EssexWorks.
For a better quality of life

DUNC

MM 9/15

Please return this book on or before the date shown above. To renew go to www.essex.gov.uk/libraries, ring 0845 603 7628 or go to any Essex library.

Essex County Council

Katie didn't answer. She couldn't. She was too conscious of his nearness, and it brought up all kinds of conflicting emotions within her.

Everything in her told her that this man was some kind of adversary. He was a danger to her peace of mind. And yet when he touched her like this she was instantly lost in a cotton wool world of warmth and comfort.

His arms were around her, his body shielding hers from all that might hurt her, and the searing impact of that tender kiss had ricocheted throughout her whole body. She didn't want to move, or speak. Why couldn't she stay here, locked in his embrace, where the world stood still and she might forget her worries?

Dear Reader

There cannot be many lovelier sights than the glorious sweep of the California coastline where it meets with the deep blue of the Pacific Ocean. I know that's where I longed to be when I wrote my story BECOMING DR BELLINI'S BRIDE.

Even more, I wanted to wander around the vineyards of the Carmel Valley, with their lush fruit hanging off the vines, just waiting to be picked.

This, I decided, was the perfect backdrop for a story of family secrets, yearnings and the desire for the return of land held for generations by the Bellini family.

Of course those cherished dreams bring Nick Bellini into sparking conflict with lovely, idealistic Katie, who is fiercely protective of her father's holdings. Too bad his land once belonged to Nick's family!

And what of the heartache Katie endures when she discovers a long-held family secret…? Will Nick be the one to soothe and comfort her?

I hope you enjoy finding out how everything works out for Nick and Katie.

Joanna Neil

BECOMING
DR BELLINI'S BRIDE

BY
JOANNA NEIL

First published in Great Britain 2011
by Mills & Boon,
an imprint of Harlequin (UK) Limited,
Large Print edition 2011
Eton House, 18-24 Paradise Road,
Richmond, Surrey TW9 1SR

© Joanna Neil 2011

ISBN: 978 0 263 21754 4

Harlequin (UK) policy is to use papers that are natural, renewable and recyclable products and made from wood grown in sustainable forests. The logging and manufacturing process conform to the legal environmental regulations of the country of origin.

Printed and bound in Great Britain
by CPI Antony Rowe, Chippenham, Wiltshire

When **Joanna Neil** discovered Mills & Boon®, her lifelong addiction to reading crystallised into an exciting new career writing Medical™ Romance. Her characters are probably the outcome of her varied lifestyle, which includes working as a clerk, typist, nurse and infant teacher. She enjoys dressmaking and cooking at her Leicestershire home. Her family includes a husband, son and daughter, an exuberant yellow Labrador and two slightly crazed cockatiels. She currently works with a team of tutors at her local education centre to provide creative writing workshops for people interested in exploring their own writing ambitions.

Recent titles by the same author:

PLAYBOY UNDER THE MISTLETOE
THE SECRET DOCTOR
HAWAIIAN SUNSET, DREAM PROPOSAL
NEW SURGEON AT ASHVALE A&E

CHAPTER ONE

KATIE stood still for a moment, her green eyes slowly scanning the horizon. Her nerves were frayed. Perhaps taking time out to look around her at this part of the sweeping California coastline was just the medicine she needed right now.

She would never have believed she would find herself in such a beautiful place as this small, quiet town, with its charming cottages and quaint shops and general sleepy atmosphere. As for the bay, it was a wide arc of golden sand, backed by rugged cliffs and rocks, a striking contrast to the clear blue of the Pacific Ocean that lapped its shores. Beyond all that was the magnificent range of the Santa Lucia Mountains, lush and green, their slopes forested with redwoods, oaks and pine.

She drank in the view for a moment or two

longer, absorbing the tranquillity of her surroundings. Then she pulled in a deep breath and
turned away to walk along the road towards a
distant building set high on a bluff overlooking
the sea.

One way or another, it had been a difficult
day so far, and she could see little chance of
things improving. She still had to meet with her
father, and even though she had become used
to seeing him over these last couple of weeks, it
was always something of a strain for her to be
with him.

'We'll have lunch,' he'd said, as though it was
an everyday, natural occurrence.

'Okay.' She'd looked at him and his expression
had been relaxed and easygoing. He seemed to
genuinely want to meet up with her again. 'I
have a half-day on Wednesday,' she told him,
'so that should work out well enough.'

And now he was waiting for her at the res-
taurant, sitting at a table on the open-air terrace, gazing out over the ocean. Katie guessed
he was watching the boats on the horizon. He
hadn't noticed her coming towards him, and she

was glad of that. It gave her the chance to compose herself, as well as an opportunity to fix his image once more in her mind.

She studied him. He was not as she remembered from all those years ago, neither did he bear any resemblance to the pictures her mother had carefully stored in the photograph album. She guessed at one time he must have been tall and vital, a vigorous man, full of energy and ambition, but at this moment he appeared frail, a shadow of his former self. His body was thin, his face faintly lined, and his brown hair was faded, threaded through with silver strands.

'Hi, there…' Katie hesitated. She was still struggling with the idea of calling this man her dad. It went against the grain to use the word, considering that he was almost a stranger to her. Instead, she asked, 'Have you been waiting long? I'm sorry I'm a bit late. I was held up at work.'

'That's all right. Don't worry about it.' Her father smiled and rose carefully to his feet to pull out a chair for her. 'You look harassed. We can't have that, can we? Sit yourself down and take a minute or two to settle. Life's too short to be getting yourself in a tizzy.'

His breathing was wheezy and laboured, and Katie was concerned. She'd heard that he had been ill for some time, but his health seemed to have taken a downturn even in the few days since she had last seen him.

'Thanks.' She sat down quickly so that he could do the same. Then she gazed around her. 'It's lovely to be able to sit out here and enjoy the fresh air… And it's all so perfect…idyllic, with the tubs of flowers and all the greenery.'

'I thought you'd like it. The food's good, too.'

A waitress approached with menus, and Katie accepted hers with a smile, opening it up to look inside and study the contents. In reality, though, her mind was in a whirl and she was finding it difficult to concentrate, so that the text became a blur.

Her father signalled to the wine waiter and ordered a bottle of Cabernet Sauvignon, before turning back to Katie. 'Why don't you tell me what sort of a day you've had?' he suggested.

'It can't have been too good, by the looks of things. Are you getting on all right at the hospital? You've been there almost a week now, haven't you?'

She nodded. 'I'm really happy to be working there. The people are great…very friendly and helpful. I'm working in Paediatrics most of the time, but I also have a couple of days when I'm on call to deal with general emergencies if they arise locally. Mostly people will ring for an ambulance if there's an accident or medical incident, but if I'm nearer and it's likely to be something serious then I'll go out as a first responder. It's a good opportunity for me to keep up with emergency work, so I was glad with this job came up.'

Her father glanced at his menu. 'It sounds as though it's the kind of work you enjoy. It's what you were doing in England, in Shropshire, isn't it?'

'That's right.'

The wine waiter arrived, pouring a small amount of clear, red wine for her father to taste, before filling two glasses.

Katie took a sip of her drink, savouring the rich, fruity flavour. She sent her father a quick, searching glance. Somehow he always managed to get her to talk about herself. He very rarely revealed anything of his lifestyle, about what had brought him to where he was now.

'What about you?' she asked. 'Did you always have it in mind to come out here—was there something about Carmel Valley that drew you—or was it *someone* who led you to this place?'

'The company I worked for sent me out here, initially,' he answered, placing his menu down on the table. He nodded towards the one she was holding. 'Have you decided what you'd like to eat yet? The filet mignon is always good.'

'Yes, I think I'll go with that. But I'd prefer the cold slices, rather than a steak, I think…with tomato, red onion and blue cheese.'

'And a Caesar salad?'

'That sounds good.'

He nodded. 'I'll grab the waitress's attention.' He studied her once more. 'So what's been happening to get you all flustered today? You've always been calm and collected whenever we've seen one another, up to now. Is it a problem at work?'

She shook her head. 'Not really… I mean, yes, in a way, I suppose.' She gave an inward sigh and braced herself. It didn't look as though he was going to give up on trying to tease it out of her, so she may as well get it off her chest.

'I saw a little boy at the clinic today,' she said. 'He was around four years old, and his mother told me he'd been unwell for some time. She hadn't known what to do because his symptoms were vague, and she put it down to the fact that he'd had a cold and sore throat. Only he took a sudden turn for the worse. When I examined him, his body was swollen with oedema, his blood pressure was high, and his heart was racing.'

Her father frowned. 'Seems that he was in a bad way, poor little chap.'

'Yes, he was. I had him admitted to the renal unit. He was losing protein in his urine, and it looks as though his kidneys are inflamed.'

He winced. 'Definitely bad news. So, what will happen to him now?'

'They'll do tests, and give him supportive treatment. Probably diuretics to bring down the swelling, and he'll be put on a low-sodium, low-protein diet.'

She glanced around once more, looking out over the redwood deck rail to the ocean beyond. The sound of birds calling to one another mingled with the soft whoosh of surf as it dashed against the rocks below.

She looked back at him. 'What about you? You haven't told me much about yourself. Mum said that you worked in the import and export trade years ago—you had to travel a lot, she said.'

'Yes, I did. I suppose that's how I first became interested in the wine business.' He beckoned the waitress and gave their orders. After the girl had left, he said gently, 'This child you treated—he isn't the reason you're not quite yourself, is he? After all, you must have come across that kind of thing many times in the course of your work.'

She nodded, brushing a flyaway tendril of chestnut hair from her cheek. Her hair was long, a mass of unruly natural curls that defied all her attempts to restrain them. 'That's true.' She pressed her lips together, uneasy at having to revisit the source of her discomfort. 'I think he reminded me of a child I treated back in Shropshire…my ex-boyfriend's son, though he was much younger, only two years old. He had the same condition.'

'Ah…' He leaned back in his chair, a thoughtful expression crossing his face. 'So it made you think about the situation back home. I see it now. Your mother told me all about the break-up.'

She sent him a sharp glance. 'You've spoken to my mother?'

'I have.' He gave a faint smile. 'She called me…naturally, when she knew you would be coming out here, she wanted to make sure that you would be all right. A mother's protective instinct at work, I guess.'

Katie frowned, and began to finger her napkin. She wasn't at all pleased with her father knowing everything there was to know about her personal life. In many ways he was an unknown quantity as far as she was concerned, and yet it appeared he knew things about her that she would much rather had remained secret.

She was still trying to take it on board when a man approached their table. He was in his mid-thirties, she guessed, a striking figure of a man with dark, smouldering good looks that sent an immediate frisson of awareness to ripple along her spine. His clothes were superb. He was wearing an immaculate dark suit that had been expertly and, no doubt, expensively tailored, while his shirt was made from a beautiful fabric, finished in a deep shade of blue that perfectly matched his eyes.

Those eyes widened as he looked at Katie, and his gaze drifted appreciatively over her, lingering for a while on the burnished chestnut curls that brushed her shoulders, before moving downwards to lightly stroke her softly feminine curves.

Katie shifted uncomfortably in her seat, trying to shake off the impact of that scorching gaze. She felt warm all over, and the breath caught in her throat. Suddenly, she was all too conscious of the closely-fitting blouse she was wearing, a pintucked design in delicate cotton, teamed with a dove-grey, pencil-slim skirt.

Getting herself together, she looked up, deciding to face him head on and return the scrutiny in full measure. He had a perfectly honed physique, long and lean, undoubtedly firm-muscled beneath all the civilised trappings. His hair was jet black, strong and crisply styled, cut short as though to tame it, but even so there was an errant kink to the strands. He had the dazzling, sensual good looks of an Italian-American.

His glance met hers and a glint of flame sparked in his blue eyes. Then he dragged his gaze from her and turned to her father.

'Jack,' he said, 'this is a pleasant surprise. It's good to see you.' He extended a lightly bronzed hand in greeting. 'I'd thought of dropping by the house in the next day or so, since you've not been looking too well of late. How are things with you?' His voice was evenly modulated, deep and soothing like a creamy liqueur brandy, and Katie's heart began to thump heavily in response. Why on earth was this man having such an effect on her?

'Things are fine, Nick, thanks.' Her father waved a hand towards Katie. 'You haven't met my daughter, Katie, have you?'

Nick looked startled. 'Your daughter? I had no idea…'

'No. Well…' Her father cut him short, his breath rasping slightly with the effort. 'It's a long story. She came over here from the UK just a fortnight ago.' He switched his attention to Katie. 'Let me introduce you,' he said. 'Katie, this is Nick Bellini. He and his family own the vineyard next to mine. He's in partnership with his father and brother.'

Katie frowned. So her father hadn't even told his friends that he had a daughter. Another small part of her closed down inside. Perhaps she had been hoping for too much. Coming out here might turn out to be the biggest mistake of her life so far.

'I'm pleased to meet you,' Katie murmured. She wasn't expecting him to respond with more than a nod, but he reached for her, taking her hand in his and cupping it between his palms.

'And I'm more than delighted to meet you, Katie,' Nick said, his voice taking on a husky, sensual note. 'I'd no idea Jack was hiding such a treasure.'

Katie felt the heat rise in her cheeks. There was nothing casual about his greeting. The way he was holding her felt very much like a caress and it was thoroughly unsettling. Her alarm system had gone into overdrive at his touch and it was way more than she could handle. As if she hadn't had enough problems with men.

As soon as it was polite enough to do so, she carefully extricated her hand. Over the last year she had worked hard to build up a shield around herself, had even begun to believe she was immune, and here, in less than two minutes, Nick Bellini had managed to shoot her defences to smithereens.

'I've a feeling I've heard the name Bellini somewhere before,' she murmured. 'In a newspaper article, I think. I just can't recall exactly what it was that I read.'

He gave her a wry smile. 'Let's hope it was something good.'

He gave his attention back to her father. 'I was hoping we could get together some time in the next week or two to talk about the vineyards. My father has drawn up some papers, and he'd appreciate it if you would look them over.'

Her father nodded. 'Yes, he mentioned them to me.' He waved a hand towards an empty chair. 'Why don't you join us, Nick…unless you have business to attend to right now? We've only just ordered.'

Katie's heart gave a disturbing lurch. She stared at him. What was her father thinking?

'Thank you.' Nick acknowledged the invitation with a nod. 'I'd like that, if you're quite sure I'm not intruding?'

He looked to Katie for an answer, but words stuck in her throat and she had to swallow down the flutter of uncertainty that rose in her. Why on earth had her father made the suggestion? They spent so little time together as it was, and there was so much she wanted to know, so many questions that still had to be answered.

She needed to be alone with him, at least until she knew him better.

But what choice did she have? To refuse after Nick had shown his willingness to accept the invitation would be churlish.

Of course, Nick Bellini must have known all that. She nodded briefly, but sent him a glance through narrowed eyes.

He pulled out a chair and sat down, a half smile playing around his mouth. She had the feeling he knew something of what she was going on in her mind, but if he had any real notion of her qualms he was choosing to ignore them.

'I came here to see the management about their wine cellar,' he said. 'After all, we might be able to tempt them into adding our new Pinot Noir to their collection—not strictly my job, but I like to keep in touch with all the restaurateurs hereabouts.' He paused as the waitress came to take his order.

'I'll have the teriyaki chicken, please, Theresa...with a side salad.' He gave the girl a careful, assessing look. 'You've done something different with your hair, haven't you?' His expression was thoughtful. 'It looks good. It suits you.'

'Thank you.' The girl dimpled, her cheeks flushed with warm colour.

Nick watched her as she walked away, and Katie observed him in the process. Did he respond like that to every woman who came his way? Were they all treated to a sample of his megawatt charm?

'Pinot Noir is a notoriously difficult wine to get right,' Jack said. 'But your father seems to have the Midas touch.'

Nick gave a fleeting smile. 'The key is to harvest the grapes in the cool of the evening and in the early morning. Then they're cold soaked before fermentation…and we use the whole berries for that process. Then, to reduce the risk of harsh tannins from the seeds and skins, they're pressed early.'

Jack nodded. 'Like I said, your father knows his business. Your vines are looking good again this year. It looks as though you'll have one of the best seasons yet.' He poured wine into a glass and passed it to Nick.

'We're hoping so.' Nick held the glass to his lips. 'Though you don't do too badly yourself. The Logan name is well respected around here… that's why we'd really like to make it part of the Bellini company.'

'It's a big undertaking.' Jack's features were sombre. 'I've worked hard to build up the business over the years. It's been my life's work.'

'Of course.' Nick tasted the wine, savouring it on his tongue before placing his glass down on the table. 'I'm sure my father will have taken all that into account.'

Katie frowned. It sounded as though the Bellinis were offering to buy out her father's company, but as usual Jack Logan was keeping his cards close to his chest. Was he thinking of selling up, or would he try to fend off their attempt at a takeover?

Nick turned towards Katie, as though remembering his manners. 'I'm sorry to talk shop…I expect this discussion of wine and grapes and company business must be quite boring for you.'

'Not at all.' Katie's expression was sincere. 'In fact I was really intrigued to learn that my father owns a vineyard, and I was actually hoping that one day soon I might get a chance to see it.'

'That won't be a problem,' Jack murmured. 'Just as soon as I get over this latest chest infection I'll take you on a tour. In the meantime, I'm sure Nick would be glad to show you around his place.'

'I'd be more than happy to do that,' Nick agreed, his gaze homing in on her. 'Maybe we could make a date for some time next week?'

'I… Possibly.' Katie was reluctant to commit herself to anything. She wasn't ready for Nick's full-on magnetism. Didn't she have enough to contend with right now, without adding to her troubles? 'I'll have to see how things work out at the hospital.'

'The hospital?'

Nick lifted a dark brow and Jack explained helpfully, 'Katie's a doctor…a paediatrician. She came out here to get a taste of California life and she's just settling into a new job.'

'Oh, I see.'

The waitress arrived with the meals just then, and Katie realised that she was hungry, despite her restless, slightly agitated frame of mind. Perhaps food would help to calm her down.

She tasted the thinly sliced beef. It was cooked to perfection, and the blend of tomatoes and cheese was sublime. She savoured the food, washing it down with a sip of red wine, and for a moment she was lost in a sweet oasis of serenity.

'So what was it that prompted you to come out here just now?' Nick asked. 'I mean, I guess you must have decided to come and see your father, but what made you choose to do it at this particular point in time?'

The peaceful moment was shattered in an instant. 'I… It just seemed to be the optimum moment,' she murmured. 'My contract back in Shropshire was coming to an end…and I'd heard that my father was ill. I wanted to see how he was doing.'

Nick studied her thoughtfully. 'There must have been more to it than that, surely? After all, Jack has suffered from lung problems for a number of years, and yet you haven't been over here to see him before this. Why now? Was it the job at the hospital that encouraged you to make the move?'

Katie frowned. Was that remark a faint dig at her because she hadn't visited her father in the last few years? What business was it of his, and who was he to judge? What did he know of their lives, of the torment she'd been through?

She made an effort to calm down. Perhaps she was being oversensitive…after all, the emotional distance between herself and her father was upsetting. It was a sore point that had festered over the years, and no one could really be expected to understand her inner hurt. And Nick was just like her father, wasn't he, probing into things she would sooner were left alone?

She said cautiously, 'The job was a factor, of course, and I suppose the idea of getting to know more of a different country held a certain appeal.'

Nick frowned. 'You could have taken a long-ish holiday, but instead you chose to come and live and work here. That must have been quite a big decision.'

Katie shrugged. 'Not necessarily.' She took a sip of her wine.

Jack shifted restlessly in his chair, as though he was impatient with the way the conversation was going. 'The truth is, Nick, Katie had a nasty break-up with a fellow back home in the UK. They'd been together for quite some time. Turns out she discovered he wasn't quite what he seemed, and she learned that he had a child by another woman. Katie still hasn't managed to get over it.'

He speared a piece of steak and held his fork aloft. 'So the long and the short of it is, she finished things with him, upped sticks and headed out here. Of course, he tried to stop her. He pleaded with her to stay with him, but she wasn't having any of it. The child was the one obstacle they couldn't overcome.'

He gave Nick a compelling stare, and Nick's eyes widened a fraction. An odd look of comprehension passed between the two men, as though somehow in that brief moment they had cemented some kind of masculine bond of understanding with one another.

Katie drew in a shocked breath. She felt as though she'd had the wind knocked out of her. Why was her father tittle-tattling her private business, especially to a man she'd only just met? Could things possibly get any worse? She was beginning to feel slightly nauseous.

'Well, that would certainly explain things.' Nick rested his fork on his plate. He studied her curiously, a faintly puzzled but sympathetic expression creasing his brow. 'I'm sorry. I imagine it must have come as a great shock to you,' he murmured. 'These things are very upsetting, of course, especially if it came out of the blue. He obviously meant a great deal to you, this man, if his fall from grace caused you to do something as drastic as to leave home and come out here. That must have been really difficult for you.'

He paused, looking at her, taking in the taut line of her jaw, and when Katie didn't respond, he added gently, 'But he was obviously very fond of you, too, and clearly he tried to explain his actions. I find it incredible that any man would do anything to cause you distress…but, in his defence, people do make mistakes, and I suppose all we can do is talk things through and try to understand how the situation came about.'

He hesitated once more, as though waiting for her to say something, but Katie stayed mute. She couldn't speak. Inside, she was a cauldron of seething emotions.

Perhaps her continuing silence had thrown him off balance because he added cautiously, 'It's not necessarily such a bad thing, fathering a child out of the confines of marriage…these things do happen sometimes. It's how people deal with the aftermath that probably matters most—they have to accept responsibility for their actions, and then perhaps we all need to take on board what's happened and move on.'

Katie took a deep breath and finally found her voice. 'So you've studied psychology along with wine production, have you, Mr Bellini?' Her gaze was frosty. 'I do appreciate you trying to help—I'm sure your theory has a good deal of merit, but, you know, I think I handled the situation the very best way I could.'

She stabbed at a slice of green pepper on her plate. 'Since I'd been with my fiancé for some three and a half years and, bearing in mind that his child was just two years old, I wasn't about to deal with his fall from grace lightly. I'm pretty sure we talked it through to the nth degree, and I have a very good idea of how the situation came about. I'm also in no doubt that James accepted full responsibility for his actions. For my part, I acknowledged totally what had happened…and I decided to move on.' Her green glance locked with his. 'That's one of the reasons why I'm here now.'

Nick looked as though he'd been knocked for six. 'It never occurred to me that any man would cheat on you,' he said in a preoccupied tone. 'I'd assumed the child was born before you met.' He held up his hands in a gesture of capitulation. 'Okay… I admit defeat. I was totally out of order. Clearly, it's none of my business and

I was wrong to try to intervene.' He frowned. 'And you must call me Nick. I insist.'

Katie gave a crooked semblance of a smile. 'Perhaps it would be for the best if we change the subject?' She glanced at her father. He had started all this, but he seemed altogether indifferent to the havoc he had caused. He simply picked up the wine bottle and began to refill her glass.

'This is an excellent vintage,' he said. 'I'll order another bottle.'

Katie took a sip of wine. 'Tell me more about the vineyards,' she said, shooting a glance towards Nick. 'How much involvement do you have, if you're in partnership with your father and brother? Do you each have separate roles?'

'We do. I deal with the wine-making process rather than the growing side of things, whereas your father is more interested in aspects of cultivation. It's intensely important to get it right, if we're to produce a select variety of wines. You must let me show you the winery—I'm sure you would enjoy a visit. Maybe you could come along for a wine-tasting session?'

'Maybe.' She wasn't about to agree to anything.

'I'll give you a call some time and see if we can arrange a date.' Clearly, he wasn't about to give up, but by now Katie was well and truly on her guard.

From then on, they kept the conversation light. The meal progressed, and Katie tried to damp down her feelings of antagonism towards this man who had cut in on her time with her father. What did her father care about her sensibilities, anyway? Perhaps she was wasting her time trying to find out why he had left all those long years ago.

And as to Nick Bellini, she had made up her mind that she would steer clear of him...no matter how hard he tried to persuade her into another meeting. He had touched a nerve with his comments, leaving her unusually rattled, and, besides, she knew it was a matter of self-preservation to avoid him. He could turn on the charm as easily as igniting a flame. She had been burned once. She wasn't going to risk body and soul all over again.

CHAPTER TWO

'No, Mum, I really don't want to go and live with my father.' Katie frowned at the idea. 'He suggested it but, to be honest, it would be like living with a stranger. After all, we barely know one another...even after three weeks I still haven't really managed to fathom him out.'

She glanced around the medical office that she had begun to call her own and leaned back in her seat, beginning to relax. There were still some ten minutes of her coffee break left, more than enough time to sit and chat with her mother.

'These things take time, I suppose...' her mother said, 'but I think it was a wise decision to go over to California to see him. You would never have been comfortable with yourself if you hadn't gone to seek him out. I suppose we all need to discover our roots, if only to find out if there are some genetic characteristics that have been passed on.' Her tone was pensive. 'I know you're like your father in some ways—you know what you want, and once you've made up your mind, you go after it. That's why you've done so well with your medical training.'

Eve Logan was thoughtful for a moment or two, and Katie could imagine her at the other end of the line, mulling things over. 'It's a shame you couldn't find a place to stay that was nearer to the hospital, though,' Eve added. 'A half-hour drive to work every day doesn't sound too good, though I expect it could have been worse.' She hesitated. 'Anyway, how is your father? From what you said last week, it sounds as though he's more ill than we suspected.'

'He has breathing problems—he's suffering from what they call chronic obstructive pulmonary disease.' Katie had spoken to her father about his difficulties, and though he'd been reluctant to dwell on his problems, he'd at least opened up enough to give her a brief outline. 'He's taking a variety of medicines to keep it under control, but I don't think they're having the desired effect. I suspect his condition's deteriorating. He puts on a show of being able to cope, but I can see that it's a struggle for him sometimes.'

She paused. 'Anyway, you're right, it makes me even more glad that I decided to come out here when I did. No matter what I think about him, he's my father, and I feel as though I have to get to know him. Trouble is, every time we meet, he manages to sidestep my questions one way or another, or we're interrupted somehow.'

It still rankled that Nick Bellini had come along to disrupt her lunch with her father, though in truth she couldn't really blame him for that. He was an innocent bystander in all this, wasn't he, and how could he know what kind of relationship they had?

Still, he'd reached her in more ways than she could have imagined. Her father's business associate wasn't someone she would easily forget.

'That must be annoying,' her mother acknowledged. 'Still, you have plenty of time to build up some kind of relationship with him. You've signed a contract for a year, haven't you, so you don't have to rush things…and if, in the end, it doesn't work out, you can always come home. There'll always be a place here for you.'

'Thanks, Mum. That's good to know.' Katie's mouth made a rueful curve. She made it sound so easy, but the truth was, her mother was making a new life for herself back in Shropshire. She was going to marry Simon, a director of the pharmaceutical company where she worked, and they were very much wrapped up in one another right now. Katie wasn't going to do anything to intrude on that.

'Anyway,' she said, 'in the meantime, the scenery around here is fantastic, and with any luck I'll get to see the vineyard before too long. It's not as big as the Bellini vineyard next to it, but by all accounts it's quite impressive.'

'Bellini—I've heard that name,' her mother commented, an inflection of interest in her voice. 'There was an article about them in the Sunday supplement some time ago…all about the different varieties of wine they produce, as I recall. Apparently their land included your father's vineyard at one time—there was something about an Italian migrant seeing the potential for development at the turn of the last century and buying up as much acreage as he could afford. But as the generations went by there were financial problems and part of the land was sold off around 1980. As far as I know, your father didn't get into the business until some twenty or so years ago.'

'Well, he's made a success of it, by all accounts,' Katie murmured. Her mother's comments about the Sunday supplements had triggered a thought process in her mind, but she still couldn't remember what it was that she'd read about Nick Bellini. Some kind of high-society gossip that kept the Sunday papers occupied for a week or two, but annoyingly the gist of it had slipped her mind.

Her pager began to bleep, and she glanced at the small screen, quickly scanning the text message from her boss. 'I'm sorry, Mum,' she said, 'but I'll have to ring you back later. I have to go out on an emergency call. Someone's had a fall at a hotel nearby, and I need to go and see what the damage is.'

'All right, Katie, love. Take care of yourself. Remember I'm always here for you.'

'I will. Bye, Mum.'

Katie grabbed her medical bag and stopped by the reception desk on her way out. 'Divert any patients to Mike O'Brien, will you, Carla? I'm going out on a call to the Pine Vale Hotel.'

'I'll do that. No problem. You'll find the hotel just off the main road out of here.' The clerk gave her a wave as Katie disappeared through the wide front doors of the building.

Pine Vale Hotel was up in the hills, only a short drive from the hospital, and Katie reached it in good time. As she slid out of her car and took a look around, she was stunned by the magnificence of the building. White painted, it was a long, symmetrical edifice with two front extending wings at either end. It stood three storeys high, and there were large, Georgian-styled windows in abundance, with green painted shutters folded back. On the ground floor several sets of French doors were set back in archways, and Katie guessed the hotel must be flooded with light.

She wasn't wrong. Inside, the foyer reflected a quiet elegance, with traditional, comfy sofas that invited people to sit and take their ease. There were low, marble-topped tables and flower arrangements everywhere, adding glorious splashes of colour to delight the eye.

'Hello.' Katie introduced herself to the woman behind the desk. 'I'm Dr Logan. I understand you have a patient for me.'

'Oh, thank goodness you're here.' The woman, around thirty years old, with fair hair cut into a neat, gently curving bob, looked relieved. 'Yes, please come with me and I'll take you to her. The ambulance is on its way…the emergency services said they were sending a doctor out as well, as there might be a head injury, so I'm really glad to see you. I'm Jenny, by the way… Jenny Goldblum. I'm the hotel manager.'

Katie nodded acknowledgement. 'I was told that the lady fell in her room and appears to be semi-conscious—did anyone see the fall? It always helps to know the circumstances.'

Jenny shook her head. She pressed the button for the lift, and frowned as the door swished open. 'It isn't clear what happened. The maid found her when she went to clean the room. We think perhaps it had only just happened because a lady in the room next door had been speaking to Mrs Wyatt just a minute or so before.'

They stepped out of the lift on to the first floor, and Katie was ushered into a large, airy room, furnished in elegant style. There was a double bed with bedside units and an oak dresser to one side of the room, but at the far end, by the window, furniture had been arranged in a seating area. There was an oval oak coffee table and a couple of brocade-covered straight-backed chairs, along with armchairs upholstered in a matching fabric.

The patient, a woman in her fifties, was lying on the floor by the dresser. 'What's her first name?' Katie asked. 'Do you know?'

'It's Laura,' Jenny answered. 'She's staying here with her husband, but he went out earlier for a walk. We haven't been able to contact him yet.'

'Okay, thanks.'

The woman was being tended by one of the

hotel staff members, but the girl moved aside as Katie approached. A rug covered the area close by, and it looked as though this had been crumpled when Mrs Wyatt fell.

Katie went to kneel down beside the injured woman. 'Mrs Wyatt…Laura…I'm Dr Logan. Can you hear me? Are you able to answer me?'

Laura Wyatt mumbled something indistinct and Katie tried again. 'Do you feel pain anywhere, Laura?' she asked gently. 'Can you tell me where it hurts?'

Again there was a muffled reply, and Katie came to the conclusion that Mrs Wyatt was too dazed to answer properly. She began a swift initial examination, checking for any obvious injuries and finishing with a neurological check.

'Laura,' she said at last, 'I think you've broken your shoulder—I know that it must be very painful, so I'm going to give you an injection to help with that. Do you understand what I'm saying?'

Laura tried to speak, but whatever she was trying to say didn't come out right, and Katie went ahead and set up an intravenous line. 'We're going to get you to hospital just as soon as possible,' she told the woman. 'In the meantime, I'm going to try to make you more comfortable with a sling that will stop you moving your arm.'

It wasn't clear whether Laura understood or simply couldn't answer, but Katie went on with her examination, checking her patient's blood pressure and listening to her heart.

'What's happened here?' A familiar male voice disturbed Katie's quiet concentration, and she looked up to see with a shock that Nick Bellini had entered the room. 'Katie?' He frowned, studying her for a moment, then turned his attention to her patient. Mrs Wyatt was groaning faintly.

His expression became grim, his eyes an intense, troubled blue.

'Nick?' Katie queried, removing the stethoscope from her ears. What was he doing here? And why had he thought it would be all right to come barging in that way? 'You really shouldn't be in here,' she told him. 'I'm examining a patient.'

'Yes… I see that. I'm sorry for intruding, but you have to understand, I own this hotel… I came as soon as I heard… I'm very concerned that someone has been injured on the premises.' His glance went to the woman once more. 'How is she?'

Katie's eyes widened. He owned this beautiful place? Was there no end to the extent of his empire? She blinked, and then hurriedly dragged her mind back to the business in hand. 'She has a fractured shoulder. I'm sure you must be very worried,' she murmured. 'That's understandable…but this lady has a right to privacy. I think you should leave.'

His head went back, a lock of midnight hair falling across his brow. He seemed stunned by her words, as though it hadn't for an instant occurred to him that anyone would ever try to evict him from where he wanted to be. She waited, bracing herself and expecting an argument, but then he said briefly, 'You'll keep me informed?'

Katie nodded, and without another word he turned and strode out of the room.

She went back to treating her patient. Nick's intrusion had set her emotions in turmoil once more. She had thought she had seen the last of him, and yet here he had turned up when she'd least expected him. His presence had thrown her completely off balance, and now, perhaps because she'd just learned of his association with the hotel, there was a snippet of a newspaper headline running through her head… Something about an heiress…the daughter of a hotel magnate…and Nick Bellini.

She made an effort to push all thoughts of him to one side, and concentrated her attention on her patient, helping the woman to sit up. Then she put the immobiliser sling in place.

'That should keep you fairly pain free until they can take care of you at the hospital,' she said.

The paramedics arrived a few minutes later, and Katie went with them to oversee her patient's transfer to the ambulance. By this time Laura's husband had arrived, and he went along with her, sitting beside his wife and holding her hand.

Katie turned to go back into the hotel, only to find that Nick was right there by her side. She gave a startled jump. He seemed to tower over her, his body firm as a rock. She took a moment to gather herself together and then she gave him a fleeting once-over. He was turned out as faultlessly as ever, dressed in a perfectly tailored dark suit that made him every inch the businessman, a force to be reckoned with.

He looked at her. 'A fractured shoulder, you said. Was she able to tell you what caused her to fall? Was it possible that it could have been the rug in her room—might she have tripped?'

She frowned, walking back with him into the foyer of the hotel. 'Are you worried about liability?' she asked. 'Is that why you rushed over here?'

'First and foremost, I came to see how the lady was doing…but, yes, I have to think about the hotel's liability in this. We take every precaution, but if someone were to be hurt on the premises, it could lead to some very worrying consequences.'

'Well, unfortunately I can't really say what caused the accident. Mrs Wyatt was too dazed to give me any answers, I'm afraid. All I know is that she'll probably need to have shoulder re-placement surgery—she fell heavily and it was a nasty injury.'

His mouth flattened as he absorbed that infor-mation. Then he said in an even tone, 'Do you have to rush on to another call, or would you have time to stay and have a drink with me?'

She hesitated. Part of her wanted to walk away and avoid getting involved with him any further than need be, but another bit of her recognised his concern. He was anxious for the woman's well-being, and as a hotel proprietor he must be all too conscious of the threat of litigation. Maybe it wouldn't hurt to stay for a while and talk things through with him.

'I don't have to be back at work—my surgery hours are finished for the day, but I'm still on call, so perhaps we should make it coffee rather than anything alcoholic?'

He smiled, his face relaxing for the first time, reminding her all too potently of that sizzling allure that had made her go weak at the knees the first time she'd met him. She had to keep a firm hold on herself. This man could annihilate her sense of security with just one look, and that wouldn't do at all. She'd been down that road, and from her experience it led to heartache…big time. Emotionally, James, her ex, had scarred her for life. She'd been blissfully unaware that he'd been cheating on her, and once his indiscretions had come to light it had torn the heart out of her.

'We'll go out on to the sun terrace,' he said. 'I'll have Jenny send us out a tray of coffee. Just give me a moment to catch up with her.' He lightly cupped Katie's elbow, as though to keep her close, and she stood still for a moment while he beckoned to Jenny. That light touch was like a searing brand on her soft flesh.

The hotel manager was waiting by the desk, talking to the receptionist, but she turned and came over immediately.

'Ask chef to make up a lunch tray, will you,

Jenny? Dr Logan will be staying for a while. We'll be out on the terrace by the shrubbery.'

Jenny nodded. 'I'll do that.' She glanced at Katie. 'Is Mrs Wyatt going to be all right?'

'I hope so,' Katie answered. 'The shoulder will give her some problems for quite a while, but those can be dealt with. I'm more concerned about her lack of response. They'll have to do tests at the hospital.'

Jenny nodded and hurried away to find the chef. Nick ushered Katie across the foyer and lounge then out through wide glass doors onto a paved area that was set out with white-painted wrought-iron tables and chairs. The scent of roses filled the air, and Katie was struck by the mass of colour all around, shades of crimson, yellow and pink shrub roses, all vying for attention in the landscaped garden.

'It's really beautiful out here,' Katie murmured as they sat down at one of the tables. 'Everything I've seen so far is overwhelmingly luxurious. I had no idea that you had other interests aside from the vineyard.'

He smiled. 'This place has been in my family's

possession for many years—as far back as I can remember. I took it over when my father decided it was time to cut back on his commitments. I bought him out, rather than see it fall to outsiders.'

She gave him a considering look. 'The family name means a lot to you, doesn't it? You're very conscious of your heritage.'

He nodded. 'That's true. Generations of my family have lived in the valley since the end of the nineteenth century, and my great-great-grandfather worked immensely hard to make a go of his enterprise. I feel that we have a duty to secure the results of his labour for generations to come.'

Two waitresses came out on to the terrace just then and placed laden trays down on the table. On one there was a porcelain coffee pot, along with cups and saucers, cream and sugar. The other held an appetising selection of food, as well as plates and cutlery.

Nick began to pour coffee for both of them. 'It isn't just about my own heritage. At the same time I believe we have to give of our best to the local community. That's why what happened this morning concerns me so much. We hold a certain position of trust out here. People look to us to set standards.'

He offered her a plate and napkin. 'Please, help yourself to food.'

'Thank you. It looks delicious.' She gazed at the tempting choices before her. There was *prosciutto*, a dry-cured Italian ham, cut in paper-thin slices, along with sun-dried tomatoes, gnocchi and a crisp salad.

She added a little of each to her plate. 'I wish I could be of more help,' she said quietly, 'but until Mrs Wyatt recovers enough to tell us what happened, we can only wait for the test results to come back from the hospital and hope that they will give us some clue.'

'Was there any head injury?'

'Not that I could see. Of course, that doesn't always mean there's nothing to be concerned about. Any kind of extreme jolting movement within the skull can cause problems that might develop later.'

He tasted a portion of the ham. 'I'll go and

see her just as soon as the doctors have had time to treat her shoulder. In the interim I've sent the under-manager along to the hospital to see if we can do anything to make her stay more comfortable.' He frowned. 'It's a dilemma. We generally make sure that the rugs in the rooms are in good condition, not easily rucked. If it was the case that she tripped, I'll have to think about having them removed.'

Katie glanced at him across the table. His concern seemed genuine, and she wondered if there was any comfort she could offer.

'It's always possible that she might have a health problem that caused her to fall—something quite unrelated to the hotel. She might have suffered a dizzy spell, for instance.'

'Or a TIA, perhaps.'

Transient ischaemic attack... Katie gave him a considering look, and slid her fork into succulent, sauce-covered potato gnocchi, giving herself time to think. 'That's a definite possibility. Any restriction of the blood supply to the brain could cause a temporary loss of consciousness.'

'Or stroke-like symptoms.'

She nodded. 'It sounds as though you have some experience of the condition. Has someone in your family had problems with TIAs?'

'No, nothing like that.' His gaze meshed with hers. 'As it happens, I'm a doctor, like yourself. I suppose that's why I didn't think twice about rushing in on you when you were examining Mrs Wyatt. I'm so used to tending these medical emergencies that it didn't cross my mind to steer clear.'

She gave a soft gasp. 'I had no idea.' She studied him afresh, a small frown indenting her brow. 'I can't imagine how you find time to practise medicine when you have a vineyard and a hotel to run.'

He laughed. 'I guess it would be difficult if I tried to do all three...but the fact is, I have managers to do the day to day work for me. They let me know if any problems arise that need my attention—like today, for instance. Jenny called me. Otherwise, I make regular checks to make sure that everything's going smoothly, but for the most part I work in the emergency department at the hospital.'

Her eyes widened. 'That must take some dedication. After all, you could have chosen to stay in the valley and reap the benefits of years of grape cultivation. Your wines are internationally famous, according to my mother.'

'That's true. But I've always wanted to be an emergency physician. When I was a teenager, I saw one of my friends injured in a traffic accident. It was horrific…and for a while it was touch and go as to whether he would survive. Thankfully, he had the best surgical team looking after him, and he made it in the end. It left a huge impression on me. So, you see, I'm passionate about my work, and I can't think of anything else I'd rather do. After all, saving lives is a job that's definitely worthwhile. It gives me more satisfaction than I could ever get from gathering in the grape harvest.'

'I can see how you would feel that way but, then, I'm biased.' She gave a faint smile. 'I have to admit, though, there are times when I'm tempted to swap it all for the kind of life I see out here…lazy days in the sunshine, a trip down to the beach to watch the surfers ride the waves…but then I come back to reality. I couldn't give up medicine. It's part of me.'

He nodded, his glance trailing over her. 'I was surprised to see you here. I remember you said you were a paediatrician…but you did a pretty good job of taking care of Mrs Wyatt, as far as I could see. She didn't appear to be in any pain, there was an IV line already in place, and you had her on oxygen. No one could complain at the standard of treatment she received.'

'Let's hope not, anyway.' She guessed he was still thinking about the repercussions of that morning's accident, and how it might affect him as a proprietor. 'I do work as a paediatrician most of the time, but I'm on call two days a week. During my training, I specialised in both paediatrics and emergency, and I wanted to keep up my skills in both those fields. This job was ideal.'

'I can imagine it would be.' He smiled, his gaze slanting over her, and then he waved a hand towards a platter. 'Won't you try our Burrata cheese? I think you'll find it's out of this world.'

'Thanks.' She helped herself to one of the cheeses, a ball wrapped in mozzarella, giving it a springy, soft texture. As she bit into it, she savoured the buttery texture of the centre, a mixture of cream and shredded mozzarella. 'Mmm,' she murmured. 'It's like a little taste of heaven.'

He chuckled, his gaze moving over her, flame glimmering in the depths of his blue eyes. 'Your expression said it all.' His glance slid to the soft fullness of her mouth and lingered there. 'What I wouldn't give to have savoured that with you,' he said on a husky note. 'You have the lips of an angel…soft, ripe and exquisitely sensual.'

She stared at him, her green eyes widening in confusion. His words took her breath away, and a tide of heat rushed through her body. 'I… Uh…' She didn't know what to say to him. She wasn't prepared for his reaction and his comment was unexpected, disarming, leaving her completely at a loss.

Nervously, she swallowed the rest of her coffee then ran the tip of her tongue over her lips, an involuntary action to make herself feel more secure, to help her to know that all was as it should be, and he made a muffled groan.

'Don't…please…' he said, his tone roughened, his gaze darkening to reflect the deep blue of the ocean. 'That just adds to the torment.'

Katie's pulse began to thump erratically, and a torrent of heat rushed to her head. Panic began to set in. Why was he having this strange effect on her? Hadn't she come all the way out here to start afresh? She didn't want any entanglements, and yet Nick seemed to be constantly in her face, a powerful, authoritative man, someone it was hard to ignore. He wasn't like other men she had met, and she was finding she couldn't trust her instincts around him. At the first foray into dangerous territory she was conscious of the ground sliding out from under her feet. She couldn't let him do this to her.

She straightened, leaning back in her chair. 'Perhaps I should leave,' she said distractedly, her thoughts spiralling out of control. He was altogether too masculine, too hot-blooded for a girl like her. With just a word, a touch he had her senses firing on overdrive.

'Surely not?' he murmured. 'Please, stay a while longer.'

She shook her head. Her bewildered mind searched for options, rocketed from one impossible scenario to the next and collapsed in a panicked heap. 'I've probably spent way too much time here already,' she managed. 'It was good of you to offer me lunch. Thank you for that, but I should be on my way now.'

He reached out to her, laying a hand over hers when she would have drawn back from the table. 'Don't let me frighten you away, Katie. It's just that you shook me to the core the first time I met you, and that feeling hasn't gone away. You're really something special and I'd do anything to see you again.'

She gently pulled her hand out from under his. 'I'm sorry... It's not that I have anything against you, Nick, but I'm not in the market for relationships right now. I just... There are too many things going on in my life, too many changes I have to deal with.'

It was all too much for her. The business with James had hurt her deeply, made her guarded and uncertain, and now she was struggling to build a new life, trying to find her niche in a new job. She couldn't deal with any distractions right now, and she sensed that Nick was way more trouble than she could ever handle.

She pulled in a deep breath and stood up, pushing back her chair. 'Thanks again for lunch,' she said, hating herself for the slight tremor in her voice. 'It was delicious…but I really must go.'

He wasn't going to make it easy for her, though, she discovered. He came to stand beside her, his body so close to hers that she could feel the heat coming from him, could register the heavy thud of his heartbeat as he leaned towards her and slid an arm around her waist. Or was that her own heart that she could feel—that pounding, intense rhythm that warned of imminent danger? His hand splayed out over her rib cage, and her whole body fired up in response.

'That's such a shame,' he murmured. 'There is so much more I want to say to you. I could even show you around the hotel if only you would stay a little longer.'

She shook her head, steeling herself to resist

the lure of his embrace. She couldn't allow herself to lean into the warmth of his long, hard
body, no matter how great the temptation. 'I
can't,' she murmured. 'I… I really ought to go
back to the office and type up my notes while
everything's fresh in my mind.' It sounded such
a weak excuse, even to her ears.

'Such mundane tasks, when life could be so
much more interesting.' He sighed, reluctantly
giving in. 'If you're determined to go, you must
at least let me walk you to your car.'

She nodded. 'Okay.' At least he was yielding
to her decision. Escape was within reach at last,
and maybe soon the fog of indecision would lift
from her mind…though it didn't help at all that
he kept his arm around her as they headed back
through the hotel.

Only when they reached her car did he let her
go and finally she began to breathe a little more
easily.

'I imagine you have to write up a report on
Mrs Wyatt's accident,' he said on an even note,
'for the inquiry.'

'Yes.' She nodded. 'There'll more than likely

be an official investigation. I gather any kind of accident on public premises causes the wheels to be set in motion.'

'Hmm…do you have any idea what will go in your report?'

She sent him a quick glance. 'I can only state the facts. Anything else would be pure conjecture.'

He considered that for a moment, a line indenting his brow. 'Yes, of course.' He pulled open the car door for her and held it while she slid into the driver's seat. 'I'd be interested in hearing the results of the tests.' He paused. 'Anyway, I expect we'll run into one another again before too long.

She nodded. 'I should think so.' He closed the door and she turned the key in the ignition, starting up the engine.

She frowned as an errant thought dropped into her mind. He'd asked about the report and what she might put in it…and for a good deal of the time while they had been eating he had been asking about the precise details of Mrs Wyatt's medical condition.

Was he worried about the outcome of the investigation and how it would affect the hotel?

Her report could sway things one way or the other. Was that the real reason he was making a play for her? Why would a man such as him be interested in her, after all, when no doubt he could take his pick of beautiful women? The thought disturbed her. She had to tread cautiously, and she couldn't take anything or anyone at face value these days, least of all Nick Bellini.

CHAPTER THREE

'I'M SURE I'd have been all right if we'd stayed at home,' Jack Logan said. His breath was wheezy, coming in short bursts, so that Katie frowned. 'There was no need for you to bring me to the hospital,' he added, struggling to gulp in air as he spoke. 'It's your day off. You shouldn't be tending to me.'

'You're ill,' she said firmly. 'And I'm your daughter, so of course I should be looking after you.' He was a proud man, not one to ask for help, and up to now she had been cautious about stepping in where she might not be wanted. Today, though, he had reached a point where medical intervention was imperative. 'You need to see a doctor right away so that we can get your medication sorted out. You can't go on like this. I won't let you.'

He didn't answer and she suspected his

strength was failing fast. She wrapped an arm around him, supporting him as she led him to a chair in the waiting room. The emergency department was busy at this time of the day, just after lunchtime, but she hoped they wouldn't have too long to wait. Her father's breathing was becoming worse by the minute, and it was worrying her.

She paused awkwardly, scanning his features. 'You have your tablets with you, don't you…and your inhaler?'

'Yes.' He eased himself down on to the padded seat, dragging in a few difficult breaths and giving himself a minute or two to recover.

'Perhaps you should have a few puffs on the inhaler now. It might help a bit.' She watched as he fumbled in his pocket for the medication. 'Will you be all right for a minute or two while I go and have a word with the clerk on duty?'

He nodded. 'I'll be fine. I don't need to be here.'

She made a wry face and turned to walk over to the reception desk. He was stubborn and in-dependent, but she wasn't going to let him get away with trying to bamboozle her. He was in a bad way, and he needed help…maybe even to be admitted to hospital.

She gave the clerk her father's details. 'He's gasping for breath and I believe he needs urgent treatment. His medication doesn't seem to be working properly.'

The clerk glanced over to where Katie's father was sitting. 'I'll see if we can have him looked at fairly quickly, Dr Logan. If you'd like to take a seat, I'll have a word with the triage nurse.'

'Thanks.' Katie went back to her father and sat down. 'We shouldn't have to wait too long,' she told him. 'Just try to relax.'

In fact, it was only a matter of minutes before they were called to go into the doctor's room, and Katie was startled to see Nick coming along the corridor to greet them. He looked immaculate, as ever, with dark trousers that moulded his long legs, a crisp linen shirt in a deep shade of blue, and a tie that gave him a businesslike, professional appearance.

She hadn't expected to run into him so soon after their meeting at the hotel. It threw her, coming across him this way, and for a moment or two she wasn't sure how to respond.

'I didn't realise that you worked here,' she said, frowning. 'I'd somehow imagined that you worked at one of the bigger city hospitals.'

He smiled. 'I prefer this one. It has all the up-to-date-facilities, and I've been familiar with it since childhood. It's become like a second home to me.'

He lent her father a supporting shoulder. 'I'm sorry to see that you're having problems, Jack,' he murmured. 'We'll go along to my office where we can be more private.' He turned and called for a nurse. 'Can we get some oxygen here, please?'

'Of course.' The nurse hurried away to find a trolley, while Nick led the way to his office.

Nick waved Katie to a leather-backed chair by the desk, and then turned his attention to Jack.

'Let me help you onto the examination couch,' he said quietly, pumping the bed to an accessible height and assisting Jack into a sitting position, propped up by pillows. 'I see you have your inhaler with you. Is it helping?'

Jack shook his head. 'Not much.' He leaned back against the pillows and tried to gather his breath. His features were drawn, his lips taking on a bluish tinge.

Nick handed him the oxygen mask and carefully fitted it over his nose and mouth. 'Take a few deep breaths,' he said. 'We'll soon have you feeling better, don't worry.'

Katie watched as Nick examined her father. He was very thorough, listening to his chest, taking his blood pressure and pulse and asking questions about the medication he was taking. All the time he was efficient, yet gentle, and she could see that he was a doctor who would put a patient's mind at ease whatever the circumstances. He set up a monitor so that he could check Jack's heart rate and blood oxygen levels. Katie saw that the results were way out of line with what they should be.

'Excuse me for a moment,' Nick murmured. 'I'm going to ask the nurse to bring a nebuliser in here. We'll add a bronchodilator and a steroid to the mix to reduce the inflammation in your airways, and that should soon make you feel a lot more comfortable.'

He went to the door and spoke to the nurse then returned a minute or two later, coming to stand beside the couch once more. 'Your blood pressure is raised,' he said, 'so I think we need to adjust your tablets to bring that down…and also perhaps we should question what's happening to bring that about.'

'I dare say I can give you an answer on that one,' Katie remarked under her breath. Her tone was cynical, and that must have alerted Nick, because he began to walk towards her, obviously conscious that she wouldn't want her father to hear.

'You know what's causing it?' he asked.

'I think so. You and your father have been pushing him to sell the vineyard, and he's worried about making the right decision. It's tearing him apart, thinking about giving up the one thing that has kept him going all these years.'

Nick raised dark brows. 'You're blaming my

father and me?' He, too, spoke in a lowered voice.

'I am. Who else would I blame?' She returned his gaze steadily. 'His health is failing, yet you bombarded him with paperwork and tried to persuade him to hand it over. He was looking at the papers this morning when he was taken ill. The vineyard means everything to him, and you've set him a huge dilemma. I don't believe he's in any state to be dealing with matters such as this.'

'I hardly think you can lay the blame at our feet. Jack has been ill for a number of years, and his lung function is way below par. As to causing him any distress, all I can say is that if he didn't want to consider our offer, he only had to say so.' His eyes darkened. 'He's perfectly capable of making his own decisions.'

Katie stiffened. He hadn't added 'without his daughter's interference', but the implication was there, all the same.

The nurse appeared just then with a trolley, and Nick broke off to go and set up the nebu-liser. 'Just try to relax and breathe deeply,' he told her father, his manner soothing. 'It'll take a few minutes, but your blood oxygen levels should gradually start to rise. In the meantime, I'm going to go and glance through your medical notes and see where we can make changes to your medication.' He halted as a thought had occurred to him. 'Katie's obviously concerned about you. Do you mind if I discuss your medical history with her, or is it something you would rather I kept private?'

Jack shook his head. 'That's fine. Go ahead. There's nothing to hide.'

'Okay.' Nick checked the monitor once more, before saying quietly, 'I'll also arrange an urgent appointment for you with your respiratory specialist.'

'Thanks,' Jack said. He looked exhausted and seemed relieved to be able to just lie back and let the drugs do their work.

Nick came back to the desk and glanced towards Katie as he sat down.

'He should start to feel better once his airways expand.' He accessed her father's medical notes on the computer, and then said quietly, 'You seem very concerned over this matter of the vineyard. Have you been out to see it?'

She nodded. 'He took me on a tour a few days ago. I was very impressed, completely bowled over by it, in fact. So much work has gone into making it what it is now. It's something to be proud of.' She looked at him through narrowed eyes. 'I can't see any reason why he would want to let it go.'

His mouth made a crooked shape. 'I'd say it was possibly becoming too much for him to handle, but it's probably better if we leave off that discussion for a while. It isn't getting either of us anywhere, is it?'

She clamped her lips shut. Nick glanced at her briefly, and then said, 'Your father's heart is taking a lot of strain—the effect of years of lung disease.' He lowered his voice as he studied her. 'I wonder if you realise just how precarious his situation is becoming.'

She nodded, her mouth making a downward turn. 'I'd guessed. I suppose I just needed to have it confirmed.'

He checked the drug schedule for a moment

or two on the computer, and then stood up and went back to her father. 'How are you feeling?' he asked.

'Much better.' Jack managed a smile. 'You've taken good care of me, as always. Thank you for that.'

'You're welcome. It's what I'm here for.' Nick glanced down at his chart. 'I want to prescribe some tablets to ease the workload on your heart, and I think we'll arrange for you to have oxygen at home. If you give me a few minutes, I'll go and see if the respiratory specialist is around. It's possible he might be able to come and see you while you're here, and that way we can finalise the details of your medication in one go.'

'Okay.' Jack nodded. 'I'm not going anywhere for a while.'

Katie could see that he was looking much better. 'The colour is coming back into your face,' she said, going over to him as Nick left the room. 'You had me worried there for a while.'

His glance trailed over her. 'You worry too much. Your mother was the same. I used to say to her, life's too short to be fretting about this and that. Seize the day—as they say. Make the most of it where you can.'

Katie's mouth flattened. 'I suppose that was back in the days when you were getting along with one another...before it all went wrong.'

'I... Yes...' He hesitated, shooting her a quick, cautious glance. 'It hasn't been easy for you, has it, Katie? We tried to make a go of things, you know, your mother and I, but there were problems... For one thing, my job took me away from home so much.'

Katie was unconvinced. 'Your job obviously meant more to you than we did, because one day you went away and never came back.' Even now, her heart lurched at the memory. 'Mum was devastated, and I could never understand why you left us that way. You were living thousands of miles from us. I was eight years old, and suddenly I'd lost my father, and my mother was in pieces. You disappeared from our lives. For a long time I thought I'd done something wrong and it was all my fault that you'd gone away.'

He frowned, his grey eyes troubled. 'I'm sorry, Katie. I should have handled things differently; I know that now.' He pulled in a deep breath. 'But your mother and I were going through a bad time, and the atmosphere was incredibly tense between us. There were lots of bitter arguments. Back then I thought it would be for the best if I stayed away. I thought it would be easier, less painful.'

She gave a short, harsh laugh. 'You were wrong. It might have been better for you, maybe, but as far as I was concerned a card here and there at birthdays and Christmas was hardly going to make up for the lack of a father. Did you really think it would? And as for presents that you sent—well, they were great but it just made me realise that you didn't even know me. I appreciated the gifts, but I couldn't help thinking that a visit would have been more to the point. But it never happened. I thought perhaps you didn't care.'

It was as though her words had cut into him like a knife. He caught his breath and seemed to slump a little, his features becoming ashen, and Katie looked on in dismay, a rush of guilt running through her. What was she thinking of, having this discussion with him in here, of all places? She had gone too far…way too far. He might have a lot to answer for, but he was ill, after all, and she was layering him with anxiety that could bring on respiratory collapse. She ought to have known better.

'That was thoughtless of me,' she said in an anxious voice. 'I didn't mean to do anything to aggravate your condition.'

'It's all right.' He paused, sucking in another breath. 'It was something I struggled with all the time—leaving you. I kept meaning to come back to see you, but somehow the longer I left it, the harder it became. I thought…if I came back to see you…' he started to gasp, fighting against the constriction in his lungs '…you might be all the more upset if I left you once more. You were very young.'

Katie's expression was bleak. 'Let's not talk about it for the moment. You're ill, and we should concentrate on making you more comfortable. Keep the mask over your face. Take deep breaths and try to relax.'

'What's going on here?' Nick came into the

room and hurried over to the bed. 'What happened?' He checked the monitor, and Katie could see that her father's heart rate and respiratory rate had increased to dangerous levels.

'It was… We were just talking. It's my fault,' she said in a halting tone. 'I said some things I shouldn't have said.' She had berated Nick for causing her father stress, and then she had done exactly the same thing, hadn't she?

She pressed her lips together. Wasn't this all part of the problem she had battled with since she had come out here? There was so much resentment locked up inside her, but none of it could gain release…not when her father was so ill. It was frustrating, an ongoing dilemma that could have no end. No matter what he had done, she would have to be inhuman to ignore his condition, wouldn't she?

'No, no…you mustn't blame yourself,' her father said, cutting in on her thoughts. 'It's only right that you should say what's on your mind. I let you down.'

Nick gave her a thoughtful glance. Perhaps he was curious about what was going on between them, but he said nothing. Instead he checked the monitors once more and handed her father a couple of tablets and a drinking cup. 'Take these,' he said. 'They'll bring your blood pressure down and calm your heart rate. Then you need to rest.' He sent Katie a warning glance and her face flushed with heat.

'It isn't Katie's fault,' Jack said, after he had swallowed the tablets. 'The old ticker isn't what it used to be. There isn't much more that you doctors can do for me—you know it, and I know it.'

'I never give up on a patient,' Nick said, his tone firm. 'You'll be fine if you take things easy. Lie back and give the medicine time to take effect.'

They sat with her father for several more minutes, watching as his breathing slowly became easier.

'I feel much better now,' he said, after a while. 'I'll be okay.'

'Maybe, but you can stay where you are for a bit longer,' Nick told him. 'The specialist will be stopping by as soon as he's finished dealing with a patient. He'll sort out your medication and make sure that you're in a good enough condition to go home.'

His pager went off and he turned to Katie. 'I have to go and deal with an emergency that's coming in,' he said. 'Maybe we could meet up some time soon for coffee or dinner? I feel there are things we need to talk about.'

He was probably thinking of her father's illness, and she acknowledged that with a slight inclination of her head. 'Actually, I have the test results on Mrs Wyatt, back in my office—the lady who fell and injured herself at your hotel. She gave me permission to share them with you, although I haven't had time to look at them properly yet. I suppose we should arrange a time to get together to talk about them.'

He nodded. 'Would it be too much of an imposition for you to come over to my beach house with them, say, later this afternoon? I have to be there because I have some people coming to do some work in the courtyard. Just say if it's a problem for you.'

She thought about it and then shook her head.

'It's not a problem. I'm off duty, and you don't live too far from my place.'

'That's great. I'll see you then.' He glanced towards her father. 'I'm glad you're feeling better, Jack. Take care. I'll see you again before too long, I expect.'

He left the room, and Jack sent Katie a questioning look. 'There was a problem at the hotel?'

She nodded and explained what had happened. 'I think he's worried in case the woman or her relatives decide to take it to court. They might try to say her fall was the fault of the hotel proprietor.'

He frowned. 'I can see how he would be worried. It won't simply be the effect this might have on trade at the hotel—the Bellinis have always taken pride in doing the right thing. Nick's father is ultra-traditional in that respect. Everything has to be done the proper way. He's a very private man, and he deplores any negative publicity.'

'I can imagine. But so far they've managed to keep things quiet, and anyway there's a lot riding on the results of various tests that were carried out at the lab.'

'And now he wants you to take the results over to the house?' Jack sent her a thoughtful glance. 'Do I detect more than just a professional collaboration going on here?'

Katie's eyes widened at the question, and she gave a faint shrug of her shoulders. 'You heard what he said. It's just easier this way.'

She wasn't going to say any more on that score. Her father hadn't earned the right to intervene in her private life, had he? Besides, how could she possibly answer him when she didn't know for sure herself what had prompted the invitation? The deed had been accomplished before she'd had time to give it much thought.

Jack was frowning. 'I could see that he was interested in you from the outset…but you should be careful how you go, with him, Katie. I know you're still recovering from what went on back in the UK, and I wouldn't want to see you hurt all over again.'

He halted for a second or two to allow his lungs to recover. 'Nick Bellini's a law unto himself where women are concerned. They seem to fall for him readily enough, but he's never yet settled down with any of them. Don't go getting your heart broken over the likes of him. He's a fine doctor—he's kept an eye on me over the last few years, just because he was concerned for me—and he's a great businessman, a wonderful friend and associate, but he's lethal to the fairer sex.'

Katie frowned. He was only telling her what she'd already guessed. That newspaper headline that had been bugging her for the last few days suddenly swam into her head once more, and this time she could see it with perfect clarity. *'Tearful heiress Shannon Draycott leaves hotel under cover of darkness. Bellini tycoon declines to comment.'* There had been more. The article had said something about a broken engagement, and there had been a lot of conjecture, along with several interviews with friends of the young woman. They all painted a picture of a tragic heiress who had been left in the lurch.

'Well, thanks for warning me. I'll be sure to keep it in mind.'

Was Nick a man who was afraid of commitment, flitting from one woman to another? Katie
was determined not to get involved with anyone
like that ever again. She had been devastated
when her relationship with James had ended.
She had trusted him and believed they might
have had a future together, but it had all gone
terribly wrong, and now she would do everything she could to steer clear of any man who
might cause her pain.

She studied her father. He was an enigma. He
looked gaunt, with prominent cheekbones and
dark shadows under his eyes, and something in
her made her want to reach out to him and wrap
her arms around him. It was confusing.

All those years he had stayed away, removing himself from her life, and yet now he was
acting like a protective father, as though her
well-being was suddenly important to him.
She couldn't quite work him out. For so long
she had tried not to think about him at all. He
had walked out on her and her mother and she
couldn't forgive him for that…and yet now her
emotions were torn.

Little by little, as she came to know him better, he was beginning to tug at her heartstrings. She didn't know how it had happened, but she felt sorry for him and in spite of herself she was worried about him. He looked so thin and wasted, and it occurred to her that he probably wasn't eating as well as he should.

As for Nick Bellini, she'd already learned to be wary of him, and she had to be grateful that her father had let her know what she was up against. Anyway, surely her fears were groundless? Her relationship with Nick was going to be strictly professional, wasn't it?

It didn't surprise her one bit to discover that he had the reputation of a compulsive heartbreaker.

A couple of hours later, Katie dropped her father off at his house and left him in the care of Libby, his housekeeper. 'I'll keep an eye on him, don't you worry,' the woman said, and Katie immediately felt reassured. Libby was kindly and capable looking, and Katie knew she was leaving him in good hands.

Then she set off for Nick's beach house. The scenery was breathtaking as she drove along, with the sun glinting on the blue Pacific Ocean and the rugged length of the coastline stretching out ahead of her.

Living here was like being dropped into a secluded corner of paradise, she reflected as she parked her car in Nick's driveway a few minutes later. She slid out of the car and looked around, gazing out over the bay and watching the surf form lacy white ribbons on the sand. Black oystercatchers moved busily amongst the rocks, seeking out mussels and molluscs with their long orange beaks.

'Katie, I'm glad you could make it,' Nick said, coming out of the house to greet her. 'I was on the upper deck when I saw you arrive.' His arms closed around her in a welcoming hug, and in spite of herself her senses immediately responded in a flurry of excitement. 'How's your father?' he asked.

'Much better.'

'I'm glad.'

His arms were warm and strong, folding her

to him, and for a wild moment or two she was tempted to nestle against him and accept the shelter he offered. She could feel the reassuring, steady beat of his heart through the thin cotton of her top.

'It's good to see you,' he murmured, stepping back a little to look at her. 'I hope you didn't mind coming out here to visit me—it's just that I have to be at the house to oversee some work I'm having done out back, as I told you. The workmen are installing a hot tub in the courtyard.'

'That sounds like fun,' she said, easing herself away from him. She ran a hand over her jeans in a defensive gesture, smoothing the denim. This closeness was doing strange things to her heart rate, and it wouldn't do to have him see what effect he was having on her. 'You certainly have the climate for it out here.'

He smiled, his hand slipping to her waist as he gently led her towards the house. 'I'm looking forward to trying it out. All those jets of water are supposed to make you feel really good, like a soothing massage.' He grinned. 'Perhaps you might like to try it with me some time?'

'I...uh...' She gave a soft intake of breath. 'I'd have to think about that.' She blinked. The prospect of sharing a hot tub with him was much more than she could handle right then. In fact, she'd have to know him a whole lot better before anything like that ever happened.

He laughed softly. 'I'll take that as a definite maybe,' he said. 'Let me show you around the house.'

'Thank you. I'd like that.' She gazed at the beautiful building as they walked along the path. It was multi-storeyed, with sloping roofs at varying levels, the tiles a soft sandstone colour that contrasted perfectly with the white-painted walls. There were arched windows and glass doors, and there were steps leading from a balconied terrace on the upper floor, providing external access to the ground below. Behind the whole edifice was a backdrop of green Monterey pines, and in the far distance she could see lush, forested mountain slopes. 'This is fantastic,' she murmured. 'It's a spectacular house.'

She turned to look back at the Pacific. 'I really envy you, living out here by the ocean. It must be lovely to look out over the water every day and gaze at the cliffs that form the bay.'

'It's very relaxing. I know I'm fortunate to be able to enjoy it.' He showed her into the house, and they stepped into a wide entrance hall whose pale-coloured walls reflected the light. The oak floor gleamed faintly.

He led the way into a room just off the hall. 'This is the lounge, as you can see. I tend to sit in here to read the paper or watch TV of an evening. It's a very peaceful room, and it looks out over the patio garden. And, of course, with the French doors it's handy for the courtyard… and, from now on, the hot tub, too,' he added with a grin.

She peered out through the open doors at the courtyard that was closed in on three sides by different wings of the building. The remaining side was made up of a decorative screen wall, providing a glimpse into the garden beyond. 'I can see the men are still working on it. It looks as though you have everything you need out there—a place to relax and enjoy the sunshine, a barbecue area, and all those lovely flowers and shrubs to enjoy. It looks like a little piece of heaven.'

She turned to gaze around the room. 'I like the pale-coloured furnishings in here, too. It just adds to the feeling of light.' Her glance took in glass shelves and a low table, before trailing over the sumptuous sofa and chairs. Pastel-coloured cushions added a delicate touch.

'I'm glad you like it,' he said, claiming her hand and leading her through an open doorway. 'Let me show you the kitchen, and I'll make us a drink. What would you like—coffee, tea? You could have iced tea, if you prefer. Or maybe you'd like something stronger?'

'Iced tea sounds fine, thanks.' She stopped to look around. 'Oh, this is lovely,' she said with a soft gasp. 'And it's such a large room, too.' The cupboards and wall units were all finished in the palest green, verging on white, and marble worktops gleamed palely in the sunlight that poured in through the windows. There were shelves filled with bright copper pans, and corner wall units with attractive ceramics on display.

'Well, it serves as a breakfast kitchen,' Nick explained, going over to the fridge. 'There's a separate dining room through the archway, but I tend to eat in here, mostly…or upstairs on the upper deck. I can look out over the ocean from there.'

'That sounds like bliss.'

He nodded, putting ice into two glasses and adding tea from a jug. 'It is. Would you like lemon and mint with this?' he asked, indicating the iced tea.

'Please. That would be good.'

He placed the two glasses on a tray, along with the jug of tea and a plate of mixed hors d'oeuvres. 'We'll take these upstairs and I'll show you the upper deck. 'It's great up there at this time of day, and you can see over the whole of the bay from the terrace.'

She followed him up the stairs, walking through a second sitting room and out through beautifully embellished glass doors onto the balcony terrace.

He was right. The view from the deck was fantastic, and Katie could even see the wildflowers that grew on the craggy slopes in the distance. He pulled out a chair for her by a wrought-iron table, and she sat down and began to relax.

Out here, there were tubs of yellow and orange California poppies, their silky petals moving gently in the faint breeze, and against the far wall, standing tall alongside a trellis, were spiky blue delphiniums. Hanging baskets provided even more colour, with exuberant displays of petunias.

'Help yourself to food,' he said, sliding a plate across the table towards her. 'I wasn't sure whether you would have eaten or not before you came.'

'Thanks.' She glanced at the food on display. There was pâté with crackers, honey-glazed chicken and a spicy tomato dip with tortilla chips. 'It looks delicious.'

He smiled. 'Not my doing, I'm afraid. I have food sent over from the hotel quite often. I don't always have time to cook.'

'I'm not surprised. You must spend the bulk of your time at the hospital, and even if you don't work on a day-to-day basis at the vineyard or the

hotel, there must be a fair amount of organisational work to deal with. I expect you're the one
who has to make the most important decisions,
aren't you?'

He nodded. 'That's true. Things tend to crop
up from time to time that need my attention—
like this unfortunate episode with Mrs Wyatt.'
He frowned. 'I went to see her, and I'm really
pleased that she's looking a lot better than she
was a few days ago.'

Katie smiled. 'Yes. I couldn't help noticing that
you arranged for her to have a private room—
the basket of fruit and the flowers you sent were
a lovely touch. I know she appreciated them.'

'It was the least I could do.' He spread pâté
onto a cracker and bit into it. 'People come to
the hotel expecting to have a good time and live
for a while in the lap of luxury. They don't want
to find themselves being taken out of there by
ambulance.'

'But you weren't obliged to pay anything towards her hospital care, were you?'

He shrugged. 'No, that's true. Her insurance
company will pay for that…but I wanted to be

certain she had the upgrade to make sure that she's comfortable, and, anyway, I count it as good customer relations.'

'Hmm. I can see that you take your role as hotelier seriously.' She dipped a tortilla chip into the fiery salsa sauce. 'You must be anxious to know what caused Mrs Wyatt to fall and break her shoulder. Would you like to hear the results of the tests?'

'Yes, definitely… I'm glad she said it would be all right for you to discuss them with me. Is it what we thought—a TIA?'

She nodded. 'It looks that way. The doctors monitored her heart and discovered that she has atrial fibrillation—as you know, that kind of abnormal heart rhythm can sometimes cause clots to form in the blood vessels. They did a CT scan, along with blood tests, and found a narrowing of the arteries. The general feeling is that she probably developed a blood clot that temporarily disturbed the flow of blood to the brain. This most likely dissolved of its own accord, but it's possible that more will form as time progresses if she doesn't have treatment.'

'So presumably they have her on anti-thrombotic therapy? And they'll give her medication to counteract the abnormal heart rhythm?'

'That's right.' She took a sip of iced tea. 'It looks as though you're in the clear—or, should I say, the hotel's in the clear?' She smiled at him. 'That must be a huge relief to you.'

'Yes, it is. I can't tell you how badly I needed to hear that. It's great news. Lucky, too, for Mrs Wyatt, because now she gets to have the treatment she needs to put her back on the road to health.' He rested back in his seat, taking a swallow of iced tea and looking the picture of contentment. 'Thanks for telling me that, Katie. I'm really obliged to you for finding out all this information.'

He set down his glass and looked her over, leaning towards her. 'In fact, if I didn't think you'd take it amiss, I could kiss you for it.' He came closer, as though, having hit on the idea, he was ready to carry it through into immediate action, regardless of the consequences.

Katie flattened herself against the back of her chair, deftly foiling his attempt. 'I think you'd better give that one a miss,' she said, her green gaze meshing with his. 'It wouldn't do if every male doctor tried to kiss me whenever I presented them with good results, would it?'

His eyes narrowed. 'Have any tried?'

'Oh, yes. From time to time.'

'And succeeded?' He was frowning now, his blue eyes darkening.

'Maybe. Once or twice.' His expression crystallised into one of seething frustration, and she laughed softly. 'Sorry about that. I couldn't resist. You looked so put out.'

He gazed at her, totally nonplussed. 'You certainly got me going there,' he said, his mouth twisting. 'My fault. I should have known any number of men would want to try their luck with you. That goes for me, too. Somehow, ever since we first met, I've been hung up on getting to know you better…much better.'

She pulled a face. 'Well, I'm not sure that's such a good idea—not in the way you mean, at least.'

He studied her thoughtfully for a moment or two, his expression serious. 'He hurt you badly, didn't he—this man from back home? You must have been very much in love with him.'

'I thought I was,' she said awkwardly. 'I thought I knew him, but perhaps I was blind to his faults. He had a lot of charisma, and I believed he was saving it all for me. It turned out I was wrong.'

And wasn't Nick so very much like James? He had that scintillating charm that could sweep a woman off her feet, and Katie was no exception. She had to be on her guard. No matter how hard he tried, she wasn't going to succumb to Nick's winning ways. Hadn't her father warned her about him?

'But let's not dwell on any of that,' she murmured. 'I'm here with you now, and we do have two things in common...our work and my father. Maybe it would be safer all round if we simply kept things between us on that level.'

'Hmm...maybe.' He sounded doubtful. His eyes were still dark, and there was a brooding quality to his expression.

Katie decided to plough on with her new diversionary tactic. She helped herself to some food and said quietly, 'Perhaps we should talk about what happened this morning—about your efforts to persuade my father to sell his land, and the effect it's having on him. Maybe we need to clear the air on that score. You know I'd sooner you put an end to any attempt at making a deal. Anyway, I have the feeling he's not at all sure about going ahead with it.'

Nick frowned. 'He hasn't said as much to me... and while there's a chance he'll concede to us, we're bound to keep trying. It would mean a lot to my father to bring the vineyard back into our keeping. My great-great-grandfather bought the land at the turn of the century, but a parcel of it was sold off some years back when the family fell on hard times. It's a matter of pride to my father to restore the vineyards into family own-ership once more. He sees it as our inheritance. It's very important to him.'

'That may be so, but I can't say it any clearer—I think you should hold off on those negotiations.'

Nick's steady gaze met hers. 'Jack doesn't

need you to hold his hand where business is concerned.'

A glint of steel came into Katie's eyes. 'I have to disagree with you on that one,' she said. 'And this is definitely not the right time to be pursuing it with him.'

Nick frowned. 'That's another matter, of course. We both saw how ill he was today.' He poured more iced tea into her glass. 'You think your father needs to be cosseted but he takes it on himself to take care of business matters, and then it becomes a matter of pride for him to see things through.'

So, no matter what she said, he wasn't giving up on his plan to secure her father's land. She drank her iced tea and studied him over the rim of her glass. Clearly, his family was not going to be satisfied with the empire they had built up. They would go after whatever they wanted. Forewarned was forearmed.

Nick's phone bleeped, and he glanced down at the screen briefly. 'It looks as though the workmen have finished installing the hot tub,' he said. 'Shall we go down and take a look?'

'Yes, of course.'

She followed him down the stairs and out to the courtyard, where the workmen waited, standing by their handiwork.

'We're all done here,' the spokesman said. 'I think you'll find everything's in order. Just turn these controls here to adjust the jets.' He began to point out the various buttons and fittings. 'This is your filter…and here's where you change the heat settings. We've left it set to around midway. Neither too hot nor too cold, but of course it's all a matter of personal preference.'

'That's great,' Nick murmured. 'It looks perfect. Thanks for all your hard work.' He turned to Katie. 'Stay and enjoy the courtyard for a minute or two, will you, while I go and see the men off? There's an ornamental fishpond that you might like to look at, over there in the corner. I'll be back in a few minutes.'

'Okay.' She watched him go, then turned and walked towards the far side of the courtyard, an attractive area, laid out with a trellised arbour and rockery. A gentle waterfall splashed into the pond where koi carp swam amongst the plants and hid beneath white waterlilies.

She gazed down at the green fronds of water plants drifting with the ripple of water from a small fountain and lost herself for a while in a reverie of a past life.

'Sorry to have left you,' Nick said, coming back to her a short time later. 'I think the men did a good job. They sited the tub perfectly and left the place looking neat and tidy. Didn't take them too long either.'

She nodded. 'I expect you'll appreciate your new tub for a good many years to come.' Turning back to the pond, she added, 'This is beautifully set out. The water's so clear, and the plants are perfect.' Her voice became wistful. 'I remember having one in our garden when I was a child… but it was never as good as this. I suppose you have to keep on top of things—make sure the filter is kept clear, and so on.'

'That's true. I tend to check it every so often. The pond is a hobby of mine. I find it totally relaxing, something you need so that you can wind down after a day in Emergency.' He sent her an oblique glance. 'Did your father set up your pond…or was it something that came with the house, so to speak?'

'It came with the house. My father was interested in it, but he wasn't around for long enough to take care of it, and the work fell to my mother.'

'And she wasn't that keen?'

'She was keen enough when my father was with us, but after he left to go and live here in California she fell apart. She lost interest in everything.'

He frowned. 'I'm sorry. That must have been hard.' He scanned her face thoughtfully. 'I've known Jack for some eighteen years, ever since he pipped us to the post and bought the vineyard from its previous owner. In all that time I had no idea he had a daughter back in the UK.'

'No. It seems he kept it quiet.'

'I suppose you had to take a lot of the burden on your shoulders—how old were you when he left?'

'I was eight. As to any burden, I must say I didn't really understand what was going on at the time. It was all very confusing. When I real-ised he wasn't coming back, I was hurt, heart-broken, and then as the years went by I became angry and resentful. There was just my mother and me, no cosy family unit with brothers and sisters to share happy times. I missed that.'

A shadow crossed his eyes. 'And that's why you never came over here until now.' He looked at her with new understanding. 'You were wait-ing for him to come back to you.'

She lowered her head. 'It wasn't going to happen, was it? So eventually I decided that if I was to make peace with myself, I had to come and find him and sort out my demons once and for all.'

He slid an arm around her shoulders. 'I'm sorry that you had to go through all that,' he said quietly. 'It must have been a terrible time for you.' He drew her close and pressed a light kiss on her forehead. 'It seems almost unforgiv-able that he should treat you that way, and yet I know Jack is a good man at heart.'

Katie didn't answer. She couldn't. She was too conscious of his nearness, and it brought up all kinds of conflicting emotions within her. Everything in her told her that this man was some kind of adversary. He was a threat to her father, and a danger to her peace of mind, and yet when he touched her like this, she was instantly lost in a cotton-wool world of warmth and comfort.

His arms were around her, his body shielding hers from all that might hurt her, and the searing impact of that tender kiss had ricocheted throughout her whole body. She didn't want to move, or speak. Why couldn't she stay here, locked in his embrace, where the world stood still and she might forget her worries?

'Do you think you can find it in you to forgive him?' Nick murmured. 'He's very ill, and there may not be too much time left.'

'I don't know.' She gave a faint sigh. The spell was broken and she straightened, gazing down into the water of the pond. Fish darted among the green fronds, oblivious to the troubles of the world around them. If only she could find such inner peace.

She took a step backwards. 'I should go,' she

said. Nick was the last person she should look to for comfort. He could well turn out to be even more of a heartbreaker than her father.

CHAPTER FOUR

'Is YOUR father really considering selling his vineyard to the Bellini family? That seems very strange to me.' Eve Logan sounded doubtful at the other end of the line. 'I haven't had a lot of contact with him over these last few years, but I did gain the impression that the business meant an awful lot to him. I wouldn't have thought it was something he would give it up lightly.'

'No, probably not,' Katie agreed. 'When I spoke to him the other day he said he hadn't thought it through yet, or words to that effect. I'm wondering if the Bellinis are putting undue pressure on him. He isn't well, and I have the strong feeling that he isn't up to it.'

'Then perhaps it's as well that you're over there and able to look out for him.'

'Yes, maybe.'

Katie cut the call to her mother a few minutes

later and gazed around the apartment. She was feeling oddly restless. Ever since her visit to Nick's home several days ago, she had been suffering from what she could only think of as withdrawal symptoms, and it was all Nick's fault.

That kiss had been the lightest, gentlest touch, and it surely had been nothing more than a gesture of comfort and understanding, but the memory of it had stayed with her ever since. Nick had a compelling, magnetic charm that could surely melt the stoniest heart, and she was proving to be no exception.

It wouldn't do at all. She was off men...they could string you along and lead you into thinking that everything was perfect, and then throw it all in your face with the biggest deception of all. No. Every instinct warned her that it would be far better to steer clear of Nick before he could work his magic on her. He spelled trouble and that was something she could definitely do without.

It didn't help that she managed to catch a glimpse of his house every time she headed along the main highway on her way to or from the hospital. Today had been no exception. Nick's home was beautiful, a jewel set in the golden, sand-fringed crown of the California coast.

Annoyingly, against all her better judgement, her thoughts kept straying to him. What was he doing...was he there, sitting outside on the upper deck, watching the seagulls perch on the distant bluffs?

But she wasn't going to waste any more time thinking about him. Enough was enough, and she had work to do. The dishwasher needed emptying and there was a stack of ironing waiting for her...though with any luck she could finish her chores and still have time to wander down to the beach and take in one of the glorious sunsets that were the norm around there.

She set to work, but she was only halfway through her ironing pile when the phone rang.

'There's been a surfing accident just a mile from where you are,' her boss told her. 'Darren Mayfield, a fourteen-year-old, was knocked unconscious and had to be pulled out of the water.

The ambulance has been called, but you'll probably reach him before it arrives. A nasty head injury, by all accounts.'

'I'll leave right away,' she told him, unplugging the iron and heading for the door. Her medical bag was in the hall, ready for such emergencies, and the rest of her supplies were in the car.

The boy's level of consciousness was waxing and waning by the time she arrived on the beach. 'Do you know anything about what happened to him?' she asked his mother, who was waiting anxiously by his side.

'He came off his board when one of the big waves hit,' the woman said, her voice shaky. 'The board sort of rose up in the air and then crashed down on him. We had to drag him out of the water. There's a gash on the back of his head and he's bleeding… He hasn't come round properly since we brought him to shore.' Her lips trembled. 'He keeps being sick, and I thought it was just concussion, but it's more than that, isn't it? He should have recovered by now.'

'I'll take a look,' Katie murmured, kneeling down beside the boy. 'How are you doing,

Darren?' she asked quietly. 'Can you hear me?' She waited, and when there was no response she added, 'Do you know what happened to you?'

He still didn't answer, and Katie began to make a swift but thorough examination. 'He's unconscious,' she told his mother, after a while. 'I'm going to put a tube down his throat, and give him oxygen, to help with his breathing, and then I need to stabilise his spine to prevent any more damage being done.' She carefully put a cervical collar in place, before checking the boy's heart rate once more. It was worryingly low, and his blood pressure was high, both signs that the pressure within his brain was rising. That didn't bode well.

Suddenly, Darren's whole body began to shake, and Katie reached in her medical bag for a syringe.

'Why's he doing that?' his mother asked in a panicked voice. 'What's happening to him?'

'He's having a seizure,' Katie answered. It was yet another indication that this boy was in trouble. 'I'm going to inject him with medication that will help to stop the fit.'

By the time the paramedics arrived, she had put in place an intravenous line so that fluids and any further drugs could be administered swiftly and easily. 'We need spinal support here,' she told the men, keeping her voice low so as not to worry the boy's mother any further. 'He has a depressed skull fracture, so we need to phone ahead and tell the trauma team what to expect. They'll most likely need to prepare him for Theatre.'

She spoke to the lead paramedic as they wheeled Darren into the ambulance a few minutes later. 'I'll ride along with him in case there are any more complications along the way.'

The paramedic nodded. 'You go ahead with Mrs Mayfield and sit by him. I'll call the emergency department and keep them up to date.'

'Thanks.'

Katie looked at her patient. He was deathly pale and she was deeply concerned for this boy as she sat beside him in the ambulance. She had placed a temporary dressing on the wound at the back of his head, but it was bleeding still, and she was worried about the extent of the damage.

The journey to the hospital seemed to take for ever, though in reality it was probably only about fifteen minutes, and as soon as they pulled into the ambulance bay, Katie was ready to move. The paramedics wheeled Darren towards the main doors.

'He had another seizure in the ambulance,' she told the doctor who came out to greet them, 'so I've boosted the anti-convulsive therapy. I'm afraid his blood pressure is high and it looks as though the intracranial pressure is rising.' Again, she spoke quietly so that the boy's mother wouldn't be unduly alarmed, but to her relief a nurse stepped forward and gently took the woman to one side.

'We'll get an x-ray just as soon as we've managed to stabilise his blood pressure,' a familiar voice said, and Katie was startled to see Nick appear at the side of the trolley. He was wearing green scrubs that only seemed to emphasise the muscular strength of his long, lean body. Her heart gave a strange little lurch.

He listened attentively to the paramedic's report and was already checking the patient's vital signs, scanning the readings on the portable heart monitor that Katie had set up. Then he looked at Katie and gave her a quick smile. 'Hi,' he said.

'Oh… I…somehow I hadn't expected to see you here.' Katie's response was muted, but she recovered herself enough to acknowledge him, and also the paramedics, who were ready to leave on another callout. She was troubled about her patient's progress, but Nick's sudden appearance had thrown her way off balance. In the heat of the moment it had completely slipped her mind that he might be on duty.

'I'm on the late shift today,' he told her, as if in answer to her unspoken thoughts, as they moved towards the trauma room. His glance ran quickly over her. 'It's great to see you again.'

'Likewise,' she said, and then tacked on hurriedly, 'I'd like to stay with Darren to see how he goes, if that's all right with you?'

'That'll be fine.' By now they had arrived in the resuscitation room and from then on he concentrated his attention on his patient, examining the boy quickly and telling the nurse who was assisting, 'We'll monitor blood glucose, renal function, electrolytes. I'll take blood for testing now and we need to consult urgently with the neurosurgeon. Given the boy's condition, it's quite likely he'll want to put him on mannitol to reduce the intracranial pressure. Ask him to come down to look at him, will you?'

Katie watched him work. He was remarkably efficient, cool, calm, and obviously concerned for this teenager. He didn't hesitate for an instant, but carried out the necessary procedures with effortless skill, delegating other tasks to members of the team. Then, when the neurosurgeon came to the side of the bed, he spent several minutes talking to him about the boy's condition.

'I'll be ready for him in Theatre in about half an hour,' the surgeon remarked as he prepared to leave the room. 'Let me have the CT images as soon as they're available.'

'Of course.' Nick checked Darren's vital signs once more, and only when he was satisfied that he had done everything possible for the boy did he turn back to Katie.

'Okay, we'll take him along to the CT unit. Let's find out exactly what's going on here.'

As soon as Darren had been placed on the CT trolley, they went into the annexe to watch the images on the computer screen as the technician began the X-ray. 'You're right,' Nick said, after a few minutes. 'It's a depressed fracture, with the bone fragments pushing down on the lining of the brain. There's a large blood clot causing a build-up of pressure. If we don't act soon, there's a risk that the brain will herniate.'

He spoke to the technician. 'Download the films to the computer in Theatre, will you? Dr Kelso will want to see them.'

The technician nodded, but Nick was already striding out of the annexe towards his patient. 'We'll have to get him to Theatre just as soon as we've cleaned the wound,' he told Katie. 'By that time Mr Kelso should be ready for him.'

They went back to the trauma room and Nick began the process of irrigating the wound while Katie looked on.

'Okay, that should be clean enough now,' he said after a while. 'We'll start him on antibiotics to prevent any infection,' he told the nurse, 'and keep on with the anticonvulsant therapy. In the meantime, give Mr Kelso a call and find out if he's ready for him up in Theatre, will you?'

The nurse nodded. 'Right away.'

A few minutes later when they had the go-ahead, Nick took his patient to the lift. 'Will you be here when I come back?' he asked Katie. 'I'm going to stay with Darren until the operation's over, but it would be good to talk to you some more.'

She nodded. 'I want to see how he does in surgery. Perhaps I should go and talk to Mrs Mayfield? I know Mr Kelso has spoken to her already, but she might appreciate having someone with her to answer any questions.'

'That would be brilliant, if you don't mind. I'm sure you and she have already managed to build up rapport and it'll be good for her to have someone familiar to be with her.'

The lift doors closed behind him, and Katie walked away, heading for the waiting room where Mrs Mayfield was sitting anxiously, hoping for news of her son.

'Can I get you anything?' Katie asked, going to sit beside her. 'A cup of coffee, perhaps?'

Mrs Mayfield shook her head. 'A nurse brought me one already, thank you.' She looked near to tears. 'I've been trying to contact my husband. He was at a conference, but he's coming straight back here now.' She looked at Katie. 'Darren's in a bad way, isn't he? He was unconscious for so long. What's going to happen to him?'

'Darren was unconscious because the impact of the surfboard pushed the bones of his skull inward, causing them to break and press down on the lining of his brain. This damaged some of the blood vessels, so that a blood clot built up quickly between the skull and the lining.'

Mrs Mayfield nodded to show that she understood. 'And this operation that he's having—Mr Kelso said they needed to bring down the pressure. How will they do that?'

'The surgeon will lift up the bone fragments that are pressing down, and at the same time he'll suck out the blood clot.'

'But will he be able to stop the bleeding? Won't the clot build up again?'

'He'll use special materials to repair the blood vessels so that shouldn't happen. You can be sure that he'll do the very best he can for your son, Mrs Mayfield.' Katie used a reassuring tone, her heart going out to this woman who was petrified for her boy's safety. She couldn't bear to think how she would feel if she had children of her own. It must be the worst thing in the world to know that they were in danger.

She stayed with her for some twenty minutes, until the door opened and Mr Mayfield walked into the room. He went over to his wife and held her tight, both of them fearful and anxious about their son.

Katie left them alone. A nurse would come by and see how they were doing in a while, and now Katie went along to the emergency room to find out if there was any news.

She knew quite a few of the doctors and nurses who worked there by now, from her work as a paediatrician and first responder. Sometimes she had to liaise with them over the phone, and occasionally, as today, she would ride along with the patient and make the handover in person.

'No news yet,' the nurse said, 'but Nick's on his way down from Theatre. He wants us to make preparations to send the boy over to the intensive care unit.'

Katie nodded. 'Thanks for letting me know, Abby. I'll wait by the nurses' station, if that's all right. I really want to know how he does.'

'Of course it is.' She smiled. 'The one consolation is that having you there from the outset must have given the boy at least a sporting chance. Too often, time drags on before people with head injuries have expert treatment. Nick reckons you did a great job.'

Katie gave a bleak smile. 'Let's hope we've all done enough to make a difference. It's such a devastating experience all round. One minute the boy's out there, enjoying the sunshine and the exhilaration of surfing the waves, and the next, in a freak accident, he's out cold and fighting for his life.' She shook her head. 'I've trained for this, but I don't think I'll ever get used to it.'

'Neither will I,' Abby said.

'You get through it by doing the best you can for your patients,' Nick commented, coming to join them. 'That way you get to sleep easier at night.'

Katie turned to face him, while the nurse left them to go and fetch linen from the supply room. 'Maybe you manage to drop off well enough,' she murmured. 'I can't say that it comes that easily to me.'

'That's a shame.' He draped an arm around her. 'Maybe I could help to remedy that?' he ventured on a husky note. 'Perhaps I could find some way to soothe you to sleep.' He lifted a quizzical brow, looking deep into her eyes.

Katie felt her colour rise. 'In your dreams,' she murmured.

He laughed. 'Well, it was worth a try, I thought.'

'Not really...and I have to say, your timing sucks.' She frowned. 'How is Darren? Did he come through the operation all right?'

His expression sobered. 'Mr Kelso managed to finish the procedure without there being any added complications,' he said. 'The boy's intra-cranial pressure is at a safer level now, but his blood pressure's still alarmingly high. ICU will monitor him closely, of course. All we can do now is wait and see if he can pull through. He's young and previously in good health, so that's in his favour.' He sent her an encouraging smile. 'The young are quite resilient, as you know. It never ceases to amaze me how they bounce back from even the most traumatic of situations.'

'I'll keep my hopes up for him.' She gazed around the emergency department. 'Everything seems very well co-ordinated around here,' she said. 'The staff all seem to work very well to-gether—I expect that has something to do with the way you run things. You're in charge here, aren't you? Everyone speaks very highly of you.'

'I'm glad of that.' He looked at her from under dark lashes. 'A lot of people, the press espe-cially, seem to think that because I come from a wealthy family I don't need to work and I'm not career orientated, but they couldn't be more wrong. I love my job.'

'I think I've seen that for myself. Though you're right...you do tend to get negative publicity from time to time, don't you?'

He sighed, leaning back against the nurses' station, crossing one long leg over the other at the ankles. 'It seems to be an occupational hazard. If you belong to a family with international holdings, I suppose you're bound to find yourself in the news from time to time.'

She nodded. 'There was a short piece about Mrs Wyatt's accident in the local press, but it was quite favourable. The journalist pointed out that you'd acted swiftly in sending for medical treatment, and that you'd helped make her stay in hospital more comfortable.'

'That's something, at least.' He made a wry smile. 'My father employs a spokesman to deal with the press. It helps to dispel any of the more outlandish stories, and gives the public our take on events.'

'Perhaps your spokesman wasn't around when the Shannon Draycott story broke?' she said softly. 'That must have caused you a few uneasy moments.'

His mouth turned down at the corners. 'I see you've been discovering my lurid past. No wonder you keep fending me off. I expect you're one of these people who believe everything you read in the papers?'

She shrugged lightly. 'Not necessarily. Though I do go along with the principle that there's no smoke without fire.' He hadn't exactly denied the story, had he? According to the papers, they had been engaged to be married—what kind of man was he that could make light of such a thing?

He winced. 'Then I'm obviously doomed.' A glint of amusement came into his eyes. 'Is there anything I can do to restore your confidence in me? I'm really one of the good guys, you know. And when I spoke to Shannon last week she seemed reasonably content with the way her life was going.'

So he was still in touch with her. The thought sounded a death knell in Katie's mind to any hopes that the stories might be a figment of someone's imagination. 'I'm glad to hear it. Perhaps she counts herself lucky to have escaped.'

'Ouch!' He clamped a hand to his chest and pretended to stagger. 'That was a well-aimed blow. I didn't realise Dr Katie Logan had such a cutting edge…though I suppose you've sharpened up your defences this last year or so.'

She nodded. 'You can count on it.' After her experience with James, she was well prepared, and on her guard, for men who had hidden secrets and a good deal of charm.

'Hmm.' He studied her thoughtfully. 'So what am I to do to persuade you that things are not as they seem? Do you think spending more time with me would help you to get to know me better?'

It was her turn to laugh. 'I have to give you eleven out of ten for trying, anyway. You're irrepressible, aren't you?'

'Where you're concerned, yes, I am.' His gaze meshed with hers. 'So how about coming along to a wine tasting at the vineyard? We're celebrating a new Pinot Noir this year, one of our finest…and you did say you'd like to see around the vineyard, didn't you? Your father's maybe, but ours is right alongside?'

'I… Um…' She thought things through. Ever since she had seen her father's land, she had been caught up in the wonder of vine culture, and now she was fascinated by everything to do with wine and wine making. She was intrigued to take a look over the Bellini land and see if it was anything like her father's. Where was the harm? It wouldn't be like going on a date, would it? After all, there would be other people around.

'A little wine tasting can be good for the soul,' Nick murmured in a coaxing tone. 'It helps you to look on life with a much more mellow attitude.'

'I'm sure that's true.' She smiled, and against all her best intentions heard herself say, 'Thanks, I think I'd enjoy that.'

. 'That's great news. I'll come and pick you up. Will you be free after work on Wednesday? I have a half-day then.'

'I will,' she murmured. 'I'll look forward to it.'

Later, though, as she waved goodbye to the paramedic who gave her a lift back to her car where she had left it on the coast road, she couldn't help wondering if she was making a mistake. Why, when every part of her knew that she should avoid getting involved with Nick, did she keep digging herself in deeper?

CHAPTER FIVE

'KATIE, Dr Bellini wants to know if you will consult with him on a young patient in the emergency department.' Carla popped her head round the door of Katie's office and waited for an answer. 'I could ask Mike to cover for you here, if you like.'

'Okay. Tell him I'll be along in five minutes.' Katie put the last suture into the cut on a small child's lip. 'There you are, young man, all finished. You've been very brave.' She smiled at the six-year-old and reached into her desk drawer for a colouring sheet and a teddy-bear badge. 'I think you deserve these, don't you?'

The boy gave a tentative nod and studied the piece of paper she'd handed him. 'A racing car!' he exclaimed in delight. 'I'm going to colour it red, and put stripes on the wings.' He looked up at her. 'Thank you.'

'My pleasure.'

She saw the boy and his mother out into the corridor, and then readied herself to go along to the emergency unit, smoothing down her pencil-line skirt and making sure that her blouse neatly skimmed the curve of her hips.

She paused, trying to make sense of her actions. Why was she doing this? Was she really so bothered about meeting up with Nick that she needed to fuss about the way she looked? Unhappily, the answer had to be a resounding 'Yes'. It gave her confidence to know that she looked okay.

A final check in the mirror showed her that her hair was the usual mass of chaotic curls, but there wasn't much she could do about that. At least it was clean and shining.

'Thanks for coming along, Katie.' Nick met her at the door of his office. His glance flicked over her, and an appreciative gleam came into his eyes. 'I'd like you to take a look at young Matthew Goren, if you will. I've asked his mother if she wouldn't mind you giving a second opinion.'

'That's okay. I'm happy to do it.'

He introduced her to the boy's mother and then to Matthew, a thin-looking eleven-year-old who looked uncomfortable and deeply troubled.

'Matt's complaining of pain in his thigh,' Nick said, as they went over to the trolley bed. 'It came on three days ago, and now he's unable to walk because of it. He has a low-grade fever, mild hypertension and slight anaemia, and he's been suffering from frequent nosebleeds in the last couple of years. Liver function, lungs and white-cell count are normal. I've done an abdominal ultrasound and an MRI of the thigh as well as X-rays, but I'm waiting on the results of other blood tests to see if they eliminate certain other possibilities.'

Nick had obviously been very thorough. This must be an unusual case or he wouldn't have brought her in on it, and she was glad that he respected her enough to ask for her opinion.

Katie gave the boy a smile. 'Hello, Matt. I'm Dr Logan. I'm sorry you're having problems with your thigh. That must be really uncomfortable.'

He nodded. 'I had it once before, when I was ten, but it went away. This is a lot worse.'

'Oh, dear.' She sent him a sympathetic glance. 'We'll have to find out what's wrong and put it right, then, won't we?' She studied his chart for a moment or two and then asked, 'Would it be all right if I examine you, Matt?'

'It's okay.'

Katie was as gentle as she could be, taking her time to assess the boy's condition. When she had finished she asked a few general questions about his symptoms.

'Has the swelling in his abdomen come on recently?' she said, looking at his mother.

Mrs Goren shook her head. 'It started just over two years ago. He says it isn't painful. To be honest, we didn't think anything of it at first— we just thought he was putting on a bit of weight around his tum.'

Katie nodded and glanced at the results of the ultrasound scan on the computer monitor. 'The spleen is definitely enlarged,' she said in a low voice, looking at Nick.

'Take a look at the radiographs and

MRI films,' he suggested. 'It looks to me as though there's a patchy sclerosis in the left femoral head…and abnormalities in the bone-marrow density.'

Katie studied the films. 'That could suggest replacement of the marrow fat by an infiltrate,' she said thoughtfully.

'That's the conclusion I came to.' Nick frowned. 'This isn't something I've ever come across before, but if my suspicions are correct it could mean subjecting the boy to more invasive tests, like a bone-marrow biopsy. I'm reluctant to do that.'

'That's understandable.' She looked over the boy's notes once more then said quietly, 'You're right—this is very rare, but given the increased erythrocyte sedimentation rate, the history of nosebleeds and two separate incidents of bone pain a year apart, I'd suggest you do a blood test for glucocerebrosidase enzyme in white blood cells.'

He pulled in a deep breath. 'So you've come to the same conclusion as me—thanks for that, Katie. I was reluctant to order specialised tests on an instinctive diagnosis, but you've picked out the associated patterns of disease and helped me to make my decision. I'll go ahead with the enzyme test.'

He turned once more to his patient and spoke to the boy's mother. 'I think we'll admit Matt to hospital overnight so that we can keep him under observation and try to reduce the inflammation in his thigh. I'll arrange for a nurse to wheel him up to the ward—I'll go and organise that now—and then, once he's settled, I'll order another blood test to check for an enzyme deficiency. The sample will have to be sent off to a specialised centre for testing, but as soon as we have the results, in maybe a week's time, I'll be able to tell you more about what's going on.'

He looked at Matt. 'In the meantime, you have to rest...so that means lots of boring things like playing games on your portable computer and watching videos or TV.' He gave an exaggerated wince, and the boy laughed. 'We'll give you some tablets to take away the pain and bring your fever down,' Nick added. 'Once the leg starts to feel more comfortable, you should be up and about again—I'm hoping that will be fairly soon.'

A few minutes later, Katie said goodbye to the boy and his mother and made her way to the door. Nick excused himself and went with her, leaving the two of them to talk about Matt's hospital stay.

'Would you let me know how he goes on?' she asked, and he nodded.

'Of course.' He smiled. 'I knew I could rely on you to pinpoint the essentials,' he said as they went out into the corridor. 'You may not have been here long, but your reputation for being an excellent doctor is already hailed throughout Paediatrics and Emergency.'

'Is it?' Katie was startled. 'I'm pleased about that, of course, but I'm just doing my job, the same as everyone else.' She sent him a fleeting glance. 'Anyway, you do pretty well yourself. I thought you were brilliant with my father the other day. He hates fuss and feeling as though he's putting people out, but you handled him perfectly and you had him feeling better in very quick time. I was impressed.'

He smiled. 'We aim to please.' Then his expression sobered and he asked, 'How is Jack? Is he coping all right with his new medication?'

She nodded. 'On the whole, it's been working well, but I think he had a bit of a setback earlier today. He wasn't feeling too good first thing, apparently.'

Katie recalled the phone conversation she'd had with her father that morning. She'd sensed he'd been holding something back, but, then, he probably kept a good deal of his thoughts hidden from her. He wouldn't want her to know the full extent of his disability, and that saddened her. He was her father, and yet there was so much that they kept hidden from one another. How could she confide her uncertainties, and how could he share his problems with her, if no bond had built up between them over the years?

'He didn't sound quite right, and I could hear the breath rasping in his lungs, but he wouldn't admit to anything more than being a bit under the weather.' She frowned. 'I know he's using his oxygen every night, and sometimes in the daytime, too, and he seems more frail every time I see him. Of course, he never tells me any of his problems. He hates being vulnerable, and it's difficult for me to reach through to him sometimes.'

'Yes, I wondered about that.' Nick sent her an oblique glance. 'Are you and he getting on all right? I know it must be difficult for you. At the hospital the other day it was fairly obvious you and he still had a lot of issues to resolve.'

She wondered how much of their conversation he had overheard. 'That's true enough.' She frowned. 'To be honest, I don't know how I feel. I've made a real effort to break down the barriers between us lately, and I think it's beginning to pay off. I've definitely grown closer to him over these last few weeks.' Even so, doubt clouded her eyes.

'Learning to forgive must be the hardest thing of all.' Nick's gaze trailed over her features, lingering on the vulnerable curve of her mouth. 'You've had to come to terms with two betrayals, haven't you…your ex's and your father's? That's why you have so much trouble contemplating any new relationship.'

'I suppose so.' She pressed her teeth into the fullness of her lower lip. 'I hope I'm succeeding with both of those. At least with James I'm beginning to see that there were already cracks in our relationship. Maybe I was too ambitious, too set on a career path…whereas James was more easygoing, taking life as it came. I'm wondering if he simply wasn't the type to settle down. He had a child, but he didn't have much contact with him.'

'Much like your father.' Nick's expression was sombre. 'No wonder your ex's weakness hit you so hard. Your father had done exactly the same thing…followed his own path and then abandoned you.'

'Yes.' She was silent for a moment, mulling things over. Could any man be trusted? Could Nick? Not according to her father.

She frowned. 'Where my father's concerned, I still don't really understand what goes on in his head. He treats me as though he's very fond of me and has my welfare at heart…but after all those years of little or no contact it takes a bit of getting used to, to believe that he cares.' And yet only yesterday he had told her how proud he was of her, how much it pleased him that his daughter was a doctor, working to save lives. 'I needed to tell you that before I pass on,' he'd said, and she'd put her arms around him and given him a hug.

'Oh, Dad, please don't say that,' she'd implored him, her throat suddenly choked up. 'Please don't talk about passing on. I'm only just getting to know you.'

He'd smiled. 'What'll be will be.'

Nick's brooding gaze rested on her, as though he sensed something of her troubled thoughts. 'I'm sure he cares very deeply for you…but unhappily something went wrong and he didn't feel able to be there for you. Perhaps distance was a problem—living out here in California meant you were so far apart that visits would be infrequent, and he might have thought it would be less painful for you if he didn't visit at all. You would be able to settle to life without him, rather than be hurt all over again every time he went away.'

'Then again,' she pointed out, 'he could have

chosen to stay in England. What was more important…his family or the job?'

He seemed to hesitate. 'That's something you
must ask him yourself. I can't answer that one
for you. But knowing him, I'm sure he had his
reasons.'

'Did he? I've no idea what they were. All I
know is that he condemned us—me and my
mother—to a lonely life.' Her expression was
bleak. 'Some people may like being an only
child, but I wasn't one of them. I always felt
there should be something more.'

He was solemn for a moment, his lips parting as though he was about to say something,
but apparently he thought better of it. He laid
a hand lightly on her shoulder. 'I'm sure it will
all come right for you in the end, Katie. You've
taken a huge step, coming out here, and you're
making great headway. Just give it a little more
time.'

He glanced at his watch. 'I'm off duty in a
couple of hours. I'll come and pick you up from
the apartment and we'll drive over to the vineyard. Perhaps that will cheer you up.'

She nodded. 'Okay. I'll be waiting.' A day or so had passed since he'd made the suggestion, and already she was beginning to regret agreeing to it. What had happened to her plan to avoid him at all costs, to steer clear of getting involved with him in any way? Working with him was proving to be a hazard in itself. It seemed that he was there at every turn…and it was impossible for her to get him out of her head.

She was beginning to realise that there was so much more to him than she had at first imagined. He was caring and perceptive and even though that made her want to get to know him a whole lot better, she was desperately afraid of the consequences. Little by little, though, he was drawing her into his electric force field and she was powerless to resist.

The vineyard, when they arrived there some time later, was bathed in late-afternoon sunlight. Nick helped her out of the passenger seat of his gleaming silver saloon and waited as she stepped out onto the wide, sweeping drive. Katie looked around. She couldn't explain it, even to herself, but just the simple fact that he was there beside her made the breath catch in her throat and in spite of herself filled her with a kind of delicious expectation. He was wearing casual clothes, a deep navy shirt, open at the neck, teamed with dark trousers, and just looking at him made her heart skip a beat.

'Let me show you round the place,' he said. 'From a high point in the gardens you can see for miles around.' He slipped an arm around her waist, his hand coming to rest on the curve of her hip in a gentle act of possession that brought heat surging throughout her body. 'I'm sure you'll love it out here,' he murmured. 'We have a beautiful day for it…the sun's shining and the vines are heavy with grapes.'

She nodded, and tried not to think about that casual touch that was so much like a caress. It only fogged her brain and left her confused and distracted.

He led the way through the house, a pretty French château-style building that had steeply pitched roofs and round towers with turrets. Painted white, it was a gem set in the middle of the Carmel Valley, and Katie fell in love with it on sight.

The gardens were exquisitely landscaped, with trees and shrubs in full bloom so that there was a mass of colour all around. Nestled among the various arbours and flowering trees there was an elevated hardwood deck, and Nick started to head towards it.

'From up here on the deck you can see the vineyard in all its glory. It's a great vantage point,' he said, mounting the wooden stairs and walking over to the balustrade.

Katie followed him and turned to gaze at the distant Carmel Valley Mountains. 'I didn't realise that you had so much land,' she murmured. 'Are all those vines yours, or do those slopes belong to another vineyard…my father's, perhaps?'

Nick followed the direction of her gaze. 'They're ours. Your father's land is a little further to the west. We've terraced the slopes here in order to grow certain types of grapes, and then we have more vines spread along the valley floor. We're incredibly lucky in this area because there's such a long season. The grapes ripen slowly and that helps to intensify the flavour.'

She nodded, trying to take it all in. In the far distance, the verdant slopes of the ever-present Santa Lucia range added to the sense of lush, rich farmland all around. 'It looks heavenly,' she murmured, 'like an Eden where everything is in harmony and the fruit is bursting off the vines.'

He smiled. 'At least, that's how we hope it will be. A good year will produce a premium vintage, but we can't rely on that. If we get too much rain at the wrong time it can cause all kinds of problems, like mould, rot or mildew. Then again, the weather one season can be too hot and another too cool. It all helps to produce a variety of flavours and different qualities of wine.'

'So you can't simply sit back and leave things to nature?'

He laughed. 'I wish! But, no, definitely not... we have to take steps to compensate for adverse conditions.' He laid an arm around her, his hand splaying out over her shoulder and sending a thrill of heat to course through her veins. 'Over the years my family has put a huge amount of effort into building up a reputation for producing quality wines…and it all came about because of my great-great-grandfather's drive and ambition.'

She was thoughtful for a moment. 'He certainly managed to pick out a piece of prime land. He must have been an astute man—and I dare say a wealthy one, too.'

Nick shook his head. 'His family were immigrants, dirt poor, and they had to scrape a living for themselves. They came out here hoping for a better life, but it was a struggle, and I think Joseph, my great-great-grandfather, made up his mind that he would carve a path for himself, come what may. He worked at all kinds of jobs, day and night, determined to earn as much money as possible. He was thrifty, too, and put aside a good part of his earnings until, after about fifteen years or so, he had saved enough money to buy this vineyard.'

'That was a huge accomplishment.'

He nodded. 'It was. But the hardest bit was

turning the vineyard around. When he first took it over they were producing inexpensive table wines, but Joseph had other ideas. He had a certain vision and he wanted to make big changes. Quality was everything to him and even though people told him he was making a big mistake, he went ahead with his plans to produce grapes that would provide superior wines. Then he had to convince the buyers that this was a product they wanted, and it all took tremendous hard work and a lot of money.'

He frowned. 'Over the years, when wine consumption declined and harvests were poor, the vineyard suffered losses that could have ruined everything for us. That's why my grandfather had to sell off a third of the land…the piece that Jack owns now. He needed the money to go on running things in keeping with Joseph's ideals.'

'And now you want it back,' Katie said flatly. 'That's why you've been asking my father to sign papers that will turn the ownership over to you once more.' She looked at him directly. 'He should have his solicitor look them over before he does anything, shouldn't he? I think I should get in touch with the law firm that deals with his affairs.' It was a subtle warning, designed to let him know that she wasn't going to stand by and see her father put under pressure. 'Only, like I said before, I don't think he's in any fit state to deal with these kinds of problems just now, do you?'

Her expression was faintly belligerent, her jaw tilted, and Nick's gaze flicked over her, taking it all in. 'I was just telling you the history of the place, that's all,' he said in an even tone. 'I don't want to get into an argument with you.'

She backed down a little. After all, she was on his territory, she was a guest here, and this was perhaps the wrong time and place to thrash out their differences.

'I'm just concerned for my father,' she said.

'I know that, and I respect you for it.' He studied her thoughtfully. 'But if you really care about him, you would probably do well to persuade him that his life would be easier if he were to offload the worries of the business onto us. That way he could relax and enjoy his remaining years.'

She stiffened. 'I think you're mistaken if you believe I'll do your deal for you.' She sent him a flinty stare. 'I haven't had many weeks to get to know him, but it's been long enough for me to begin to care what happens to him. I didn't know what it was to have a father until now, and I've started to realise that it's something precious. I never imagined I would feel this way, about him or his land—so I'm not likely to suggest that he changes anything.'

She threw him a quick glance. 'I expect you're equally protective of your parents—more so, in fact.'

He nodded. 'I'm not criticising you in any way. It's natural that you should want to protect Jack's interests…but I'm sure he's astute enough to recognise a good deal when he sees one, and ours is far above anything he would get on the open market. Instead of trying to shield him, you could show him that it's the sensible route to follow.'

'I don't think so. I think you and your father

need to back off.' She hesitated as a thought struck her. 'I don't believe you've ever mentioned your mother...'

'No.' His eyes were briefly troubled. 'She passed away some years ago...it was a virus, a nasty one that attacked her heart. The doctors did everything they could, but it wasn't enough to save her. I think she was already weak from a chest infection that laid her low.' He looked at Katie. 'I loved her dearly. She was a wonderful woman.'

'I'm sorry.' Katie pressed her lips together in a moment of regret. 'That must have been hard for all of you—your brother and your father.'

He nodded. 'Alex—my brother—was in Canada when he heard she was ill, but he came back as soon as he found out. At least we were all able to be with her at the end, and that makes it a little easier for us to bear.'

He moved away from the deck rail, becoming brisk and ready for action as though he wanted to shake off such sombre thoughts. 'Shall we go over to the winery? I said I'd take you on a tour after all.'

'Yes, I think maybe we should.' She followed him down the steps, saying, 'I was expecting some of your family to be here today—your father, maybe, or your brother.'

He shook his head. 'My father had to go into town, and Alex is in Los Angeles on business. I told him all about you, and I know he wants to meet you.'

Katie wasn't sure how to respond to that. Why would he have spoken to his brother about her? Unless, of course, he'd simply confided in his brother that a new girl had wandered in on his horizon…but perhaps she was misjudging him. It could be that her father was the factor in all this. The Bellinis were strongly allied to him through their business dealings, and it was prob- ably only natural that they would be interested in the fact that he had a daughter—one that he had kept secret for a good many years.

They walked along a path leading from the house towards a collection of buildings some five hundred yards away. Nick pointed out a large stone-built complex where the grapes were processed, and then indicated another outbuilding where the offices and labs were housed. 'I'll show you around there later on,' he said, moving on.

She nodded. 'I know next to nothing about wine-making, I'm afraid.'

'You're not alone in that,' he murmured. He paused by a heavy wooden door set into a stone arch. 'Through here is the entrance to the cellar,' he told her. 'It has walls that are some fifteen inches thick, and it's a cool, well-ventilated environment, essential for producing good wine.'

The wine-tasting room was in a building set a little apart from these processing areas. The outer walls were painted in a soft sunshine yellow, and there were tubs of flowers and hanging baskets facing out on to the courtyard, giving it a mellow, cottage-style appearance.

'This is so pretty,' Katie said, glancing at the winery and looking back at the chateau in the distance. 'Your father must be really pleased to live in such an idyllic place.'

'I'm sure he is. I know I loved it. I was brought up here, and it was a wonderful childhood.' He looked around. 'It might be a good idea to sample the wines out here. Perhaps a table in the shade would be best.' He indicated a table in a far corner that was bordered by diamond-patterned trellises on two sides.

'Come and make yourself comfortable,' he said, holding out a seat for her, 'while I go and fetch the wines.'

He returned a moment later, bearing a tray. 'We'll try a Burgundy-style Pinot Noir first of all. It's our pride and joy, the best vintage yet. See what you think of it. It's made from black grapes that grow on the cooler slopes.'

Once she was settled, he handed her a glass filled with dark red wine, and she took a sip. It was rich and smooth, with a hint of spice and an aftertaste of black cherry plum. Katie savoured it, letting it roll over her tongue before she swallowed it. 'I can see why you're excited about this,' she said. 'I'm not a wine buff, but I do know what I like, and this is delicious.'

Nick said quietly, 'Joseph Bellini would have been proud.' He turned to Katie. 'This is what his hard work was all about, and nowadays we do our level best to live up to his vision. As

well as this special wine, we produce our own
Cabernet Sauvignon. It's stored in barrels made
of French oak and allowed to mature over many
years. The oak helps to smooth out the harsh
tannins and introduces softer, wood tannins.'

Katie nodded and tasted the wine once more.
'Don't you have a problem if my father's vineyard produces similar wines? Doesn't that put
you in direct competition with one another?'

He shook his head. 'Your father concentrates
on Chardonnay. He had a really good season last
year, and the result should be a superb wine.'
He picked out another bottle. 'This is one of
his Chardonnays,' he said, pouring white wine
into a glass and handing it to her. 'Try it. I think
you'll like it. It's full of fruit flavours—like pear,
apple and melon.'

Katie sipped the wine and tried to forget for
the moment that Nick and his family were doing
their level best to pull her father's business out
from under his feet. How could she be drawn to
a man who would do that? He was the enemy
and yet she was calmly sipping wine with him

and enjoying the comfort of his home. She felt like a traitor.

She would simply have to be on her guard and watch out for Jack's interests whenever possible, she decided. Maybe she would carry out her threat and get in touch with the law firm that dealt with his business affairs. The Garcias were in the phone book, and a straightforward call might do the trick. They could advise her what to do and monitor her father's dealings at the same time.

'Mmm.' She nodded. 'This is lovely.' She raised her glass to him and then looked at the tray of wines. 'I see you have at least a dozen bottles on the trolley,' she said quietly. 'At this rate I shall be tipsy before dinner.'

Nick smiled and answered under his breath, 'I think I'd quite like to see that.' Then he pulled a wry face. 'I do have a secret stash of crackers and cheese hidden away, designed to soak up the alcohol, once we've had a taster. It's a pity that we have to eat them,' he added, his voice low and husky. 'With your senses blurred, I might have been able to persuade you that

I'm everything you ever wanted in a man.' His expression was mournful, and Katie stifled a laugh.

'Give it up,' she murmured. 'I wouldn't want your hopes to be dashed.'

They tasted several more wines, including the Merlot, which her father seemed to favour most of all. It was another red wine, rich and fruity with notes of currant and cherry.

Katie was glad of the savoury biscuits and the cheese platter that Nick brought out a short time later. She had missed lunch and she was beginning to feel more than a little heady. Alongside the various cheeses, there were pizza slices and *bruschetta*—slices of toasted bread topped with *prosciutto* and tomato. He had provided a selection of nuts, too, served with slices of dried apricot.

'This has been such a great experience,' she told him. 'I've never been to a wine tasting before, and to be here surrounded by greenery and row on row of vineyard slopes has been wonderful.'

'I'm glad you've enjoyed it,' he said, giving her

an appreciative smile. 'Perhaps we should go along and have a look at the processing complex, before the wine goes right to your head. You're looking a trifle flushed, and it might help if you were to stretch your legs for a bit.'

'Okay.'

He helped her to her feet, and they strolled slowly over to the stone-built production plant. Nick explained some of the processes involved— the pressing of the grapes, the addition of yeast and the many checks that were done to test each stage of the fermentation process. In each separate room there were photos and clear text descriptions on the walls to enable visitors to understand what went on there. There were photos, too, of Joseph Bellini, his son Sebastian, Nick's grandfather, Thomas, and finally Robert and his two sons. Katie stared at them in wonder. They all had the same rugged good looks, the strong bone structure, and that dark, Italian machismo.

'I had no idea such a lot of effort went into producing a bottle of wine,' she told Nick a while later as they stood by the window in the scrupulously clean barn where the grapes were poured into a giant hopper. The building's double doors were open to allow a cooling drift of air into the room. 'It must be tremendously satisfying to overcome all the hazards of production and finally taste the result—and discover that it's perfection.'

'It is. Wine-making is in our blood. It has become a part of us, much as the hills and valleys all around have become our home. I wouldn't want to be anywhere else than this small corner of the world.' He gave a crooked smile. 'My brother chose to travel, to go from place to place marketing our wines, but that wouldn't do for me. My roots are here. I love this valley and my beach house. I'm very content.'

'I imagine you are.' She gazed out of the window at the surrounding hills and then looked back at him. 'You must be very proud of your ancestors…all the dedication, strength of mind and sheer stamina that has gone into making the business what it is now. No wonder you're such a fit-looking family—what I've seen of it so far. It must be in the genes.'

He leaned against a guard rail, turning to face her full on, his dark eyes glinting. 'Fit is good, isn't it?' He slightly raised dark brows. 'Does this mean you're beginning to alter your opinion of me?' He reached for her in a leisurely fashion, his hands at the base of her spine, drawing her to him and holding her lightly within the circle of his arms. 'Perhaps there's still hope I could persuade you that I'm the sort of man you could go for?'

She laughed softly. 'There's always hope, I suppose.' She looked at him from under her lashes. 'But I wouldn't get too carried away if I were you.'

'A good thing you're not me, then,' he murmured huskily, 'because I have entirely different ideas on that score. Carried away sounds just about right to me. Carried away is a chink in the armour, and definitely something I'd like to explore a little further.'

He came towards her, his arms tightening around her waist, and as his head lowered she finally began to realise his intention. He was going to kiss her, and even though, way down in the depths of her mind, she knew she really ought to be doing something to stop him, she did nothing at all. And as his lips brushed hers in a touch that was as light as the drift of silk over her skin, she discovered the last thing on earth she wanted was to pull away.

Just the opposite, in fact. Instead, she wanted to lean into him, to revel in his warm embrace, and delight in the strength of those muscular thighs that were pressuring her softly against the cool, steel wall of the hopper. And he must have known what she wanted because he drew her ever closer until her breasts were softly crushed against the wall of his chest and she could feel the heavy thud of his heartbeat marching in time with her own.

He kissed her, tenderly at first and then with rising passion, so that his breathing became ragged and his hands began to smooth over her curves.

Katie was lost in a haze of fevered pleasure. The sun was bright in an azure sky, and for a moment or two time seemed to stand still. There was only the sensual glide of his lips as they slowly explored the contours of her face, her throat and the creamy expanse of her shoulder, laid bare by the thin straps of the cotton top she wore. And with each lingering kiss her senses soared in response.

It was all so exhilarating, so perfect, and nothing like anything she had ever experienced before. What was it about him that made her feel this way? Did he have some kind of magical touch? If so, she wanted more, much more.

Only, as his lips began to slide lower, drifting into unsafe territory, alarm bells started to ring inside her. He gently nudged aside the delicate cotton strap and ventured even further into the danger zone, trailing soft kisses over the rounded swell of her breasts and leading her to a heady, disturbing place where feeling and emotion were all, and logical thought was banished.

Even so, a tiny sliver of common sense began to filter through the mist that spread, unbidden, through her brain. Perhaps it was the swish of sprinklers being started up on the lawns outside that alerted her, or maybe it was the soft flap of a bird's wings that dragged her attention back to the reality of what was happening. What was she thinking? How could she have let this happen?

She struggled to get herself together. Wasn't Nick the man who avoided commitment? Wasn't he the one who was trying to persuade her father to sign away his land?

And here she was, betraying every instinct she possessed by falling into his arms at the first opportunity. She was a fool. She ought to have known better.

'Are you all right?' Nick lifted his head, depriving her of that heavenly, forbidden contact, and she tried to answer, but no words came. 'Have I done something wrong?' His voice was a soft murmur against her cheek.

'No... I... Yes...' She tried to ease herself away from him, her hands flattening against his chest as though she would put an end to his kisses. Why, then, did she feel the urge to stroke the velvet-covered wall of his rib cage and let her fingers explore the broad expanse of his shoulders? His muscles were firm and supple, inviting her to touch him and savour the moment.

Truly, she was a basket case—a woman at the mercy of her hormones and not to be trusted with the slightest task. 'I don't think I'm ready for this,' she said huskily. 'I shouldn't have let things get this far.'

'Are you quite sure about that?' His hands caressed her, and his tone was soft and coaxing, inviting her to drift back into the shelter of his arms once more. 'Life could be so much sweeter if only you'd allow yourself to taste it.'

She pulled in a shaky breath, willing herself to resist temptation. 'I'm sure...absolutely sure.' Even as she said it she wondered if she was trying to convince him or herself. She straightened and took a step away from him. 'I don't know how you manage to do this to me,' she said huskily, her gaze troubled. 'I need to feel good about myself, and none of this is helping. I'm very confused. I need time to think.'

'Okay.' He gave a soft, ragged sigh and moved to lay his forehead gently against hers. 'But I can't help thinking that you'd do better to throw caution to the wind. Life isn't easy. It's full of what-ifs and might-have-beens, and if you thought hard about all of them you might never experience the good side of things. I know you've been hurt, but sometimes you have to get back into the fray if you're to have another chance of happiness. Sometimes you simply have to go with your instinct and trust in people.'

Slowly, he released her, and then stood with his hands to either side of him on the guard rail, so that she finally began to breathe a little easier.

He straightened. 'I'll walk you back to the courtyard.' He gave a crooked smile. 'You'll be safe there.'

CHAPTER SIX

KATIE placed the consultant's letter back in her tray and tried to steer her thoughts towards work. 'Good news there, at least,' she told Carla, the desk clerk, indicating the sheet of headed notepaper. 'My young patient who was rushed to hospital from here a few weeks ago is back home and on the mend.'

'The child with kidney problems? I remember his mother was so upset.' Carla gave a relieved smile. 'It's good to know he's pulled through all right. I've been worrying about him...about the poor boy with the head injury, too.'

Katie nodded. 'Me, too. Last I heard, they were thinking about moving him from the intensive care unit. I was hoping I might find time to ring and check up on him some time today, but the time has simply rushed by.' She frowned, straightening up and easing the slight ache in her back. Earlier today she had rung her father to find out how he was doing, but things weren't good, and that was playing on her mind. His nurse, Steve, was worried about his condition.

She dragged her mind back to work. 'Do I have any more patients to see this afternoon? There's nothing on my list and the waiting room's empty.'

Carla glanced at her screen once more. 'No, but there was a message from Dr Bellini. He said Matthew Goren was coming in to hospital as an outpatient today. He thought you might like to be in on the consultation with him. His appointment's scheduled for four o'clock—that gives you a quarter of an hour to get over there.'

'Right…thanks, Carla. I'd better run.'

She hurried over to the emergency department. She wasn't at all sure how she was going to cope with seeing Nick again—his scorching kisses had seared a memory into her brain that would last for all time. It made her feel hot and bothered even now, just thinking about it. And she had also been mulling over his words of advice… 'Sometimes you have to go with your instinct and trust in people.' Could she do that? Was she ready to put the past behind her and accept that she might be able to find happiness in his arms?

She went along the corridor in search of his room.

'Katie, I'm glad you could make it.' Nick's voice was deep and warm, smooth like honey drizzled over caramelised pears. He gave her a quick smile and invited her into his office. 'I thought you might like to be in on this one. The lab results are back, and this is the last appointment of the day so there will be time to break the news to the boy and his mother without having to rush things.'

'Break the news—it's what we thought, then?'

He nodded. 'Gaucher's disease. Fortunately, even though it's rare, there are treatments for it, so it isn't as bad as it might have been some years ago. And Matt has the mildest form of the disease, so that's another point in his favour.'

He accessed the boy's notes on his computer, and they both took time to sift through the various test results and read the letter from the consultant. When the clerk paged them a few minutes later, they were both ready to receive mother and son with smiles of greeting.

'I know you're anxious to hear the results of the tests,' Nick told them after he had made some general enquiries about the boy's state of health. 'As you know, I was concerned because Matt's spleen appeared to be enlarged and because he's been having pain in his joints. We discovered there was also some slight enlargement of the liver.'

Mrs Goren nodded. 'You took some blood for testing, and he had an MRI scan.'

'That's right.' Nick brought up the film of the scan on his computer monitor and turned to Katie. 'Do you want to explain the results?' he asked.

Katie nodded, and looked at the boy. He was a thin child, slightly underweight, with cropped brown hair that gave him an elfin look. He was looking at her now with large eyes and a faintly worried expression.

'What we discovered,' she said, 'was that you

have a fatty substance in your liver and spleen. It shouldn't be there, and so we needed to find out what was going on inside you that would have caused it.'

Matt nodded, but looked puzzled and, picking up on that Katie said quickly, 'I want you to feel free to ask me questions at any time, Matt. If there's anything you don't understand, or anything you'd like to say, just go ahead.'

He frowned. 'Have you found out what caused it? Is it something I've done? The boys at school tease me.'

Katie gave him a sympathetic smile. 'No, it's nothing that you've done, and I'm sorry that you're being teased. Perhaps when you explain to the boys what's wrong, they'll understand a bit better and stop making fun of you.'

She glanced at his mother. 'Matt has a condition called Gaucher's disease. Basically, it means that he was born without an enzyme that breaks down a substance called glucocerebroside.' She turned to Matt. 'Because you don't have this enzyme in your body, the fatty substance isn't broken down and has to find somewhere to go. Unfortunately, when it finds a home in places like your liver, your spleen or even your bones, for example, it stops those parts of you from working properly. That's why you've been having pain in your thigh, and it's the reason for you being tired all the while.'

'You're saying he was born with it?' His mother was frowning. 'Does that mean it's a hereditary disease?'

Mrs Goren's gaze flew in alarm from Katie to Nick, and Nick answered quietly, 'That's right. You and your husband may not suffer from the disease, but it's possible that either one or both of you may be a carrier. It can go back through generations, although there may not be anyone in the family that you know of directly who has the disease.'

All at once Mrs Goren looked close to tears and Katie hurried on to say, 'The *good* news is that we do have treatment for it.' She smiled at Matt. 'There's something called enzyme replacement therapy, which helps to break down this fatty substance and should soon start to improve things for you.'

Matt's brow cleared, and his mother dabbed at her eyes with a tissue and did her best to pull herself together. She looked at Nick. 'Can we start him on this treatment straight away?'

He responded cautiously. 'I can arrange an appointment for him at the hospital. The answer isn't as simple as taking a tablet, I'm afraid, but what happens is that Matt will be given an infusion—it takes about an hour to administer, and the treatment is given once a fortnight. He'll need to stay with the treatment for life, until such time as science comes up with a better answer. It's a rare disease. Of course, he'll be carefully monitored on a regular basis, so that we can check how he's responding.'

Katie was silent, watching as mother and son tried to absorb what he had just told them. Nick waited, too, before gently asking if they had any questions for him. He was unfailingly patient and kind, and her respect for him grew. In fact, every time she saw him at work, she marvelled at his caring, conscientious manner.

Mrs Goren and Matt both remained quiet for a moment or two longer. Perhaps they had all the information they could handle for the time being. It was a lot to take in, but the consolation was that from now on they would receive masses of help from the clinic at the hospital… along with ongoing input from Nick and herself, of course.

'Will the treatment cause the swelling to go down?' Mrs Goren asked, and Nick nodded.

'You should see a great improvement.' He looked at Matt. 'And the pain will go away.'

After answering a few more questions, and doing what he could to put the mother's mind at ease, he said, 'Let me leave you with some reading material that I've printed out for you. I'm sure there will be things that you think of once you leave here, but I'm hoping that these papers will help answer any immediate queries…and, of course, you can always come and see me again if you want to talk.'

Katie glanced at Nick. That was a thoughtful touch—he had gone that one step further to give his patient everything he could, and she could see that Mrs Goren was pleased.

Nick gave his attention to Matt, and said, 'The

nurses and doctors at the clinic will look after you and explain anything you want to know. Next time you come to the hospital for an out-patient appointment, I'm sure you'll be feeling a whole lot better. In the meantime, keep taking the painkillers if you have any more trouble with your thigh, and get plenty of rest. Once you get started on the treatment, I'm certain you'll begin to feel much more energetic.'

Matt nodded. 'Thanks,' he said, and gave a shuddery sigh. 'I thought I had some horrible illness that was going to make me die, but it's not as bad as that, is it?'

'No, it isn't,' Nick told him with a reassuring smile, and Katie's heart went out to this child who had suffered in silence all this time. 'And if you ever have worries of any kind,' Nick added, 'please speak up. Don't keep it to yourself. Often things aren't nearly as bad as you think, and we're here to help you in any way we can.'

After they left, Nick invited Katie to stay awhile and made coffee for both of them. 'I need to write up my notes while they're fresh in my mind—but perhaps we can talk after that?'

'Okay.' She sipped her coffee and leaned back in her chair, thinking about the day's events. From a medical standpoint at work, things had gone well, but she felt uneasy somehow. There was still that niggling worry over her father's health.

She gave a faint sigh, and then stretched. What she needed right now was a complete change of scene, a trip to the beach, perhaps or maybe even a walk through the cobbled streets of the town. But that wasn't likely to happen for a while… Perhaps she ought to go and see her father, see how he was bearing up. There might be something she could do for him.

'Are you okay?' Nick asked.

Caught off guard, Katie quickly tried to collect her thoughts. She hadn't realised he'd been watching her. 'I'm fine, thanks.'

His gaze flicked over her. 'You seem…pensive. If there's something wrong, perhaps I can help?'

She shook her head. 'I was just thinking about my father—I feel that I should go over to his place to see if he's all right. I rang this morning and he was having a bad day, according to the nurse, Steve. It's a bit worrying—apparently he was talking but not making much sense.'

Nick winced. 'That happens sometimes when the blood oxygen levels are low.'

'Yes. Even so, I asked Steve to send for the doctor to see if he would prescribe a different medication. He hasn't called me yet to let me know what happened. I suppose he's been too busy, with one thing and another, or perhaps he didn't want to tie up the phone line if the doctor was likely to call.'

'That's probably the case.' He studied her thoughtfully. 'Would you like me to go with you to see him? It's never easy when someone in the family is ill, is it?'

'No, it isn't.' She might have known Nick would understand. He had been through diffi-cult times with his mother in the past, and it said a lot about his compassion and perception that he was offering to be by her side. 'Thank you,' she said softly. 'I'd really like it if you would be there with me.'

'We'll go as soon as I've finished up here,' he

said, becoming brisk and ready for action. 'Give me five minutes.'

A feeling of relief swept over her. She didn't know why she had involved Nick in any of this, there was no accounting for her actions, and she was working purely on instinct. All at once, though, she felt that with him by her side, she could handle anything.

They went out to his car a short time later, which was in a leafy, private space in the car park. She glanced at him. Even after a day's work, he looked cool and fresh, dressed in dark trousers and crisp linen shirt that perfectly outlined his long, lean figure. His black hair glinted with iridescent lights as they walked in the sunlight, and she gazed at him for a moment or two, wondering what it was about him that stirred her blood and made her want to be with him.

He touched her hand, clasping it within his, and suddenly she felt safe, cherished, as though all was right with the world. 'I'm here for you, Katie,' he said softly. 'Any time you need me.'

Her heart swelled with joy. The truth was, he had never been anything but good towards her.

He had treated her with warmth and respect, with care and attention, and he was here now, ready to be by her side at a moment's notice and support her through what promised to be a difficult time. What more could she ask?

She stood in the shade of a cypress tree, watching him as he paused to unlock the car, and it finally hit her that she was bedazzled by him. He made her heart thump and her thoughts go haywire, and there was no knowing why it was happening. Why was she holding back? She might just as well cast her fears to one side and start living again, mightn't she?

Okay, so she had been hurt once before. Her ex had had a child by another woman and had shocked her to the core with his infidelity, but that didn't have to mean all men were of a similar nature, did it? Was she going to let that experience ruin her life for evermore?

Nick came to stand beside her, his lips curving in a faint smile, and he said softly, 'Are you feeling all right? You look different somehow.'

A faint bubble of laughter rose in her throat. 'I'm fine. I'm just so glad that you're here with me. Whatever happens, I feel as though I'll be able to cope with it, just as long as we're together.'

'That's good to know.' His voice faded on a shuddery sigh. 'I've waited a long while for you to learn to trust me, Katie. I won't let you down, I promise.'

He wrapped his arms around her and kissed her gently on the mouth. His touch was light as the drift of silk, but it sent fiery signals to every nerve ending in her body, and she wanted to cling to him, to savour that moment and make it last for ever.

Her fingers lightly stroked his arms and then moved up to tangle with the silky hair at his nape. She belonged in his arms, it felt right, as though it was the only place to be at that moment.

He kissed her again, trailing kisses over her cheek, her throat, and then with a soft, ragged sound he reluctantly dragged himself away from her.

'Wrong place,' he said in a roughened tone, as though that explained things. 'I can think of better places where I can show you how much I care.'

Katie stared at him, blankly, her lips parting, a tingle of delicious sensation still running through her from head to toe.

He sent her an oblique glance in return, his mouth twisting a little. 'Did I go too far again?' he asked. 'I hope not, because I really wanted to do that. In fact, it's on my mind every time I see you—and even sometimes when we're apart.'

She didn't answer, still lost in that haze of delirious excitement. He'd kissed her…he cared about her… All at once the world was bright and new. Was this love?

Nick pulled in a deep breath, as though to steady himself. He held open the passenger door for her and she slid dazedly into the air-conditioned comfort of his car. Then he went around to the driver's side, coming to sit beside her.

He turned the key in the ignition, starting up the car. 'I need to get my head right,' he said. 'Perhaps we should talk about everyday kind of things for a while—like work, for instance.'

She blinked and closed her mouth, trying her

utmost to bring her thoughts back down to a level plane, and he went on cautiously, 'I thought you might like to know—I checked up on Darren Mayfield this afternoon.'

'You did?' She finally found her voice. 'Oh, I'm glad of that. I haven't had time to ring the unit yet today. How's he doing? I know they were thinking of moving him from Intensive Care.'

He nodded. 'That's right. I know you've been keeping tabs on his condition over the last week or so. Anyway, he's on the main ward now and he seems on course to make a full recovery. There's some weakness in his limbs apparently, but the physiotherapist is going to be working with him and he looks set to be back to normal within a few weeks.'

Her face lit up. 'Oh, that's wonderful news… the best.'

He nodded. 'I knew you'd be pleased.' He set the car in motion and turned his attention to the road, leaving her to gaze out at the passing landscape.

'You said you'd been to see your father's

vineyard,' Nick remarked as he turned the car on to the valley road. 'Of course, he doesn't live on the property—his manager is the one who stays on the premises. I expect you'll have met him when you went over there.'

Katie nodded. 'Yes, I've been introduced to Toby. He seems a very friendly and approachable man. At least he was willing to answer all my naïve questions. Like I said, I've been fascinated with the whole process of growing vines and turning the fruit into wine ever since I came over here and learned what my father was doing.'

Nick frowned. 'You could always ask me anything you want to know…anytime. I'd be only too glad to tell you. We could even combine it with dinner out or supper at one of the ocean view restaurants around here, if you like. Or a stroll along the beach if that takes your fancy more.'

Her mouth curved. 'I'll definitely think about it. They all sound good to me.'

He relaxed, a look of satisfaction crossing his face. 'Wow! I think I'm actually winning for a change! Wake me up, I think I might be dreaming!'

'I seriously hope not,' she said with a laugh, 'or any minute now you'll be crashing the car into my father's gatepost.'

They had reached her father's property, a stone-built house set in a secluded area some short distance from the coastal stretch where Nick had his home. They approached it along a sweeping drive that cut through well-kept lawns, bordered in part by mature trees and flowering shrubs.

The house was a solid, rectangular building on two storeys, with the ground-floor windows placed symmetrically either side of a wide doorway.

Katie frowned as Nick drew the car to a halt. 'It looks as though my father has a visitor,' she said. 'I don't recognise that four by four, do you?'

'It's the doctor's car. Dr Weissman—I've known him for some years now.'

'Oh, yes.' Katie collected her thoughts. 'I think I've bumped into him once or twice.' Her gaze was troubled. 'I wonder if my father's taken a turn for the worse?'

Nick was already sliding out of the car, and she hurried to join him on the gravelled fore-court. It was a fresh, warm summer's day, but the sun went behind a cloud just then and a sudden sense of foreboding rippled through her. She walked quickly towards the oak front door and rang the bell.

Libby, the housekeeper, came to answer it, looking unusually flustered. 'Oh, Katie, there you are.' She pulled open the door and ushered them inside. 'I was just about to call you,' she said, pulling at a wayward strand of soft brown hair. 'The doctor and Steve are with your father now. Jack's been having a bad time of it all day. It's his heart, I think. At least, that's what the doctor said.'

'I need to go and see him,' Katie said, a thread of unease edging her words. The feeling of dread that clutched at her midriff since she'd arrived at the house was intensifying by the minute.

'I understand how you must be feeling,' Libby answered, worry lines creasing her brow, 'but the doctor said he would come and let us know as soon as there was any news.'

Katie frowned. 'But I'm his daughter. I want to be with him. I want to know what's going on.'

The housekeeper's face seemed to crumple, and she made a helpless, fluttering gesture with her hands, as though this was all getting too much for her, and Katie said quickly, 'It will be all right, Libby, I promise. We made up our differences a while ago, my father and I…he'll want me to be there with him. I know he will.'

Libby was still fraught with indecision. 'I should have rung you earlier, I know I should, but I had to ring for an ambulance and try to contact the others and that took up so much time. It's been such an awful day, one way and another. And the ambulance still hasn't arrived.'

Katie frowned. What others? What was Libby talking about? But perhaps she had tried to phone Jack's friends, the people who knew him best…along with the doctor, of course. Katie might be his daughter, but she had only been in town for a couple of months at most.

Nick took hold of her arm, as though to add

a helping hand, and she turned to him in gratitude. 'Thanks for bringing me here. It looks as though things are much more serious than I thought. Otherwise why would Dr Weissman have wanted an ambulance?'

'It does sound as though he's concerned,' Nick admitted, 'but let's wait and hear what he has to say.'

'I must go to my father,' she said again. She knew the way to Jack's room from the first time she had been there, when her father had shown her around, and despite Libby's distressed expression she made an instant decision and began to head in that direction.

Nick went with her, but as they came to the first floor and walked along the corridor, the door of her father's room opened and Steve walked out.

He stopped as soon as he saw them and pulled in a deep, calming breath. 'Katie,' he greeted her. 'I don't think you should go in there just yet. Let me talk to you for a while. Shall we find somewhere to sit down?' He glanced at Nick, and an odd look passed between them. Katie didn't understand it. Hadn't that same mysterious kind of glance occurred when she and her father had had dinner together and she'd met Nick for the first time?

She allowed Nick to lead her away, following Steve along the corridor and back down the stairs to the sitting room.

'Please, sit down, Katie.' Steve indicated a comfortable sofa and then turned to Nick. 'You, too, Nick,' he said.

Katie did as he suggested, feeling for the settee with the back of her legs and not once taking her gaze off Steve. Nick sat down beside her, and the nurse took the armchair opposite.

She was more bewildered than ever. Something was going on here and she had no idea what it could be. Right now, though, she wanted more than anything to know what was happening with her father.

'Katie,' Steve began quietly, 'I'm really sorry to be the one to tell you this…but I'm afraid your father passed away a few minutes ago. In the end his heart simply gave out.'

'No…' Katie's mind refused to take it in. 'That

can't be… I only spoke to him on the phone this morning. How can this be happening?' For all her training as a doctor, coming face to face with the death of a loved one was turning out to be every bit as difficult for her as it was for her patients. She had no idea it could be so hard to accept.

Nick put his arm around her and held her tight. 'I'm so sorry, Katie. It's a shock—in fact, it's a shock for both of us.'

Steve pressed his lips together in a fleeting moment of sadness. 'Dr Weissman did everything he could to try to resuscitate him, but in the end it was impossible. There was nothing more he could do.'

Katie was bewildered. 'I just can't take it in. I came here thinking he was just having one of those bad days. He always seemed so stoical, so determined to get the best out of life.'

'And I'm sure he did, Katie.' Nick leant his cheek against hers. 'He was over the moon because you had come out here to see him. These last few weeks he was always talking about you, saying how well you'd done for yourself.'

'Was he?' Tears began to trickle slowly down her face. 'It seems such a waste. All these years I've waited, wanting to get to know him but always holding back because I was afraid of what I might find. It took me such a long time to forgive him for walking out on my mother and me. It was such a strange sort of life…as if it was somehow off key. And now he's gone.'

He held her close, letting her weep for what might have been, and all the time he stroked her hair, comforting her just by being there for her when she needed him most.

Libby brought in a tray of tea and quietly set it down on the coffee table. 'The doctor's gone into the kitchen to fill in his forms. He's very sad. They were good friends—your father always spoke highly of him.'

Katie glanced up at Libby. The woman was ashen-faced, struggling to keep her emotions in check.

'Perhaps you should sit down and give yourself some time,' Katie suggested softly, still shaken but subdued. 'You must be as upset as the rest of us. More so, perhaps…my father told me you'd been with him for years.'

Libby put a tissue to her face. 'I have, yes, that's true.' She wrung her hands. 'I ought to go and…' She turned distractedly, as though to go out of the door, and then changed her mind and came to sit down on one of the straight-backed chairs by a polished mahogany desk. 'I don't know what to do,' she said in a broken voice.

'Don't do anything. Just sit for a while and I'll get you some tea.' Katie moved as though to go and pour a cup, but Nick gently pressured her back into the sofa.

'I'll do it,' he said. 'You stay there.'

Steve looked towards the sitting-room door while Nick poured tea and handed it around. 'I should go and have a word with the doctor,' he murmured. 'He'll need someone to see him out…and I'd better call the paramedics and tell them what's happened.'

He walked over to the door and opened it, walking out into the hallway. The sound of voices coming from there alerted Katie and made her sit up and take notice. Had the paramedics arrived already?

'We just want to talk to Libby for a minute or two,' a male voice said. 'There will be things to arrange.'

Steve said quietly, 'Perhaps it can wait for a while. Libby's in shock, as we all are. Do you want to go and talk to the doctor instead, in the kitchen?'

'Not just yet.' The sound of the man's voice drew nearer, and Katie looked across the room as the door opened. A young man walked in, followed by a slender girl who looked to be slightly older than him, about twenty-three or twenty-four years old. She was pretty, with auburn hair that fell in bright curls about her shoulders, but right now her features were taut, as though she was doing her best to hold herself together.

Katie stood up, dragging her thoughts away from all that had happened and making an effort to behave in the way that Jack would have expected. He would want her to politely greet his guests and make them welcome, even now.

'Hello,' she said, going over to them. 'I don't

think we've met before, have we? I'm Katie. For a moment there I thought you were the paramedics.'

The young man shook his head. 'I think the doctor rang and told them there was no urgency.'

'Yes, that would be the sensible thing to do.' Katie studied him briefly. He had black hair and hazel eyes, and she had the impression he was struggling to keep his emotions under control, his face showing signs of stress, with dark shadows under his eyes and a gaunt, hollowed-out appearance to his cheeks.

'I'm Tom Logan,' he said, 'and this is my sister, Natasha.' He put an arm around the girl's shoulders. 'You've caught us at a bad time. I expect you've heard that our father has just died. Did you know him? Were you a friend of his?'

Katie almost reeled back in shock. She stared at him. *Their father?* Surely there had to be some mistake? She felt as though all the breath had been knocked out of her and for a moment or two she simply stood there and tried to absorb his words.

'I didn't realise…' she began after a while, but broke off. There couldn't be any mistake, could there? *Logan*, he had said. How much clearer could he have made it?

'Are you all right?' Tom was frowning, looking perplexed, and his sister pulled in a shaky breath and tried to show her concern, too.

It wasn't fitting that she should be here, Katie decided suddenly. These were Jack's children, and they had the right to grieve in peace. She had to get out of here. 'Yes, I…' She swallowed hard. 'I have to go… I need to get some air…' This wasn't the time or the place to explain who she was and where she had come from, was it? They'd obviously had no idea that she existed before this.

She swivelled round, desperate to get out of there, away from all these people. All at once she felt as though she was part of a topsy-turvy world where nothing made sense any more. She needed to be alone, to try to take it all in.

'Katie's upset,' she heard Nick saying. 'This has all been a bit too much for her. Excuse us, please. I think I'd better take her home.'

Katie was already out of the front door, standing on the drive, when she realised that she didn't have her own car there. But perhaps that was just as well. She was probably in no state to drive.

Was it too far away for her to walk home? She could always get a taxi, couldn't she? But for now she just needed to keep moving, to get away from there, to get her head straight.

'Katie, wait, please.' Nick dropped into step beside her.

'Why would I do that?' She shot the words at him through gritted teeth. 'I really don't have anything to say to you.' She kept on walking. Hadn't he known all along?

'But we need to talk this through,' he said. 'You've had a shock—a double shock, given what's happened to Jack.'

'Yes, I've had a shock—and whose fault is that, precisely?' The words came out flint sharp. 'Did you really think you could hide it from me for ever? Why would you want to do that?' She clamped her lips together. 'No, don't answer that. I don't want to hear it. You colluded with him, let me go on thinking I was the daughter he loved and cared about, when all the time he…' She couldn't get the words out. Her anger was rising in a tide of blood that rushed to her head. It made her feel dizzy, and it thumped inside her skull like the stroke of a relentless mallet.

'It wasn't the way you think…believe me…'

'Believe you?' She gave a harsh laugh. 'Why should I believe you?' She looked at him, her green eyes glinting with barely suppressed fury. 'Why should I listen to anything you have to say? I was foolish enough to think that you had some integrity, that you were different to the others…that you could be honest with me. Well, I was wrong.' She was still walking, her footsteps taking her out through the large wrought-iron gates, flanked on either side by stone-built gateposts.

'Katie, this is madness. At least stop and talk to me. Let me explain.'

'There's nothing to explain, is there? I know exactly how it went. You knew all along that my father had another family, a family he didn't want me to know about…or my mother, for that matter. How old is Natasha, do you imagine? Twenty-four? That means she was born while he was still married to my mother. How do you think I feel about that? Can you imagine? And yet I still would have wanted to know that they existed. Don't you think I had a right to know?'

'Of course you did. And he would have told you, given time. It's just that he wanted to pick his moment. You were getting along so well together. He didn't want to spoil that.'

He frowned. 'Katie, you've only just discovered that he's passed on. You're bound to be upset and not thinking clearly about things. You're emotional and overwrought, and you should give yourself time to get used to the idea that he's gone before you start dissecting his behaviour and giving yourself grief over it. You'll have a much more balanced outlook in a day or so's time.'

'Will I? I think I have a pretty firm handle on the situation right now. I might even forgive my father for his deception…after all, I've been there before. He left us back in England and eventually I managed to come to terms with what he had done. I know what kind of man he is...' her voice lowered to a whisper. 'Was.'

She stopped walking and faced him head on. 'It's you I have a problem with. You're the one who kept the pretence going. You banded together to keep me in the dark about it, about my family—my brother and sister, for heaven's sake.'

She shook her head as though to throw out all the debris of broken dreams that had gathered there. 'You knew how lonely I was through all those years after he left us,' she said, her eyes blurred with tears. 'You knew how much it hurt me to be rejected and how desperately I needed to know the reason for that. You should have told me the truth...that he had another family out here, one that he was prepared to stand by, to love and protect. It would have helped me to understand. I wouldn't have kept my hopes up that my relationship with my father could have been something more than it was.'

Her gaze locked with his. 'Instead, you let me flounder and lose my way. You made it so that

I stumbled across his children at the worst possible moment. You could have stopped all that, and yet you did nothing.'

'Katie, I had to keep it from you. Jack made me promise. He wanted to tell you himself when the time was right.'

'Well, you should never have made that promise,' she told him flatly. 'Because of it, all my illusions are shattered. I thought I knew you. I thought I could trust you…but I was wrong.' She took in a shuddery breath. 'You should go back to the house, Nick. I need to be alone.'

CHAPTER SEVEN

'IF THERE's anything at all that I can do to help you through these next few weeks, Dr Logan, please be sure to give me a call…at any time.' The lawyer handed Katie his embossed card. 'I know this must be a particularly difficult time for you.'

'Thank you.' Katie accepted the card and slipped it into her bag. She was still numb from everything that had happened over the last couple of weeks. Her father had died, the will had been read and now she had to try to pick up the pieces and go on with her life.

How was she to do that? Nick had betrayed her. The one man she'd thought she could trust had let her down, with devastating consequences. He'd once told her that she was special and that she'd shaken him to the core, and yet those had been empty words. It seemed those feelings were fragile, and he was easily diverted.

His duplicity left her feeling utterly lost and alone and she couldn't see how she was ever going to recover from this.

Even now, Nick was watching her from across the room. It was bad enough that he was there at all, but there was nothing she could do about that. She could feel his dark gaze homing in on her, piercing like a laser, but she was determined to ignore him. She wanted to avoid him at all costs. He'd known all along about Tom and Natasha, but he had said nothing. How could he have left her to find out about them that way? If he had cared anything for her, wouldn't he have told her?

'It can't have been easy for you, discovering that you had a family out here in California,' the lawyer commented.

'No,' she confessed. She'd had two long weeks to think about that awful day at her father's house, and now she was here with her half-brother and -sister, gathered together under the same roof once more, and it was every bit as unsettling now as it had been then. 'I'm finding it all a bit of a strain, I must admit. I'm still struggling to take it all in. It hadn't occurred to me that my father would leave the vineyard, the house—everything, in fact—to the three of us.' She frowned. 'I'm not sure what I expected, really...after all, I hadn't been part of his life for some twenty years.'

'The terms of the will were very precise.' His brows drew together in a dark line. 'After his second wife died, he stipulated that the property and the land should go to his children, and he named each one of you specifically. It wasn't an afterthought. He had the will drawn up several years ago. Other bequests were added later— like the monetary gifts to his housekeeper and manager.'

'And the collection of rare books that went to Nick Bellini.' That was the reason for him being there, wasn't it, on a day when she'd thought she would be safe?

He nodded. 'Jack knew that he had a special interest in them, and he wanted to thank him for his help over the years. He said Nick had always been there to advise him about matters to do with the vineyard, and lately he had looked out for him when he was ill.'

'It sounds as though you knew my father very well.' Her mouth softened. 'He must have talked to you quite a bit about these things.'

'That's true. I often had occasion to meet with him, so we got to know one another on a friendly as well as a professional basis. I had a lot of respect for your father.'

Katie's mouth made a faint downward curve. It was a pity she couldn't share that opinion. Her world had been turned upside down when she had discovered her father's secret. Now she would remember him as a weak man who hadn't had the courage to admit to his shortcomings. How much grief would he have spared his family if he had done that? Even her mother had echoed those thoughts at his funeral.

For Katie's part, she wanted to weep. What was it about her that made people treat her this way? As a child, for a long time after her father left she had felt that she was unlovable...worthless…and now those feelings of rejection and isolation were intensified.

Was there anyone she could rely on? Her ex had cheated on her, and her own father had left her so that he could be with his other family. And now Nick had hurt her deeply by keeping her in the dark about her brother and sister. If he'd cared about her at all, wouldn't he have confided in her, tried to smooth her path and let her know about something so significant as a family that was being hidden from her?

'How are you bearing up?' Nick came to join them, and the lawyer discreetly excused himself to go and talk to her new siblings. 'If there's anything I can do—'

'You could stay away,' she said, slanting him a brief, cool stare.

'I'm sorry you feel that way.' His gaze flicked over her, taking in the silky sheen of her chestnut hair, the troubled curve of her mouth, and then shifted downwards over the slender lines of her dove-grey suit. The jacket nipped in at the waist, emphasising the flare of her hips, while the slim skirt finished at the knee, showing off an expanse of silk-smooth legs. 'I was hoping by now you'd have had time to think things through…and maybe come to the conclusion that I'd acted with the best of intentions.'

'Then you'll be disappointed. I won't forgive you for holding back from me. You let me down. You betrayed my trust…my faith in you. I'd begun to think you were someone I could believe in, but it turns out you're no different from any of the other men in my life.'

His head went back at that and sparks flared in his eyes, as though she had slapped him. A moment later, though, he recovered himself and said in an even tone, 'I can see I've a lot of fences to mend. I hoped you would understand that I did what I felt was right. I had to keep my promise to your father.'

She gave an indifferent shrug. 'That's as may be. I'm not disputing that. You made your choice and you stuck by it. That's fine. Just don't expect me to agree with you. If you had any thought for my feelings at all, you would have warned me. Instead, you let me blunder on, thinking I actually had a father who loved me but who had simply made a mistake.' Her jaw clenched. 'But, of course, it turns out that *I* was the mistake. That's laughable, isn't it? The offspring who really mattered to him are standing over there, talking to his lawyer.' Her gaze was steel sharp. 'You colluded with him.' She gave an imitation of a smile. 'I must have thrown the cat among the pigeons, turning up here out of the blue.'

His mouth compressed. 'You know I'm not to blame for any of that, Katie. You're putting the sins of your father onto me. Don't you think you're mixing things up in your head just a little?'

'No, I don't. Not at all.' Her mouth tightened. 'You should have told me, and you could at the very least have persuaded my father to tell me, instead of leaving things until it was too late.'

She started to turn away from him. 'I'm going to talk to Libby for a while,' she said, 'and maybe I'll go and help myself to something from the buffet.' She threw him a warning glance. 'I hope that doesn't mean you'll feel obliged to butt in there as well.'

A muscle flicked in his jaw. 'You're mistaking

concern for interference, Katie. I only want what's best for you.'

Katie's mouth twisted. 'Whatever. I don't need your help or your concern. It's way too late for that.' She walked away from him, going over to the buffet table where Libby was standing alone, looking lost. She had to get away from him.

The truth was, she still could not sort out in her mind where everything had gone wrong. He had stolen into her heart and she had glimpsed a snapshot of how wonderful her life might be with him as part of it. She had begun to care for him and those feelings lingered on, in spite of herself. It wrenched her heart to know what a fool she had been to fall for him.

Natasha came to join them a minute or so later. 'I'm just going to grab a quick bite to eat and then I'll go and fetch Sarah down from upstairs.' She bit into a cheese topped cracker, savouring it as though she hadn't eaten for hours.

Katie frowned. 'Who's Sarah?' she asked.

'Oh, of course, you don't know, do you?' Natasha smiled. 'She's my little girl. I laid her down in the cot upstairs before you arrived. Even with the excitement of a house full of people, she was ready for sleep.' She helped herself to a sandwich. 'I thought I heard her stirring a minute ago. She usually naps for a couple of hours in the afternoon, so I take my opportunities while I can.' She waved the sandwich in explanation.

'I'd no idea,' Katie said. 'You look so young, and I'd assumed you were single, like Tom.'

Natasha smiled. 'She's eighteen months old— I've been married for four years, but Greg and I separated a few months ago, so it's just Sarah and me now.' Her mouth flattened briefly. 'Not that she's any trouble. Lately, she just wants to sit quietly and play with her dolls. None of that racketing about that she used to do when she first started to walk.' She frowned, thinking about it. 'Perhaps I ought to take her to the doctor. She's definitely not as lively as she used to be…but, then, I don't want to be labelled as a fussy mother, and it could be that she's fretting over her father.' She crammed another cracker into her mouth, brushed the crumbs from her hands and hurried away. 'Must go and check on her,' she said.

Katie watched her go, feeling a little sad. There were so many things she didn't know about her newfound family. They had at least twenty-four years of catching up to do.

'We ought to get together over the next day or so,' Tom said, coming to the table to pour himself a cup of coffee from the ceramic pot. 'There's been a lot to take in today, and the land and holdings are all a bit complex, so we really need to iron out what we're going to do.' He looked around. 'There's no use doing it here. I can't think straight in this house…too many memories. I can see Dad in my mind everywhere I go. And if today's anything to go by, there are likely to be interruptions, with visitors stopping by to pay their respects over the next week or so.'

He swallowed his drink. 'Nick has offered us the use of a conference room at his hotel. It's quiet there, and the lawyer, Antony, has said he'll come along and talk us through things in detail. I thought Wednesday would be a good day for it—you have a half-day then, don't you, Katie?'

'Um…yes, that's right.' Katie was looking at Nick, who had somehow managed to appear by Tom's side. The last thing she wanted to do was spend time at Nick's hotel. He must surely be aware of that.

His gaze meshed with hers and in that moment she knew without a doubt that he had set this up. There was a hint of satisfaction in the faint curve of his mouth. She might run, his blue eyes were telling her, but he would always be there, in her wake.

'I ran it by Natasha, and she's okay with that,' Tom said, 'so if it's all right with you, Katie, we could go ahead and make arrangements.'

She could hardly disrupt their plans for her own selfish reasons, could she? Katie flinched inwardly, but heard herself saying, 'Wednesday's fine by me,' and Nick's mouth curved.

'Juice!' A child's voice cut into their conversation, sounding clear and sharply commanding, and Katie looked round to see Natasha crossing the room. 'Juice, Mummy.' A chubby little hand appeared from out of the blanket-wrapped bundle that Natasha was carrying, the fingers curling and uncurling as the child poked her head above the fleece and spied the jugs of orange juice on the table. Pale faced, she had a mass of auburn curls that quivered around her cheeks with her excitement at seeing the buffet table.

'There's a girl who knows exactly what she wants.' Nick laughed, glancing from the infant to Natasha. 'Would you like me to get it for you? You seem to have your hands full.'

'Would you? Thanks.' Natasha handed him the child's drinking cup. 'She's such a fussy madam, this one…and you're right, she's very clear about what she wants. She'll never settle for second best.'

'Seems to me that's a good enough way to go through life.' Nick filled the cup, pressing the lid into place before handing it to the child.

'Tanka,' Sarah said, giving him a beaming smile and sucking on the spout of the cup as though she hadn't seen a drink in twenty-four hours.

'Um…tanka?' Nick echoed, looking at Natasha for an explanation.

'I'm trying to teach her please and thank you,' Natasha answered. 'She hasn't quite got the hang of thank you yet.'

'Oh, I see.' Nick chuckled. He glanced at Sarah once more and commented softly, 'I see you made short work of that, missie. I guess sleeping made you thirsty.'

'More!' Sarah reached out and waved the cup in front of his nose, and as he gently took it from her, she lunged towards him and planted an open-mouthed kiss on his cheek, letting her face linger there as though she was testing him out for touch and taste.

'Well, that was nice,' Nick murmured with a smile, gently disentangling himself from a mound of blanket as Sarah finally retreated. 'It's good to be appreciated.'

Watching the two of them brought a lump to Katie's throat. Nick seemed perfectly at home with the child's gloriously uninhibited behaviour. Seeing him relate to her, she could almost imagine him as a father—he would be a natural from the looks of things.

Her heart flipped over, even as her mind veered away from that startling thought. Over the last few years she had wondered what it would be like to have a family of her own, but she felt totally ill equipped for the role. Perhaps with the right man by her side, it would be different. She glanced at Nick once more, this time with wistfulness in her gaze. Why did all her hopes and dreams come to nothing? First her ex, and then her relationship with her father, and now Nick had let her down. What was wrong with her that these things kept happening? Why couldn't she be happy?

Nick caught her glance, sending her a thoughtful look in return, and she quickly turned away.

'Do you have any nieces or nephews back in England?' Tom was saying, and she came out of her reverie with a start. 'You haven't told us much about yourself up to now.'

'Uh—no, I don't, I'm afraid.' She smiled briefly. 'I'm an only child—or at least I thought

I was until now. I wish I'd known about you and Natasha before this. I would have liked to be part of a family—or to feel that I was, anyway. It makes me regret that I didn't have the confidence to come out here earlier. I feel I've missed out on so much.' What must it be like to know the intimacy and joy that came from having young people around, from sharing a household with siblings?

'Perhaps that's why you chose to work with children,' Nick suggested, his glance moving over her, almost as though he had read her thoughts. 'That way you get to have the contact with youngsters that was missing from your life. It isn't the same, I know, but it must help in some way.'

He was perceptive, she had to give him that... far more perceptive than any man she'd known up to now. 'I expect you're right,' she murmured. 'I hadn't thought about it that way.'

'It must be very fulfilling work, being a paediatrician,' Natasha commented. She set Sarah down on the floor so that she could toddle along to a corner of the room where Libby had set out a box of toys. 'We rely on doctors so much when things go wrong. I know when Sarah had a nasty virus a few weeks ago I was really worried, but it helped to talk things through with my doctor.'

She frowned. 'I don't do anything nearly so grand as you—I work in an office, part time, and Libby looks after Sarah for me while I'm away from home. I don't know what I'd do without her. The job doesn't pay very well, but I didn't want to work full time and lose out on Sarah's young years.' She grimaced. 'I suppose things will be a little easier once we've sorted out the inheritance, though everything's tied up in land and property from the sound of things... and stocks and shares.' She hesitated, thinking through what she had said. 'That sounds awful, doesn't it, thinking about the estate when we've only just lost our father?'

'I know what you mean, though,' Tom said. 'I started up my business a year ago—glass manufacture,' he added, for Katie's benefit, 'but without injecting extra capital I can't see how the company will survive for much longer.'

Katie looked from one to the other. 'Did neither of you want to follow in your father's footsteps?'

Natasha shook her head. 'It was very much his thing, you know. He didn't really involve us in it, and we didn't exactly badger him to let us know the ins and outs of it. We knew when the harvest had been good, or when it had been disastrous, and I suppose that's what put me off. I couldn't give my all to something that relied on the vagaries of the weather or could be destroyed by a disease of some sort. I like to know where I stand.'

Tom nodded agreement. 'I feel much the same way. I suppose we both take after our mother. She was always the practical one, the one who wanted to do something other than work a vineyard…but it was Dad's dream, and so she went along with him.'

Natasha smiled. 'Yes. Do you remember the time when she'd planned a day out and Dad didn't want to leave because he wanted to go out and inspect the crops?'

Their conversation faded into the distance.

Katie found it hard to take in this glimpse of family life. It seemed strange to hear them talk about their relationships, the way that they had been at odds with their father. And yet they had loved him, there was no doubting it. That was what her father had denied her for so long. And now Nick was also to blame.

CHAPTER EIGHT

THE hotel's Garden Room was aptly named. Patio doors opened up onto a terrace, enlivened with stone tubs that were filled with bright, trailing begonias in shades of scarlet and yellow. Beyond that was a lawned area, bordered by trees and shrubs, with trellised archways and rustic fences providing support for scrambling clematis in various hues of pink and lilac.

The room was comfortably furnished with soft-cushioned sofas and low, glass-topped occasional tables. It was the perfect setting for a family meeting, but the atmosphere was tense, and Katie was feeling distinctly uncomfortable.

'I can't believe you're doing this.' A faint scowl marred Tom's features as he turned on Katie. 'You're acting on a whim, and your idea of holding onto the vineyard is going to ruin me. My business is failing and selling the vineyard is my way out. It would be different if we could sell our individual assets, but we can't, according to the will. It's all or nothing.'

'And I'm in arrears with my rent,' Natasha put in, 'and there are so many bills to pay I hardly dare open the envelopes when they come through the door. I even tried asking my ex for help, but he's struggling, too.' She hesitated, her gaze clouding momentarily. 'But, then, that's half the reason we split up. He couldn't make a go of his business and the strain was too much for us.'

'I can see why you're both upset,' Katie answered cautiously, 'and it's true I've only just come to know about the vineyard and all it represents…but it has been long enough for me to realize that it's very important to me.' She tilted her chin. 'You're forgetting that Jack was my father, too. I was his firstborn, and that means something to me. It means that I have his genes, and now I have a heritage that I want to safeguard. I'm sorry if that causes problems for you, but it's the way I feel.'

They stared at her in stunned silence, their

expressions totally hostile. She didn't want to be at odds with either of them, and a surge of guilt ran through her, but with every fibre of her being she felt she had to stick to her guns.

She had been battling with them for the last hour and at times the argument had been heated and bitter. It left her feeling shaky inside, and it hurt that they had turned on her in such a savage way. It was easy enough to understand how they felt, but this was a once-in-a-lifetime opportunity and everything in her told her that she didn't want to let it go.

Was it selfish of her to want to carry on what her father had started? He might not have been the greatest father in the world. He'd let her down, but the vineyard was his handiwork, something to be proud of, the one solid achievement that she could preserve for posterity.

Her pager began to bleep. She checked the text message and said flatly, 'I have to go. There's been a road traffic accident.' She glanced at her half-brother and -sister. 'I'm sorry…perhaps Antony can help you to come to some arrangement over finances that will help you both out…

but I've made my decision. Believe me, it wasn't an easy one…but I've been thinking about it for these last few weeks and I've made up my mind. I'm not prepared to sell.'

She left the room and hurried along to the hotel foyer, but she was taken aback to see Nick standing by the reception desk. He was talking to the manageress, looking through a brochure with her, but as Katie approached he turned away from the desk and let his glance drift over her.

Katie felt her stomach clench. She had been right to push him away, hadn't she? For all his careful attention and sweet-talking ways, he had shown that he was just like everyone else.

And what would he make of her dispute with her brother and sister? Most likely he would side with them and encourage them to pressurise her into selling. It would be in his interests to do that, wouldn't it?

'You're leaving already?' Nick said with a frown. 'I'd expected the meeting to go on for much longer.'

'I have to go out on an emergency.' Her voice

was terse. 'There's been an accident on the main highway, with several cars involved, and they're calling for medics to attend.'

Nick's brows drew together, and as he handed the brochure to the manageress his phone began to bleep, signalling a text message. He quickly scanned it and then said, 'Me, too. It must be a bad one.' He turned to the woman once more. 'I have to go,' he murmured. 'Change the layout as we discussed and I'll look over the copy as soon as soon as you have it.'

She nodded. 'That's fine. You go ahead. I'll deal with this.'

'We should go,' Nick said, taking Katie by the arm. 'I can give you a lift—there's no sense in taking two cars, is there?'

'I suppose not.' Katie shrugged. 'I'll get my medical kit from the boot of my car.'

They set off just a few minutes later, driving along the main road from the hotel towards the coastal highway. Katie watched the rolling hills pass by, took in the magnificent cypress trees forming silhouettes against the skyline, and tried not to think about the fact that she was in Nick's car, that her heart was encased in ice, or that her siblings hated her.

'You're very quiet,' Nick said, turning the car on to the highway. 'How were things back there?'

'Not too good. Natasha was a bit edgy—she's worried about her little girl. She said she's tired all the while, but the doctor thinks the child's just a bit run down and it will pass.'

She frowned. From her experience she knew that doctors ought never to ignore a mother's instinct. But the toddler's symptoms were vague, and you could hardly expect the physician to be too worried at this stage. 'Tom seems to think the little girl is a fussy eater, and that might have led to her problems.'

'He could be right,' Nick murmured. 'At least the doctor's given her a check-up.'

'I suppose so.'

'So, how did the meeting go? You seem quite subdued. Was it not as you expected? It's a shame that you didn't get to finish it.'

'Perhaps it's just as well we were interrupted,' she answered with a faint sigh. 'Things weren't going too well. Tom and Natasha are very upset with me, and I'm sad about that because I want to get on well with them.'

He sent her a sideways glance. 'Why would they be upset with you? You only had to talk over what you were going to do about the estate, didn't you? I would have thought that was a positive thing, albeit tinged with a good deal of sadness. It's not every day you get to decide how to manage an inheritance like that.'

'Well, there's the rub.' She made a face. 'We couldn't agree on how to deal with it.'

He frowned. 'You'll have to explain. I've no idea what could have gone wrong. I know they were very keen on selling to my father and me. It was agreed that Toby would stay on as manager, so there shouldn't be any hitches.'

'No, there shouldn't…but you see, even you believe it's all a foregone conclusion. Except that isn't how it is at all.' She shot him a quick glance. He must have been feeling very satisfied, thinking all was going to plan.

The thought depressed her. How could she have had him so wrong? She had fallen for him, been caught up in a whirlwind of emotion that had threatened to overwhelm her, and life had become bright with the intense colours seen through the eyes of new love. But it had all faded, and she'd realised that she didn't know him at all.

'Katie?' His quiet voice jerked her out of her reverie.

'I told them I don't want to sell.'

His eyes widened. 'Are you quite sure you know what you're doing?' he asked, his tone incredulous. 'How on earth are you going to handle things? You have absolutely no experience of running a vineyard.'

'Then I'll have to learn, won't I?'

'Do you think it's just a matter of harvesting the crop and sitting back while the money rolls in?' He shook his head. 'It doesn't happen that way, Katie. It takes a lot of hard work and dedication.'

Her eyes narrowed on him. 'Do you think I'm not capable of that?'

His mouth twisted. 'That's not what I'm saying.

I'm just pointing out that if you go ahead with this, it's quite possible you'll come a cropper.'

'And there wouldn't be just a hint of sour grapes in your reaction, would there?' she challenged him. 'I know how much you wanted the vineyard for yourself.'

'For my family.' The correction was brusque and to the point. 'Yes, we want it.' His eyes darkened. 'And I'm not giving up on that. The offer still stands.'

Her gaze was troubled. 'But I'm not going to accept it. Okay, I'm not at all sure I'm doing the right thing, and I really don't want to upset my family. I know they're going through a difficult time. But instinct tells me I shouldn't be making such a big decision about selling so soon after my father's death. If I let the vineyard go now, I might come to regret it some months or years down the line. I'm really keen on the idea of owning a stretch of land—my father's land—that produces some of the finest wines in California. For me, that's far more important than the money.'

'It's a huge undertaking. I think you're making a big mistake.'

'I know.' She frowned. Clearly, she was on her own in this, and if things went wrong, she would only have herself to blame. He was right. What did she know about owning a vineyard? The enormity of what she was planning to do began to crowd in on her, overwhelming her with all sorts of dire possibilities, and to distract herself she looked out of the window and gave her attention to the road once more.

They were passing through scenic countryside right now, and she could see the ocean in the near distance and she watched as waves crashed on to the rocky shore. It seemed to perfectly echo the way she was feeling right now.

A minute or so later they reached the point in the road where the accident had happened. Police officers had sealed off the area and set up diversionary routes for other drivers.

Katie looked around and then let out a slow breath. 'This is a mess,' she said softly.

Nick's mouth made a grim line. 'It looks as though an SUV turned over. From the skid marks, I'd say he tried to avoid something up ahead and everyone else piled in. You're right, it's a mess.'

'There are a couple of drivers in the cars who look to be in a bad way,' a police officer told them as they went over to the cordoned-off area and introduced themselves. 'The fire department is working to free them right now. We've led the walking wounded away to a place of safety, but there are two women in the SUV who look as though they have serious injuries. Seems the driver had to slam on the brakes when someone pulled out in front of her. She swerved and lost control of the vehicle and then ended up on the embankment at the side of the road. There are some others who are injured, but the paramedics don't seem to be too worried about them at the moment.'

'Thanks for letting us know,' Nick said. 'We'll go and check them out.'

Two ambulances were already on the scene, and the paramedics were doing triage, trying to find out which people needed attention first.

'Glad to have you along, Doc.' The lead

paramedic nodded towards Nick and then gave Katie a brief acknowledgement. The two men obviously knew one another.

'The drivers of the cars have fractures of the legs and arms,' he said. 'They're in a lot of pain and discomfort, but we're doing what we can to stabilise them right now. It's the women in the SUV who need looking at. I think one of them is going into shock. My colleague did an initial assessment and we're giving them oxygen.'

'Okay, we'll see to them.'

Nick and Kate hurried over to the SUV. It was partially on its side, having come to rest on the embankment, but at least both women were accessible, albeit with some difficulty. Katie manoeuvred herself into the doorway of the vehicle and assessed the woman in the passenger seat, while Nick attended to the driver.

'Can you tell me your name?' she asked. The woman appeared to be in her early forties, and her companion was of a similar age, she guessed.

'Frances...Frances Delaney.' She struggled to

get the words out, and Katie could see that she was having trouble with her breathing.

'Okay, Frances,' she murmured. 'I'm Dr Logan and I'm here to help you. Can you tell me where it hurts?'

'My chest. It's a bad pain.' The woman tried to point to her upper rib cage, but then she tried to look round and became agitated. 'What's happening to Maria...to my sister?' she asked. 'She's not speaking—is she all right?'

Katie glanced to where Nick was carefully examining the driver. 'She's conscious,' she told Frances. 'Dr Bellini is looking after her.'

'She's hypotensive,' Nick murmured, 'and her heart rate is low. There's a contusion where the steering-wheel must have impacted, so I think we're looking at some kind of abdominal injury.' He looked at his patient. 'As soon as I've finished examining you, Maria, I'll give you something for the pain.'

Maria tried to say something, but couldn't get the words out. Katie's strong guess was that she might be asking for Frances, but the sound was indistinct and faded on her lips. 'Try not to worry, we're going to take good care of you and your sister,' Nick told her. He must have come to the same conclusion as Katie.

He had a soothing way with his patients, Katie reflected. He was gentle and soft spoken, and at the same time very thorough and methodical. Maria was in excellent hands.

She went on with her own examination of Frances. 'It looks as though you have some broken ribs,' she said quietly. 'And as far as I can tell, your forearm is fractured in two places. I'll give you an injection for the pain and immobilise it with a sling, but you're going to need surgery to fix the bones in place.'

Frances was white-faced and it was fairly obvious that her condition was deteriorating by the minute…something that started alarm bells ringing in Katie's head.

'Yes. Thank you for helping me.' The taut lines of the woman's expression relaxed a little as Katie administered the injection. 'It's my sister I'm worried about,' she said, her voice husky with emotion. 'She's always looked out for me…we look out for each other. I can't bear the thought that…' her voice began to fail '…that something might happen to her.'

'Try not to fret yourself.' Katie frowned. Despite the nature of the arm injuries, it was the rib fractures that concerned her most. Her patient was already experiencing severe pain and breathlessness. As a doctor, Katie knew that first and second rib fractures were often associated with damage to important blood vessels, and if that was happening, time was fast running out. It was imperative that Frances be taken to hospital as soon as possible.

She set up an intravenous line so that she could give her patient fluids, a first stage in defence against shock and blood-pressure problems that stemmed from traumatic injury. Nick was doing the same for Maria, but his expression was serious, and she guessed he was concerned for his patient.

'How is she doing?' Frances whispered the words, straining to summon the energy from a well that was beginning to run dry. 'I can't hear her. I need…to know…she's all right.'

Nick's gaze met Katie's. He made a small

shake of his head. Maria had lapsed into unconsciousness and he had secured an artificial airway in place in her throat.

'We're doing everything we can for her,' Katie said softly. 'We'll be taking her to hospital with you, just as soon as we can.'

Nick called for the paramedics to assist with spinal boards for both women, and within a matter of minutes they had stabilised the sisters sufficiently so that they could be transferred to the ambulance.

Katie went to check on the other injured people. She checked vital signs and applied dressings to stem bleeding where necessary, and when she looked around some time later, she saw that Nick was doing the same.

The injured drivers had finally been freed from their cars, and were at that moment being taken into the second ambulance.

As soon as he was certain everyone was secure, Nick started to gather together his medical kit. 'I want to follow them to the hospital and oversee things from there,' he told Katie. 'Is that all right with you? Otherwise I could arrange for someone from the hotel to come and pick you up.'

'No, it's okay. I want to go with you.' She walked with him to his car. 'I'm worried about both of them. I want to make sure that Frances has an angiogram—I'm pretty sure there's some internal bleeding, and if it isn't dealt with quickly she'll be in bad trouble.'

He nodded. 'Same here. Maria's heart rate is way too low, and her abdomen felt full and doughy when I examined her. I'm sure there's some bleeding into the abdominal cavity, and the problems with her lower rib cage make me think there could be damage to her liver or spleen. An ultrasound scan should tell us what's going on there. If we can't find where the bleeding is coming from, we'll have to do a peritoneal lavage…but whatever happens, we need to do it quickly.'

They set off, and Nick drove as fast as was possible towards the hospital, arriving there as the paramedics were unloading their patients from the ambulance.

Both he and Katie made their reports to the

emergency teams, and followed the women into the trauma room. 'Is Dr Wainwright on duty?' Nick asked as a nurse, Abby, hurried to assist.

She nodded.

'That's good.' He turned to Katie. 'He's the best vascular surgeon we have. If there's any damage to your patient's subclavian or innominate artery—or both—he's the man to put it right.'

'That's a relief.' A patient could die from an injury like that if it wasn't picked up in time, or if the surgeon was unable to stem the bleeding.

Nick was talking to the doctor in charge of the emergency room. 'I'd like to oversee my patient's ultrasound scan. I hope that's all right with you?'

'Of course. Any time. You don't need to ask, Nick.'

Katie went to discuss her patient's case with the doctor who was taking care of her, and a few minutes later she watched as Frances was whisked away to the angiography suite. The woman was agitated, distressed at having to leave her sister behind, and, unnacountably, as she saw the lift doors close on the trolley bed, Katie was overcome by a sudden tide of unhappiness.

Perhaps it had come about because this was the end of a long day. She had been hard at work in the paediatric unit this morning, before hurrying to the meeting with her half-brother and -sister, and now, in the aftermath of the traffic accident, she was beginning to register the dreadful impact of tending injured people in the wreckage of vehicles that had been slewn across the highway. She didn't know what had caused these feelings to well up inside her. She couldn't explain it, but her heart was heavy and she felt desperately sad.

'I need to go and get a breath of air,' she told Abby. 'I'll be outside in the courtyard if there's any news.'

'That's all right. I'll come and find you if there are any developments.'

'Thanks.'

Katie went out into the courtyard, a quiet, paved area where hospital staff could sit for a while on wooden benches set at intervals on the perimeter. There were a couple of cherry trees out there, along with tubs of velvet-petalled petunias that provided bright splashes of colour.

She sat down and tried to sort out the bewildering thoughts that were crowding in on her. She was feeling overwhelmed and off balance, and it scared her quite a bit because she wasn't used to feeling that way.

'Are you okay?' Nick came out into the courtyard a few minutes later and sat down on the bench beside her. He handed her a cup of coffee. 'Sorry it's a styrofoam cup—the coffee machine was closest to hand. I doubt you had time to enjoy the coffee and sandwiches I sent round earlier at the hotel...you seemed to come out of the room almost as soon as the waitress took them.'

'No, you're right, I didn't.' She frowned. 'Come to think of it, I haven't had anything to eat or drink since first thing this morning.' She sent him a quick look as she sipped the hot liquid. 'We had a few difficult cases to deal with in the paediatric unit this morning and I had to stay on for a couple of hours after my shift finished to

make sure everything was sorted out properly.'
She took another swallow of her drink. 'This
is good…thanks.' Even the delectable aroma of
the coffee teased her taste buds.

He smiled. 'Are you going to tell me what's
wrong, or do I have to prise it out of you? I know
there's something, because you were very quiet
back there and you had that far-away, hurting
kind of look in your eyes.'

She hadn't realised that he'd been watching
her. 'And there I thought your mind was all on
your patient.' She cradled the cup in her hands
and swallowed down the rest of the liquid.

He shook his head. 'You're the one who's always
on my mind,' he said quietly. 'Everywhere I go.
I think about you, wonder what you're doing
or whether you're okay. And I know you're not
okay right now, so you should tell me what it is
that's bothering you. What's upset you?'

'I don't know,' she said simply. Did he really
think about her all the time? She put the empty
cup down on the floor. 'I watched Frances being
wheeled away and this bleak feeling swept over

me. She looked so devastated, so torn, because she was being separated from her sister.'

She looked up at him, her eyes troubled. 'Perhaps that was it. She and her sister seem to be so close to one another, and maybe I wish things could have been like that for me. I never had any siblings until now, and it was all I ever wanted, to share that family feeling with people close to me. Finding out about Tom and Natasha was a shock, but once I got used to the idea I realised that a whole new world had opened up for me. And then I went and ruined it by throwing a spanner in the works. I don't think they'll ever forgive me.'

'But you have to be true to yourself in the end, don't you? And that means sticking by your decision.' He put an arm around her and drew her close and she didn't have it in her to pull away from him. The truth was, she missed that closeness, that feeling of being cherished. A lump formed in her throat. 'Isn't that what your father would have wanted?' Nick asked. 'Either way you choose, you risk losing out in some way.'

'Maybe.' Her eyes clouded. 'I suppose you

were just pointing out what I already know when you said I haven't a clue about running a vineyard. And that's perfectly true. Perhaps the enormity of what I'm taking on is just beginning to sink in. It's one thing to do it when you have back-up, but quite another when everyone who matters is against you.'

'And I'm included in that group, aren't I?' His mouth made a crooked shape. 'I don't want to cause you any hurt, Katie…but the vineyard is my heritage, mine and my brother's. Running the family business is in our blood, it flows through our veins as though it's part of our being. You're just beginning to feel something of that with this inheritance from your father.'

'And I'm finding just the thought of it a little overwhelming, as you said I would. But I can't turn my back on it. I just need to find the strength, from somewhere, to go on.'

She pressed her lips together. 'I've had to come to terms all over again with the kind of man my father was. I was hurt when I found he had another family who had been kept from me, and perhaps I overreacted.' She gazed up at him. 'It was like a betrayal, and I thought I'd done with all that. I thought I had this tough outer shell that couldn't be broken, but it wasn't so. I crumbled at the first blow. I'm every bit as weak as he was. I can't even hold it together in the emergency room.'

'You know that isn't true, Katie.' He wrapped both arms around her and folded her to him. 'You're forgetting that you've only just lost your father in these past few weeks. You can't make decisions—any kind of decisions—when you're still grieving. And you *are* grieving, even though you feel he let you down.'

His lips lightly brushed her temple and Katie realised that more than anything she wanted to nestle against him and accept the comfort he offered. 'You'd grown to love him,' he murmured. 'That's why you want to hold on to what he left behind. You see his touch in every row of vines, in every grape that ripens. That's how I feel, too, when I think about how my ancestors carved out this valley and planted their crops. We can't let it go, Katie. We're no different from one another, you and I.'

'Aren't we?' She gazed up at him, her features troubled. 'You seem to be so confident, in everything you do. I'm still struggling to find my way.'

'Then let me help you,' he said softly, bending his head to gently trace her lips with his own. 'Let me help you to forget your worries for a while.'

He kissed her again, a lingering, wonderful kiss that filled her with aching need and made her want to run her hands through the silk of his hair. She ought to have been wary of him, because she knew that he would never stop trying to make her change her mind and relinquish her inheritance. Wasn't that what he'd meant when he'd said it was the wrong time to be making decisions?

She was at war with herself. On the one hand she felt he had the power to destroy everything that mattered to her...what was there to stop him from piling on the pressure until she gave in and sold out to him? And on the other, she wanted to drink him in, as though he was the water of life, a fount of everything that could save her from herself and make her whole again.

But the moment was short-lived. He eased back from her, reluctantly dragging his mouth from hers, and she stared at him, her senses befuddled, until she gradually began to realise that she could hear the rustle of someone approaching.

'I thought you'd like to know that your patient is back from her angiography,' the nurse said. 'Mr Wainright is going to operate. And the other lady is in a bad way, too, by the looks of things. They've called for someone from the surgical team to come and look at her.'

'Thanks, Abby,' Katie managed in a low voice. 'I'll come back in and take a look at the films.' Reality began to set in once more. She felt as though she'd had a near miss...a brush with danger...but she didn't think she'd come away unscathed. She felt as though the life was being sucked out of her.

Nick stooped to pick up her abandoned coffee cup then straightened and waited for her to come and stand beside him. 'Ready?' he said.

She nodded, but she wasn't ready at all. Far from it. After that kiss, she was more bewildered than ever.

CHAPTER NINE

THE doorbell pealed, and Katie checked her watch as she went out into the hallway. It was mid-afternoon and she wasn't expecting anyone—though there was always the slim chance that Tom or Natasha might drop by to talk things through with her. It would be a relief if they did. She desperately wanted to try to clear the air between them.

It was neither of them. Instead, she opened the door to discover that Nick was standing there, casually waiting, one hand planted flat against the wall as he gazed around the vestibule.

'Katie,' he said, straightening up. 'I'm glad I've found you at home.'

His gaze travelled over her and already her body was on full alert. He looked good, too good for her peace of mind, dressed in dark trousers that moulded his hips and thighs and emphasised the taut line of his stomach and a loose cotton shirt that sat easily on his broad shoulders.

She pulled the door open wider and waved him into the hallway. 'Come in,' she said. 'This is unexpected. Is everything all right? Is there a problem at the hospital?' She led the way to the living room and tried not to think about the way he'd held her just the day before or the way his kisses had melted the ice around her heart.

'It's nothing like that. Everything's fine. I just thought you might want an update on the Delaneys. I know you've been asking about them.'

She nodded. 'No one was very forthcoming. I know Frances had arterial grafts to repair her damaged blood vessels, and her forearm fracture was so bad that both bones had to be fixed with metal plates and screws. She was still in a fragile condition this morning when I rang. But no one seems to be able to give me much information on Maria.'

'I think that's because the situation was complicated,' Nick explained. 'Both her liver and

spleen were lacerated, but the surgeon managed to repair the damage. The biggest problem
was that while he was operating he discovered
damage to the pancreas. He did what he could
to preserve the organ, but it's touch and go from
here on.'

Katie sucked in her breath. 'Poor Maria.'
Pancreatic trauma was often not detected until
it was too late. Sometimes, if it was a simple
contusion, it could be cleaned up and drained,
but in Maria's case it sounded as though the
damage was extensive. All they could do now
was wait and see what happened.

'Thanks for coming here and telling me,' she
said. 'I was hoping you'd follow up on them and
let me know how they were doing.'

His glance touched her, moving over her features in a lingering, thoughtful manner. 'That's
one of the things I love so much about you…
that you care about people. They're not just patients to you, but people with families and lives
outside the hospital.' His mouth flattened. 'Of
course, that can be a hazard in itself. Getting

too involved isn't always a good thing—not if you want to feel easy in yourself.'

Katie's gaze met his briefly. There were things he loved about her? She looked away. She'd been through too much heartache to start hoping all over again...hadn't she? How many times was she going to get up on to her feet, only to have life knock her down again?

If Nick wondered what she was thinking, he made no mention of it. Instead, he cast an appreciative glance around the room, his gaze lingering on the shelves that decorated one wall. 'It looks as though you've picked up one or two pieces from the fine-art shops around here,' he murmured.

'Yes.' She pulled herself together. 'I wasn't able to bring much with me from England, so I thought it would be good to brighten up the apartment with a few colourful touches here and there.'

He nodded, and turned his attention to the glassware on display. 'I like these bowls...the etchings on the glass make me think of sea life, with all those fronds and water plants.'

'They're similar to some my mother has at home.' Her mouth made a straight line. 'She and my father brought quite a bit of glassware from Murano. She likes to collect special pieces, paperweights and so on.'

Nick's gaze flicked over her. 'Have you forgiven him yet?'

The breath left her lungs in a sudden rush. 'I don't know. Perhaps.' After all, she'd been living with her father's imperfections for some twenty years. In the end, maybe she simply had to accept that he'd had genuine feelings for her. He'd told her he was proud of her, and he'd taken the trouble to warn her against falling for Nick. Though that was probably a warning that had come too late. Wasn't she already living with the consequences?

'And me?'

Her gaze faltered. 'Where you're concerned, I just think it's safer if I try to keep my wits about me.'

His mouth twisted. 'There must be some way I can get back into your good books,' he said softly. 'Maybe I could drive you over to Jack's vineyard so that you could have another look at the place? I know you've been so busy lately that you haven't been able to go over there.'

'And you think when I do I'll perhaps decide that I've made the wrong decision about keeping it?'

He laughed. 'Well, maybe that, too.' His expression became thoughtful. 'Actually, I heard Natasha was thinking of going over there this afternoon, and I guessed it might be a good opportunity for you to talk to her again—to the manager, Toby, as well, of course. He's usually up at the house at this time of day.'

She hesitated. Why was he doing this? Was it really as he said, to try to win her over, or did he have an ulterior motive? Did he think that when she saw the vast extent of the place once more she would realise she had taken on too much?

'It sounds like a great idea,' she murmured. 'Though I don't know how Natasha is going to react to me. I'm not altogether sure that there's anything I can say to her that will put things right.'

'I wouldn't worry too much about that. At least you'll have made the effort.'

'I suppose so.' She sent him a quick glance. 'Won't I be putting you out, though?'

'Not at all. I've been meaning to see Toby about a planting programme we were talking about last month. Your father and he were thinking about trying a new variety of grape, and my father wants to try it out, too.'

'Okay, then.' She hesitated. 'Are we ready to go now? I'll fetch my jacket.'

The approach to her father's vineyard took them through a glorious green valley, with pine-clad hills that soon gave way to row upon row of vines. The fruit was lush, soft hued as it began to ripen, and Katie felt an overwhelming sense that all was right with the natural world as she gazed at the sun-dappled slopes. If only her own life could be so serene.

Toby was at the front of the house, talking to Natasha, when they arrived, but they both turned to look in their direction as Nick drove on to the forecourt.

Natasha was holding Sarah in her arms, but

she set the infant down on the ground once Nick had parked the car. A black Labrador had been padding about, sniffing amongst the flower-beds, but he came to greet them, tail wagging, as they stepped out of the car.

'Hi, there, Benjy.' Nick patted the dog on the head and received a boisterous welcome in return, the Labrador's whole body moving in excited recognition. Then it was Katie's turn, and she gently stroked the dog, tickling him behind the ears.

She smiled at Natasha but received a blank stare in return. Toby, on the other hand, nodded to both of them.

'Hi, there,' he said. 'I wondered if you might drive over today.' He was a tall man in his early forties, with brown hair and a face that was bronzed from many hours spent out in the sun. 'My wife had to go out, but she made some oat-meal cookies before she left, so we can enjoy them with a pot of tea. I'll put the kettle on and we can sit outside on the patio for a while, if you like. Then I'll show you around.'

Satisfied he had made his presence known,

the dog went to lie down at his feet, regarding them all in a slightly curious fashion, raising an eyelid every now and again in case he was missing something.

'Thanks,' Katie said. 'That sounds good. I wanted to talk to you for a while, about the vineyard and so on.'

His expression was serious. 'I thought you might.'

'We were just going to take a look around the house,' Natasha said, glancing at Nick. 'There are one or two maintenance problems that have cropped up—like a couple of broken fences and some roof tiles that need to be replaced. Toby said he didn't mind fixing them, but I think he probably has enough to do already.' She looked at Katie, her expression cool and vaguely antagonistic. 'I suppose the ball's in your court. You were keen to take this on, so I dare say we can leave the decisions to you. Tom and I never wanted the stress of running the business and everything associated with it.'

Katie pulled in a deep breath. 'If that's what you want, then of course I'll deal with everything that comes along. I'll keep you up to date with what's happening.' She was disappointed by her cool reception, but she could hardly have expected anything else in the circumstances. Natasha was still annoyed with her, from the looks of things, but there was no point in getting into a state about it, was there?

Sarah toddled over to Katie and stood, gazing up at her. Her bright curls quivered and shone in the sunlight. 'Pwetty,' she said, and for a moment or two Katie was taken aback, until the little girl pointed to her necklace. 'Pwetty,' she said again, and Katie smiled.

'You like it? It is pretty, isn't it?' She fingered the silver filigree necklace and crouched down so that the infant could take a better look. 'My mother gave it to me, so it's very special.'

'Best not let Sarah get her fingers round it, then,' Natasha said flatly. 'She doesn't distinguish between special or worthless. She grabs everything. One tug and it's ruined.'

'Oh, dear. Well, I'd best protect it, then, hadn't I?' Katie placed her fingers over the necklace and glanced towards Nick, wondering what she could do to distract the child.

'You can play with my keys for a while, if you like, Sarah,' he said, coming to the rescue by jangling them temptingly in front of the child's face. Her eyes widened and she turned her attention to Nick, the pink tip of her tongue coming out to touch her bottom lip as she gazed up at him. The keys were irresistible, it seemed, and she held up her hands, trying to grasp them as he gently teased her, darting them about in a catch-me-if-you-can kind of game.

It didn't have quite the effect he was looking for, though, because being thwarted proved altogether too much for her, and the toddler burst into tears.

Nick's jaw dropped, and Katie looked on in consternation. 'I was just playing with her,' Nick said. 'I didn't mean to upset her.' He turned to Natasha. 'Do you think she'll let me pick her up and comfort her?'

'You can try,' Natasha said. 'It isn't your fault, mind. She's been like this for some time now, fretful and tearful, on and off. I just haven't been able to work out what's wrong with her. I've put it down to tiredness. She's been sleeping an awful lot lately, so perhaps the doctor was right when he said she was run down. I've just been letting her rest as and when she needs it.'

Nick picked up the little girl and cradled her in his arms, offering her the keys, but by now she had lost interest in them. She sobbed, large hiccuping sobs that racked her body, and tears trickled down her face, giving her a woeful expression.

'I'm sorry, cherub,' Nick said in a soothing tone. 'I was only teasing. I didn't mean to upset you.' He was thoughtful for a moment or two, and then asked quietly, 'How about I give you a rock-a-bye swing—would you like that, hmm?' He began to rock her gently to and fro in his arms, and after a while she stopped crying and stared up at him, her face pale.

Katie watched him with the little girl and felt a pang of emotion well up inside her. He was so natural with her, so caring and gentle, so obviously concerned for her well-being.

'You definitely have the knack,' Toby said

with a laugh. 'I expect Natasha will be calling on you for babysitting duties from now on.'

'Heaven forbid!' Nick looked aghast. 'I'd need a bit more practice before I took up that kind of challenge.' He looked at Katie, a questioning, odd kind of look, and an unbidden thrill of expectation ran through her. What would it be like to have his children?

Toby showed them the way through the house to the kitchen, the dog following at his heels. It was a large breakfast kitchen with glass doors to one side leading out on to a terrace. 'Make yourselves at home out there,' Toby said, waving them out towards a teak wood table and chairs. 'I'll make the tea and bring it out to you.'

Nick was still holding his precious bundle, but now he looked over at Natasha. 'Do you want to take her?' he asked. 'She looks as though she's settled now.'

'Okay. I'll put her in her buggy,' Natasha murmured. 'She can sit and watch us while we talk.'

Katie glanced at the child as she lay back in her buggy a short time later. She was white faced, her curls slightly damp against her forehead as though she was a little feverish. Her breathing was rapid, and it occurred to her that the child looked exhausted.

Toby arrived with the tea, and once he had seated himself and they had chatted for a while, Katie brought up the subject of the management of the vineyard.

'I hope you'll stay on here and run things for us as you've always done,' she said. 'I know how much my father valued your work here.'

'Thank you. I'd like that.' Toby looked relieved. 'Does that mean my family can go on living here at the house?'

'Of course. I've asked Antony to draw up the paperwork to give you a more secure tenancy.'

Natasha sent her a quick look, but said nothing, and Katie said evenly, 'I'm assuming that will be all right with you and Tom?'

Her sister nodded, and soon after that Nick began to talk to Toby about the new planting programme. Benjy, who had been supposedly dozing at Toby's feet, was disturbed by a butterfly and decided he needed to go and check

things out. As the butterfly flitted away to the
flower border, he got to his feet and went after
it.

'Up, Mummy!' Sarah suddenly exclaimed,
looking at Natasha. 'Up.' She stretched out her
arms to her mother, and Natasha frowned.

'If I lift you up, what then?' she said, giving
her daughter a quizzical look. 'You'll be demanding to be set down, then, won't you?' She
frowned. 'You want to play with Benjy, don't
you?'

Sarah's expression was gleeful. 'Up...play
Benjy,' she said, and by now her fingers were
doing their familiar clasping and unclasping as
if she was clutching at the air.

'Okay, then, young madam,' Natasha murmured, lifting the child out of the buggy. 'But
try and stay out of trouble. No pulling at the
flowers.'

'F'owers,' Sarah echoed happily. 'Benjy
f'owers.'

Benjy was indeed exploring the flowers, Katie
noticed. His nose was pressed up against them
as he drank deeply of their scent, and a moment

later he drew his head back and gave an enormous sneeze. Sarah giggled.

The dog's nose was covered with pollen, and Katie smiled. She looked at Nick and saw that he was chuckling, too. Their glances met in a shared moment of amusement.

Sarah toddled off to where Benjy was getting ready for another sneeze. She patted him vigorously in sympathy and then wandered away to inspect the scarlet begonias.

Katie watched her go, and saw how the little girl seemed to slow down and come to a standstill. It seemed that she had stopped to look at a ladybird or some such, but there was something about the way she was standing that had Katie's instincts on alert all of a sudden. Then the child's legs seemed to crumple under her and in an instant Katie was out of her seat. She hurried over to her, catching her as she would have fallen.

'What's wrong with her? What's happened?' Natasha was beside herself with worry. She rushed over and began to stroke her little girl's hair as though by touch alone she would bring her back to normal.

'She just collapsed,' Katie said softly. She used the second hand on her watch to carefully check the infant's pulse. Then she glanced at Nick, who had come to kneel down beside her. 'Her heart rate is very fast, and she's much too pale. I think perhaps she ought to have a proper check-up at the hospital.'

He nodded. 'I agree with you.' The dog came to find out what was going on, and Nick said softly, 'We should take her into the house.' He glanced at Natasha and she nodded.

'You could lay her down on the sofa in the living room,' Toby suggested. 'It's cooler in there. Maybe she had a touch too much sun.'

'It's possible,' Katie said, gently handing the child over to Nick, who lifted her into his arms and carried her into the house. 'We'll give her a few minutes to see if she comes round, but I think it's something more than that.'

'You thought she was ill earlier, didn't you?' Natasha glanced sharply at Katie as they gathered in the living room a moment or two later.

'I saw you looking at her when she was in her buggy.'

Katie nodded. 'If I'm right, I don't think it's anything too serious.'

'Tell me.' Natasha crouched down beside the sofa, holding her child's hand, letting her know that she was there with her the whole time.

'Her main symptoms seem to be the tiredness and her pallor,' Katie murmured. 'You haven't mentioned anything else that's bothering you, apart from the fact that she's been quite fretful lately.'

'That's right.'

'And you mentioned some time ago that she had suffered from a viral infection—I'm guessing that this has been going on since then?'

'Yes… I think so.' Natasha's brows drew together. 'It's hard to know exactly when it started. It's been coming on gradually. What do you think is wrong with her?'

Sarah began to stir, rubbing her eyes and shifting to a more comfortable position.

Katie glanced at Nick. 'I'm thinking some kind of transient anaemia.'

'Yes.' He nodded. 'That sounds about right. Of course, we would need to confirm it with tests.'

'Anaemia?' Natasha's voice was filled with stress. 'Is that because of something I've been doing wrong? Haven't I been feeding her properly?'

Katie recognised the guilt in her voice. Parents often blamed themselves where no blame was due.

'No, it's nothing at all like that,' Nick said quietly. 'You don't often see this, but sometimes, after certain types of viral illness in young children, their bodies stop making red blood cells for a while. That would account for Sarah's tiredness and pale appearance.'

Natasha was horrified. 'That sounds awful,' she said. 'Can something be done? Is there a cure?'

He nodded. 'Usually it sorts itself out after two or three months.'

'But she collapsed. She can't go on like that, surely? That can't be right.'

Katie laid a hand gently on her arm. 'I know

this is really worrying for you, Natasha, but Nick's right. Usually this type of illness clears up of its own accord. When a child collapses, though, as Sarah just did, it's best to get things checked out. She might need a transfusion. If this is what we think it is, that will help a lot and she'll soon start to feel better…though it's possible she'll need another transfusion before she recovers completely. At some point her bone marrow will start manufacturing the cells once more.'

Natasha had a panicked look about her. 'But I need to go and get help now. I want to take her to the emergency room.' She looked around distractedly. 'I shan't rest until I find out exactly what's happening.'

'I could take you to the hospital,' Toby offered, but Nick intervened.

'I'll go with her,' he said quietly. 'You stay and show Katie around the vineyard. I'm sure you must have a lot to talk about. Natasha and Sarah will be fine with me.'

'You don't mind?' Natasha asked. 'Are you

sure? I don't mean to break things up, but I'm really worried about her.'

'Of course you are,' Nick said. 'I would have suggested it anyway. Sarah needs to be checked out.' He turned to look at Katie. 'Here, take my car keys. I'll take Natasha's car, and if we're delayed at the hospital for any reason, you can drive yourself home in mine. I'll pick it up later. Don't worry if you're not around when I come to collect it, I'll use my spare set of keys.'

'Okay.' Katie wasn't at all sure how she felt about driving his beautiful, streamlined car, but she judged that now wasn't the moment to dither or argue. It said a lot about him that he'd thought of her in this moment of crisis.

Natasha hurried away to gather together everything she needed to take with her while Nick secured Sarah in her car seat. The child was still drowsy, not really taking any notice of what was going on around her.

'Will she be all right?' Toby asked as he and Katie watched them drive away a few minutes later. 'I know you said it would clear up on its own, but it sounded pretty horrific to me.

Anything to do with bone marrow not working properly is pretty scary, isn't it?'

'You're right,' Katie answered. 'Normally, it would be very worrying, but I'm hoping that this is one of those instances where she'll make a full recovery. We won't really know until we have the results of the tests.'

'It's a difficult situation—a worrying time all round.'

Katie nodded. 'Yes, it is.' She was glad Nick had gone with Natasha. He would be a comfort to her, and he would be able to explain anything that she didn't understand. He was a man to be relied on, a good man to have by your side in times of trouble. Or at any time, come to think of it.

She sighed inwardly. Her feelings for Nick were complex and very unsettling. Could it be that she was falling in love with him? In fact, the more she thought about it, the more certain she became that he was the one man who could make her happy…if only she could be sure that she could put her faith in him.

'Perhaps you'd like to look around the parts

of vineyard you haven't already seen while we're waiting to hear what's happening?' Toby suggested. 'I know you were interested in the vines and the type of grapes that produce the Chardonnay. We have a separate area for the new planting on the west side.'

'Thanks. That would be great.'

The hills were bathed in sunshine at this time of day, and as they walked around, Katie was glad that she was wearing a simple, sleeveless cotton dress that kept her relatively cool and fresh. Even so, she was thankful for the occasional ocean breeze that fanned her hot cheeks.

Row upon row of glorious vines stretched out ahead of her, all of them in full leaf and heavy with fruit. 'You're doing a great job here, Toby,' she said.

'I do my best.' He sent her a quick look. 'These two vineyards, the Logans' and the Bellinis', have always been interconnected and run in a harmonious fashion. That might be under threat now that Tom and Natasha have shown that they're not interested.'

She frowned. 'You're afraid it will affect the smooth running of the place?'

'I think it might. At the moment they're happy for you to make the decisions, but that might not always be the case. There could be problems.'

She thought it over. 'I can see how that's a possibility—but right now I don't see any way round the situation. I can't afford to buy them out.'

'No.' Toby was quiet for a moment or two then added, 'I know Nick has an idea for smoothing things out. I expect he's spoken to you about it?'

She shook her head. 'No, he hasn't—except to say that he'd like to buy us out? Is that what he meant?'

Toby put up his hands as though to ward off any more questions. 'I'd better leave it to him to tell you his thoughts on that subject. Anyway, he wasn't specific, and I'm only concerned for the smooth operation of the vineyard.' He gave a wry smile. 'I don't want to get involved in sibling rivalry and multi-million-dollar takeovers.'

Katie stayed silent for a while after that. Toby's

words had set up a welter of turbulent emotions inside her. Was Nick intending to increase his offer for the vineyard? How could he go on with his bid when he knew how much her father's legacy meant to her? She had begun to think he might have deep feelings for her, might actually come to love her, but now all her dreams were dashed once more. Her hopes had been reduced to ashes.

CHAPTER TEN

KATIE wandered barefoot along the beach, picking her way over craggy rocks and alternately feeling the warm sand glide between her toes.

There was so much to think about, so many questions that niggled at the back of her mind. What could Nick be planning? Would he really do anything to upset her? Why hadn't he rung to let her know what had happened at the hospital yesterday?

She missed him, she wanted to hear his voice, but instead there had just been a brief note pushed into her mailbox that morning to tell her that he had come along and collected his car while she was out—and to say that Sarah was being admitted to the paediatric ward so that the doctors could do tests. When Katie had tried to phone him, there had been no answer and the service had cut straight away to voice mail.

She stopped for a moment to listen to the calls of gulls overhead and to look around at the rugged, coastal bluffs. Out in the ocean, sea stacks rose majestically, carved out of ancient volcanic rock, a playground for sea otters that played offshore, feeding off the underwater kelp.

It was somehow soothing to be at one with nature...but in the end it didn't take away her inner torment. How could it? Her life had changed so much in these last few months, and she'd had no choice but to confront her demons. Where had that left her? She was afraid and uncertain, full of doubt. And yet one thing shone clearly through the gloom—Nick had been a constant support to her, showing her how much he wanted her, gently coaxing her into loving him.

Just yesterday he had taken her to meet Natasha, and surely that was because he hoped they might somehow manage to heal the rift that had opened up between them. Would he have done all that if she meant nothing to him, if their relationship was just a spur-of-the-moment thing, a casual fling? She had to hope there was more. She couldn't go on this way.

For once, she had to take him at his word and trust in him. From now on she was going to meet life head on, which was why she walking along this stretch of sand, heading towards Nick's beach house.

Of course, she had rung Natasha. She had been desperate for news of her young niece, and at least her half-sister had recognised that she cared about the child and was worried about her.

'They're keeping her in overnight,' Natasha had said. 'It was late by the time the doctors worked out what they were going to do, but Nick was by my side all the while, explaining everything about the tests and so on. I don't know what I'd have done without him.' She pulled in a deep breath. 'Anyway, I'm going to stay here at the hospital so that I can be with Sarah. My husband—Greg—said he'd try to get here as soon as he can. He's been working away in the next county. We're both worried sick about her.'

'That's understandable,' Katie murmured. 'This must have come as quite a shock to you. I hope things turn out all right for you—will you let me know what happens?'

'Yes, I will.' Natasha hesitated. 'Thanks, Katie. I know you've been concerned for her all along and you were looking out for her. We've perhaps been hard on you, Tom and I. We both feel that we've misjudged you.'

'You've had a lot to deal with,' Katie said simply. 'You're my family. I just want to know that you're all doing well.'

It was a huge relief to know that they no longer bore her any ill-will, but the problems were still there. If she refused to sell the vineyard, they would go on struggling to keep their heads above water. What was Nick planning to do that would change all that? If things were to work out well for her half-brother and -sister, there could only be one loser.

She was overcome by doubts. If she was ever to make sense of any of this, she needed to see him, be with him…talk to him.

Katie pushed away a strand of chestnut hair

that blew across her cheek in the faint breeze and walked closer to the water's edge. She paused to pick up a pebble and launch it into the ocean. It made a satisfying splash, and water droplets sprayed over her cotton dress. Waves lapped at her feet, cool, even after the heat of the day.

She halted for a moment, peering into the distance. From here she could just about make out Nick's house sheltered in the curve of the bay, and she set off once more towards it.

It was late afternoon, still warm, with the sun casting its glow over all and sundry. Surely Nick would have finished his shift at the hospital by now?

It wasn't long before she reached the smooth stretch of sand that fronted his house, and straight away she saw that he was there. He was standing outside on the terrace, beneath the overhead deck, and he was facing her way. But he didn't see her because he wasn't alone and at this moment his companion was claiming all his attention.

A young woman was talking to him earnestly, her hand resting tenderly on his arm.

Katie recognised her from her picture in the paper. This was Shannon, the woman he had once been engaged to, the girl he had suppos edly abandoned.

Katie couldn't move. She stood and watched them, and after a second or two she saw Nick move closer to the girl and give her a hug.

The breath caught in Katie's lungs. She felt as though she had been winded, and she didn't know how to react. There was such a wealth of affection in that embrace, and it broke her heart. She stood transfixed, her pulse racing, a feeling of despair washing over her.

What was she doing, thinking that there might be a future for her with Nick? She was wishing on a moonbeam if she thought there was any chance he might have fallen for her. Hadn't Shannon always been there in the background? He'd made no secret of their relationship, had he? And in the end, hadn't he proved to be no different from her ex, professing to want Katie and at the same time making a play for someone else?

Slowly, her mind clouded by doubt and

uncertainty, she started to turn away. She would talk to him later, when she had her head together a bit more. Seeing him with another woman was way more than she could bear right now. She loved him, and knowing that he was with someone else was just one more betrayal, perhaps the biggest betrayal of all because she had finally come to realise that he meant more to her than anyone in the whole world.

Her feet sank into the sand, slowing her down, but she made a huge effort to hurry away from there, even as she saw him glance in her direction and heard him call her name. She didn't look back but kept on going, putting as much distance as she could between her and the house.

'Katie…stop…let me talk to you.'

Still she kept on going. There was nothing to say, was there? She had made a mistake, and this was one from which she might never recover.

After a while he stopped calling after her, and even the silence was a rebuke. How could she have been so reckless as to fall for him? She meant nothing to him, did she? He had let her go without a fight. Perhaps he'd never wanted her in the first place, despite what he'd said.

She trudged on, oblivious to the call of the birds around her. She paid scant attention to the rare sight of brown pelicans nesting on the high bluffs or the black-headed terns that were searching for crustaceans among the rocks.

Minutes later, though, she stirred as she heard the drone of an engine in the distance. It was coming nearer, gaining steadily on her, the sound becoming louder and mingling with the crash of surf against the distant crags. She turned to see what was disturbing the peace and tranquillity of the bay.

'Nick!' Her eyes widened in astonishment as a dune buggy swung alongside her. 'What are you doing? Where did that come from?'

'It's mine. Hop in, I'll give you a ride along the beach.'

'No, thank you.' She shrank away from him. 'I don't think so. I really don't want to go any-where with you.'

'Of course you do...you're just not thinking straight. Come on up here beside me.' The engine chugged to a slow, idling pace.

'I can't for the life of me think why I'd want to do that,' she muttered. 'I'd just as soon be on my own right now.' She frowned, looking the contraption over, studying the sturdy wheels and the open rails that allowed the warm air to move freely over its occupant. 'Anyway, I've never been in one of those things before. What's it for?'

He cut the engine. 'It's for catching up with headstrong young women who won't stop and take notice when they're called,' he said, reaching out a hand and grasping her by the wrist. 'Up you come. You'll like it…only hold onto the rail because the ride might get a bit bumpy around the rocks.'

She tried to resist, but his hold on her was firm and unyielding and after a while she realised that her struggles were fruitless and she may as well give in. There was no one around within shouting distance to come to her rescue, anyway.

Triumphant, he tugged her into the seat beside

him. She glowered at him then settled herself more comfortably and brushed the sand off her feet before slipping on her sandals.

'Where are we going?' she asked as he started up the engine once more. 'And what about Shannon—shouldn't you be with her? I saw you together. What happened? Have you just abandoned her? I'm sure she won't be very pleased to know that you're here with me.'

'Heaven forbid that I'd abandon her. No, she had to leave. She was only there on a quick visit—all she wanted was to let me know that she'd sorted out her problems.' He sent her a quick sideways glance. 'I thought we'd head along the beach to a nice, secluded spot…you never know when people are going to come along and disturb us on this section of the beach…and then you can tell me what's going on, why you came to see me and then turned away.'

'I decided what I had to say could wait until you were less busy,' she said in a pithy tone. 'It seemed to me that you had your hands full.'

'I thought that might be it.' The buggy gathered speed. 'You have a bee in your bonnet about Shannon, don't you?' he said, raising his voice to combat the sound of the engine. 'I keep telling you not to believe what you read in the papers. She's just a friend and she's been going through a bad time, but I guess you don't believe me, do you?'

Katie's mouth turned down at the corners. 'Perhaps it would help if you told me why she was at the hotel with you that night when the press caught up with you—and why, when I saw you with her just now, you had your arms around her?'

'Does that bother you?' He studied her thoughtfully for a moment and then turned his attention back to the beach ahead. 'Does it matter to you if I'm with someone else?'

'If it's another woman…yes, it matters.' She swallowed hard. There, it was out, she'd said it, something she'd hated to admit because it made her incredibly vulnerable.

'Good,' he said, in a satisfied tone, and she looked at him in shocked surprise. 'I hope that means you're jealous. I was beginning to think you'd never take me seriously.' He manoeuvred the buggy around an outcrop of rocks and steered it into a sheltered cove.

'I don't follow your reasoning,' she said awkwardly, looking at him wide-eyed. 'How can you care about me the way you say you do, if you're still seeing Shannon?'

His mouth flattened. 'Shannon is just a friend,' he said. 'I couldn't explain the situation before because she wanted to keep everything under wraps. The truth is, she's in love with someone her father doesn't approve of—he decided some time ago that he was a fortune hunter and did everything he could to break up the relationship. Of course, that was totally the wrong thing to do because it just encouraged them to have more clandestine meetings. Personally, I think the man she's chosen is okay. He cares about Shannon and wants the best for her.'

He parked the buggy by the foot of a cliff. 'Shannon was upset because her boyfriend was becoming wary of what her father might do— he'd threatened to cut her out of his life. So the boyfriend was thinking of going away because he didn't want her life to be ruined because of him. I was at the hotel that night when he'd tried to break it off with her, and she confided in me. We left the hotel separately, but the press had wind she was there and caught both of us on camera. They put two and two together and came up with five.'

'And now? After all, that was some time ago, wasn't it?' Katie looked at him doubtfully.

'Now she's trying to gain command of her life once more. She's made up her mind to go ahead and marry the man she fell in love with.' He gave a wry smile. 'To be honest, I don't think her father will cut her off. He loves her too much for that.'

'Oh, I see.' Katie's green eyes were troubled.

'I hope you do,' he said. 'But either way I'm glad you came to see me. Was there something special, or was it just because you couldn't stay away?' He grinned. 'I hope it was the last one.'

She pressed her lips together, still anxious. Even though he had put her mind at rest over Shannon, there was still a huge hurdle to face.

She had to know what was on his mind when he spoke to Toby.

'I wanted to talk to you this morning,' she said, 'but I couldn't get through to your mobile.'

He nodded. 'I was swamped at work. We were inundated.'

'Yes, of course, I should have known.' She frowned. 'Is there any more news about Sarah?'

'They gave her a transfusion this morning and they're waiting to see if she perks up. From what the nurse said, she seems to be improving.' He paused for a moment. 'I think the doctors were worried about the cause of the anaemia initially, but now that the test results are back it appears it's as we thought. In time, she'll start to recover naturally. They say she just needs supportive care at the moment…rest, fresh air, a balanced diet.'

Katie let out a slow breath. 'That's good to know.'

'It is…and another snippet of good news is that I think Natasha and Greg will be getting back together. They were always well suited—it was just that their money worries took over once Sarah came along. The fact that she's ill has brought them close to one another again.'

'I'm glad for them…and it's good to know that Sarah will have her father back with her.'

'Yes. It's always good when families are reunited. Which applies to the Delaneys, too, by the way. They moved Maria out of Intensive Care this afternoon. Apparently, her sister went to see her and they were able to talk for a while.'

'Oh, that's brilliant news.' Her face broke into a smile. 'That's been weighing on my mind for some time.'

'A lot of things seem to have been weighing you down lately.' He lifted a hand and gently stroked her face. 'Like this business of the vineyard. You're not happy about how it has affected Tom and Natasha, are you? I know things have been difficult between you.' His hand was warm against her cheek and she revelled in his comforting touch.

'It's worrying me,' she admitted. 'Though at least Tom and Natasha seem to have forgiven me. But I know they're going to have heavy burdens on their shoulders for some time to come, and I can't help feeling I might have done something to help them avoid that situation.'

'You still could.' He fingered the silky strands of her hair. 'If you let me help you.'

Her gaze meshed with his. 'Sell to you, you mean? I won't do that, Nick. I'm sorry. I made up my mind.'

'I know. I meant you could buy them out.'

She shook her head. 'How could I do that? I just don't have the means.'

'You could...' he paused to drop a kiss gently on her mouth, catching her off guard and setting off a flurry of warm sensation to fizz inside her '...if you'd allow me to lend you the money.'

She stared up at him, open-mouthed. 'But... but why would you want to do that?'

'Because I care about you.' He gazed down at the pink fullness of her lips. 'Because I want you to be happy. Because it's in my power to do it.'

Katie was shocked, thrown completely off balance by the enormity of his gesture. So this was his plan? To help her to keep the land that meant so much to his family? Words failed her, and her head was swimming with all kinds of thoughts, all of them leading to nowhere but utter confusion.

'I need to think about this,' she said huskily. 'I don't know why you're saying this to me. I never dreamed...'

She suddenly needed to escape the confines of the buggy. She slid down onto the sand and stared about her for a second or two, her mind in a daze. What he was suggesting was something she had never even contemplated...but why would he do such a thing?

He came to stand beside her, his arms folding her to him, his body close to hers, so close that it was all she could do not to cling to him and bask in the heady comfort of his warm embrace.

'What you're suggesting is incredibly generous,' she said huskily, her words muffled against the velvet column of his throat, 'but I don't see how I could accept. There's such a huge sum of money involved and I've no way of knowing if I could pay you back in the short or the long term. But thank you… I'm overwhelmed that you would even make the offer.'

The palm of his hand drifted lightly over the gentle curve of her spine, stroking her as though he would memorise every line, shifting to caress the rounded swell of her hip.

'You don't need to worry about any of that,' he murmured. 'It doesn't matter to me. All that matters is that you're happy and free from worry.' He gazed down at her. 'I don't know how it happened, Katie, but I've fallen for you big time. I'm completely out of my depth for the first time in my life and there's nothing I can do about it but accept it. I realised that some time ago. I love you… I need you… But most of all I want to make sure that you're safe and secure.'

The breath caught in her throat. 'I never imagined you would ever say that to me. I wanted it so much, but there was always this doubt at the back of my mind. I was scared. I'm still scared. I tried so hard not to love you because I was so sure I would be hurt…but it happened all the same, and now I'm…overwhelmed…elated…

over the moon…' She closed her eyes briefly and absorbed the moment. 'I love you, Nick.'

He let out a ragged sigh and stooped to kiss her, exploring her lips with tender passion, sparking a trail of fire that flamed in every part of her being. 'Then nothing else matters,' he said softly, his voice rough edged as he came up for air. 'I'll always be here for you, Katie. You just have to learn to trust in me. I'll never hurt you, I promise you. You're part of me now. You've found your way into my heart, and we're bound together for all time.'

He darted kisses over her cheek, her throat, the bare curve of her shoulder. 'Will you marry me, Katie? Please say that you'll be my wife.' His expression was intent, his eyes as dark as the ocean on a stormy day, and she realised that he was holding his breath, waiting for her answer.

'Yes… Oh, yes… I will,' she said in a soft whisper, gazing up at him, her heart filled with joy. She reached up to lightly stroke his face. She kissed him, running her hands along his arms, his back, wanting him, desperate to have him hold her closer, and he obliged, drawing her against him, moulding his thighs to hers and pressuring her into the safe haven of the cliff side.

'I want you so much,' he murmured, his voice husky with emotion. 'I can't get enough of you, Katie. You're everything I could ever want in a woman…so gentle, thoughtful, so considerate of everyone around you.' His mouth indented in a smile. 'When I saw you with young Sarah, holding her in such a worried fashion, I thought there was the woman I would want to be the mother of my children. You're the only one for me, Katie. I love you so much.'

She gave a sigh of contentment, her fingers roaming lightly over his chest. 'I'd like to have your children some day,' she murmured. Her gaze softened as she looked up at him. 'Of course, if we should be lucky that way, you know what it will mean, don't you?'

He shook his head and clasped her hand lightly, kissing her fingertips as though he would confirm his love for her with each tender kiss.

'That we'll face the future together as a family, come what may?'

'As a family,' she echoed. 'The Bellini family. And the name will go on through the generations, just as you wanted. Our vineyards would be linked under the same name as they were once before.'

'I hadn't thought of that,' he said. 'But, of course, it's true.' He smiled. 'It sounds like a perfect solution to me.' He wrapped his arms more firmly about her, and then he hugged her close and kissed her passionately, thoroughly, until her senses whirled and she was lost in a thrilling world of heady delight.

'I feel as though I've drunk too much wine,' she murmured contentedly. 'I feel as though my head is spinning and I'm so full up of happiness that I'm brimming over with it. Everything is turning out to be just perfect…you and me, and the solution to my brother and sister's worries. I never imagined things could turn out like this.'

'I'm glad you feel that way. I want to smooth out every glitch and make things perfect for you.' He laughed softly, running his hands over her as though to make sure she was really there, that he wasn't dreaming.

'I love you, Nick…only you. There's no other man I want in my life.'

He breathed a long sigh of relief. 'That's good. Because I really, really love you, Katie'

He bent his head and kissed her once more, and Katie clung to him and kissed him in return, loving him, loving the feel of him and wanting nothing more than to be with him for all time. For now she realised he was a man she could trust, a man who would be there for her always. It had taken her a long while to let down her guard, and finally she understood that he wasn't like other men. He would keep his promise to her, she could feel it in every part of her being, and she knew that she could look forward to a love that would last for ever.

She settled into his arms, kissing him tenderly, an ache of desire burning like a flame inside her. Why had she waited so long?

* * * * *

MEDICAL ROMANCE™

Large Print

Titles for the next six months...

September

SUMMER SEASIDE WEDDING — Abigail Gordon
REUNITED: A MIRACLE MARRIAGE — Judy Campbell
THE MAN WITH THE LOCKED AWAY HEART — Melanie Milburne
SOCIALITE...OR NURSE IN A MILLION? — Molly Evans
ST PIRAN'S: THE BROODING HEART SURGEON — Alison Roberts
PLAYBOY DOCTOR TO DOTING DAD — Sue MacKay

October

TAMING DR TEMPEST — Meredith Webber
THE DOCTOR AND THE DEBUTANTE — Anne Fraser
THE HONOURABLE MAVERICK — Alison Roberts
THE UNSUNG HERO — Alison Roberts
ST PIRAN'S: THE FIREMAN AND NURSE LOVEDAY — Kate Hardy
FROM BROODING BOSS TO ADORING DAD — Dianne Drake

November

HER LITTLE SECRET — Carol Marinelli
THE DOCTOR'S DAMSEL IN DISTRESS — Janice Lynn
THE TAMING OF DR ALEX DRAYCOTT — Joanna Neil
THE MAN BEHIND THE BADGE — Sharon Archer
ST PIRAN'S: TINY MIRACLE TWINS — Maggie Kingsley
MAVERICK IN THE ER — Jessica Matthews

MILLS & BOON

MEDICAL ROMANCE™

Large Print

December

January

February

MILLS & BOON

MODES OF INDIVIDUALISM
AND COLLECTIVISM

MODES OF
INDIVIDUALISM AND
COLLECTIVISM

edited by

JOHN O'NEILL

HEINEMANN
LONDON

Heinemann Educational Books Ltd

LONDON EDINBURGH MELBOURNE AUCKLAND TORONTO
HONG KONG SINGAPORE KUALA LUMPUR
IBADAN NAIROBI JOHANNESBURG
NEW DELHI

ISBN 0 435 82664 6

Paperback ISBN 0 435 82665 4

First published 1973

Published by Heinemann Educational Books Ltd
48 Charles Street, London WIX 8AH

Printed in Great Britain by Morrison and Gibb Ltd
London and Edinburgh

For Paul Baran 1910–1964

CONTENTS

viii *Contents*

ACKNOWLEDGEMENTS

The essays contained in this volume originally appeared in the journals and books listed below, and the author and publishers are grateful to the following for permission to reproduce them:

F. A. Hayek and *Economica* for the essay from 'Scientism and the Study of Society', *Economica*, August 1942 and February 1943.

Professor Sir Karl Popper and Routledge and Kegan Paul for 'The Poverty of Historicism', sections 29 to 32.

May Brodbeck and the Williams and Wilkins Company for 'On the Philosophy of the Social Sciences', *Philosophy of Science*, Vol. 21, 1954, pp. 140–156.

Alan Gewirth and the Williams and Wilkins Company for 'Subjectivism and Objectivism in the Social Sciences', *Philosophy of Science*, Vol. 21, 1954, pp. 157–163.

Richard S. Rudner and the Williams and Wilkins Company for 'Philosophy and Social Science', *Philosophy of Science*, Vol. 21, 1954, pp. 164–241.

Alan Gewirth and the Williams and Wilkins Company for 'Can Men Change Laws of Social Science?', *Philosophy of Science*, Vol. 21, 1954, pp. 229–241.

J. W. N. Watkins and Cambridge University Press for the revised and expanded version of 'Ideal Types and Historical Explanation' that originally appeared in *The British Journal for the Philosophy of Science*, 3, 1952.

J. W. N. Watkins and Cambridge University Press for 'Historical Explanation in the Social Sciences', *The British Journal for the Philosophy of Science*, 8, 1957.

J. W. N. Watkins and the Williams and Wilkins Company for 'Methodological Individualism: A Reply', *Philosophy of Science*, Vol. 22, 1955, pp. 58–62.

Joseph Agassi and *The British Journal of Sociology* for 'Methodological Individualism', *The British Journal of Sociology*, II, 1960, pp. 244–270.

K. J. Scott and Cambridge University Press for 'Methodological and Epistemological Individualism', *The British Journal for the Philosophy of Science*, Vol. II, February 1961.

Maurice Mandelbaum and *The British Journal of Sociology* for 'Societal Facts', *The British Journal of Sociology*, 6, 1955.

Maurice Mandelbaum and Cambridge University Press for 'Societal Laws', *The British Journal for the Philosophy of Science*, 8, 1957.

E. A. Gellner and The Aristotelian Society for 'Explanations in History', *The Proceedings of the Aristotelian Society*, 1956.

L. J. Goldstein and *The Journal of Philosophy* for 'The Inadequacy of the Principle of Methodological Individualism', *The Journal of Philosophy*, Vol. LIII, No. 25, December 1956.

L. J. Goldstein and Cambridge University Press for 'Two Theses of Methodological Individualism', *The British Journal for the Philosophy of Science*, 9, 1958.

May Brodbeck and the Williams and Wilkins Company for 'Methodological Individualisms: Definition and Reduction', *Philosophy of Science*, Vol. 25, 1958, pp. 1–22.

A. C. Danto and *Filosofia* for 'Methodological Individualism and Methodological Socialism', *Filosofia*, 4 November 1962.

Part 1

Scientism and Historicism

JOHN O'NEILL

Scientism, Historicism and the Problem of Rationality

The following collection of essays has the natural unity of a live discussion which originally took place in a scatter of philosophical and social science journals. It is unnecessary therefore to impose a conventional editorial introduction on the issues contained in the debate, particularly since they are so ably exposed by the protagonists. This would only conceal that these are issues on which it is essential to have an opinion. I am aware that aspects of the issues argued in this volume have been discussed by continental writers such as Lukács,[1] Sartre[2] and Goldmann,[3] to mention a few. However, I have decided to preserve the actual exchange rather than extend the dialogue artificially into an anthology. Though it is certainly no substitute for selections from other European writers, not to mention Marx and Weber, I shall attempt in the light of the wider tradition to sketch the nature of historicism[4] and scientism[5] against the background of the problem of rationality which the methodological analysis of individualism and collectivism presupposes. I have preferred to attempt to complement the discussion in this way rather than deal exclusively with the

[1] G. Lukács, *History and Class Consciousness*, Studies in Marxist Dialectics, Translated by Rodney Livingstone, London, Merlin Press, 1971.

[2] J. P. Sartre, *Critique de la Raison dialectique*, Paris, Librairie Gallimard, 1960.

[3] L. Goldmann, *Recherches dialectiques*, Paris, Librairie Gallimard, 1959.

[4] 'Popper's use of the term "historicism" to mean a methodology that "aims at *historical prediction*" would seem unfortunate because almost all the proponents of historicism repudiate any search for the "laws" in the physical science sense, and hence deny that history offers a basis for prediction . . . we suggest two brief definitions: (a) the belief that the truth, meaning and value of anything i.e., the basis of any evaluation, is to be found in its history; and, more narrowly, (b) the anti-positivistic and anti-naturalistic view that historical knowledge is a basic, or the only requirement for understanding and evaluating man's present political, social and intellectual position or problems,' D. E. Lee and R. N. Beck, 'The Meaning of "Historicism" ', *American Historical Review*, Vol. LIX, No. 3, April, 1954, pp. 568–577.

[5] What I consider to be basic in the attitude of 'scientism' is the cultural value set upon science in general, and in particular the physical sciences, so that there arises a dispute about the paradigm value of the latter for the social and human sciences, as well as meta-scientific discussions about the meaning of science as a human enterprise.

3

methodological issues—upon which I readily subscribe to the collectivist position.

Whatever choice one makes between the principles of individualism and collectivism as methodological and normative principles, it can only be a choice enlightened by the dialogue initiated by Professors Hayek and Popper, the willingness of Watkins to suffer the arrows of outrageous fortune and the general care exercised to sustain the dialogue beyond premature frustration and hostility. Once we attempt to specify the nature of the interaction between individual conduct and its institutional contexts, we are involved in disagreement about the instrumental, rational and value matrices of social action, particularly when it is recognized that we possess few universal generalizations about human nature and social structure. Fortunately, none of the discussants is concerned to withdraw into an epistemological or methodological limbo, to work out a social science guaranteed immunity from conflict and controversy, if ever times show themselves propitious for its introduction. On the contrary, in every case the argument proceeds on the assumption that the texture of individual and social experience is vitally affected by the manner in which action is governed by conceptions of human nature, social structure, trends and laws of history. Though, indeed, it is sometimes argued as though a particular view of these problems derives from simple fallacies, false analogies, or even wish-fulfilment, such claims are not derived from the claim to an ultimate knowledge of the nature of social reality, which would overlook its intentional and practical constitution. This is dimly acknowledged in our reluctance to crush alternative ideologies, as we might otherwise do, were they to represent nothing but the preference for error over truth, rather than conscientious varieties of truth, each with its partial errors.

The essays which follow range over the disciplines of history, sociology, anthropology, economics, psychology and politics. They are concerned with the intellectual tradition of the social sciences, as well as with their formal and methodological properties. The argument focuses upon the nature of concept formation and the logic of explanation in the social sciences. It is an argument that is a central and perennial topic of the social sciences. The most recent context of the debate over the Popperian conception of the social sciences has been the *Methodenstreit*[6]

---

[6] *Der Positivismusstreit in der deutschen Soziologie*, Herausgeben von Heinz Maus und Friedrich Fürstenberg, Neuwied und Berlin, Luchterhand Verlag, 1969. For a very clear review of the issues between the Marxists, critical theorists and Popperians on the German debate see, George Lichtheim, 'Marx or Weber: Dialectical Methodology', in his *From Marx to Hegel And Other Essays*, London, Orbach and Chambers, 1971. David Frisby, 'The Popper-Adorno Controversy: the Methodological Dispute in German Sociology', *Philosophy of the Social Sciences*, Vol. 2, Number 2, June 1972, pp. 105–119.

between members of the Frankfurt school of critical theory and the positivist exponents of empirical sociology in Germany. Once again, it is important to understand that what is at stake besides methodological issues, is the question of the conservative and radical roots of social science knowledge. The original *Methodenstreit*, with which these issues are continuous, arose over the merits of the institutional and analytic approaches to political economy. This debate issued in Weber's reflections on the question of value-free social research which have borne so distinctly upon the professional practice of sociology and its articulation with a society whose need for sociology is itself never questioned.[7] In taking up the cudgels against Popper's positivist ideal of social science research, Adorno develops the critique of methodological individualism using the language of reification to describe the social ontology assumed by positivism. The objectivism of positivist knowledge, he argues, ignores the institutional praxis through which facts and trends are constituted; it thereby reproduces them through the ideology of value-neutral research. It is therefore the task of critical theory, by means of '*ideologie-kritik*', to unmask the positivist reification of scientific praxis and its institutional presuppositions. Adorno, therefore, rejects Popper's restriction of social science practice to problems of knowledge, rather than the problems of the society in which sociology is practised, as well as the rule of undertaking only small-scale problems with neat solutions. The ideals of knowledge become truly ideological when translated into norms of social and political practice. Indeed, the basic question is whether we can restrict the practice of social criticism to the model of the development of scientific knowledge through the formation of specific and testable hypotheses. For, in doing so, we risk reifying the praxis of science, in particular of the natural sciences, which have usually not been attuned to the nature of the social and political order in which they function. However, as Habermas remarked in the same debate, Popper has at least raised the question of the extrapolation of the meta-scientific discussion of rationality from the community of science to the political public (*Öffentlichkeit überhaupt*). Critical sociology cannot rest upon conjectures and refutations; it aims at the transformation of individual and social conduct. Critical sociology, therefore, cannot be content with the logic of its own formal possibility; it seeks the practical realization of its understanding. But this is a task wider than the interests of the

[7] Alvin W. Gouldner, 'Anti-Minotaur: The Myth of a Value-free Sociology', and other essays in *The Relevance of Sociology*, edited by Jack D. Douglas, New York, Appleton-Century-Crofts, 1970; compare a positivist development of Weber's value-free thesis along Popperian lines by Hans Albert, 'Social Science and Moral Philosophy: A Critical Approach to the Value Problem in the Social Sciences', in *The Critical Approach to Science and Philosophy*, edited by M. Bunge, Glencoe, N.Y., Free Press, 1964.

community of scientists, even though it is a gain to recognize, as do Popper and others, that the objectivity of knowledge rests upon the praxis of specific epistemic communities. The task involved calls for a substantive sociology of the structures of work, politics and communication in which the insights of critical theory and Marxism might merge.[8] We shall return to these themes in the latter part of this essay.

Though there are differences between them, Popper and Hayek are both concerned with the moral and political consequences of the view that the processes of society may be subject to engineering prediction and control, analogous to systems of control in the physical sciences. Both argue that this 'scientistic' aspiration of the social sciences is based upon a false understanding of the nature of the physical sciences.

Hayek regards scientism as a complex of attitudes, which he labels objectivism, collectivism and historicism. The error in objectivism lies in the assimilation of mental events to physical events, or the reduction of the operations of mind to electro-physical brain processes. Social entities, Hayek argues, are not found or given objects, but meaningful wholes, constituted by the participants' interactions, or for the sake of questions raised by the social scientist. Scientism, in seeking objectivity, falls into the error of identifying ideas which are *constitutive* of the phenomena to be explained with those ideas which the participants or the social scientist may have formed *about* these phenomena and which are not causes, but only more or less fruitful theories about social behaviour and institutions. Hayek's arguments to save mind from the physicalist reduction may well serve to defend the principle of individualism against bio-chemical strategies for brave new world totalitarianisms. Having resisted the physicalist attempt to undermine individualism, Hayek then couples his psychic holism with the 'resolutive-compositive method',[9] designed to ward off absorption from over-arching social collectivities. The limits of this method, however, are apparent from Hobbes's application of it, inasmuch as there is evidently no way of moving from private protocol to public consensus except through the alienation of individual rights and reason in favour of Leviathan. Having suppressed the precontractual bases of protocol, it is only possible to reintroduce consensus—which was to be explained —through the containment of violence. Where Hobbes saw a fearful

[8] For contributions to this task, see Trent Schroyer, 'Toward a Critical Theory for Advanced Industrial Society', in *Recent Sociology No. 2*, edited by Hans Peter Dreitzel, New York, The Macmillan Company, 1970, and John O'Neill, 'The Responsibility of Reason and the Critique of Political Economy', in *Phenomenology and the Social Sciences*, edited by Maurice Natanson, Evanston, Northwestern University Press, 1973.

[9] J. W. N. Watkins, *Hobbes' System of Ideas*, London, Hutchinson University Library, 1965, Ch. III, Scientific Tradition.

violence in the privacy of the individual, Hayek finds a political virtue inasmuch as the privacy of mind resists social science generalizations and thereby rescues us from their totalitarian potential. Popper would not accept Hayek's argument that the subject matter of the social sciences, even when not characterized in terms of scientistic and holist preconceptions, necessitates a method of analysis and explanation wholly different from that of the natural sciences. He would, however, agree that ultimately the ground of sociological behaviour is furnished by individual dispositions, not in the psychologistic sense of starting analysis from these individual dispositions but requiring that explanation come to rest in them. The sense of this ultimate explanatory basis has been developed by Watkins in his account of the ideal typical dispositions of 'anonymous individuals'.

Apart from purely methodological arguments, Hayek and Popper are equally concerned to trace the historical sources of scientism and historicism. While Popper has painted his own gallery of the enemies of the open society,[10] Hayek appears to have made a more thorough documentation of the counter-revolutionary origins of scientism. However, even a brief examination of the socialist attitude to the autonomy of science at the time of the French Revolution is sufficient to show that the engineers of the new social order were no friends of scientism. After remarking on this specific context of scientism, we may then proceed to a more general discussion of the role of scientism in Western knowledge.

Hayek traces the two great intellectual movements of the nineteenth century—socialism and scientism—to their roots in the engineering mentality of the École Polytechnique and the 'ideological' outlook of the neighbouring Collège de France. Though they are not accountable for the evils of scientism, Hayek still regards the interest that d'Alembert and Condorcet showed in mathematics, physics and the philosophy of history as fateful for the scientistic and positivistic treatment of social phenomena. For a time their influence was held in check by their Cartesianism; however, ultimately this too proved a weakness. French political thought failed to separate itself from the rationalism of Natural Law thought and ignored the pragmatic liberalism of Condillac and Say in favour of the revolutionary rationalism of Quesnay and Condorcet. Although Hayek notices that Condorcet fell victim to the Revolution, he does not stop to consider what scandal Condorcet gave to the Revolution, along with Lavoisier, Lagrange,

[10] K. R. Popper, *The Open Society and its Enemies*, New York and Evanston, Harper Torchbook, 1963.

Delambre, Carnot and Coulamb—surely, all spiritual sources of scientism, if not of the Revolution. In fact, their fate is indicative of a tactical shift in the relations between revolutionary politics and science. In this case, the general alliance between science and the revolution against feudal authority had to be sacrificed in the face of the ultimate split between the principles of determinism and interventionism, as options which divide the social and natural sciences.

The developments which Hayek attributes to Saint-Simon and Comte have their origins much earlier. Indeed, these earlier facts may account for the division of the French sciences between the École Polytechnique and the Collège de France. This division, which Hayek notices, actually reflects a fundamental division of outlook in what he regards as a uniformly positivist outlook. The division is symbolized in the rivalry between mechanistic and organismic models of the universe and is as ancient as the rivalry between idealism and materialism. The argument has to be considered in the specific context of the attitude of Jacobin socialism to the physical and mathematical sciences. It has been argued quite cogently that the basic philosophy of science, not only of the French Revolution, but even of the Enlightenment, was not in fact based on Newtonian science, as is so often thought.[11] Newtonian science proposed an abstract mechanical picture of the universe which offered very little encouragement to the political impulse of the time to participate in the direction of universal history. The result was a modern revival of Stoicism which differed importantly from anything like abject scientism. The demands of a messianic democracy, combined with the essentially utilitarian employment of science and technology in the interests of the general welfare, dictated an attack upon the learned academies.[12]

On 8 August, 1793, in view of their interests in abstract mathematical knowledge and purely theoretical science, the learned academies were abolished as contrary to the interests of the new Republic. The Revolution demanded a philosophy of science in which man participates. Nature had to be seen as a whole, as d'Alembert saw it in his Dream. Accordingly, there was fostered a great interest in and devotion to natural history, chemistry, physiology, history, technology—in fact all the sciences which promised to benefit man. This is the source from

[11] C. C. Gillispie, 'The Encyclopédie and the Jacobin Philosophy of Science', in M. Clagett (ed.), *Critical Problems in the History of Science*, Madison, University of Wisconsin Press, 1959, pp. 255–289.

[12] H. Guerlac, 'Science During the French Revolution', in P. S. Frank (ed.), *The Validation of Scientific Theories*, Boston, Beacon Press, 1954, pp. 171–191; C. C. Gillispie, 'Science in the French Revolution', *Proceedings of the National Academy of Science*, Vol. XLV (1959), p. 679. These developments reveal the lack of subtlety in arguments such as Eric Voeglin, 'The Origins of Scientism', *Social Research*, 1948, pp. 462–494.

which arose the École Polytechnique, Collège de France, École Normale and Musée d'Histoire Naturelle. From the start, Jacobin socialism raised moral objections against Newtonianism which represented a political critique rather than an espousal of anti-science.[13] It was in fact the Napoleonic suppression of the idéologues, and the subordination of science to military engineering, which ushered in the sort of fate which science experiences in the closed society.[14] Hayek ignores the extent to which the totalitarianism of counter-revolutionary France had its origins in the political centralization of the ancient régime and the bitter suppression of the revolutionary class struggles from 1789 to 1848 and 1870.

Popper's critique of certain misguided conceptions of social science, now known as historicism and scientism, has been so persuasive that there appears to be no alternative philosophy of social science other than methodological individualism.[15] The Popperian critique of inductivism as a logic of method of natural science is indeed destructive of certain positivist interpretations of the logic of scientific discovery. What is questionable is whether pre-Popperian social science ever modelled itself upon a second-hand positivist interpretation of the method of natural science.[16] For the critique of natural science positivism also has its roots in neo-Kantianism, which cannot be overlooked as a corrective in the pre-Comtean, and, particularly, the Marxist-Hegelian tradition of social thought.[17]

The Popperian critique is aimed in general against positivist characterizations of the method of natural sciences. The positivist logic of induction yields an inadequate account of the theoretical framework of natural science. Moreover, inductivism stultifies the practical development of sciences which adopt it as a methodological model.

---

[13] L. Pearce Williams, 'The Politics of Science in the French Revolution', in *Critical Problems in the History of Science*, pp. 291–308.

[14] L. Pearce Williams, 'Science, Education and Napoleon I', *ISIS*, Vol. XLVII, December, 1956, pp. 369–382.

[15] Popper's perspective, together with Habermas' theory of critical sociology, is regarded as the most vital force in shaping the goals of social science, in Gerard Radnitzky, *Contemporary Schools of Metascience*, Göteborg, Akademiförlaget, 1970. While critical theorists attack Popperian positivism, Radnitzky sees Popper as the founder of critical rationalism. The problem here is that Popper is certainly a critical positivist and a rationalist in this sense. What is at issue is the nexus between Popper's views on scientific method and the scientific community and their implications for the wider political community affected by scientific praxis.

[16] W. M. Simon, *European Positivism in the Nineteenth Century*, New York, 1963. Ch. IX. Positivism in Germany, provides a corrective to the account in F. A. Hayek, *The Counter-Revolution of Science*, Glencoe, 1952.

[17] H. Marcuse, *Reason and Revolution*, Boston, Beacon Press, 1968, Pt. II. Ch. II. The Foundations of Positivism and the Rise of Sociology.

The epistemological errors of positivism are consequently moral errors, because they hinder the development of social-scientific knowledge which is the foundation of a rational society. In effect, the Popperians advance a rationalist theory of social development based upon a comparative epistemology. They challenge alternative conceptions of the social sciences on the ground that they are based upon primitive epistemologies which must be rejected by the guardians of the open society. Their political position is the consequence of methodological individualism: the basic unit of social structure is the individual and social change is the product of individual purposes and their unintended consequences; the degree to which the outcome of individual behaviour is the result of purpose, or the secondary effect of 'the logic of the situation', is the measure of the degree of rational social control in a given society. The Popperian concept of rationalism is functional and not substantive, that is to say, it is concerned with the adaptation of means to given ends. There is, however, a tendency to provide a definition of substantive rationality by taking the hypothetical form of reasoning about means to be a constitutive feature of the rational society. Thus a comparative sociology is substituted for a theory of social change on the basis of a type-distinction between epistemologies.[18]

Jarvie, for example, complains that a unified conception of social knowledge as a moral and scientific project has been destroyed by a mistaken characterization of the nature of scientific method. The fault lies in the ritualization of the Baconian tradition of the power of the inductive method in yielding knowledge which would transform man's natural and social environment. Bacon's directions for avoiding the speculative errors of the hypothetical method have resulted in the banishment of theoretical imagination and the institution of a fetishism of facts. This is the situation which accounts for the present stultification of the social sciences. Indeed, the clincher is that the contemporary difficulties of social anthropology, as evidenced by its failure to explain the cargo cults, is due to its own cargo-cult expectations of positivistic scientific method. The error here, as Jarvie rightly observes, is that the facts, however numerous, can never be made to deliver of themselves; they require fertilization by the theoretical constructs which it is the task of the scientist to bring to his material. In the encounter between

---

[18] 'Both we westerners and the savages have a degree of rationality in believing what we do. But our reasons for believing what we do are somewhat better than their reasons, at least by our standard of critical discussion. And our standards of critical discussion are better than no standards of critical discussion, and the latter is the situation of the savage.' I. C. Jarvie, *The Revolution in Anthropology*, London, Routledge and Kegan Paul, 1964, p. 143. Compare this argument with Lévi-Strauss's argument upon the relation between the logic of 'hot' and 'cold' societies in his *La Pensée Sauvage*, Paris, Plon, 1962. Ch. VIII. Le Temps Retrouvé.

fact and theory the objectivist attitude is entirely abortive. The question remains whether holism is conceptually on the same level as the cargo-cults with regard to its expectations of social science.

The inductivist model of scientific procedure, apart from blocking theoretical orientation to the data of the social sciences, also leads to the suppression of the normative dimension of social studies. The Popperians propose to substitute for positivism and relativism the metaphysics of 'conventionalism and objectivism' which will provide a basis for comparative judgments about moral development and an interventionist policy in social development. Underlying the distinction between conventionalism and naturalism as conflicting attitudes to the nature of social institutions is Popper's comparative model of the open and closed societies.[19] The closed society is absorbed in the natural world and does not distinguish the laws of its development from the laws of nature. The open society draws a distinction between the (descriptive) laws of development of natural phenomena and the (prescriptive) laws of social development. Failure to make these distinctions has important consequences for the possibilities of social change. In the closed society, the naturalist conception of social laws is reinforced by considering all laws the unalterable prescriptions of a higher agency. It is the 'supernaturalist' attitude of the closed society which defines any departure from the *status quo* as taboo. Such a disposition precludes any analysis of the sources of tension in the social structure. Social changes (due to contact with Western culture) are experienced as crises in the religious framework, as a heightened expectation of the good life, accompanied by ritual modifications, i.e. the cargo-cults, for dealing with the new expectations. The (super), naturalism of the closed society prevents it from achieving a rational understanding of the laws of social development and consequently inhibits it from intervening in the rational control of its growth. It remains underdeveloped. As a reaction to the capitalist break-up of feudal society, Marxism merely produces socialism as another version of the closed society.

The contrast between the conventionalism or interventionism of the open society and the naturalism of the closed society is perhaps better understood as an epistemological distinction rather than a contrast of historical types. Viewed in this way, it is easy to see that it is hardly illegitimate to extend the critique of Marxist social science into the argument that Marxist knowledge represents a potential rebarbarization of the open society. The elements of historicism relevant to our discussion are its structuralism and its fatalism. It is worth noting that Popper is not the opponent of analytic struc-

[19] *The Open Society and Its Enemies*, Vol. 1, Ch. 5, Nature and Convention.

turalism that his followers take him to be.[20] The concept of structure is more general than its biological and physical variants with which the social sciences have been traditionally concerned.[21] A sympathetic understanding of historicism amounts to seeing it as an attempt to regard physical structures as particular systems within a more general class of systems, biological and social. Popper nevertheless proceeds to the destruction of historicism as the view that social systems are analogous to physical systems, in particular the planetary system. It is, of course, short work to dispose of the argument that the laws of society are not like the irreversible laws of planetary motion. Yet this analysis is offered in explanation of the contradiction between the interventionist politics of Marxism and its historical fatalism derived from its misconception of the nature of scientific laws. The methodological individualists have joined issue with collectivists by locating the errors of scientism in the very notion of system or structure. The total effect is to characterize alternative conceptions of social science, principally Marxism, as modern cargo-cults founded upon the naturalist mentality of the closed society.[22]

It is a curiosity of scholarship that Hegel and Marx have come to be identified with a deterministic conception of history and the place

---

[20] *The Open Society and Its Enemies*, Ch. 14, The Autonomy of Sociology. Popper's stand on methodological individualism is not consistent in quite the way that his students demand. K. J. Scott, 'Methodological and Epistemological Individualism', in this volume, argues that Popper's criterion of the testability of sociological laws is independent of any epistemological thesis; methodological individualism is subscribed to by Popper as a criterion of satisfactory explanation of sociological laws. But in discussing Mill's reduction of the law of progress to a law of human nature, Popper points out that the principle of falsifiability yields conditions which are favourable and unfavourable to a psychological propensity, and thus an *institutional* and technological analysis of the conditions of progress is needed. (*The Poverty of Historicism*, p32.) See note 22 below.

[21] C. Lévi-Strauss, *Structural Anthropology*, New York, 1963, Ch. XV. Social Structure. Lévi-Strauss sees in communications theory a general theory of the exchange relationships which structure kinship, language and economic systems; compare R. Bastide (ed.) *Sens et Usages du Terme Structure*, S. Gravenhage, 1962; P. L. Van den Berghe, 'Dialectic and Functionalism: Toward a Theoretical Synthesis', *American Sociological Review*, 1963, 28, pp. 695–705.

[22] Marxian methodology is critized as a species of collectivism, i.e., it is implied that the analytic use of type-concepts results in the depreciation of the ethical value of the individual. Here again an epistemological or ontological theory is subscribed as the foundation of comparative politics. (F. A. Hayek, 'The Individualist and Compositive Method of the Social Sciences'.) Methodological individualism confuses the logical question of descriptive emergence with regard to concepts, which depends upon criteria of meaning, with the empirical question of the possibility of the reduction of laws and theories of the social sciences. (M. Brodbeck, 'Models, Meanings and Theories', in L. Gross (ed.), *Symposium on Sociological Theory*, New York, Row and Petersen, 1959, pp. 373–403.) It is quite possible for certain purposes to redefine group concepts in terms of relations

in it of human freedom, whereas both conceived of history as the story of freedom. Indeed, it is precisely the historical consciousness which the individual achieves though the stages of his own awareness and collective development that is the foundation of the openness of the future. Now this metaphysics of history is quite compatible with the recognition of levels of social system determinism *vis-à-vis* individual action and with the decisiveness of individual action at certain conjunctures of history. Meta-historicism, as we may call it, is by no means the same thing as the claim that historical events determine individual conduct from behind. Rather, the suppression of meta-historicist concerns is more likely to lead to this effect through the ideological neglect of the meta-principles underlying the interaction between social and individual behaviour in given historical situations. Popper's *Open Society and Its Enemies* is explicitly directed to the meta-historical question of the ultimate values of the open society. I argue that this works fails because, instead of remaining at the meta-historical level of the meaning or value of scientific rationality, it reduces its argument to a comparative epistemology which assumes the values of science.[23] Moreover the *Poverty of Historicism* deals only with a particularly rigid or fatalist version of historicism thereby nullifying the practical connections between political action and sociological research, which is the real constellation of Marxist-historicism. Popper's basically empiricist position requires him to break the hermeneutic circle of action and meaning in history. In his view, history is nothing but individual goals and decisions. But today we need, more than ever, a philosophy of history if we are not to reduce human action to a product of technical

---

between individuals. But the prediction of group behaviour from member behaviour is not possible without empirical composition laws or *axiomata media*, as John Stuart Mill called them in Book VI of his *Logic*. The latter establish determinate relations between the behaviour of individuals within a system and the resultant behaviour of that system. Karl Popper's criticism that Marx deduced historical laws on the assumption that social systems are analogous to planetary systems (*The Poverty of Historicism*, Boston, 1957) completely overlooks Marx's own criticism of the 'natural laws' of classical economics, i.e., that they are dependent upon an historically specific set of sociological preconditions— the bourgeois property and class structure. I have developed these arguments in 'The Concept of Estrangement in the Early and Late Writings of Karl Marx', *Philosophy and Phenomenological Research*, Vol. XXV, No. 1, September 1964, pp. 64–84.

[23] I cannot agree with Radnitzky's view that the *Open Society and Its Enemies* contains a devastating moral criticism of fatalist-historicism, since, as I say, it is false to the problematic of Western rationality that has prevailed from Plato to Marx. Cf. *Contemporary Schools of Metascience*, Vol. II, p. 115. The whole of Volume Two, however, deserves attention for its attempt to merge Popper's 'criticistic rationalism' with 'hermeneutic-dialectic' or the critical social science of Habermas.

decisions—which is the basis of the totalitarianism *within* liberal society. This, however, challenges the self-image of social science fostered by logical empiricism, which insists upon the dichotomy of knowledge and decision. In effect, this amounts to a rejection of the meta-scientific problems of knowledge through the reduction of science to the tasks of technical reason. It is the value placed upon instrumental rationality as productive of science which is masked by the positivistic value-free position on questions of substantive rationality. But this only leaves positivist social science open to the domination of the interests of the society from which it affects a critical distance. 'Thus the rationality concept underlying a positivistically oriented criticism of ideologies is that of means-ends-rationality; simply, efficiency and economy of means to given ends. These values are accorded a privileged status since they are implied in "rational" procedure itself. Thus the aim of this ideology-critique can be seen, more specifically as the enforcement of this positivistic type of rationality, and as an attempt to provide it with a monopolistic position. That means that—*in the name of value-freedom—this criticism of ideologies dictates the value-system for all realms of human life, viz., its own.* Or, in other words, its value-freedom is hypothetical to a preceding position-taking. That the allocation of a monopolistic position to purely technical interest goes unnoticed is due to the fact that it is so deeply rooted in our form of life: in it is rooted the basis of our industrialized society—technology; the basis upon which our system of life literally depends for its survival (and by which too, our life is threatened today, for the same reasons).'[24]

The Popperians have developed a comparative sociology organized around the polar concepts of the open and closed societies. The latter typology is proposed as a basis for comparative moral judgments. Popperian sociology is actually more a study in comparative epistemology, and is thus a species of rationalism—but not its norm. The Popperian type-constructs are drawn on the basis of a distinction between societies which cast their knowledge in the form of hypotheses and those which do not. The closed society is not an historical stage. It is a state of mind in which man's condition is looked upon as given, naturally or supernaturally and beyond the influence of human intervention. Such a condition can only be altered by some deus ex machina or spiritual metamorphosis. The closed society does not institute processes of directed social change because it fails to cast its knowledge in a form instrumental to such development.

The theory of social change is not reducible to a sub-theorem of astronomy. The Popperians rightly emphasize the logical difference between physical and social systems. The point of the argument, how-

[24] Radnitzky, *loc. cit*, p. 133.

ever, is that a theory of social change is a theory of the transformation of social orders. In this case it is clear that the Popperian philosophy of social science is less general than its comparative epistemology suggests. It is tied to an individualistic theory of technological-scientific change which abstracts (normatively) from the social framework. Popperian sociology is the instrument of a social order whose individualist norm is an obstacle to the diagnosis of the structural changes involved in its present transformation.

Primitive ontology may have been too luxuriant. But nothing is to be gained from epistemological strictures which deprive us of adequate theoretical structures. The Popperians are aware that the working method of science is always to provide itself with the ontological scaffolding needed to get a job done. Despite much meta-talk about the relationship between natural science method and the social sciences, the Popperians in practice adopt as their model the science of economics. Unfortunately, they seem not to have noticed certain revolutionary changes in modern economics. The Keynesian revolution, for example, represented a critique of the macro-irrationality of a social order based upon the micro—or functional—rationalism of individual economic units.[25] The Keynesian diagnosis resulted in the treatment of a number of structural variables, income, saving and investment functions, which determine the aggregate level of performance of the economic system. In short, Keynes, in the very interests of an ethic of individualism, expanded the ontological assumptions of economics from the awareness that it is 'the ought' which provides the framework of 'what is'. As Keynes himself put it, 'We need a new set of convictions which spring naturally from a candid examination of our own inner feelings in relation to the outside facts'. The Popperians, on the other hand, attempt to defend the values of individualism with an outworn conception of the social sciences, retarding the transformation of the social order that might be built upon them.

The crux of the issue between individualists and collectivists is the locus of power.[26] Hayek and Popper are concerned with the alienation of power from individuals to totalitarian states. Their accounts of this historical process attribute it largely to a series of erroneous conceptions of scientific knowledge and its procedures of concept-formation and generalization. Revolutionaries, they say, have by and large alienated

---

[25] J. M. Keynes, 'The End of Laissez-Faire' (1926) in *Essays in Persuasion*, London, 1952; *The General Theory of Employment Interest and Money*, London, 1957, ch. 24, Concluding Notes on the Social Philosophy Towards Which The General Theory Might Lead.

[26] J. O. Wisdom, 'Situational Individualism and Emergent Group-Properties', in *Explanations in the Behavioral Sciences*, edited by Robert Borger and Frank Cioffi, Cambridge University Press, 1970, pp. 271–296.

individual powers by appealing to deterministic laws of social systems. This criticism, however, fails to distinguish, for example, the Marxist use of holist analysis and its ethical aim of the creation of a set of social institutions in which *human* and not narrowly individualistic values would prevail. Methodological individualism, both Marx and Hegel would argue, is the mode in which it is plausible to analyse individual behaviour in market society, although this conceals, as Durkheim, Toennies and Weber have shown, the historical, legal and institutional preconditions of such individualism. Moreover, it obscures the phenomenon of the distribution of power which, under market conditions, belongs to some individuals only, and not all. In other words, the *class* distribution of power and social privilege is obscured by methodological individualism.

It might be argued that there is a certain emancipatory interest in the attempt to reduce statements about institutions to statements about individuals. Thus the goals of clarity and simplicity espoused by logical empiricists are advanced as pillars of liberal freedom, ridding us of totalitarian states and clearing the skies of historicist laws. At any rate, it might be said, Popper's reduction of the weight of institutions to the logic of situationally unintended consequences of individual action materially demystifies the power of institutions. In the end, however, the question of power is a residual for Popper. He intends to fight off the enemies of the open society, so far as he can see them coming—that is to say, as he identifies them—but seems unaware of the problematic nature of the liberal social order itself.

The same complex of questions underlies Popper's account of historicism. Just as he is not always clear whether he means to settle the question of power through a simple reductionist individualism (though on balance I believe he does not), so it is not clear whether he means to attack a fatalist version of historicism, or only the view that we can have some knowledge of the future. Again the first view, if anyone ever held it, would make nonsense of political practices aimed at changing the course of human affairs. So far from having bad political consequences, from which Popper's critique of historicism would preserve us, fatalist historicism, strictly speaking, would have no political consequences at all, since it serves to suppress altogether the category of political action. More serious, because of the way it relates to the problem of power, is the argument over the degree of confidence we can have in planning human affairs. Human plans are often self-defeating. But they may also be self-fulfilling. The odds against the Viet Cong or Castro result neither in automatic victory for those they favour, nor in a simple capitulation, but in a resolve to fight, which is an essential ingredient in the way men make history and politics. In this example, what is at stake is the different attention paid to the analysis of social and political developments by the revolutionaries and the technocrat adviser of imperialism. However, although technological extrapolations run aground on political forces, the revolutionaries, for all that, still dodge bombs! Moreover, behind the imperialist bombing there is a behaviouralist theory of social engineering which certainly has the merits of being 'piecemeal', if only because it will, if successful, have to start from a totally shattered society. As Chomsky has shown,[27] it is quite possible to combine the rhetoric of experimental science with imperialist intervention to produce nightmares to equal anything that supposedly results from non testable utopias.

It seems to me that the problem of the relation between the natural and the social sciences, or moral sciences, cannot be discussed solely in terms of the unity of method in abstraction from the axiological assumption of man's domination of nature which radicalizes the subject-object split and propels knowledge towards quantification and rationalization. As Weber has argued, we need to understand the nature of the 'vocation' of Western science before we attribute our disenchantment to peculiar misapprehensions of science. Modern science is chained to progress through invention. Every scientific finding asks to be surpassed in the light of further knowledge. Every scientist must be resigned to making only the smallest contributions to a task that is conceived as limitless. 'And with this we come to inquire into the meaning of science. For, after all, it is not self-evident that something subordinate to such a law is sensible and meaningful in itself. Why does one engage in doing something that in reality never comes, and never can come to an end.'[28] We can give practical or extrinsic reasons for the scientist's vocation in terms of its technological and material pay-off for society. But we have still to understand the intrinsic satisfactions in the insatiable pursuit of knowledge. Between them Marx and Weber raised the question of the meaning of accumulation and rationalization beyond its purely practical and technical significance. How shall we understand the pursuit of economic and cultural values in the absence of any self-imposed or socially imposed limit which would make the acquisition of these values a meaningful end rather than an essentially ever-distant and unattainable goal? It is the concern with the ordered disorder or the anomie of industrial society which histori-

[27] Noam Chomsky, *American Power and the New Mandarins*, New York, Pantheon Books, 1969.
[28] 'Science as a Vocation', *From Max Weber: Essays in Sociology*, translated, edited and with an Introduction by H. Gerth and C. Wright Mills, New York, Oxford University Press, 1958, p. 138.

cists have brought to our attention at least as much as any concern
with the nature of historical 'laws'.[29]

In Marx and Weber we have the elements of a phenomenology of
the logic of technological domination in Western culture. This is the
intuitive focus of their comparative studies of Western philosophy, social
science and social structure. It is from this standpoint that we best
understand what Marx and Weber aimed at in their ideal typical constructions of capitalism. The model of economic rationality is not
simply a construction of the social scientist's understanding. It also
reflects the shift from a social structure in which power was based on
status to a social structure in which all statuses are ascribed on the
basis of economic power. In short the ideal type of capitalism is, as
Hegel would put it, the truth of subjectivity as it experiences itself
under the conditions of liberal society which has broken the bonds of
traditional sentimentality in favour of a vast machinery of individual
rights, exchange and private property. In their use of the ideal-type
Marx and Weber, so far from reducing social facts to natural or technological factors, understood the latter as middle principles (Mill's *prin-
cipia media*) whose meta-economic significance is the self-transformation
of human nature through the market as a generator of wants and needs.

Methodological criticism of scientism is certainly in order as far as it
goes, but it deals with symptoms and suggests that all our troubles stem
only from the misunderstanding of the practice of science. This
assumption is itself covertly scientistic for it assumes that science is
intrinsically unproblematic whereas this is precisely something Weber
questions. 'Science has created this cosmos of natural causality and has
seemed unable to answer with certainty the question of its own
ultimate presuppositions.'[30] This is not a question about the meaning
of the vocation *for* science but about the *value of science* and the commitment to progress to which it is a motive. And this question Weber
compares to Tolstoi's question about the meaning of death in modern
civilization. Modern man, in virtue of being pitted against an ever
expanding universe of ideas, problems, and values, though he can be
weary of life, always encounters death as meaningless, for it robs him
of infinity. 'And because death is meaningless, civilized life as such is
meaningless; but its very "progressiveness" gives death the imprint
of meaninglessness.'[31]

Scientism is not simply a product of nineteenth-century positivism
aggravated by the utopianism of Saint-Simon and Marx. Scientism lies
at the roots of Western civilization. It is the source of the adventure

[29] Cf. note 4 above.
[30] 'Religious Rejections of the World and Their Directions', *From Max Weber*,
p. 355.
[31] 'Science as a Vocation', *From Max Weber*, p. 140.

and the ambiguity of Western knowledge. It is science which opens tribal society and rescues it from the fatalism of an eternal past; but science also commits the open society to the control of its future so that organization and planning are essential to the open society and with these the problems of heartless bureaucracy and disenchanted rationalization. Modern science and modern politics are not in search of a truth whether of nature or of man, and the sense in which they are theoretical is not with respect to ends but in regard to the implementation of means. The accumulation of knowledge and the accumulation of economic and political power, in short, the expansion of the modern 'world', implies an undertaking whose meaning and value lies outside the sciences upon which it relies. In the absence of a science of ends, which might illuminate the image of man and the norm of change and accumulation implicit in the expansion of Western knowledge, Weber attempted to confront the polytheism of modern values with the notions of the 'calling' and the 'ethic of responsibility'. These notions provide us with a situated understanding of the nature of Western economics, science and politics not in order to relativize their experience but to accept heroically their ambiguity and even violence.

> Integrity, however, compels us to state that for the many who today tarry for new prophets and saviors, the situation is the same as resounds in the beautiful Edomite watchman's song of the period of exile that has been included among Isaiah's oracles:

> He calleth to me out of Seir, Watchman, what of the night?
> The watchman said, The morning cometh, and also the night: if ye will enquire, enquire ye: return, come.

> The people to whom this was said has enquired and tarried for more than two millenia, and we are shaken when we realize its fate. From this we want to draw the lesson, that nothing is gained by yearning and tarrying alone, and we shall act differently. We shall set to work and meet 'the demands of the day', in human relations as well as in our vocation. This, however, is plain and simple, if each finds and obeys the demon who holds the fibers of his very life.[32]

We cannot meet the 'demands of the day' either with sheer fatalism or cynical opportunism.[33] Fatalism is out because the Western tradition is an activist tradition which may well in the flush of youth have thought of its powerful ascendancy as the working of an inevitable progress. But this is a rhetoric no more deceiving than the mood of despair and contingency that invades Western society confronted with the complex issues of maturity that force upon it a conception of its

[32] 'Science as a Vocation', *loc. cit.*, p. 156.
[33] On this see the soulful reflections upon Europe and the third world in the conclusion of Frantz Fanon, *The Wretched of the Earth*, Preface by Jean-Paul Sartre, translated by Constance Farrington, London, Penguin Books, 1967.

essential nature as a choice which it must continue and even open to the third world. The demands of the day are for the control of the human environment undistorted by world political and social inequality. This is the imperative behind the sudden vogue of the comparative social sciences. It also furnishes a new context for the relation between scientism and historicism. Today, every society wishes to enter history whether with the introduction of a simple birth-control device or the construction of giant dams and atomic power-plants. There is nothing inevitable about this process, for it is always introduced with violence and fought with violence. In such times the appeal to history is an appeal to the very history we are making; it is an appeal to a norm that is becoming historical by smashing a past history which no longer furnishes a basis for humane and social relations.

Popper argues that there is no inevitable law of history. But, as I think he himself recognizes,[34] contemporary history is an adventure which may be dangerous and colossally destructive but not something from which 'we' can opt out and still expect to retain our identity. Nowadays, what we are and what we expect of ourselves is very much the same question as the nature and process of industrialization. It is within this matrix that we meaningfully raise questions about the nature of the individual and society, order and freedom, science and government.[35] There is indeed no necessary connection between the goods promised by industrialization and the goods it delivers. The critics of chiliastic and millenarian attempts to close this gap are therefore not to be ignored. It may be true that the prospect of industrialization represents a greater emancipation for those countries about to experience it, than for more mature societies in which affluence, at least in the context of certain social and political institutions, no longer appears an unmixed blessing. Yet however difficult the solution to these problems may be, there can be little doubt that they do not deter contemporary societies from embracing the industrialization process for better or worse. And this is because the industrialization process is seen to some extent as a socially self-correcting process, precisely because of the knowledge and resources that it makes available. This does not happen automatically, of course. What happens is that a break is made with past history and the shape of the future is gradually framed through the accumulation and criticism of natural and social science knowledge. Under these conditions it is proper to raise questions about the nature of social structures, and the conditions of their emergence and change. Indeed such questions are essential to the nature of the enterprise; and in this the strictures of Hayek and Popper upon scientism and

---

[34] *The Open Society and its Enemies*, Vol. I, p. ix.
[35] E. Gellner, *Thought and Change*, London, Weidenfeld and Nicolson, 1964.

historicism are out of tune with the moral vision of our times, to see things broadly and to see ahead to cope with the scale and complexity of issues which face us.

We need also to view the issues raised in the arguments over individualism and collectivism in the wider framework of the sociology of knowledge conceived as the clarification of the methodological and existential premises of our times in its concern with humanism and historicity. From this perspective the Western experience is an unfinished one and is not justified solely by the determination of relatively unindustrialized countries to enter the path of 'development'. At the same time, we cannot separate ourselves from the projection of our experience in various forms of 'planning'. Rather, the sense of future progress lies only in facing its ambiguity and trying to comprehend its adventure without invoking its certainty.

I would suggest that the Popperian critique of historicism and scientism is ultimately a reflection upon one of the dilemmas of Western rationalism, which may be expressed in terms of the antinomy of naturalism and conventionalism, but not resolved thereby. The growth of Western rationalism owes much to a naturalist understanding of the social and historical roots of Reason. At the same time, the relativist and sceptical tendencies of naturalism were suspended in the Natural Law conception of Reason as a progressive moral force in the historical and social order. In the nineteenth century, both history and the natural sciences disputed the claim to have discovered that history and nature belong to the same reality. The unity of man and nature established by Natural Law thought yielded to the historical differences between man and man. This development opened up two options, namely, *naturalistic* historicism, whose ultimate tendency was to resolve history into sociology, and *metaphysical* historicism which resolved history and nature into stages of the Idea.[36] These oscillations are not simply contradictions, to be resolved by the distinction between descriptive and prescriptive laws. For in the social sciences the search for the 'laws' of social development is both naturalistic and normative, inasmuch as the ultimate goal is the transvaluation of history and the social order on the basis of its own discoveries.

All this, of course, flies in the face of the ritual distinction between fact and value which derives from the Galilean and Newtonian take-off in the physical sciences. In Galileo's mathematical universe everything is objective, in the sense that its laws of behaviour are entirely independent of human perception and intervention. Where Copernicus

[36] Carlo Antoni, *From History to Sociology, The Transition in German Historical Thinking*, translated and with an Introduction by Hayden V. White, p. xiv.

moved human consciousness off-centre, Galileo succeeded in sending it off the field altogether. Yet even in mathematics Gödel and Tarski have shown that it is not possible to develop a self-validating logic which relieves us of the *choice* of axioms and the assumption of *responsibility* for the particular grammar in which we frame a problem.[37] It is no longer possible to pursue the objectivity of science in abstraction from its subjective sources in the *praxis* which constitutes nature as a neutral instrumentality established for the sake of *control* and *domination*. 'The science of nature develops under the *technological a priori* which projects nature as potential instrumentality, stuff of control and organization. And the apprehension of nature as (hypothetical) instrumentality *precedes* the development of all particular technical organization.'[38] It is this *technological a priori* which is axiomatic in the neutrality of science and technology with respect to their practical applications, inasmuch as both are ultimately only intelligible as instruments of emancipation.[39]

The tension between the purely technological domination of nature and the social organization of the means of production is evidence that 'power' and 'freedom' are essential moments in the Western concept of 'knowledge'. The dialectic of Western science is essentially a self-reflexive or self-fulfilling *prophecy*. The discovery of an 'objective' order, precisely because of the *technological a priori* which motivates it, is naturally fed into the social matrix of action which is the proper end of 'scientific communication', or the mediation of 'pure' and 'applied' science. In the Preface to *The Phenomenology of Mind*, Hegel shows that the difference between philosophy and mathematics, for example, lies precisely in the nature of the relevance of the two modes of knowledge to the existence of their objects. The truth of the Pythagorean proposition is external to any empirical right-angle triangle and does not enter into its constitution. By contrast man's realization that he is a rational and free agent is a discovery which fulfils itself in the actual history of man. Indeed, the truth of human nature is in no way external to the history of man; it rests upon nothing else for its foundation.[40]

[37] R. Rudner, 'The Scientist *Qua* Scientist Makes Value Judgments', *Philosophy of Science*, Vol. XX (1955).

[38] H. Marcuse, *One-Dimensional Man*, Studies in the Ideology of Advanced Industrial Society, Boston, Beacon Press, 1964, p. 153.

[39] Jurgen Habermas, *Knowledge and Human Interests*, translated by Jeremy J. Shapiro, London, Heinemann Educational Books, 1972.

[40] 'The concept of war belongs *essentially* to my behavior. But the concept of gravity does not belong essentially to the behavior of a falling apple in the same way: it belongs rather to the physicists' explanation of the apple's behavior', P. Winch, *The Idea of a Social Science*, London, Routledge and Kegan Paul, 1958, p. 128.

To this Marx merely added what was implicit in Hegel, namely, that the relation between consciousness and its objects is a relation wholly within social reality, grounded in the nature of man as embodied consciousness. Of course, at any point in time the descriptive proposition that man is a free and rational agent is not true. But its falsity is only a historical moment in the dialectic between the descriptive and the prescriptive condition of man's humanity, which is not a fixed subjectivity, but one which actively seeks its own truth. Thus the 'laws' of human development can never be laws independent of the comprehension of self-consciousness, which enters into its own history so that it becomes rational and free. Popper and Hayek entirely overlook the Hegel-Marx critique of the positivist conception of knowledge. As a result, they attribute to Hegel and Marx the very errors of reification which they were first to criticize in the commonsense and natural science attitudes.[41] We have already remarked upon Hayek's failure to appreciate the 'revolutionary' demands of the social sciences which preserved them from slavish dependence upon the natural sciences that would indeed have 'counter-revolutionary' consequences, wherever it is the model. This is the problem which underlies Marx's critique of the basic postulate of classical realist epistemology, that the objective structure of the world precedes our consciousness of it, or that knowing makes no difference to the object known.[42] In the *Theses on Feuerbach* Marx argued that the objectivism of classical epistemology overlooks that man is a situated being and that knowledge and truth rest upon nothing outside of human *praxis*, which opens up nature and humanity to their mutual possibilities. In his critique of classical political economy, Marx pointed out that the 'laws' of economics only hold within a given social structure, constituted by a set of middle principles, which define regularities or patterns of behaviour within that institutional matrix. Marx defines capitalism in terms of specific property relations or class relations with respect to the means of production. In the socio-economic system defined by 'capitalism' there is created a socially structured focus for behaviour oriented towards acquisition, accumulation and profit-making. Weber's analysis of the prerequisites of capitalism stresses the importance of the rationalization of accounting, technology, law and the permanent enterprise. However, both Marx and Weber agreed that the psychology of capitalism, rationalized through the Protestant ethic, is ultimately dependent upon a definite historical and sociological constellation of the forces of production. The difference between Weber and Marx, in the end, is that,

[41] John O'Neill, *op. cit.*, note 22 above.
[42] See my 'On Theory and Criticism of Marx', in John O'Neill, *Sociology as a Skin Trade, Essays Towards a Reflective Sociology*, London, Heinemann Educational Books, 1972.

unlike Weber, Marx believed that the formal rationalization of industrial society might be turned from the rule of a 'blind' law into a principle of substantively rational social and economic planning.

The so-called laws of society are derivations of a basic societal orientation towards the nexus between the human condition and human action. Social action is not an unlimited projection of possibilities: it starts from an understanding of the human situation which is simultaneously a structure of limits and possibilities. The problem of the relation between knowledge and social action centres upon the antinomy between the micro-rationality of the processes of modern industrial society and the macro-irrationality of its technological culture.[43] As we have tried to show earlier, the historical background of this problem lies in the reduction of knowledge to technical knowledge, which is simultaneously an axiological reduction of the realm of use-values to exchange-value. The meaning of modern knowledge can only be grasped historically and sociologically in relation to its roots in a logic of domination and accumulation which creates the split between 'subjective' and 'objective' experience. But the attempt to understand this split sociologically is itself infected with the same logic of self-conquest, so long as it attempts to totalize human experience.

In Marx's *Economic and Philosophical Manuscripts* we have the beginnings of a redefinition of the nexus between knowledge, technology and work which is grounded in the nature of man as sensuous being or embodied consciousness.[44] The Marxian concept of alienation may provide us with a final formulation of the modes of individual and collective being in an industrial society. Now, the Marxian concept of alienation hardly makes sense except as a critique of scientism, in which the true nature of science, society and individualism are sketched. Capitalism is historically unique in the way that it has created an unprecedented expansion of man's control over nature, through a transvaluation of values grounded on the relations of a class of men over the mass of men. The interplay between the dialectic of man and nature, and the dialectic between man and society, is crucial to the understanding of the structure and genesis of the capitalist order. Marx thought the basic contradiction of the capitalist order lay in the conflict between the principle of rationalization applied to the means of production, which determinies its economic order, and the irrational and

[43] Paul A. Baran, *The Longer View*, Essays Towards a Critique of Political Economy, edited and with an Introduction by John O'Neill, New York and London, Monthly Review Press, 1970.

[44] John O'Neill, 'Hegel and Marx on History as Human History', in Jean Hyppolite, *Studies on Marx and Hegel*, translated with Notes and Bibliography by John O'Neill, New York, Basic Books, 1969.

immoral nature of capitalism as a social and political order, determined by that same principle of rationality.

Thus, in our own day, from a Marxist standpoint, the corporate economy promotes the most highly rationalized forms of production process, business administration and market control, while simultaneously, and on the same principle, undermining the culture and humanity of the social order it professes to serve. What is called the productive strength of monopoly capitalism is its power to over-produce for the private sector, relative to the class distribution of income, while underproducing or mis-producing in the public sector, as presently determined by the liberal ideology and corporate interests.[45] Measured by the standard of its ability to produce such basic ingredients of humane society as a universal 'minimum' standard of health, housing, education and public safety, the performance of monopoly capitalism is glaringly lopsided. The conflict between the 'micro-reason' demanded by the accumulation needs of the capitalist system and the 'macro-madness' induced by the expression of wants in order to realize expectations on given levels of investment is reflected in the individual's fractured experience as worker and consumer. His off-work time is invaded by a quantitative ethic of wants, which seduces him into co-operating with the alienation of his conscious sensibilities at work in order to satisfy a phantasy of wants conjured up in the 'privacy' of the home. The individual is torn in the conflict between the ideology of rationality and responsibility dictated in his working life and the image of spontaneity and carefree living projected for his off-work hours. Everywhere he finds himself upon a treadmill of wants which alienate him further and further from human needs.

The loss of a common world separates modern society into a corporate hierarchy and multitude of individuals in whom the other directedness of consumption substitutes for the lost contexts of community. In keeping with the liberal ideology of individualistic familism, any attempt to relate private troubles to public or institutional contexts is regarded as a projection of problems better suited for individual therapy. The result is that men lack bridges between their private lives and the indifference of the publics that surround them.

The task which faces the political imagination of our times is to build bridges between men's private troubles and the institutions of public and political action.[46] It is, I think, the basic conception of Marxian social science that human reason is a power in history and

---

[45] John O'Neill, 'Public and Private Space', in J. T. McLeod and T. Lloyd (eds.), *Agenda 1970, Proposals for a Creative Politics*, Toronto, University of Toronto Press, 1965.

[46] C. Wright Mills, *The Sociological Imagination*, New York, Grove Press Inc., 1961, ch. 1.

society, responsible for the foundation of a social order which releases its potentialities both in the individual and the collective. In this task there are no historical guarantees. The vision of a rational social order is an option to which many are committed but it is equally an option that men may refuse. And this is so, not because a rational society represents one value among others, for it is the matrix of all values; it happens because the truth which is the birth of truth only enters the world in a struggle with partial truths.

F. A. HAYEK

From Scientism and the Study of Society

Before we proceed further to consider the effect of scientism on the study of society it will be expedient briefly to survey the peculiar object and the methods of the social studies. They deal, not with the relations between things, but with the relations between men and things or the relations between man and man. They are concerned with man's actions and their aim is to explain the unintended or undesigned results of the actions of many men.

Not all the disciplines of knowledge which are concerned with the life of men in groups, however, raise problems which differ in any important respect from those of the natural sciences. The spread of contagious diseases is evidently a problem closely connected with the life of man in society and yet its study has none of the special characteristics of the social sciences in the narrower sense of the term. Similarly the study of heredity, or the study of nutrition, or the investigation of changes in the number or age composition of populations, do not differ significantly from similar studies of animals. And the same applies to certain branches of anthropology, or ethnology, in so far as as they are concerned with racial characteristics or other physical attributes of men. There are, in other words, natural sciences of man which do not necessarily raise problems with which we cannot cope with the methods of the natural sciences. Wherever we are concerned with unconscious reflexes or processes in the human body there is no obstacle to treating and investigating them 'mechanically' as caused by objectively observable external events. They take place without the knowledge of the person concerned and without his having power to modify them; and the conditions under which they are produced can be established by external observation without recourse to the assumption that the person observed classifies the external stimuli in any way differently from that in which they can be defined in purely physical terms.

The social sciences in the narrower sense, i.e., those which used to be described as the moral sciences,[1] are concerned with man's con-

---

[1] Sometimes the German term *Geisteswissenschaften* is now used in English to describe the social sciences in the specific narrow sense with which we are here

27

scious or reflected action, actions where a person can be said to choose between various courses open to him, and here the situation is essentially different. The external stimulus which may be said to cause or occasion such actions can of course also be defined in purely physical terms. But if we tried to do so for the purposes of explaining human action, we would confine ourselves to less than we know about the situation. It is not because we have found two things to behave alike in relation to other things, but because they appear alike to us, that we expect them to appear alike to other people. We know that people will react in the same way to external stimuli which according to all objective tests are different, and perhaps also that they will react in a completely different manner to a physically identical stimulus if it affects their body in different circumstances or at a different point. We know, in other words, that in his conscious decisions man classifies external stimuli in a way which we know solely from our own subjective experience of this kind of classification. We take it for granted that other men treat various things as alike or unlike as we do, although no objective test, no knowledge of the relations of these things to other parts of the external world justifies this. Our procedure is based on the experience that other people as a rule (though not always—e.g., not if they are colourblind or mad) classify their sense impressions as we do.

But we not only know this. It would be impossible to explain or understand human action without making use of this knowledge. People do behave in the same manner towards things, not because these things are identical in a physical sense, but because they have learnt to classify them as belonging to the same group, because they can put them to the same use or expect from them what to the people concerned is an equivalent effect. In fact, most of the objects of social or human action are not 'objective facts' in the special narrow sense in which this term is used by the Sciences and contrasted to 'opinions', and cannot at all be defined in physical terms. So far as human actions are concerned the things *are* what the people acting think they are.

This is best shown by an example for which we can choose almost any object of human action. Take the concept of a 'tool' or 'instrument', or of any particular tool such as a hammer or a barometer. It is easily seen that these concepts cannot be interpreted to refer to 'objective facts', i.e., to things irrespective of what people think about them. Careful logical analysis of these concepts will show that they all express relationships between several (at least three) terms, of which one is the acting or thinking person, the other some desired or imagined effect,

concerned. But considering that this German term was introduced by the translator of J. S. Mill's *Logic* to render the latter's 'moral sciences', there seems to be little case for using this translation instead of the original English term.

and the third a thing in the ordinary sense. If the reader will attempt a definition he will soon find that he cannot give one without using some terms such as 'suitable for' or 'intended for' or some other expression referring to the use for which it is designed by somebody.[2] And a definition which is to comprise all instances of the class will not contain any reference to its substance, or shape, or other physical attribute. An ordinary hammer and a steam-hammer, or an aneroid barometer and a mercury barometer, have nothing in common except the purpose for which men think they can be used.

It must not be objected that these are merely instances of abstractions to arrive at generic terms just as those used in the physical sciences. The point is that they are abstractions from *all* the physical attributes of the things in question and that their definitions must run entirely in terms of mental attitudes of men towards the things. The significant difference between the two views of the things stands out clearly if we think, e.g., of the problem of the archaeologist trying to determine whether what looks like a stone implement is in truth an 'artefact', made by man, or merely a chance product of nature. There is no way of deciding this but by trying to understand the working of the mind of prehistoric man, of attempting to understand how he would have made such an implement. If we are not more aware that this is what we actually do in such cases and that we necessarily rely on our own knowledge of the working of a human mind, this is so mainly because of the difficulty (or impossibility) of conceiving of an observer who does not possess a human mind and interprets what he sees in terms of the working of his own mind.

There are no better terms available to describe this difference between the approach of the natural and the social sciences than to

---

[2] It has often been suggested that for this reason economics and the other theoretical sciences of society should be described as 'teleological' sciences. This term is, however, misleading as it is apt to suggest that not only the actions of individual men but also the social structures which they produce are deliberately designed by somebody for a purpose. It leads thus either to an 'explanation' of social phenomena in terms of ends fixed by some superior power or to the opposite and no less fatal mistake of regarding all social phenomena as the product of conscious human design, to a 'pragmatic' interpretation which is a bar to all real understanding of these phenomena. Some authors, particularly O. Spann, have used the term 'teleological' to justify the most abstruse metaphysical speculations. Others, like K. Englis, have used it in an unobjectionable manner and sharply distinguished between 'teleological' and 'normative' sciences. (See particularly the illuminating discussions of the problem in K. Englis, *Teleologische Theorie der Wirtschaft*, Brünn, 1930.) But the term remains nevertheless misleading. If a name is needed the term 'praxeological' sciences, deriving from A. Espinas, adopted by T. Kotarbinsky and E. Slutsky, and now clearly defined and extensively used by L. v. Mises (*Nationalökonomie*, Geneva, 1940), would appear to be the most appropriate.

call the former objective and the latter subjective. Yet these terms are ambiguous and without further explanation their use might prove misleading. While for the natural scientist the contrast between objective facts and subjective opinions is a simple one, the distinction cannot as readily be applied to the object of the social sciences. The reason for this is that the object, the 'facts' of the social sciences are also opinions—not opinions of the student of the social phenomena, of course, but opinions of those whose actions produce his object. In one sense his facts are thus as little 'subjective' as those of the natural sciences, because they are independent of the particular observer; but what he studies is not determined by his fancy or imagination but is equally given to the observation by different people. But in another sense in which we distinguish facts from opinions the facts of the social sciences are merely opinions, views held by the people whose actions we study. They differ from the facts of the physical sciences in being beliefs or opinions held by particular people, beliefs which as such are our data, irrespective of whether they are true or false, and which, moreover, we cannot directly observe in the minds of the people but recognize from what they do and say merely because we have ourselves a mind similar to theirs.

In the sense in which we here use the contrast between the subjectivist approach of the social sciences and the objectivist approach of the natural sciences it says little more than what is commonly expressed by saying that the former deal in the first instance with the phenomena of individual minds, or mental phenomena, and not directly with material phenomena. They deal with phenomena which can be understood only because the object of our study has a mind of a structure similar to our own. That this is so is no less an empirical fact than our knowledge of the external world. It is shown not merely by the possibility of communicating with other people—we act on this knowledge every time we speak or write; it is confirmed by the very results of our study of the external world. So long as it was naïvely assumed that all the sense qualities (or their relations) which different men had in common were properties of the external world it could be argued that our knowledge of other minds is no more than our common knowledge of the external world. But once we have learnt that our senses make things appear to us alike or different which prove to be alike or different in none of their relations between themselves, but only in the way in which they affect our minds, this fact that men classify external stimuli in a particular way becomes a significant fact of experience. While qualities disappear from our scientific picture of the external world they must remain part of our scientific picture of the human mind. In fact the elimination of qualities from our picture of the external world does not mean that these qualities do not 'exist', but that when we study qualities we study not the physical world but the mind of man.

The reason why it is expedient to retain the terms 'subjective' and 'objective' for the contrast with which we are concerned, although they inevitably carry with them some misleading associations, is not only that the terms 'mental' and 'material' carry with them an even worse burden of metaphysical associations and that at least in economics[3] the term 'subjective' has long come to be used precisely in the sense in which we use it here. What is more important is that the term 'subjective' stresses another important fact to which we shall yet have to refer: that the knowledge and beliefs of different people, while possessing that common structure which makes communication possible, will yet be different and often conflicting in many respects. If we could assume that all the knowledge and beliefs of different people were identical, or if we were concerned with a single mind, it would not matter whether we described it as an 'objective' fact or as a subjective phenomenon. But the concrete knowledge which guides the action of any group of people never exists as a consistent and coherent body. It only exists in the dispersed, incomplete, and inconsistent form in which it appears in many individual minds and this dispersion and imperfection of all knowledge is one of the basic facts from which the social sciences have to start. What philosophers and logicians often contemptuously dismiss as 'mere' imperfections of the human mind becomes in the social sciences a basic fact of crucial importance. We shall later see how the opposite 'absolutist' view, as if knowledge, and particularly the concrete knowledge of particular circumstances, were given 'objectively', i.e., as if it were the same for all people, is a source of constant errors in the social sciences.

The 'tool' or 'instrument' which we have before used as an illustration of the objects of human action can be matched by similar instances from any other branch of social study. A 'word' or a 'sentence', a 'crime' or a 'punishment',[4] are of course not objective facts in the sense that they can be defined without referring to our knowledge of people's conscious intentions with regard to them. And the same is true quite generally wherever we have to explain human behaviour towards things; these things must then not be defined in terms of what we might

---

[3] I believe also in the discussions on psychological methods.

[4] It is sheer illusion when some sociologists believe that they can make 'crime' an objective fact by defining it as those acts for which a person is punished. This only pushes the subjective element a step further back, but does not eliminate it. 'Punishment' is still a subjective thing which cannot be defined in objective terms. If, e.g., we see that every time a person commits a certain act he is made to wear a chain round his neck, this does not tell us whether it is a reward or a punishment.

find out about these things by the objective methods of science, but in terms of what the person acting thinks about them. A medicine or a cosmetic, e.g., for the purposes of social study, are not what cures an ailment or improves a person's looks, but what people think will have that effect. Any knowledge which we may happen to possess about the true nature of the material thing, but which the people whose action we want to explain do not possess, is as little relevant to the explanation of their actions as our private disbelief in the efficiency of a magic charm will help us to understand the behaviour of the savage who believes in it. If in investigating our contemporary society the 'laws of nature' which we have to use as a datum because they affect people's actions are approximately the same as those which figure in the works of the natural scientists, this is for our purposes an accident which must not deceive us about the different character of these laws in the two fields. What is relevant in the study of society is not whether these laws of nature are true in any objective sense, but solely whether they are believed and acted upon by the people. If the current 'scientific' knowledge of the society we study included the belief that the soil will bear no fruit till certain rites or incantations are performed, this would be quite as important for us as any law of nature which we now believe to be correct. And all the 'physical laws of production' which we meet, e.g., in economics, are not physical laws in the sense of the physical sciences but people's beliefs about what they can do.

What is true about the relations of men to things is, of course, even more true of the relations between men, which for the purposes of social study cannot be defined in the objective terms of the physical sciences but only in terms of human beliefs. Even such a seemingly purely biological relationship as that between parent and child is in social study not defined in physical terms and cannot be so defined for their purposes: it makes no difference as regards people's actions whether their belief that a particular child is their natural offspring is mistaken or not.

All this stands out most clearly in that among the social sciences whose theory has been most highly developed, economics. And it is probably no exaggeration to say that every important advance in economic theory during the last hundred years was a further step in the consistent application of subjectivism.[5] That the objects of economic activity cannot be defined in objective terms but only with reference

[5] This is a development which has probably been carried out most consistently by L. v. Mises and I believe that most peculiarities of his views which at first strike many readers as strange and unacceptable are due to the fact that in that consistent development of the subjectivist approach he has for a long time moved ahead of his contemporaries. Probably all the characteristic features of his theories, from his theory of money (so much ahead of his time in 1912!) to what he calls his

to a human purpose goes without saying. Neither a 'commodity' or an 'economic good', nor 'food' or 'money', can be defined in physical terms but only in terms of views people hold about things. Economic theory has nothing to say about the little round disks of metal as which an objective or materialist view might try to define money. It has nothing to say about iron or steel, timber or oil, or wheat or eggs as such. The history of any particular commodity indeed shows that as human knowledge changes the same material thing may represent quite different economic categories. Nor could we distinguish in physical terms whether two men barter or exchange or whether they are playing some game or performing some religious ritual. Unless we can understand what the acting people mean by their actions any attempt to explain them, i.e., to subsume them under rules which connect similar situations with similar actions, are bound to fail.

This essentially subjective character of all economic theory, which it has developed much more clearly than any other branch of the social sciences, but which I believe it has in common with all the social sciences in the narrower sense, is best shown by a closer consideration of one of its simplest theorems, e.g., the 'law of rent'. In its original form this was a proposition about changes in the value of a thing defined in physical terms, namely land. It stated, in effect,[6] that changes in the value of the commodities in the production of which land was required would cause much greater changes in the value of land than in the value of the other factors whose co-operation was required. In this form it is an empirical generalization which tells us neither why nor under what conditions it will be true. In modern economics its place is taken by two distinct propositions of different character which combined lead to the same conclusion. One is part of pure economic theory and asserts that whenever in the production of one commodity different (scarce) factors are required in proportions which can be varied, and of which one can be used only for this (or only for comparatively few) purposes while the others are of a more general usefulness, a change in the value of the product will affect the value of the former more than that of the latter. The second proposition is

---

a priorism, his views about mathematical economics in general and the measurement of economic phenomena in particular, and his criticism of planning all follow directly (although, perhaps, not all with the same necessity) from this central position. See particularly his *Grundprobleme der Nationalökonomie* (Jena, 1933) and *Nationalökonomie* (Geneva, 1940).

[6] In the extreme Ricardian form the statement is, of course, that a change in the value of the product will affect *only* the value of the land and leave the value of the co-operating labour altogether unaffected. In this form (connected with Ricardo's 'objective' theory of value) the proposition can be regarded as a limiting case of the more general proposition given in the text.

the empirical statement that land is as a rule in the position of the first kind of factor, i.e., that people know of many more uses for their labour than they will know for a particular piece of land. The first of these propositions, like all propositions of pure economic theory, is a statement about the implications of certain human attitudes towards things and as such necessarily true irrespective of time and place. The second is an assertion that the conditions postulated in the first exist at a given time and with respect to a particular piece of land because the people dealing with it hold certain beliefs about its usefulness and the usefulness of other things required in order to cultivate it. As an empirical generalization it can of course be disproved and frequently will be disproved. If, e.g., a piece of land is used to produce some special fruit the cultivation of which requires a certain rare skill, the effect of a fall in the demand for the fruit may fall exclusively on the wages of the men with the special skill, while the value of the land may remain practically unaffected. In such a situation it would be labour to which the 'law of rent' applies. But when we ask: 'why?' or: 'how can I find out whether the law of rent will apply in any particular case?', no information about the physical attributes of the land, the labour, or the product can give us the answer. It depends on the subjective factors stated in the theoretical law of rent; and only in so far as we can find out what the knowledge and beliefs of the people concerned are in the relevant respects shall we be in a position to predict in what manner a change in the price of the product will affect the prices of the factors. What is true of the theory of rent is true of the theory of price generally: it has nothing to say about the behaviour of the price of iron or wool, of things of such and such physical properties, but only about things about which people have certain beliefs and which they want to use in a certain manner. And our explanation of a particular price phenomenon can therefore also never be affected by any additional knowledge which we (the observers) acquire about the good concerned, but only by additional knowledge about what the people dealing with it think about it.

We cannot here enter into a similar discussion of the more complex phenomena with which economic theory is concerned and where in recent years progress has been particularly closely connected with the advance of subjectivism. We can only point to the new problems which these developments make appear more and more central, such as the problem of the compatibility of intentions and expectations of different people, of the division of knowledge between them, and the process by which the relevant knowledge is acquired and expectations formed.[7] We are not here concerned, however, with the specific prob-

[7] For some further discussion of these problems see the author's article 'Economics and Knowledge', *Economica*, February, 1937.

lems of economics, but with the common character of all disciplines which deal with the results of conscious human action. The points which we want to stress are that in all such attempts we must start from what men think and mean to do, from the fact that the individuals which compose society are guided in their actions by a classification of things or events in a system of sense qualities and concepts which has a common structure and which we know because we, too, are men, and that the concrete knowledge which different individuals possess will differ in important respects. Not only man's action towards external objects but also all the relations between men and all the social institutions can be understood only in terms of what men think about them. Society as we know it is, as it were, built up from the concepts and ideas held by the people; and social phenomena can be recognized by us and have meaning to us only as they are reflected in the minds of men.

The structure of men's mind, the common principle on which they classify external events, provide us with the knowledge of the recurrent elements of which different social structures are built up and in terms of which we can alone describe and explain them. While concepts or ideas can, of course, exist only in individual minds, and while, in particular, it is only in individual minds that different ideas can act upon another, it is not the whole of the individual minds in all their complexity, but the individual concepts, the views people have formed of each other and the things, which form the true elements of the social structure. If the social structure can remain the same although different individuals succeed each other at particular points, this is not because the individuals which succeed each other are completely identical, but because they succeed each other in particular relations, in particular attitudes they take towards other people and as the objects of particular views held by other people about them. The individuals are merely the *foci* in the network of relationships and it is the various attitudes of the individuals towards each other (or their similar or different attitudes towards physical objects) which form the recurrent, recognizable and familiar elements of the structure. If one policeman succeeds another at a particular post, this does not mean that the new man will in all respects be identical with his predecessor, but merely that he succeeds him in certain attitudes towards his fellow man and as object of certain attitudes of his fellow men which are relevant to his function as policeman. But this is sufficient to preserve a constant structural element which can be separated and studied in isolation.

While we can recognize these elements of human relationships only because they are known to us from the working of our own minds, this does not mean that the significance of their combination in a particular pattern relating different individuals must be immediately obvious to us. It is only by the systematic and patient following up of the implications of many people holding certain views that we can understand, and often even only learn to see, the unintended and often uncomprehended results of the separate and yet interrelated actions of men in society. That in this effort to reconstruct these different patterns of social relations we must relate the individual's action not to the objective qualities of the persons and things towards which he acts, but that our data must be man and the physical world as they appear to the men whose actions we try to explain, follows from the fact that only what people know or believe can enter as a motive into their conscious action.

At this point it becomes necessary to interrupt the main argument for a little in order to safeguard ourselves against a misconception which might arise from what has just been said. The stress which we have laid on the fact that in the social sciences our data or 'facts' are themselves ideas or concepts must, of course, not be understood to mean that all the concepts with which we have to deal in the social sciences are of this character. There would be no room for any scientific work if this were so; and the social sciences no less than the natural sciences aim at revising the popular concepts which men have formed about the objects of their study, and at replacing them by more appropriate ones. The special difficulties of the social sciences and much confusion about their character derive precisely from the fact that in them ideas appear in two capacities, as it were, as part of their object and as ideas about the object. While in the natural sciences the contrast between the object of our study and our explanation of it coincides with the distinction between ideas and objective facts, in the social sciences it is necessary to draw a distinction between those ideas which are *constitutive* of the phenomena we want to explain and the ideas which either we ourselves or the very people whose actions we have to explain may have formed *about* these phenomena and which are not the cause of, but theories about, the social structures.

This special difficulty of the social sciences is a result not merely of the fact that we have to distinguish between the views held by the people which are the object of our study and our views about them, but also from the fact that the people who are our object themselves not only are motivated by ideas but also form ideas about the un-designed results of their actions—popular theories about the various social structures or formations which we share with them and which our study has to revise and improve. The danger of substituting 'concepts' (or 'theories') for the 'facts' is by no means absent in the social sciences and failure to avoid it has exercised as detrimental an effect here as in the natural sciences;[8] but it appears on a different plane and is very inadequately expressed by the contrast between 'ideas' and 'facts'. The real contrast is between ideas which by being held by the people become the causes of a social phenomenon and the ideas which people form about that phenomenon. That these two classes of ideas are distinct (although in different contexts the distinction may have to be drawn differently[9]) can easily be shown. The changes in the opinions which people hold about a particular commodity and which we recognize as the cause of a change in the price of that commodity stand clearly in a different class from the ideas which the same people may have formed about the causes of the change in price or about the 'nature of value' in general. Similarly, the beliefs and opinions which lead a number of people regularly to repeat certain acts, e.g., to produce, sell, or buy certain quantities of commodities, are entirely different from the ideas they may have formed about the whole of the 'society', or the 'economic system', to which they belong and which the aggregate of all their actions constitutes. The first kind of opinions and beliefs are a condition of the existence of the 'wholes' which would not exist without them; they are, as we have said, 'constitutive', essential for the existence of the phenomenon which the people refer to as 'society' or the 'economic system', but which will exist irrespectively of the concepts which the people have formed about these wholes.

It is very important that we should carefully distinguish between the motivating or constitutive opinions on the one hand and the speculative or explanatory views which people have formed about the wholes; confusion between the two is a source of constant danger. It is the ideas which the popular mind has formed about such collectives as 'society' or the 'economic system', 'capitalism' or 'imperialism', and other such collective entities, which the social scientist must regard as no more than provisional theories, popular abstractions, and which he

[8] Cf. the excellent discussions of the effects of *Begriffsrealismus* on economics in W. Eucken, *Die Grundlagen der Nationalökonomie*, Jena, 1940, pp. 29 *et seq.*

[9] In some contexts concepts which by another social science are treated as mere theories to be revised and improved upon may have to be treated as data. One could, e.g., conceive of a 'science of politics' showing what kind of political action follows from the people holding certain views on the nature of society and for which these views would have to be treated as data. But while in man's actions towards social phenomena, i.e., in explaining his political actions, we have to take his views about the constitution of society as given, we can on a different level of analysis investigate their truth or untruth. The fact that a particular society may believe that its institutions have been created by divine intervention we would have to accept as a fact in explaining the politics of that society; but it need not prevent us from showing that this view is probably false.

must not mistake for facts. That he consistently refrains from treating these pseudo-entities as 'facts', and that he systematically starts from the concepts which guide individuals in their actions and not from the results of their theorizing about their actions, is the characteristic feature of that methodological individualism which is closely connected with the subjectivism of the social sciences. The scientistic approach, on the other hand, because it is afraid of starting from the subjective concepts determining individual actions, is, as we shall presently see, regularly led into the very mistake it attempts to avoid, that of treating as facts those collectives which are no more than popular generalizations. Trying to avoid using as data the concepts held by individuals where they are clearly recognizable and explicitly introduced as what they are, people brought up in scientistic views frequently and naïvely accept the speculiative concepts of popular usage as definite facts of the kind they are familiar with.

We shall have to discuss the nature of this collectivist prejudice inherent in the scientistic approach more fully in a later section.

A few more remarks must be added about the specific theoretical method which corresponds to the systematic subjectivism and individualism of the social sciences. From the fact that it is the concepts and views held by individuals which are directly known to us and which form the elements from which we must build up, as it were, the more complex phenomena follows another important difference between the method of the social disciplines and the natural sciences. While in the former it is the attitudes of individuals which are the familiar elements and by the combination of which we try to reproduce the complex phenomena, the results of individual actions, which are much less known—a procedure which often leads to the *discovery* of principles of structural coherence of the complex phenomena which had not (and perhaps could not) be established by direct observation—the physical sciences must needs commence with the complex phenomena of nature and work backwards to infer the elements from which they are composed. The place where the human individual stands in the order of things brings it about that in one direction what he perceives are the comparatively complex phenomena which he analyses, while in the other direction what is given to him are elements from which more complex phenomena are composed which he cannot observe as wholes.[10]

---

[10] Cf. Robbins, *An Essay on the Nature and Significance of Economic Science*, 2nd ed., 1935, p. 105: 'In Economics . . . the ultimate constituents of our fundamental generalisations are known to us by immediate acquaintance. In the natural sciences they are known only inferentially.' Perhaps the following quotation from an earlier essay of my own (*Collectivist Economic Planning*, 1935, p. 11) may help further to explain the statement in the text: 'The position of man, midway between natural and social phenomena—of the one of which he is an effect and

While the method of the natural sciences is in this sense analytic, the method of the social sciences is better described as compositive[11] or synthetic. It is the so-called wholes, the groups of elements which are structurally connected, which we learn to single out from the totality of observed phenomena only as a result of our systematic fitting together of the elements with familiar properties, and which we build up or reconstruct from the known properties of the elements.

It is important to observe that in all this the various types of individual beliefs or attitudes are not themselves the object of our explanation, but merely the elements from which we build up the structure of possible relationships between individuals. In so far as we analyse individual thought in the social sciences the purpose is not to explain that thought but merely to distinguish the possible types of elements with which we shall have to reckon in the construction of different patterns of social relationships. It is a mistake, to which careless expressions by social scientists often give countenance, to believe

---

of the other a cause—brings it about that the essential basic facts which we need for the explanation are part of common experience, part of the stuff of our thinking. In the social sciences it is the elements of the complex phenomena which are known to us beyond the possibility of dispute. In the natural sciences they can be at best surmised.' Cf. also C. Menger, *Untersuchungen über die Methoden der Socialwissenschaften*, 1883, p. 157, note: 'Die letzten Elemente, auf welche die exacte theoretische Interpretation der Naturphänomene zurückgehen muss, sind "Atome" und "Kräfte". Beide sind unempirischer Natur. Wir vermögen uns "Atome" überhaupt nicht, und die Naturkräfte nur unter einem Bilde vorzustellen, und verstehen wir in Wahrheit unter den letzteren lediglich die uns unbekannten Ursachen realer Bewegungen. Hieraus ergeben sich für die exacte Interpretation der Naturphänomene in letzter Linie ganz ausserordentliche Schwierigkeiten. Anders in den exacten Socialwissenschaften. Hier sind die menschlichen *Individuen* und *ihre Bestrebungen*, die letzen Elemente unserer Analyse, empirischer Natur und die exacten theoretischen Sozialwissenschaften somit in grossem Vortheil gegenüber den exacten Naturwissenschaften, Die "Grenzen des Naturerkennens" und die hieraus für das theoretische Verständnis der Naturphänomene sich ergebenden Schwierigkeiten bestehen in Wahrheit nicht für die exacte Forschung auf dem Gebiete der Socialerscheinungen. Wenn A. Comte die "Gesellschaften" als reale Organismen, und zwar als Organismen komplicirterer Art, denn die natürlichen, auffasst und ihre theoretische Interpretation als das unvergleichlich komplicirtere und schwierigere wissenschaftliche Problem bezeichnet, so findet er sich somit in einem schweren Irrthume. Seine Theorie wäre nur gegenüber Socialforschern richtig, welche den, mit Rücksicht auf den heutigen Zustand der theoretischen Naturwissenschaften, geradezu wahnwitzigen Gedanken fassen würden, die Gesellschaftsphänomene nicht in specifisch socialwissenschaftlich, sondern in naturwissenschaftlich-atomistischer Weise interpretiren zu wollen.'

[11] I borrow the term 'compositive' from a manuscript note of Carl Menger who in his personal annotated copy of Schmoller's review of his *Methoden der Socialwissenschaften* (*Jahrbuch für Gesetzgebung*, etc., N.F., 7, 1883, p. 42) wrote it above the word 'deductive' used by Schmoller.

that their aim is to *explain* conscious action. This, if it can be done at all, is a different task, the task of psychology. For the social sciences the types of conscious action are data[12] and all they have to do with regard to these data is to arrange them in such orderly fashion that they can be effectively used for their task.[13] The problems which they try to answer arise only in so far as the conscious action of many men produce undesigned results, in so far as regularities are observed which are not the result of anybody's design. If social phenomena showed no order except in so far as they were consciously designed, there would indeed be no room for theoretical sciences of society and there would be, as is often argued, only problems of psychology. It is only in so far as some sort of order arises as a result of individual action but without being designed by any individual that a problem is raised which demands a theoretical explanation. But although people dominated by the scientistic prejudice are often inclined to deny the existence of any such order (and thereby the existence of an object for theoretical sciences of society), few if any would be prepared to do so consistently: that at least language shows a definite order which is not the result of any conscious design can scarcely be questioned.

The reason of the difficulty which the natural scientist experiences in admitting the existence of such an order in social phenomena is that these orders cannot be stated in physical terms, that if we define the elements in physical terms no such order is visible, and that the units which show an orderly arrangement do not (or at least need not) have any physical properties in common (except that men react to them in the 'same' way—although the 'sameness' of different people's reaction will again, as a rule, not be definable in physical terms). It is an order in which things behave in the same way because they mean the same thing to man. If, instead of regarding as alike and unlike what appears so to the acting man, we were to take for our units only what Science shows to be alike or unlike, we should probably find no recognizable order whatever in social phenomena— at least not till the natural sciences had completed their task of analysing all natural phenomena into their ultimate constituents and psychology had also

---

[12] As Robbins (*loc. cit.*, p. 86) rightly says, economists in particular regard 'the things which psychology studies as the data of their own deductions'.

[13] That this task absorbs a great part of the economist's energies should not deceive us on the fact that by itself this 'pure logic of choice' (or 'economic calculus') does not explain any facts. For the precise relationship between the pure theory of the economic calculus and its use in the explanation of social phenomena I must once more refer to my article 'Economics and Knowledge' (*Economica*, February 1937). It should perhaps be added that while economic theory might be very useful to the director of a completely planned system in helping him to see what he ought to do to achieve his ends, it would not help us to explain his actions—except in so far as he was actually guided by it.

fully achieved the reverse task of explaining in all detail how the ultimate units of physical science come to appear to man just as they do, i.e., how that apparatus of classification operates which our senses constitute.

It is only in the very simplest instances that it can be shown briefly and without any technical apparatus how the independent actions of individuals will produce an order which is no part of their intentions; and in those instances the explanation is usually so obvious that we never stop to examine the type of argument which leads us to it. The way in which tracks are formed in a wild broken country is such an instance. At first everyone will seek for himself what seems to him the best path. But the fact that such a path has been used once is likely to make it easier to traverse and therefore more likely to be used again; and thus gradually more and more clearly defined tracks arise and come to be used to the exclusion of other possible ways. Human movements through the district come to conform to a definite pattern which, although the result of deliberate decisions of many people, has yet not been consciously designed by anyone. This explanation of how this happens is an elementary 'theory' applicable to hundreds of particular historical instances; and it is not the observation of the actual growth of any particular track, and still less of many, from which this explanation derives its cogency, but from our general knowledge of how we and other people behave in the kind of situation in which the successive people find themselves who have to seek their way and who by the cumulative effect of their action create the path. It is the elements of the complex of events which are familiar to us from every-day experience, but it is only by a deliberate effort of directed thought that we come to see the necessary effects of the combination of such actions by many people. We 'understand' the way in which the result we observe can be produced, although we may never be in a position to watch the whole process or to predict its precise course and result.[14]

[14] It makes no difference for our present purpose whether the process extends over a long period of time as it does in such cases as the evolution of money or the formation of language, or whether it is a process which is constantly repeated anew as in the case of the formation of prices or the direction of production under competition. The former instances raise theoretical (i.e., generic) problems (as distinguished from the specifically historical problems in the precise sense which we shall have to define later) which are fundamentally similar to the problems raised by such recurring phenomena as the determination of prices. Although in the study of any particular instance of the evolution of an 'institution' like money or the language the theoretical problem will frequently be so overlaid by the consideration of the particular circumstances involved (the properly historical task), this does not alter the fact that any explanation of a historical process involves assumptions about the kind of circumstances that can produce certain kinds of effects—assumptions which, where we have to deal with results which were not directly willed by somebody, can only be stated in the form of a generic scheme, in other words a theory.

The physicist who wishes to understand the problems of the social sciences with the help of an analogy from his own field would have to imagine a world in which he knew by direct observation the inside of the atoms and had neither the possibility of making experiments with lumps of matter nor opportunity to observe more than the interactions of a comparatively few atoms during a limited period. From his knowledge of the different kinds of atoms he could build up models of all the various ways in which they could combine into larger units and make these models more and more closely reproduce all the features of the few instances in which he was able to observe more complex phenomena. But the laws of the macrocosm which he could derive from his knowledge of the microcosm would always remain 'deductive'; they would, because of his limited knowledge of the data of the complex situation, scarcely ever enable him to predict the precise outcome of a particular situation; and he could never verify them by controlled experiment—although they might be disproved by the observation of events which according to his theory are impossible.

In a sense some problems of theoretical astronomy are more similar to those of the social sciences than those of any of the experimental sciences. Yet there remain important differences. While the astronomer aims at knowing all the elements of which his universe is composed, the student of social phenomena cannot hope to know more than the types of elements from which his universe is made up. He will scarcely ever even know of all the elements of which it consists and he will certainly never know all the relevant properties of each of them. The inevitable imperfection of the human mind becomes here not only a basic datum about the object of explanation but, since it applies no less to the observer, also a limitation on what he can hope to accomplish in his attempt to explain the observed facts. The number of separate variables which in any particular social phenomenon will determine the result of a given change will as a rule be far too large for any human mind to master and manipulate them effectively.[15] In consequence our knowledge of the principle by which these phenomena are produced will rarely if ever enable us to predict the precise result of any concrete situation. While we can explain the principle on which certain phenomena are produced and can from this knowledge exclude the possibility of certain results, e.g., of certain events occurring together, our knowledge will in a sense be only negative, i.e., it will merely enable

---

[15] Cf. M. R. Cohen, *Reason and Nature*, p. 356: 'If, then, social phenomena depend upon factors than we can readily manipulate, even the doctrine of universal determinism will not guarantee an attainable expression of laws governing the specific phenomena of social life. Social phenomena, though determined, might not to a finite mind in limited time display any laws at all.'

us to preclude certain results but not enable us to narrow the range of possibilities sufficiently so that only one remains.

The distinction between an explanation merely of the principle on which a phenomenon is produced and an explanation which enables us to predict the precise result is of great importance for the understanding of the theoretical methods of the social sciences. It arises, I believe, also elsewhere, e.g., in biology, and certainly in psychology. It is, however, somewhat unfamiliar and I know no place where it is adequately explained. The best illustration in the field of the social sciences is probably the general theory of prices as represented, e.g., by the Walrasian or Paretian systems of equations. These systems show merely the principle of coherence between the prices of the various types of commodities of which the system is composed, but without knowledge of the numerical values of all the constants which occur in it and which we never do know, this does not enable us to predict the precise results which any particular change will have.[16] Quite apart from this particular case, a set of equations which shows merely the form of a system of relationships but does not give the values of the constants contained in it, is perhaps the best general illustration of an explanation merely of the principle on which any phenomenon is produced.

This must suffice as a positive description of the characteristic

[16] Pareto himself has clearly seen this. After stating the nature of the factors determining the prices in his system of equations, he adds (*Manuel d'économie politique*, 2nd ed., 1927, pp. 233–234): 'It may be mentioned here that this determination has by no means the purpose of arriving at a numerical calculation of prices. Let us make the most favourable assumptions for such a calculation; let us assume that we have triumphed over all the difficulties of finding the data of the problem and that we know the *ophélimités* of all the different commodities for each individual, and all the conditions of production of all the commodities, etc. This is already an absurd hypothesis to make. Yet it is not sufficient to make the solution of the problem possible. We have seen that in the case of 100 persons and 700 commodities there will be 70,699 conditions (actually a great number of circumstances which we have so far neglected will still increase that number); we shall, therefore, have to solve a system of 70,699 equations. This exceeds practically the power of algebraic analysis, and this is even more true if one contemplates the fabulous number of equations which one obtains for a population of forty millions and several thousand commodities. In this case the roles would be changed: it would not be mathematics which would assist political economy, but political economy which would assist mathematics. In other words, if one really could know all these equations, the only means to solve them which is available to human powers is to observe the practical solution given by the market.' Compare also A. Cournot, *Researches into the Mathematical Principles of the Theory of Wealth* (1838), translated by N. T. Bacon, New York, 1927, p. 127, where he says that if in our equations we took the entire economic system into consideration 'this would surpass the powers of mathematical analysis and of our practical methods of calculation, even if the values of all the constants could be assigned to them numerically'.

problems of the social sciences. It will become clearer as we contrast in the following sections the specific procedure of the social sciences with the most characteristic aspects of the attempts to treat their object after the fashion of the natural sciences.

Closely connected with the 'objectivism' of the scientistic approach is its methodological collectivism, its tendency to treat 'wholes' like 'society' or the 'economy', 'capitalism' (as a given historical 'phase') or a particular 'industry' or 'class' or 'country' as definitely given objects about which we can discover laws by observing their behaviour as wholes. While the specific subjectivist approach of the social sciences starts, as we have seen, from our knowledge of the inside of these social complexes, the knowledge of the individual attitudes which form the elements of their structure, the objectivism of the natural sciences tries to view them from the outside;[17] it treats social phenomena not as something of which the human mind is a part and the principles of whose organization we can reconstruct from the familiar parts, but as if they were objects directly perceived by us as wholes.

There are several reasons why this tendency should so frequently show itself with natural scientists. They are used to seek first for empirical regularities in the relatively complex phenomena that are immediately given to observation, and only after they have found such regularities to try to explain them as the product of a combination of other, often purely hypothetical, elements (constructs) which are assumed to behave according to simpler and more general rules. They are therefore inclined in the social field, too, to seek first for empirical regularities in the behaviour of the complexes before they feel that there is need for a theoretical explanation. This tendency is further strengthened by the experience that there are few regularities in the behaviour of individuals which can be established in a strictly objective manner; and they turn therefore to the wholes in the hope that they will show such regularities. Finally, there is the rather vague idea that as 'social phenomena' are to be the object of study, the obvious procedure is to start from the direct observation of these 'social phenomena', where the existence in popular usage of such terms as 'society' or 'economy' is naïvely taken as evidence that there must be definite 'objects' corresponding to them. The fact that people all talk

[17] The description of this contrast as one between the view from the inside and the view from the outside, though, of course, metaphorical, is less misleading than such metaphors usually are and perhaps the best short way to indicate the nature of the contrast. It brings out that what of social complexes is directly known to us are only the parts and that the whole is never directly perceived but always reconstructed by an effort of our imagination.

about 'the nation' or 'capitalism' leads to the belief that the first step in the study of these phenomena must be to go and see what they are like, just as we should if we heard about a particular stone or a particular animal.[18]

The error involved in this collectivist approach is that it mistakes for facts what are no more than provisional theories, models constructed by the popular mind to explain the connection between some of the individual phenomena which we observe. The paradoxical aspect of it, however, is, as we have seen before,[19] that those who by the scientistic prejudice are led to approach social phenomena in this manner are, by their very anxiety to avoid all merely subjective elements and to confine themselves to 'objective facts', induced to commit the mistake they are most anxious to avoid, namely to treat as facts what are no more than vague popular theories. They thus become, when they least suspect it, the victims of the fallacy described by an expressive German term as *Begriffsrealismus* and made familiar to us by Professor Whitehead as the 'fallacy of misplaced concreteness'.

The naïve realism which uncritically assumes that where there are commonly used concepts there must also be definite 'given' things which they describe is so deeply embedded in current thought about social phenomena that to free ourselves from it needs a deliberate effort of will. While most people will readily admit that in this field there may exist special difficulties in recognizing definite wholes because we have never before us many specimens of a kind and therefore cannot readily distinguish their constant from their merely accidental attributes, few are aware that there is a much more fundamental obstacle: that the wholes as such are never given to our observation but are without exception constructions of our mind. They are not 'given facts', objective data of a similar kind which we spontaneously recognize as similar by their common physical attributes. They cannot be perceived at all apart from a mental scheme that shows the connection between some of the many individual facts which we can observe. Where we have to deal with such social wholes we cannot, as we do in the natural sciences, start from the observation of a number of instances which we recognize spontaneously by their common sense attributes as instances of 'societies' or 'economies', 'capitalisms' or 'nations', 'languages' or 'legal systems', and where only after we have

[18] It would, of course, be false to believe that the first instinct of the student of social phenomena is any less to 'go and see'. It is not ignorance of the obvious but long experience which has taught him that directly to look for the wholes which popular language suggests to exist leads nowhere. It has, indeed, rightly become one of the first maxims which the student of social phenomena learns (or ought to learn) never to speak of 'society' or a 'country' acting or behaving in a certain manner, but always and exclusively to think of individuals as acting.

[19] Cf. pp. 37–38 above.

collected a sufficient number of instances we begin to seek for common laws which they may obey. Social wholes are not given to us as what we may call 'natural units' which we recognize as similar with our senses, as we do with flowers or butterflies, minerals or light-rays, or even forests or ant-heaps. They are not given to us as similar things before we even begin to ask whether what looks alike to us also behaves in like manner. The terms for collectives which we all readily use do not designate definite things in the sense of stable collections of sense attributes which we recognize as alike by inspection; they refer rather to certain structures of relationships between some of the many things we can observe within given spatial and temporal limits and which we select because we think we can discern connections between them— connections which may or may not exist in fact.

What we group together as instances of the same collective or whole are different complexes of individual events, in themselves perhaps quite dissimilar, but believed by us to be related to each other in a similar manner; they are classifications or selection of certain elements of a complex picture on the basis of a theory about their coherence. They do not stand for definite things or classes of things (if we understand the term 'thing' in any material or concrete sense) but for a pattern or order in which different things may be related to each other —an order which is not a spatial or temporal order but can be defined only in terms of relations which are intelligible human attitudes. This order or pattern is as little perceptible as a physical fact as these relations themselves; and it can be studied only by following up the implications of the particular combination of relationships. In other words, the wholes about which we speak exist only if, and to the extent to which, the theory is correct which we have formed about the connection of the parts which they imply and which we can explicitly state only in the form of a model built from those relationships.[20]

The social sciences, thus, do not deal with 'given' wholes but their task is to *constitute* these wholes by constructing models from the familiar elements—models which reproduce the structure of relationships between some of the many phenomena which we always simultaneously observe in real life. This is no less true of the popular concepts of social wholes which are represented by the terms current in ordinary language; they too refer to mental models, but instead of a precise description they convey merely vague and indistinct suggestions of the way in which certain phenomena are connected. Sometimes the wholes constituted by the theoretical social sciences will roughly correspond with the wholes to which the popular concepts refer,

[20] Cf. F. Kaufmann, 'Soziale Kollektiva', *Zeitschrift für Nationalökonomie*, Vol. I, 1930.

because popular usage has succeeded in approximately separating the significant from the accidental; sometimes the wholes constituted by theory may refer to entirely new structural connections of which we did not know before systematic study commenced and for which ordinary language has not even a name. If we take current concepts like those of a 'market' or of 'capital', the popular meaning of these words corresponds at least in some measure to the similar concepts which we have to form for theoretical purposes, although even in these instances the popular meaning is far too vague to allow the use of these terms without first giving them a more precise meaning. If they can be retained in theoretical work at all it is, however, because in these instances even the popular concepts have long ceased to describe particular concrete things, definable in physical terms, and have come to cover a great variety of different things which are classed together solely because of a recognized similarity in the structure of the relationships between men and things. A 'market', e.g., has long ceased to mean only the periodical meeting of men at a fixed place to which they bring their products to sell them from temporary wooden stalls. It now covers any arrangements for regular contacts between potential buyers and sellers of any thing that can be sold, whether by personal contact, by telephone or telegraph, by advertising, etc., etc.[21]

When, however, we speak of the behaviour of, e.g., the 'price system' as a whole and discuss the complex of connected changes which will correspond in certain conditions to a fall in the rate of interest, we are not concerned with a whole that obtrudes itself on popular notice or that is ever definitely given; we can only reconstruct it by following up the reactions of many individuals to the initial change and its immediate effects. That in this case certain changes 'belong together', that among the large number of other changes which in any concrete situation will always occur simultaneously with them and will often swamp those which form part of the complex in which we are interested, a few form a more closely interrelated complex, we do not know from observing that these particular changes regularly occur together. That would indeed be impossible because what in different circumstances would have to be regarded as the same set of changes could not be determined by any of the physical attributes of the things but only by singling out certain relevant aspects in the attitudes of men towards the things; and this can be done only by the help of the models we have formed.

The mistake of treating as definite objects 'wholes' that are no more

---

[21] It should be noted that though observation may assist us to understand what people mean by the terms they use, it can never tell us what a 'market' or 'capital', etc., really is, i.e., which are the significant relations which it is useful to single out and combine into a model.

than constructions, and that can have no properties except those which follow from the way in which we have constructed them from the elements, has probably appeared most frequently in the form of the various theories about a 'social' or 'collective' mind[22] and has in this connection raised all sorts of pseudo-problems. The same idea is frequently but imperfectly concealed under the attributes 'personality' or 'individuality' which are ascribed to society. Whatever the name, these terms always mean that, instead of reconstructing the wholes from the relations between individual minds which we directly know, a vaguely apprehended whole is treated as something akin to the individual mind. It is in this form that in the social sciences an illegitimate use of anthropomorphic concepts has had as noxious an effect as the use of such concepts in the natural sciences. The remarkable thing here is, again, that it should so frequently be the empiricism of the positivists, the arch-enemies of any anthropomorphic concepts even where they are in place, which leads them to postulate such metaphysical entities and to treat humanity, as for instance Comte does, as one 'social being', or as a kind of super-person. But as there is no other possibility than either to compose the whole from the individual minds or to postulate a super-mind in the image of the individual mind, and as positivists reject the first of these alternatives, they are necessarily driven to the second. We have here the root of that curious alliance between nineteenth-century positivism and Hegelianism which will occupy us in a later study.

The collectivist approach to social phenomena has not often been so emphatically proclaimed as when the founder of sociology, Auguste Comte, asserted with respect to them that, as in biology, 'the whole of the object is here certainly much better known and more immediately accessible'[23] than the constituent parts. This view has exercised a lasting influence on that scientistic study of society which he attempted to create. Yet the particular similarity between the objects of biology and those of sociology, which fitted so well in Comte's hierarchy of the sciences, does not in fact exist. In biology we do indeed first recognize as things of one kind natural units, stable combinations of sense properties, of which we find many instances which we spon-

---

[22] On this whole problem, see M. Ginsberg, *The Psychology of Society*, 1921, chapter IV.—What is said in the text does of course not preclude the possibility that our study of the way in which individual minds interact may reveal to us a structure which operates in some respects similarly to the individual mind. And it might be possible that the term collective mind would prove the best term available to describe such structures—though it is most unlikely that the advantages of the use of this term would ever outweigh its disadvantages. But even if this were the case the employment of this term should not mislead us into thinking that it describes any observable object that can be directly studied.

[23] *Cours de philosophie positive*, Vol. IV (2nd–4th ed.), p. 258.

taneously recognize as alike. We can, therefore, begin by asking why these definite sets of attributes regularly occur together. But where we have to deal with social wholes or structures it is not the observation of the regular coexistence of certain physical facts which teaches us that they belong together or form a whole. We do not first observe that the parts always occur together and afterwards ask what holds them together; but it is only because we know the ties that hold them together that we can select a few elements from the immensely complicated world around us as parts of a connected whole.

We shall presently see that Comte and many others regard social phenomena as given wholes in yet another, different, sense, contending that concrete social phenomena can be understood *only* by considering the totality of everything that can be found within certain spatio-temporal boundaries, and that any attempt to select parts or aspects as systematically connected is bound to fail. In this form the argument amounts to a denial of the possibility of a theory of social phenomena as developed, e.g., by economics, and leads directly to what has been misnamed the 'historical method' with which, indeed, methodological collectivism is closely connected. We shall have to discuss this view below under the heading of 'historism'.

The endeavour to grasp social phenomena as 'wholes' finds its most characteristic expression in the tendency to gain a distant and comprehensive view in the hope that thus regularities will reveal themselves which remain obscure at closer range. Whether it is the conception of an observer from a distant planet, which has always been a favourite with positivists from Condorcet to Mach,[24] or whether it is the survey of long stretches of time through which it is hoped that constant configurations or regularities will reveal themselves, it is always the same endeavour to get away from our inside knowledge of human affairs and to gain a view as, it is supposed, would be commanded by somebody who was not himself a man but stood to men in the same relation as that in which we stand to the external world.

This distant and comprehensive view of human events at which the scientistic approach aims is now often described as the 'macroscopic view'. It would probably be better called the telescopic view (meaning simply the distant view—unless it be the view through the inverted

---

[24] Cf. Ernst Mach, *Erkenntnis und Irrtum*, 3rd ed., 1917, p. 28, where, however, he points out correctly that 'Könnten wir uns die Menschen aus grösserer Entfernung, aus der Vogelperspektive, vom Monde aus beobachten, so würden die feineren Einzelheiten mit den von individuellen Erlebnissen herrührenden Einflüssen für uns verschwinden, und wir würden nichts wahrnehmen, als Menschen, die mit grosser Regelmässigkeit wachsen, sich nähren, sich fortpflanzen.'

telescope!) since its aim is deliberately to ignore what we can see only from the inside. In the 'macrocosm' which this approach attempts to see, and in the 'macrodynamic' theories which it endeavours to produce, the elements would not be individual human beings but collectives, constant configurations which, it is presumed, could be defined and described in strictly objective terms.

In most instances this belief that the total view will enable us to distinguish wholes by objective criteria proves, however, to be just an illusion. This becomes evident as soon as we seriously try to imagine of what the macrocosm would consist if we were really to dispense with our knowledge of what things *mean* to the acting men, and if we merely observed the actions of men as we observe an ant-heap or a bee-hive. In the picture such a study could produce there could not appear such things as means or tools, commodities or money, crimes or punishments, or words or sentences; it could contain only physical objects defined in terms of the sense attributes they present to the observer. And since the human behaviour towards the physical objects would show practically no regularities discernible to the observer, since men would in a great many instances not appear to react alike to things which would seem the same to the observer, nor differently to what appeared as different to him, he could not hope to achieve an explanation of their actions unless he had first succeeded in reconstructing in all detail the way in which men's senses and men's minds pictured the external world to them. The famous observer from Mars, in other words, before he could understand even as much of human affairs as the ordinary man does, would have to reconstruct from our behaviour those immediate data of our mind which to us form the starting-point of any interpretation of human action.

If we are not more aware of the difficulties which would be encountered by an observer not possessed of a human mind this is so because we never seriously imagine the possibility that any being with which we are familiar might command sense perceptions or knowledge which are denied to us. Rightly or wrongly we tend to assume that other minds we encounter can differ from ours only by being inferior, so that everything which they perceive or know can also be perceived or be known to us. The only way in which we can form an approximate idea of what would be our position if we had to deal with an organism as complicated as ours but organized on a different principle, so that we should not be able to reproduce its working on the analogy of our own mind, is to conceive that we had to study the behaviour of people with a knowledge vastly superior to our own. If, e.g., we had developed our modern scientific technique while still confined to part of our planet, and then made contact with other parts inhabited by a race which had advanced knowledge much further, we clearly could not hope to understand many of their actions by merely observing what they did and without directly learning from them their knowledge. It would not be from observing them in action that we should acquire their knowledge, but it would be through being taught their knowledge that we should learn to understand their actions.

There is yet another argument which we must briefly consider which supports the tendency to look at social phenomena 'from the outside' and which is easily confused with the methodological collectivism of which we have spoken though it is really distinct from it. Are not social phenomena, it may be asked, from their definition mass phenomena, and is it not obvious, therefore, that we can hope to discover regularities in them only if we investigate them by the method developed for the study of mass phenomena, i.e., statistics? Now this is certainly true of the study of certain phenomena, such as those which form the object of vital statistics and which, as has been mentioned before, are sometimes also described as social phenomena, although they are essentially distinct from those with which we are here concerned. Nothing is more instructive than to compare the nature of these statistical wholes, to which the same word 'collective' is sometimes also applied, with that of the wholes or collectives with which we have to deal in the theoretical social sciences. The statistical study is concerned with the attributes of individuals, though not with attributes of particular individuals, but with attributes of which we know only that a certain quantitatively determined proportion of all the individuals in our 'collective' or 'population' possess them. In order that any collection of individuals should form a true statistical collective it is even necessary that the attributes of the individuals whose frequency distribution we study should not be systematically connected or, at least, that in our selection of the individuals which form the 'collective' we are not guided by any knowledge of such a connection. The 'collectives' of statistics on which we study the regularities produced by the 'law of large numbers' are thus emphatically not wholes in the sense in which we describe social structures as wholes. This is best seen from the fact that the properties of the 'collectives' which statistics studies must remain unaffected if from the total of elements we select at random a certain part. Far from dealing with structures of relationships, statistics deliberately and systematically disregard the relationships between the individual elements. It is, to repeat, concerned with the properties of the *elements* of the 'collective', though not with the properties of particular elements, but with the frequency with which elements with certain properties occur among the total. And, what is more, it assumes that these properties are *not* systematically connected with the different ways in which the elements are related to each other.

The consequence of this is that in the statistical study of social phenomena the structures with which the theoretical social sciences are concerned actually disappear. Statistics may supply us with very interesting and important information about what is the raw material from which we have to reproduce these structures, but it can tell us nothing about these structures themselves. In some field this is immediately obvious as soon as it is stated. That the statistics of words can tell us nothing about the structure of a language will hardly be denied. But although the contrary is sometimes suggested, the same holds no less true of other systematically connected wholes such as, e.g., the price system. No statistical information about the elements can explain to us the properties of the connected wholes. Statistics could produce knowledge of the properties of the wholes only if it had information about statistical collectives, the elements of which were wholes, i.e., if we had statistical information about the properties of many languages, many price systems, etc. But, quite apart from the practical limitations imposed on us by the limited number of instances known to us, there is an even more serious obstacle to the statistical study of these wholes: the fact which we have already discussed, that these wholes and their properties are not given to our observation but can only be formed or constituted by us from their parts.

What we have said applies, however, by no means to all that goes by the name of statistics in the social sciences. Much that is thus described is not statistics in the strict modern sense of the term, does not deal with mass phenomena at all, but is called statistics only in the older, wider sense of the word in which it is used for any descriptive information about the State or society. Though the term will today be used only where this description is of a quantitative nature, this should not lead us to confuse it with the science of statistics in the narrower sense. Most of the economic statistics which we ordinarily meet, such as trade statistics, figures about price changes, and most 'time series', or statistics of the 'national income', are not data to which the technique appropriate to the investigation of mass phenomena can be applied. They are just 'measurements' and frequently measurements of the type already discussed at the end of Section VI above. If they refer to significant phenomena they may be very interesting as information about the conditions existing at a particular moment. But unlike statistics proper, which may indeed help us to discover important regularities in the social world (though regularities of an entirely different order from those with which the theoretical sciences of society deal), there is no reason to expect that these measurements will ever reveal anything to us which is of significance beyond the particular place and time at which they have been taken. That they cannot produce generalizations does not, of course, mean that they may not be useful, even very useful; they will often provide us with the data to which our theoretical generalization must be applied to be of any practical use. They are an instance of the historical information about a particular situation the significance of which we must further consider in the next sections.

To see the 'historism' to which we must now turn described as a product of the scientistic approach may cause surprise since it is usually represented as the opposite to the treatment of social phenomena on the model of the natural sciences. But the view for which this term is properly used (and which must not be confused with the true method of historical study) proves on closer consideration to be a result of the same prejudices as the other typical scientistic misconceptions of social phenomena. If the suggestion that historism is a form rather than the opposite of scientism has still somewhat the appearance of a paradox this is so because the term is used in two different and in some respects opposite and yet frequently confused senses: for the older view which justly contrasted the specific task of the historian to that of the scientist and which denied the possibility of a theoretical science of history, and for the later view which, on the contrary, affirms that history is the only road which can lead to a theoretical science of social phenomena. However great is the contrast between these two views sometimes called 'historism' if we take them in their extreme forms, they have yet enough in common to have made possible a gradual and almost unperceived transition from the historical method of the historian to the scientistic historism which attempts to make history a 'science' and the only science of social phenomena.

The older historical school, whose growth has recently been so well described by the German historian Meinecke, though under the misleading name of historism,[25] arose mainly in opposition to certain generalizing and 'pragmatic' tendencies of some, particularly French, eighteenth-century views. Its emphasis was on the singular or unique (*individuell*) character of all historical phenomena which could be understood only genetically as the joint result of many forces working

---

[25] G. Meinecke, *Die Entstehung des Historismus*, 1936. The term historian applied to the older historical school discussed by Meinecke is inappropriate and misleading since it was introduced by Carl Menger (*Die Irrthümer des Historismus*, 1884) to describe the distinguishing features of the younger historical school in economics of Schmoller and his associates. Nothing shows more clearly the difference between the younger historical school and the earlier movement from which it inherited the name than that it was Schmoller who accused Menger of being an adherent of the 'Burke-Savigny school' and not the other way round. (Cf. G. Schmoller, 'Zur Methodologie der Staats und Sozialwissenschaften', *Jahrbuch für Gesetzgebung*, etc., N.F., Vol. VII, 1886, p. 250.)

through long stretches of time. Its strong opposition to the 'pragmatic' interpretation, which regards social institutions as the product of conscious design, implies in fact the use of a 'compositive' theory which explains how such institutions can arise as the unintended result of the separate actions of many individuals. It is significant that among the fathers of this view Edmund Burke is one of the most important and Adam Smith occupies an honourable place.

Yet, although this historical method implies theory, i.e., an understanding of the principles of structural coherence of the social wholes, the historians who employed it not only did not systematically develop such theories and were hardly aware that they used them; but their just dislike of any generalization about historical developments also tended to give their teaching an anti-theoretical bias which, although originally aimed only against the wrong kind of theory, yet created the impression that the main difference between the methods appropriate to the study of natural and to that of social phenomena was the same as that between theory and history. This opposition to theory of the largest body of students of social phenomena made it appear as if the difference between the theoretical and the historical treatment was a necessary consequence of the differences between the objects of the natural and the social sciences; and the belief that the search for general rules must be confined to the study of natural phenomena, while in the study of the social world the historical method must rule, became the foundation on which later historism grew up. But while historism retained the claim for the pre-eminence of historical research in this field, it almost reversed the attitude of the older historical school to history and under the influence of the scientistic currents of the age came to represent history as the empirical study of society from which ultimately generalization would emerge. History was to be the source from which a new science of society would spring, a science which should at the same time be historical and yet produce what theoretical knowledge we could hope to gain about society.

We are not here concerned with the actual steps in that process of transition from the older historical school to the historism of the younger. It may just be noticed that historism in the sense in which the term is here used, was created not by historians but by students of the specialized social sciences, particularly economists, who hoped thereby to gain an empirical road to the theory of their subject. But to trace this development in detail and to show how the men responsible for it were actually guided by the scientistic view of their generation must be left to the later historical account.[26]

---

[26] Although in its German origins the connection of historism with positivism is less conspicious than is the case with its English followers such as Ingram or

The first point we must briefly consider is the nature of the distinction between the historical and the theoretical treatment of any subject which makes it in fact a contradiction in terms to demand that history should become a theoretical science or that theory should ever be 'historical'. If we understand that distinction, it will become clear that it has no necessary connection with the difference of the concrete objects with which the two methods of approach deal and that for the understanding of any concrete phenomenon, be it in nature or in society, both kinds of knowledge are equally required.

That human history deals with events or situations which are unique or singular when we consider all aspects which are relevant for the answer of a particular question we may ask about them, is, of course, not peculiar to human history. It is equally true of any attempt to explain a concrete phenomenon if we only take into account a sufficient number of aspects—or, to put it differently, so long as we do not deliberately select only such aspects of reality as fall within the sphere of that system of connected propositions which we call one theoretical science. If I watch and record the process by which a plot in my garden that I leave untouched for years is gradually covered with weeds, I am describing a process which in all its detail is no less unique than any event in human history. If I want to explain any particular configuration of different plants which may appear at any stage of that process, I can do so only by giving an account of all the relevant influences which have affected different parts of my plot at different times. I shall have to consider what I can find out about the differences of the soil in different parts of the plot, about differences in the radiation of the sun, of moisture, of the air-currents, etc., etc.; and in order to explain the effects of all these factors I shall have to use, apart from the knowledge of all these particular facts, various parts of the theory of physics, of chemistry, biology, meteorology, and so on. The result of all this will be the explanation of a particular phenomenon, but not a science of how garden plots go out of cultivation.

In an instance like this the particular sequence of events, their causes and consequences, will probably not be of sufficient general interest to make it worth while to write them up or to develop their study into a distinct discipline. But there are large fields of natural knowledge, represented by recognized disciplines, which in their methodological character are no different from this. In geography, e.g., and at least in a large part of geology and astronomy, we are mainly concerned with particular situations, either of the earth or of the universe; we aim at

Ashley, it was no less present and is overlooked only because historism is erroneously connected with the historical method of the older historians, instead of with the views of Roscher, Hildebrandt and particularly Schmoller and his circle.

explaining a unique situation by showing how it has been produced by the operation of many forces subject to the general laws studied by the theoretical sciences. In the specific sense of a body of general rules in which the term 'science' is often used[27] these disciplines are not 'sciences', i.e., they are not theoretical sciences but endeavours to apply the laws found by the theoretical sciences to the explanation of particular 'historical' situations.

The distinction between the search for generic principles and the explanation of concrete phenomena has thus no necessary connection with the distinction between the study of nature and the study of society. In both fields we need generalizations in order to explain concrete and unique events. Whenever we attempt to explain or understand a particular phenomenon we can do so only by recognizing it or its parts as members of certain classes of phenomena, and the explanation of the particular phenomenon presupposes the existence of general rules.

There are very good reasons, however, for a marked difference in emphasis, reasons why, generally speaking, in the natural sciences the search for general laws has the pride of place while their application to particular events is usually little discussed and of small general interest, while with social phenomena the explanation of the particular and unique situation is as important and often of much greater interest than any generalizations. In most natural sciences the particular situation or event is generally one of a very large number of similar events, which as particular events are only of local and temporary interest and scarcely worth public discussion (except as evidence of the truth of the general rule). The important thing for them is the general law applicable to all the recurrent events of a particular kind. In the social field, on the other hand, a particular or unique event is often of such general interest and at the same time so complex and so difficult to see in all its important aspects, that its explanation and discussion constitutes a major task requiring the whole energy of a specialist. We study here particular events because they have contributed to create the particular environment in which we live or because they are part of that environment. The creation and dissolution of the Roman Empire or the Crusades, the French Revolution or the Growth of Modern Industry are such unique complexes of events, which have helped to contribute the particular circumstances in which we live and whose explanation is therefore of great interest.

It is necessary, however, to consider briefly the logical nature of

---

[27] It will be noted that this, still restricted, use of the term 'science' (in the sense in which the Germans speak of *Gesetzeswissenschaft*) is wider than the even narrower sense in which its meaning is confined to the theoretical sciences of nature.

these singular or unique objects of study. Probably the majority of the many disputes and confusions which have arisen in this connection are due to the vagueness of the common notion of what can constitute *one* object of thought—and particularly to the misconception that the totality (i.e., all possible aspects) of a particular situation can ever constitute one single object of thought. We can here touch only on a very few of the logical problems which this belief raises.

The first point which we must remember is that, strictly speaking, *all* thought must be to some degree abstract. We have seen before that all perception of reality, including the simplest sensations, involves a classification of the object according to some property or properties. The same complex of phenomena which we may be able to discover within given temporal and spatial limits may in this sense be considered under many different aspects; and the principles according to which we classify or group the events may differ from each other not merely in one but in several different ways. The various theoretical sciences deal only with those aspects of the phenomena which can be fitted into a single body of connected propositions. It is necessary to emphasize that this is no less true of the theoretical sciences of nature than of the theoretical sciences of society, since an alleged tendency of the natural sciences to deal with the 'whole' or the totality of the real things is often quoted by writers inclined to historism as a justification for doing the same in the social field.[28] Any discipline of knowledge, whether theoretical or historical, can, however, deal only with certain selected aspects of the real world; and in the theoretical sciences the principle of selection is the possibility of subsuming these aspects under a logically connected body of rules. The same thing may be for one science a pendulum, for another a lump of brass, and for a third a convex mirror. We have already seen that the fact that a pendulum possesses chemical and optical properties does not mean that in studying laws of pendulums we must study them by the methods of chemistry and optics—though when we apply these laws to a particular pendulum we may well have to take into account certain laws of

[28] Cf. e.g., E. F. M. Durbin, 'Methods of Research—A Plea for Co-operation in the Social Sciences', *Economic Journal*, June 1938, p. 191, where the writer argues that in the social sciences 'unlike the natural sciences, our subdivisions are largely (though not entirely) *abstractions from* reality rather than *sections* of reality' and asserts of the natural sciences that 'in all these cases the object of study are real independent objects and groups. They are not aspects of something complex. They are real things'. How this can be really asserted, e.g., of Crystallography (one of Mr Durbin's examples) is difficult to comprehend. This argument has been extremely popular with the members of the German historical school in economics, though, it should be added, Mr Durbin is probably entirely unaware how closely his whole attitude resembles that of the *Kathedersozialisten* of that school.

chemistry or optics. Similarly, as has been pointed out, the fact that all social phenomena have physical properties does not mean that we must study them by the methods of the physical sciences.[29]

The selection of the aspects of a complex of phenomena which can be explained by means of a connected body of rules is, however, not the only method of selection or abstraction which the scientist will have to use. Where investigation is directed, not at establishing rules of general applicability, but at answering a particular question raised by the events in the world about him, he will have to select those features that are relevant to the particular question. The important point, however, is that he still must select a limited number from the infinite variety of phenomena which he can find at the given time and place. We may, in such cases, sometimes speak as if he considered the 'whole' situation as he finds it. But what we mean is not the inexhaustible totality of everything that can be observed within certain spatio-temporal limits, but certain features thought to be relevant to the question asked. If I ask why the weeds in my garden have grown in this particular pattern no single theoretical science will provide the answer. This, however, does not mean that to answer we must know everything that can be known about the space-time interval in which the phenomenon occurred. While the question we ask designates the phenomena to be explained, it is only by means of the laws of the theoretical sciences that we are able to select the other phenomena which are relevant for its explanation. The object of scientific study is never the totality of all the phenomena observable at a given time and place, but always only certain selected aspects. and according to the question we ask the same spatio-temporal situation may become any number of different objects of study. The human mind indeed can never grasp a 'whole' in the sense of all the different aspects of a real situation.

The application of these considerations to the phenomena of human history leads to very important consequences. It means nothing less than that a historical process or period is never a single definite object of thought but becomes this only by the question we ask about it; and that according to the question we ask, what we are accustomed to regard as a single historical event can become any number of different objects of thought.

It is confusion on this point which is mainly responsible for the doctrine now so very much in vogue that all historical knowledge is necessarily relative, determined by our 'standpoint' and bound to

---

[29] It is significant that all of H. Rickert's well-known work on the difference-between the *Naturwissenschaften* and *Kulturwissenschaften* is based on the assertion that since all phenomena which we can observe are physical phenomena, all generalizing (theoretical) science must be physical science.

change with the lapse of time.[30] This view is a natural consequence of the belief that the commonly used names for historical periods or complexes of events, such as 'the Napoleonic Wars', or 'France during the Revolution', or 'the Commonwealth Period', stand for definitely given objects, unique individuals[31] which are given to us in the same manner as is the case with the natural units in which biological specimens or planets are given to us. Those names of historical phenomena define in fact little more than a period and a place and there is scarcely a limit to the number of different questions which we can ask about events which occurred during the period and within the region to which they refer. It is, however, only the question that we ask which will define our object; and there are, of course, many reasons why at different times people will ask different questions about the same period.[32] But this does not mean that history will at different times and on the basis of the same information give different answers to the same question. This alone, however, would entitle us to assert that historical knowledge is relative. The kernel of truth in the assertion about the relativity of historical knowledge is that historians will at different times be interested in different objects, but not that they will necessarily hold different views about the same object.

We must dwell a little longer on the nature of the 'wholes' which the historian studies, though much of what we have to say is merely an application of what has been said before about the 'wholes' which some authors regard as objects of theoretical generalizations. What we said then is just as true of the wholes which the historian studies. They are never given to him as wholes, but always reconstructed from their elements which alone can be directly perceived. Whether he

---

[30] For a good survey of the modern theories of historical relativism see M. Mandelbaum, *The Problem of Historical Knowledge*, New York, 1938.

[31] Cf. below, p. 61, footnote.

[32] It is not possible to pursue further here the interesting question of the reasons which make the historian ask particular questions and which make him ask at different times different questions about the same period. We ought, however, perhaps briefly to refer to one view which has exercised wide influence since it claims application not only to history but to all *Kulturwissenschaften*. It is Rickert's contention that the social sciences, to which, according to him, the historical method is alone appropriate, select their object exclusively with reference to certain values with respect to which they are important. Unless by 'value consideration' (*Wertbezogenheit*) any kind of practical interest in a problem is meant so that this concept would include the reasons which make us, say, study the geology of Cumberland, this is certainly not necessarily the case. If, merely to indulge my taste in detective work, I try to find out why in the year x Mr N. has been elected mayor of Cambridge, this is no less historical work though no known value may have been affected by the fact that Mr N. rather than somebody else has been elected. It is not the reason why we are interested in a problem but the character of the problem which makes it a historical problem.

speaks about the government that existed or the trade that was carried on, the army that moved, or the knowledge that was preserved or disseminated, he is never referring to a constant collection of physical attributes that can be directly observed, but always to a system of relationships between some of the observed elements which can merely be inferred. Words like government or trade or army or knowledge do not stand for single observable things but for structures of relationships which can be described only in terms of a schematic representation or 'theory' of the persistent system of relationships between the ever-changing elements[33] These 'wholes', in other words, do not exist for us apart from the theory by which we constitute them, apart from the mental technique by which we can reconstruct the connections between the observed elements and follow up the implications of this particular combination.

The place of theory in historical knowledge is thus in forming or constituting the wholes to which history refers; it is prior to these wholes which are not visible except by following up the system of relations which connects the parts. The generalizations of theory, how-ever, do not refer, and cannot refer, as has been mistakenly believed by the older historians (who for that reason opposed theory), to the concrete wholes, the particular constellations of the elements, with which history is concerned. The models of 'wholes', of structural con-nections, which theory provides ready-made for the historian to use (though even these are not the given elements about which theory generalizes but the results of theoretical activity), are not identical with the 'wholes' which the historian considers. The models provided by any one theoretical science of society consist necessarily of elements of one kind, elements which are selected because their connection can be explained by a coherent body of principles and not because they help to answer a particular question about concrete phenomena. For the latter purpose the historian will regularly have to use generaliza-tions belonging to different theoretical spheres. His work, thus, as in all attempts to explain particular phenomena, presupposes theory; it is, as is all thinking about concrete phenomena, an application of generic concepts to the explanation of particular phenomena.

If the dependence of the historical study of social phenomena on theory is not always recognized this is mainly due to the very simple nature of the majority of theoretical schemes which the historian will employ and which brings it about that there will be no dispute about

---

[33] It does not alter the essential fact that the theorizing will usually already have been done for the historian by his source which in reporting the 'facts' will use such terms as 'state' or 'town' which cannot be defined by physical char-acteristics but which refer to a complex of relationships which, made explicit, is a 'theory' of the subject.

the conclusions reached by their help and little awareness that he has used theoretical reasoning at all. But this does not alter the fact that in their methodological character and validity the concepts of social phenomena which the historian has to employ are essentially of the same kind as the more elaborate models produced by the systematic social sciences. All the unique objects of history which he studies are in fact either constant patterns or relations, or repetitive processes in which the elements are of a generic character. When the historian speaks of a State or a battle, a town or a market, these words cover coherent structures of individual phenomena which we can comprehend only by understanding the intentions of the acting individuals. If the historian speaks of a certain system, say the feudal system, persisting over a period of time, he means that a certain pattern of relationships continued, a certain type of actions were regularly repeated, structures whose connection he can understand only by mental reproduction of the individual attitudes of which they were made up. The unique wholes which the historian studies, in short, are not given to him as individuals,[34] natural units of which he can find out by observation which features belong to them, but constructions made by the kind of technique that is systematically developed by the theoretical sciences of society. Whether he endeavours to give a genetic account of how a particular institution arose, or a descriptive account of how it functioned, he cannot do so except by a combination of generic considerations applying to the elements from which the unique situation is composed. Though in his work of reconstruction he cannot use any elements except those he empirically finds, not observation but only the 'theoretical' work of reconstruction can tell him which among those that he can find are part of a connected whole.

Theoretical and historical work are thus logically distinct but complementary activities. If their task is rightly understood, there can be no conflict between them. And though they have distinct tasks,

---

[34] The confusion which reigns in this field has evidently been assisted by a purely verbal confusion apt to arise in German in which most of the discussions of this problem have been conducted. In German the singular or unique is called the *Individuelle*, which almost inevitably calls forth a misleading association with the term for the individual (*Individuum*). Now, individual is the term which we employ to describe those natural units which in the physical world our senses enable us to single out from the environment as connected wholes. Individuals in this sense, whether human individuals or animals or plants, or stones, mountains or stars, are constant collections of sense attributes which, either because the whole complex can move together in space relatively to its environment, or for cognate reasons, our senses spontaneously single out as connected wholes. But this is precisely what the objects of history are not. Though singular (*individuell*), as the individual is, they are not definite individuals in the sense in which this term is applied to natural objects. They are not given to us as wholes but only found to be wholes.

neither is of much use without the other. But this does not alter the fact that neither can theory be historical nor history theoretical. Though the general is of interest only because it explains the particular and though the particular can be explained only in generic terms, the particular can never be the general and the general never the particular. The unfortunate misunderstandings that have arisen between historians and theorists are largely due to the name 'historical school' which has been usurped by the mongrel view better described as historism and which is indeed neither history nor theory.

The naïve view which regards the complexes which history studies as given wholes naturally leads to the belief that their observation can reveal 'laws' of the development of these wholes. This belief is one of the most characteristic features of that scientistic history which under the name of historism was trying to find an empirical basis for a theory of history or (using the term philosophy in its old sense equivalent to 'theory') a 'philosophy of history' and to establish necessary successions of definite 'stages' or 'phases', 'systems' or 'styles' which followed each other in historical development. This view on the one hand endeavours to find laws where in the nature of the case they cannot be found, in the succession of the unique and singular historical phenomena, and on the other hand denies the possibility of the kind of theory which alone can help us to understand unique wholes, the theory which shows the different ways in which the familiar elements can be combined to produce the unique combinations we find in the real world. The empiricist prejudice thus led to an inversion of the only procedure by which we can comprehend historical wholes, their reconstruction from the parts; it induced scholars to treat as if they were objective facts vague conceptions of wholes which were merely intuitively comprehended; and it finally produced the view that the elements which are the only thing that we can directly comprehend and from which we must reconstruct the wholes could, on the contrary, be understood only from the whole, which had to be known before we could understand the elements.

The belief that human history, which is the result of the interaction of innumerable human minds, must yet be subject to simple laws accessible to human minds is now so widely held that few people are at all aware what an astonishing claim it really implies. Instead of working patiently at the humble task of rebuilding from the directly known elements the complex and unique structures which we find in the world, and at tracing from the changes in the relations between the elements the changes in the wholes, the authors of these pseudo-theories of history pretend to be able to arrive by a kind of mental short cut at a direct insight into the laws of succession of the immediately apprehended wholes. However doubtful their status, these theories of development have achieved a hold on public imagination much greater than any of the results of genuine systematic study. 'Philosophies' or 'theories' of history (or 'historical theories') have indeed become the characteristic feature, the 'darling vice'[35] of the nineteenth century. From Hegel and Comte, and particularly Marx, down to Sombart and Spengler these spurious theories came to be regarded as representative results of social science; and through the belief that one kind of 'system' must as a matter of historical necessity be superseded by a new and different 'system' they have even exercised a profound influence on social evolution. This they achieved mainly because they looked like the kind of laws which the natural sciences produced; and in an age when these sciences set the standard by which all intellectual effort was measured, the claim of these theories of history to be able to predict future developments was regarded as evidence of their preeminently scientific character. Though merely one among many characteristic nineteenth-century products of this kind, Marxism more than any of the others has become the vehicle through which this result of scientism has gained so wide an influence that many of its opponents equally with its adherents are thinking in its terms.

Apart from setting up a new ideal this development had, however, also the negative effect of discrediting the existing theory on which past understanding of social phenomena had been based. Since it was supposed that we could directly observe the changes in the whole of society or of any particular changed social phenomenon, and that everything within the whole must necessarily change with it, it was concluded that there could be no timeless generalizations about the elements from which these wholes were built up, no universal theories about the ways in which they might be combined into wholes. All social theory, it was said, was necessarily historical, *zeitgebunden*, true only of particular historical 'phases' or 'systems'.

All concepts of individual phenomena, according to this strict historism, are to be regarded as merely historical categories, valid only in a particular historical context. A price in the twelfth century or a monopoly in the Egypt of 400 B.C., it is argued, is not the same 'thing' as a price or a monopoly today, and any attempt to explain that price or the policy of that monopolist by the same theory which we would use to explain a price or a monopoly of today is therefore vain and bound to fail. This argument is based on a complete misapprehension of the function of theory. Of course, if we ask why a particular price

[35] L. Brunschvicg, in *Philosophy and History, Essays presented to E. Cassirer*, ed. by R. Klibansky and H. J. Paton, Oxford, 1936, p. 30.

was charged at a particular date, or why a monopolist then acted in a particular manner, this is a historical question which cannot be fully answered by any one theoretical discipline; to answer it we must take into account the particular circumstances of time and place. But this does not mean that we must not, in selecting the factors relevant to the explanation of the particular price, etc., use precisely the same theoretical reasoning as we would with regard to a price of today.

What this contention overlooks is that 'price' or 'monopoly' are not names for definite 'things', fixed collections of physical attributes which we recognize by some of these attributes as members of the same class and whose further attributes we ascertain by observation; but that they are objects which can be defined only in terms of certain relations between human beings and which cannot possess any attributes except those which follow from the relations by which they are defined. They can be recognized by us as prices or monopolies only because, and in so far as, we can recognize these individual attitudes and from these as elements form the structural pattern which we call a price or monopoly. Of course the 'whole' situation, or even the 'whole' of the men who act, will greatly differ from place to place and from time to time. But it is nothing but our capacity to recognize the familiar elements from which the unique situation is made up which enables us to attach any meaning to the phenomena. Either we cannot thus recognize the meaning of the individual actions, they are nothing but physical facts to us, the handing over of certain material things, etc., or we must place them in the mental categories familiar to us but not definable in physical terms. If the first contention were true, however, this would mean that we could not know the facts of the past at all because in that case we could not understand the documents from which we derive all knowledge of them.[36]

Consistently pursued historism necessarily leads to the view that the human mind is itself variable and that not only are most or all manifestations of the human mind unintelligible to us apart from their historical setting, but that from our knowledge of how the whole situations succeed each other we can learn to recognize the laws according to which the human mind changes, and that it is the knowledge of these laws which alone puts us in a position to understand any particular manifestation of the human mind. Historism, because of its refusal to recognize a compositive theory of universal applicability, unable to see how different configurations of the same elements may produce altogether different complexes, and unable, for the same reason, to comprehend how the wholes can ever be anything but what the human

---

[36] Cf. C. V. Langlois and C. Seignobos, *Introduction to the Study of History*, translated by G. C. Berry, London, 1898, p. 222: 'If former humanity did not resemble humanity of to-day documents would be unintelligible'.

mind consciously designed, was bound to seek the cause of the changes in the social structures in changes of the human mind itself—changes which it claims to understand and explain from changes in the directly apprehended wholes. From the extreme assertion of some sociologists that logic itself is variable, and the belief in the 'prelogical' character of the thinking of primitive people, to the more sophisticated contentions of the modern 'sociology of knowledge', this approach has become one of the most characteristic features of modern sociology. It has raised the old question of the 'constancy of the human mind' in a more radical form than has ever been done before.

This phrase is, of course, so vague that any dispute about it without giving it further precision is not likely to be profitable. That not only any human individual in its historically given complexity, but also certain types predominant in particular ages or localities, differ in significant respects from other individuals or types is, of course, beyond dispute. But this does not alter the fact that in order that we should be able to recognize or understand them at all as human beings or minds there must be certain invariable features present. We cannot recognize 'mind' in the abstract. When we speak of mind what we mean is that certain phenomena can be successfully interpreted on the analogy of our own mind, that the use of the familiar categories of our own thinking provides a satisfactory working explanation of what we observe. But this means that to recognize something as mind is to recognize it as something similar to our own mind, and that the possibility of recognizing mind is limited to what is similar to our own mind. To speak of a mind with a structure fundamentally different from our own, or to claim that we can observe changes in the basic structure of the human mind is not only to claim what is impossible; it is a meaningless statement. Whether the human mind is constant can never become a problem—because to recognize mind cannot mean anything but to recognize something as operating in the same way as our own thinking.

To recognize the existence of a mind always implies that we add something to what we perceive with our senses, that we interpret the phenomena in the light of our own mind, or find that they fit into the ready pattern of our own thinking. This kind of interpretation of human actions may not be always successful, and, what is even more embarrassing, we may never be absolutely certain that it is correct in any particular case; all we know is that it works in the overwhelming number of cases. Yet it is the only basis on which we ever understand what we call other people's intentions or the meaning of their actions; and certainly the only basis of all our historical knowledge since this is all derived from the understanding of signs or documents. As we pass from men of our own kind to different types of beings we may, of course, find that what we can thus understand becomes less and less. And we cannot exclude the possibility that one day we may find beings who, though perhaps physically resembling men, behave in a way which is entirely unintelligible to us. With regard to them we should indeed be reduced to the 'objective' study which the behaviourists want us to adopt towards men in general. But there would be no sense in ascribing to these beings a mind different from our own. We should know nothing of them which we could call mind, we should indeed know nothing about them but physical facts. Any interpretation of their actions in terms of such categories as intention or purpose, sensation or will, would be meaningless. A mind about which we can intelligibly speak must be like our own.

The whole idea of the variability of the human mind is a direct result of the erroneous belief that mind is an object which we observe as we observe physical facts. The sole difference, however, between mind and physical objects, which entitles us to speak of mind at all, is precisely that wherever we speak of mind we interpret what we observe in terms of categories which we know only because they are the categories in which our own mind runs. There is nothing paradoxical in the claim that all mind must run in terms of certain universal categories of thought, because where we speak of mind this means that we can successfully interpret what we observe by arranging it in these categories. And anything which can be comprehended through our understanding of other minds, anything which we recognize as specifically human, must be comprehensible in terms of these categories.

Through this theory of the variability of the human mind, to which the consistent development of historism leads, it cuts, in fact, the ground under its own feet: it is led to the self-contradictory position of generalizing about facts which, if the theory were true, could not be known. If the human mind were really variable so that, as the extreme adherents of historism assert, we could not directly understand what people of other ages meant by a particular statement, history would be inaccessible to us. The wholes from which we are supposed to understand the elements would never be visible to us. And even if we disregard this fundamental difficulty created by the impossibility of understanding the documents from which we derive all historical knowledge, without first understanding the individual actions and intentions the historian could never combine them into wholes and never explicitly state what these wholes are. He would, as indeed is true of so many of the adherents of historism, be reduced to talking about 'wholes' which are intuitively comprehended, to making uncertain and vague generalizations about 'styles' or 'systems' whose character could not be precisely defined.

It follows indeed from the nature of the evidence on which all our historical knowledge is based that history can never carry us beyond the stage where we can understand the working of the minds of the acting people because they are similar to our own. Where we cease to understand, where we can no longer recognize categories of thought similar to those in terms of which we think, history ceases to be human history. And precisely at that point, and only at that point, do the general theories of the social sciences cease to be valid. Since history and social theory are based on the same knowledge of the working of the human mind, the same capacity to understand other people, their range and scope is necessarily co-terminus. Particular propositions of social theory may have no application at certain times, because the combination of elements to which they refer does not occur.[37] But they remain nevertheless true. There can be no different theories for different ages, though at some times certain parts and at others different parts of the same body of theory may be required to explain the observed facts, just as, e.g., generalizations about the effect of very low temperatures on vegetation may be irrelevant in the tropics but still true. Any true theoretical statement of the social sciences will cease to be valid only where history ceases to be human history. If we conceive of somebody observing and recording the doings of another race, unintelligible to him and to us, his records would be in a sense history as, e.g., the history of an ant-heap. Such history would have to be written in purely objective, physical terms. It would be the sort of history which corresponds to the positivist ideal, such as the proverbial observer from another planet might write of the human race. But such history could not help us to understand any of the events recorded by it in the sense in which we understand human history.

When we speak of man we necessarily imply the presence of certain familiar mental categories. It is not the lumps of flesh of a certain shape which we mean, nor any units performing definite functions which we could define in physical terms. The completely insane, none of whose actions we can understand, is not a man to us—he could not figure in human history except as the object of other people's acting and thinking. When we speak of man we refer to one whose actions we can understand. As old Democritus said:

$$\text{ἄνθρωπός ἐστιν ὁ πάντες ἴδμεν}^{38}$$

[37] Cf. W. Eucken, *Grundlagen der Nationalökonomie*, 1940, pp. 203–205.

[38] 'Man is what is known to all.' Cf. H. Diehls, *Die Fragmente der Vorsokratiker*, 4th ed., Berlin, 1922; Democritus, Fragment No. 165, Vol. II, p. 94. I owe the reference to Democritus in this connection to Professor Alexander Rüstow.

K. R. POPPER

From The Poverty of Historicism

THE UNITY OF METHOD

I am going to propose a doctrine of the unity of method; that is to say, the view that all theoretical or generalizing sciences make use of the same method, whether they are natural sciences or social sciences. At the same time, some of these doctrines of historicism which I have not yet sufficiently examined will be touched upon, such as the problems of Generalization; of Essentialism; of the role played by Intuitive Understanding; of the Inexactitude of Prediction; of Complexity; and of the application of Quantitative Methods.

I do not intend to assert that there are no differences whatever between the methods of the theoretical sciences of nature and of society; such differences clearly exist, even between the various natural sciences themselves, as well as between the various social sciences. (Compare, for example, the analysis of competitive markets and of Romance languages.) But I agree with Comte and Mill—and with many others, such as C. Menger—that the methods in the two fields are fundamentally the same (though the methods I have in mind may differ from those they had in mind). The methods always consist in offering deductive causal explanations, and in testing them (by way of predictions). This has sometimes been called the hypothetical-deductive method,[1] or more often the method of hypothesis, for it does not achieve absolute certainty for any of the scientific statements which it tests; rather, these statements always retain the character of tentative hypotheses, even though their character of tentativeness may cease to be obvious after they have passed a great number of severe tests.

Because of their tentative or provisional character, hypotheses were considered, by most students of method, as *provisional in the sense that they have ultimately to be replaced by proved theories* (or at least by theories which can be proved to be 'highly probable', in the sense of some calculus of probabilities). I believe that this view is mistaken and

---

[1] See V. Kraft, *Die Grundformen der wissenschaftlichen Methoden* (1925).

that it leads to a host of entirely unnecessary difficulties. But this problem[2] is of comparatively little moment here. What is important is to realize that in science we are always concerned with explanations, predictions, and tests, and that the method of testing hypotheses is always the same. From the hypothesis to be tested—for example, a

[2] See my *Logic of Scientific Discovery*, on which the present section is based, especially the doctrine of tests by way of deduction ('deductivism') and of the redundancy of any further 'induction', since theories always retain their hypothetical character ('hypotheticism'), and the doctrine that scientific tests are genuine attempts to falsify theories ('eliminationism'); see also the discussion of testability and falsifiability.

The opposition here pointed out, between *deductivism* and *inductivism*, corresponds in some respects to the classical distinction between *rationalism* and *empiricism*: Descartes was deductivist, since he conceived all sciences as deductive systems, while the English empiricists, from Bacon on, all conceived the sciences as collecting observations from which generalizations are obtained by induction.

But Descartes believed that the principles, the premises of the deductive systems, must be secure and self-evident—'clear and distinct'. They are based upon the insight of reason. (They are synthetic and *a priori* valid, in Kantian language.) As opposed to this, I conceive them as tentative conjectures, or hypotheses.

These hypotheses, I contend, must be refutable in principle: it is here that I deviate from the two greatest modern deductivists, Henri Poincaré and Pierre Duhem.

Poincaré and Duhem both recognized the impossibility of conceiving the theories of physics as inductive generalizations. They realized that the observational measurements which form the alleged starting point for the generalizations are, on the contrary, *interpretations in the light of theories*. And they rejected not only inductivism, but also the rationalistic belief in synthetic *a priori* valid principles or axioms. Poincaré interpreted them as analytically true, as definitions; Duhem interpreted them as instruments (as did Cardinal Bellarmino and Bishop Berkeley), as means for the ordering of the experimental laws—the experimental laws which, he thought, were obtained by induction. Theories thus cannot contain either true or false information: they are nothing but instruments, since they can only be convenient or inconvenient, economical or uneconomical; supple and subtle, or else creaking and crude. (Thus, Duhem says, following Berkeley, there cannot be logical reasons why two or more theories which contradict one another should not all be accepted.) I fully agree with both these great authors in rejecting inductivism as well as the belief in the synthetic *a priori* validity of physical theories. But I cannot accept their view that it is impossible to submit theoretical systems to empirical tests. Some of them are testable, I think; that is, refutable in principle; and they are therefore synthetic (rather than analytic); *empirical* (rather than *a priori*); and *informative* (rather than purely instrumental). As to Duhem's famous criticism of crucial experiments, he only shows that crucial experiments can never *prove* or establish a theory; but he nowhere shows that crucial experiments cannot *refute* a theory. Admittedly, Duhem is right when he says that we can test only huge and complex theoretical systems rather than isolated hypotheses; but if we test two such systems which differ in one hypothesis only, and if we can design experiments which refute the first system while leaving the second very well corroborated, then we may be on reasonably safe ground if we attribute the failure of the first system to that hypothesis in which it differs from the other.

universal law—together with some other statements which for this purpose are not considered as problematic—for example, some initial conditions—we deduce some prognosis. We then confront this prognosis, whenever possible, with the results of experimental or other observations. Agreement with them is taken as corroboration of the hypothesis, though not as final proof; clear disagreement is considered as refutation or falsification.

According to this analysis, there is no great difference between explanation, prediction and testing. The difference is not one of logical structure, but rather one of emphasis; it depends on *what we consider to be our problem* and what we do not so consider. If it is not our problem to find a prognosis, while we take it to be our problem to find the initial conditions or some of the universal laws (or both) from which we may deduce a *given* 'prognosis', then we are looking for an *explanation* (and the given 'prognosis' becomes our 'explicandum'). If we consider the laws and initial conditions as given (rather than as to be found) and use them merely for deducing the prognosis, in order to get thereby some new information, then we are trying to make a *prediction*. (This is a case in which we *apply* our scientific results.) And if we consider one of the premises, i.e., either a universal law or an initial condition, as problematic, and the prognosis as something to be compared with the results of experience, then we speak of a *test* of the problematic premise.

The result of tests is the *selection* of hypotheses which have stood up to tests, or the *elimination* of those hypotheses which have not stood up to them, and which are therefore rejected. It is important to realize the consequences of this view. They are these: all tests can be interpreted as attempts to weed out false theories—to find the weak points of a theory in order to reject it if it is falsified by the test. This view is sometimes considered paradoxical; our aim, it is said, is to establish theories, not to eliminate false ones. But just because it is our aim to establish theories as well as we can, we must test them as severely as we can; that is, we must try to find fault with them, we must try to falsify them. Only if we cannot falsify them in spite of our best efforts can we say that they have stood up to severe tests. This is the reason why the discovery of instances which confirm a theory means very little if we have not tried, and failed, to discover refutations. For if we are uncritical we shall always find what we want: we shall look for, and find, confirmations, and we shall look away from, and not see, whatever might be dangerous to our pet theories. In this way it is only too easy to obtain what appears to be overwhelming evidence in favour of a theory which, if approached critically, would have been refuted. In order to make the method of selection by elimination work, and to ensure that only the fittest theories survive, their struggle for life must be made severe for them.

This, in outline, is the method of all sciences which are backed by experience. But what about the method by which we *obtain* our theories or hypotheses? What about *inductive generalizations*, and the way in which we proceed from observation to theory? To this question I shall give two answers. (a) I do not believe that we ever make inductive generalizations in the sense that we start with observations and try to derive our theories from them. I believe that the prejudice that we proceed in this way is a kind of optical illusion, and that at no stage of scientific development do we begin without something in the nature of a theory, such as a hypothesis, or a prejudice, or a problem—often a technological one—which in some way *guides* our observations, and helps us to select from the innumerable objects of observation those which may be of interest.[3] But if this is so, then the method of elimination—which is nothing but that of trial and error—can always be applied. However, I do not think that it is necessary for our present discussion to insist upon this point. For we can say (b) that it is irrelevant from the point of view of science whether we have obtained our theories by jumping to unwarranted conclusions or merely by stumbling over them (that is, by 'intuition'), or else by some inductive procedure. The question, 'How did you first *find* your theory?' relates, as it were, to an entirely private matter, as opposed to the question, 'How did you *test* your theory?' which alone is scientifically relevant. And the method of testing described here is fertile; it leads to new observations, and to a mutual give and take between theory and observation.

Now all this, I believe, is not only true for the natural but also for the social sciences. And in the social sciences it is even more obvious than in the natural sciences that we cannot see and observe our objects before we have thought about them. For most of the objects of social science, if not all of them, are abstract objects; they are *theoretical* constructions. (Even 'the war' or 'the army' are abstract concepts, strange as this may sound to some. What is concrete is the many who are killed; or the men and women in uniform, etc.) These objects, these theoretical constructions used to interpret our experience, are the result of constructing certain *models* (especially of institutions), in order to explain certain experiences—a familiar theoretical method in the natural sciences (where we construct our models of atoms, molecules, solids, liquids, etc.). It is part of the method of explanation by way of reduction, or deduction from hypotheses. Very often we are unaware of the fact that we are operating with hypotheses or theories, and we

---

[3] For a surprising example of the way in which even botanical observations are guided by theory (and in which they may be even influenced by prejudice), see O. Frankel, 'Cytology and Taxonomy of Hebe, etc.', in *Nature*, vol. 147, 1941, p. 117.

therefore mistake our theoretical models for concrete things. This is a kind of mistake which is only too common.[4] The fact that models are often used in this way explains—and by so doing destroys—the doctrines of methodological essentialism. It explains them, for the model is abstract or theoretical in character, and so we are liable to feel that we see it, either within or behind the changing observable events, as a kind of permanent ghost or essence. And it destroys them because the task of social theory is to construct and to analyse our sociological models carefully in descriptive or nominalist terms, that is to say, *in terms of individuals*, of their attitudes, expectations, relations, etc.— a postulate which may be called 'methodological individualism'.

The unity of the methods of the natural and social sciences may be illustrated and defended by an analysis of two passages from Professor Hayek's *Scientism and the Study of Society*.[5]

In the first of these passages, Professor Hayek writes:

'The physicist who wishes to understand the problems of the social sciences with the help of an analogy from his own field would have to imagine a world in which he knew by direct observation the inside of the atoms and had neither the possibility of making experiments with lumps of matter nor the opportunity to observe more than the interactions of a comparatively few atoms during a limited period. From his knowledge of the different kinds of atoms he could build up models of all the various ways in which they could combine into larger units and make these models more and more closely reproduce all the features of the few instances in which he was able to observe more complex phenomena. But the laws of the macrocosm which he could derive from his knowledge of the microcosm would always remain *"deductive"*; they would, because of his limited knowledge of the data of the complex situation, scarcely ever enable him to predict the precise outcome of a particular situation; and he could never verify them by controlled experiment—although they might be *disproved* by the observation of events which according to his theory are impossible.'

I admit that the first sentence of this passage points to certain differences between social and physical science. But the rest of the passage, I believe, speaks for a complete *unity of method*. For if, as I do not doubt, this is a correct description of the method of social science, then it shows that it differs only from such interpretations of the

---

[4] With this and the following paragraph, cf. F. A. von Hayek, 'Scientism and the Study of Society', Parts I and II, *Economica*, Vols. ix and x. [See pp. 36–53 above], where methodological collectivism is criticized and where methodological individualism is discussed in detail.

[5] For the two passages see *Economica*, Vol. ix, p. 289 f. [p. 42 f. above] (italics mine).

method of natural science as we have already rejected. I have in mind, more especially, the 'inductivist' interpretation which holds that in the natural sciences we proceed systematically from observation to theory by some method of generalization, and that we can 'verify', or perhaps even prove, our theories by some method of induction. I have been advocating a very different view here—an interpretation of scientific method as deductive, hypothetical, selective by way of falsification, etc. And this description of the method of natural science agrees perfectly with Professor Hayek's description of the method of social science. (I have every reason to believe that my interpretation of the methods of science was not influenced by any knowledge of the methods of the social sciences; for when I developed it first, I had only the natural sciences in mind,[6] and I knew next to nothing about the social sciences.)

But even the differences alluded to in the first sentence of the quotation are not so great as may appear at first sight. It is undoubtedly true that we have a more direct knowledge of the 'inside of the human atom' than we have of physical atoms; but this knowledge is intuitive. In other words, we certainly use our knowledge of ourselves in order to frame *hypotheses* about some other people, or about all people. But these hypotheses must be tested, they must be submitted to the method of selection by elimination. (Intuition prevents some people from even imagining that anybody could possibly dislike chocolate.) The physicist, it is true, is not helped by such direct observation when he frames his hypotheses about atoms; nevertheless, he quite often uses some kind of sympathetic imagination or intuition which may easily make him feel that he is intimately acquainted with even the 'inside of the atoms'—with even their whims and prejudices. But this intuition is his private affair. Science is interested only in the hypotheses which his intuitions may have inspired, and then only if these are rich in consequences, and if they can be properly tested.

These few remarks may also indicate the way in which the historicist doctrine should be criticized—that is to say, the doctrine that social science must use the method of intuitive understanding.

In the second passage, Professor Hayek, speaking of social phenomena, says: '. . . our knowledge of the principle by which these phenomena are produced will rarely if ever enable us to predict the precise result of any *concrete* situation. While we can explain the principle on which certain phenomena are produced and can from this knowledge *exclude the possibility of certain results*, e.g., of certain events occurring together, our knowledge will in a sense be only negative, i.e., it will

---

[6] Cp. *Erkenntnis*, III, p. 426 f., and my *Logik der Forschung*, 1934, whose subtitle may be translated: 'On the Epistemology of the Natural Sciences'.

merely enable us to preclude certain results but not enable us to narrow the range of possibilities sufficiently so that only one remains.'

This passage, far from describing a situation peculiar to the social sciences, perfectly describes the character of natural laws which, indeed, can never do more than *exclude certain possibilities*. ('You cannot carry water in a sieve'.) More especially the statement that we shall not, as a rule, be able 'to predict the precise result of any *concrete* situation' opens up the problem of the inexactitude of prediction. I contend that precisely the same may be said of the concrete physical world. In general it is only by the use of artificial experimental isolation that we can predict physical events. (The solar system is an exceptional case—one of natural, not of artificial isolation; once its isolation is destroyed by the intrusion of a foreign body of sufficient size, all our forecasts are liable to break down.) We are very far from being able to predict, even in physics, the precise results of a *concrete* situation, such as a thunderstorm, or a fire.

A very brief remark may be added here on the problem of complexity. There is no doubt that the analysis of any concrete social situation is made extremely difficult by its complexity. But the same holds for any concrete physical situation.[7] The widely held prejudice that social situations are more complex than physical ones seems to arise from two sources. One of them is that we are liable to compare what should not be compared; I mean on the one hand concrete social situations and on the other hand artificially insulated experimental physical situations. (The latter might be compared, rather, with an artificially insulated social situation—such as a prison, or an experimental community.) The other source is the old belief that the description of a social situation should involve the mental and perhaps even physical states of everybody concerned (or perhaps that it should even be reducible to them). But this belief is not justified; it is much less justified even than the impossible demand that the description of a concrete chemical reaction should involve that of the atomic and subatomic states of all the elementary particles involved (although chemistry may indeed be reducible to physics). The belief also shows traces of the popular view that social entities such as institutions or associations are concrete natural entities such as crowds of men, rather than abstract models constructed to interpret certain selected abstract relations between individuals.

But in fact, there are good reasons, not only for the belief that social science is less complicated than physics, but also for the belief that concrete social situations are in general less complicated than concrete

[7] A somewhat similar argument can be found in C. Menger, *Collected Works*, Vol. II, 1883 and 1933, pp. 259–260.

physical situations. For in most social situations, if not in all, there is an element of *rationality*. Admittedly, human beings hardly ever act quite rationally (i.e., as they would if they could make the optimal use of all available information for the attainment of whatever ends they may have), but they act, none the less, more or less rationally; and this makes it possible to construct comparatively simple models of their actions and inter-actions, and to use these models as approximations.

The last point seems to me, indeed, to indicate a considerable difference between the natural and the social sciences—perhaps *the most important difference in their methods*, since the other important differences, i.e., specific difficulties in conducting experiments and in applying quantitative methods (see below), are differences of degree rather than of kind. I refer to the possibility of adopting, in the social sciences, what may be called the method of logical or rational construction, or perhaps the 'zero method'.[8] By this I mean the method of constructing a model on the assumption of complete rationality (and perhaps also on the assumption of the possession of complete information) on the part of all the individuals concerned, and of estimating the deviation of the actual behaviour of people from the model behaviour, using the latter as a kind of zero co-ordinate.[9] An example of this method is the comparison between actual behaviour (under the influence of, say, traditional prejudice, etc.) and model behaviour to be expected on the basis of the 'pure logic of choice', as described by the equations of economics. Marschak's interesting 'Money Illusion', for example, may be interpreted in this way.[10] An attempt at applying the zero method to a different field may be found in P. Sargant Florence's comparison between the 'logic of large-scale operation' in industry and the 'illogic of actual operation'.[11]

In passing I should like to mention that neither the principle of methodological individualism, nor that of the zero method of constructing rational models, implies in my opinion the adoption of a psychological method. On the contrary, I believe that these principles can be combined with the view[12] that the social sciences are comparatively independent of psychological assumptions, and that psycho-

[8] See the 'null hypothesis' discussed in J. Marschak, 'Money Illusion and Demand Analysis', in *The Review of Economic Statistics*, Vol. XXV, p. 40. The Method described here seems partly to coincide with what has been called by Professor Hayek, following C. Menger, the 'compositive' method.

[9] Even here it may be said, perhaps, that the use of rational or 'logical' models in the social sciences, or of the 'zero method', has some vague parallel in the natural sciences, especially in thermodynamics and in biology (the construction of mechanical models, and of physiological models of processes and of organs). (Cf. also the use of variational methods.)

[10] See J. Marschak, *op. cit.*

[11] See P. Sargant Florence, *The Logic of Industrial Organisations* (*1933*).

[12] This view is more fully developed in ch. 14 of my *Open Society*.

logy can be treated, not as the basis of all social sciences, but as one social science among others.

In concluding this section, I have to mention what I consider to be the other main difference between the methods of some of the theoretical sciences of nature and of society. I mean the specific difficulties connected with the application of quantitative methods, and especially methods of measurement.[13] Some of these difficulties can be, and have been, overcome by the application of statistical methods, for example in demand analysis. And they *have to be overcome* if, for example, some of the equations of mathematical economics are to provide a basis even of merely qualitative applications; for without such measurement we should often not know whether or not some counteracting influences exceeded an effect calculated in merely qualitative terms. Thus merely qualitative considerations may well be deceptive at times; just as deceptive, to quote Professor Frisch, 'as to say that when a man tries to row a boat forward, the boat will be driven backward because of the pressure exerted by his feet.[14] But it cannot be doubted that there are some fundamental difficulties here. In physics, for example, the parameters of our equations can, in principle, be reduced to a small number of natural constants—a reduction which has been successfully carried out in many important cases. This is not so in economics; here the parameters are themselves in the most important cases quickly changing variables.[15] This clearly reduces the significance, interpretability, and testability of our measurements.

THEORETICAL AND HISTORICAL SCIENCES

The thesis of the unity of scientific method, whose application to theoretical sciences I have just been defending, can be extended, with certain limitations, even to the field of the historical sciences. And this can be done without giving up the fundamental distinction between theoretical and historical sciences—for example, between sociology or economic theory or political theory on the one hand, and social, economic, and political history on the other—a distinction which has been so often and emphatically reaffirmed by the best historians. It is the distinction between the interest in universal laws and the interest in particular facts. I wish to defend the view, so often attacked as old-fashioned by historicists, that *history is characterized by its interest in actual, singular, or specific events, rather than in laws or generalizations*. This view is perfectly compatible with the analysis of scientific

[13] These difficulties are discussed by Professor Hayek.
[14] See *Econometrica*, I, 1933, pp. 1 f.
[15] See Lionel Robbins, in *Economica*, Vol. V, especially p. 351.

method, and especially of causal explanation, given in the preceding sections. The situation is simply this: while the theoretical sciences are mainly interested in finding and testing universal laws, the historical sciences take all kinds of universal laws for granted and are mainly interested in finding and testing singular statements. For example, given a certain singular 'explicandum'—a singular event—they may look for singular initial conditions which (together with all kinds of universal laws which may be of little interest) explain that explicandum. Or they may *test* a given singular hypothesis by using it, along with other singular statements, as an initial condition, and by deducing from these initial conditions (again with the help of all kinds of universal laws of little interest) some new 'prognosis' which may describe an event which has happened in the distant past, and which can be confronted with the empirical evidence—perhaps with documents or inscriptions, etc.

In the sense of this analysis, *all* causal explanation of a singular event can be said to be historical in so far as the 'cause' is always described by singular initial conditions. And this agrees entirely with the popular idea that to explain a thing causally is to explain how and why it happened, that is to say, to tell its 'story'. But it is only in history that we are really interested in the causal explanation of a *singular* event. In the theoretical sciences, such causal explanations are mainly means to a different end—the testing of universal laws.

If these considerations are correct, then the burning interest in questions of origin shown by some evolutionists and historicists, who despise old-fashioned history and wish to reform it into a theoretical science, is somewhat misplaced. *Questions of origin are 'how and why' questions. They are comparatively unimportant theoretically* and usually have only a specific historical interest.

Against my analysis of historical explanation[16] it may be argued that history *does* make use of universal laws contrary to the emphatic declaration of so many historians that history has no interest whatever in such laws. To this we may answer that a singular event is the cause of another singular event—which is its effect—only relative to some universal laws.[17] But these laws may be so trivial, so much part of our

---

[16] My analysis may be contrasted with that of Morton G. White, 'Historical Explanation' (*Mind*, N.S., Vol. 52, pp. 212 ff.), who bases his analysis on my theory of causal explanation as reproduced in an article by C. C. Hempel. Nevertheless he reaches a very different result. Neglecting the historian's characteristic interest in singular events, he suggests that an explanation is 'historical' if it is characterized by the use of *sociological terms* (and theories).

[17] This has been seen by Max Weber. His remarks on p. 179 of his *Ges. Schr. zur Wissenschaftslehre*, 1922, are the closest anticipation of which I know to the analysis offered here. But he is mistaken, I believe, when he suggests that the difference between theoretical and historical science lies in the degree of generality of the laws used.

common knowledge, that we need not mention them and rarely notice them. If we say that the cause of the death of Giordano Bruno was being burnt at the stake, we do not need to mention the universal law that all living things die when exposed to intense heat. But such a law was tacitly assumed in our causal explanation.

Among the theories which the political historian presupposes are, of course, certain theories of sociology—the sociology of power, for example. But the historian uses even these theories, as a rule, without being aware of them. He uses them in the main not as universal laws which help him to test his specific hypotheses, but as implicit in his terminology. In speaking of governments, nations, armies, he uses, usually unconsciously, the 'models' provided by scientific or pre-scientific sociological analysis (see the foregoing section).

The historical sciences, it may be remarked, do not stand quite apart in their attitude towards universal laws. Whenever we encounter an actual application of science to a singular or specific problem we find a similar situation. The practical chemist, for example, who wishes to analyse a certain given compound—a piece of rock, say—hardly considers any universal law. Instead, he applies, possibly without much thought, certain routine techniques which, from the logical point of view, are tests of such *singular* hypotheses as 'this compound contains sulphur'. His interest is mainly a historical one—the description of one set of specific events, or of one individual physical body.

I believe that this analysis clarifies some well-known controversies between certain students of the method of history.[18] One historicist group asserts that history, which does not merely enumerate facts but attempts to present them in some kind of causal connection, must be interested in the formulation of historical laws, since causality means, fundamentally, determination by law. Another group, which also includes historicists, argues that even 'unique' events, events which occur only once and have nothing 'general' about them, may be the cause of other events, and that it is this kind of causation that history is interested in. We can now see that both groups are partly right and partly wrong. Universal law and specific events are together necessary for any causal explanation but, outside the theoretical sciences, universal laws usually arouse little interest.

This leads us to the question of the *uniqueness* of historical events. In so far as we are concerned with the historical explanation of typical events they must necessarily be treated as typical, as belonging to kinds or classes of events. For only then is the deductive method of causal explanation applicable. History, however, is interested not only in the explanation of specific events but also in the description of a

---

[18] See, for example, Weber, *op. cit.*, pp. 8 f., 44 f., 48, 215 ff., 233 ff.

specific event as such. One of its most important tasks is undoubtedly to describe interesting happenings in their peculiarity or uniqueness; that is to say, to include aspects which it does not attempt to explain causally, such as the 'accidental' concurrence of causally unrelated events. These two tasks of history, the disentanglement of causal threads and the description of the 'accidental' manner in which these threads are interwoven, are both necessary, and they supplement each other; at one time an event may be considered as typical, i.e., from the standpoint of its causal explanation, and at another time as unique.

These considerations may be applied to the question of *novelty*. The distinction made there between 'novelty of arrangement' and 'intrinsic newness' corresponds to the present distinction between the standpoint of causal explanation and that of the appreciation of the unique. So far as newness can be rationally analysed and predicted, it can never be 'intrinsic'. This dispels the historicist doctrine that social science should be applicable to the problem of predicting the emergence of intrinsically new events—a claim which may be said to rest ultimately on an insufficient analysis of prediction and of causal explanation.

SITUATIONAL LOGIC IN HISTORY: HISTORICAL INTERPRETATION

But is this all? Is there nothing whatever in the historicist demand for a reform of history—for a sociology which plays the role of a theoretical history, or a theory of historical development? Is there nothing whatever in the historicist idea of 'periods'; of the 'spirit' or 'style' of an age; of irresistible historical tendencies; of movements which captivate the minds of individuals and which surge on like a flood, driving, rather than being driven by, individual men? Nobody who has read, for example, the speculations of Tolstoy in *War and Peace*—historicist, no doubt, but stating his motives with candour—on the movement of the men of the West towards the East and the counter movement of the Russians towards the West,[19] can deny that historicism answers a real need. We have to satisfy this need by offering something better before we can seriously hope to get rid of historicism.

Tolstoy's historicism is a reaction against a method of writing history which implicitly accepts the truth of the principle of leadership; a method which attributes much—too much, if Tolstoy is right, as he undoubtedly is—to the great man, the leader. Tolstoy tries to show, successfully I think, the small influence of the actions and decisions of

[19] This anticipates the problems recently laboured but not answered by Professor Toynbee.

Napoleon, Alexander, Kutuzov, and the other great leaders of 1812, in the face of what may be called the logic of events. Tolstoy points out, rightly, the neglected but very great importance of the decisions and actions of the countless unknown individuals who fought the battles, who burned Moscow, and who invented the partisan method of fighting. But he believes that he can see some kind of historical determination in these events—fate, historical laws, or a plan. In his version of historicism, he combines both methodological individualism and collectivism; that is to say, he represents a highly typical combination—typical of his time, and, I am afraid, of our own—of democratic-individualist and collectivist-nationalistic elements.

This example may remind us that there are *some* sound elements in historicism; it is a reaction against the naïve method of interpreting political history merely as the story of great tyrants and great generals. Historicists rightly feel that there may be something better than this method. It is this feeling which makes their idea of 'spirits'—of an age, of a nation, of an army—so seductive.

Now I have not the slightest sympathy with these 'spirits'—neither with their idealistic prototype nor with their dialectical and materialistic incarnations—and I am in full sympathy with those who treat them with contempt. And yet I feel that they indicate, at least, the existence of a lacuna, of a place which it is the task of sociology to fill with something more sensible, such as an analysis of problems arising within a tradition. There is room for a more detailed analysis of the *logic of situations*. The best historians have often made use, more or less unconsciously, of this conception: Tolstoy, for example, when he describes how it was not decision but 'necessity' which made the Russian army yield Moscow without a fight and withdraw to places where it could find food. Beyond this *logic of the situation*, or perhaps as a part of it, we need something like an analysis of social movements. We need studies, based on methodological individualism, of the social institutions through which ideas may spread and captivate individuals, of the way in which new traditions may be created, and of the way in which traditions work and break down. In other words, our individualistic and institutionalist models of such collective entities as nations, or governments, or markets, will have to be supplemented by models of political situations as well as of social movements such as scientific and industrial progress. These models may then be used by historians, partly like the other models, and partly for the purpose of explanation, along with the other universal laws they use. But even this would not be enough; it would still not satisfy all those real needs which historicism attempts to satisfy.

If we consider the historical sciences in the light of our comparison between them and the theoretical sciences, then we can see that their lack of interest in universal laws puts them in a difficult position. For in theoretical science laws act, among other things, as centres of interest to which observations are related, or as points of view from which observations are made. In history the universal laws, which for the most part are trivial and used unconsciously, cannot possibly fulfil this function. It must be taken over by something else. For undoubtedly there can be no history without a point of view; like the natural sciences, history must be *selective* unless it is to be choked by a flood of poor and unrelated material. The attempt to follow causal chains into the remote past would not help in the least, for every concrete effect with which we might start has a great number of different partial causes; that is to say, initial conditions are very complex, and most of them have little interest for us.

The only way out of this difficulty is, I believe, consciously to introduce a *preconceived selective point of view* into one's history; that is, to write *that history which interests us*. This does not mean that we may twist the facts until they fit into a framework of preconceived ideas, or that we may neglect the facts that do not fit.[20] On the contrary, all available evidence which has a bearing on our point of view should be considered carefully and objectively. But it means that we need not worry about all those facts and aspects which have no bearing upon our point of view and which therefore do not interest us.

Such selective approaches fulfil functions in the study of history which are in some ways analogous to those of theories in science. It is therefore understandable that they have often been taken for theories. And indeed, those rare ideas inherent in these approaches which can be formulated in the form of *testable hypotheses*, whether singular or universal, may well be treated as scientific hypotheses. But as a rule, these historical 'approaches' or 'points of view' *cannot be tested*. They cannot be refuted, and apparent confirmations are therefore of no value, even if they are as numerous as the stars in the sky. We shall call such a selective point of view or focus of historical interest, if it cannot be formulated as a testable hypothesis, a *historical interpretation*.

Historicism mistakes these interpretations for theories. This is one of its cardinal errors. It is possible, for example, to interpret 'history' as the history of class struggle, or of the struggle of races for supremacy, or as the history of religious ideas, or as the history of the struggle between the 'open' and the 'closed' society, or as the history of scientific and industrial progress. All these are more or less interesting points of view, and *as such* perfectly unobjectionable. But historicists do not present them as such; they do not see that there is necessarily a

[20] For a criticism of the 'doctrine . . . that all historical knowledge is relative', see Hayek, in *Economica*, Vol. X, pp. 55 ff [pp. 58 ff. above].

plurality of interpretations which are fundamentally on the same level of both suggestiveness and arbitrariness (even though some of them may be distinguished by their *fertility*—a point of some importance). Instead, they present them as doctrines or theories, asserting that 'all history is the history of class struggle', etc. And if they actually find that their point of view is fertile, and that many facts can be ordered and interpreted in its light, then they mistake this for a confirmation, or even for a proof, of their doctrine.

On the other hand, the classical historians who rightly oppose this procedure are liable to fall into a different error. Aiming at objectivity, they feel bound to avoid any selective point of view; but since this is impossible, they usually adopt points of view without being aware of them. This must defeat their efforts to be objective, for one cannot possibly be critical of one's own point of view, and conscious of its limitations, without being aware of it.

The way out of this dilemma, of course, is to be clear about the necessity of adopting a point of view; to state this point of view plainly, and always to remain conscious that it is one among many, and that even if it should amount to a theory, it may not be testable.

THE INSTITUTIONAL THEORY OF PROGRESS

In order to make our considerations less abstract, I shall try to sketch, in very brief outline, a *theory of scientific and industrial progress*. I shall try to exemplify, in this way, the ideas developed; more especially the idea of situational logic, and of a methodical individualism which keeps clear of psychology. I choose the example of scientific and industrial progress because undoubtedly it was this phenomenon which inspired modern nineteenth-century historicism, and because I have previously discussed some of Mill's views on this subject.

Comte and Mill, it will be remembered, held that progress was an unconditional or absolute trend, which is *reducible to the laws of human nature*. 'A law of succession,' writes Comte, 'even when indicated with all possible authority by the method of historical observation, ought not to be finally admitted before it has been rationally reduced to the positive theory of human nature . . .'[21] He believes that the law of progress is deducible from a tendency in human individuals which impels them to perfect their nature more and more. In all this, Mill follows him completely, trying to reduce his law of progress to what he calls the 'progressiveness of the human mind'[22] whose first 'impelling

[21] Comte, *Cours de philosophie positive*, IV, p. 335.
[22] Mill, *Logic*, Book VI, Ch. X, section 3; the next quotation is from section 6 where the theory is worked out in more detail.

force . . . is the desire of increased material comforts'. According to both Comte and Mill the unconditional or absolute character of this trend or quasi-law enables us to deduce from it the first steps or phases of history, without requiring any initial historical conditions or observations or data.[20] In principle, the whole course of history should be thus deducible; the only difficulty being, as Mill puts it, that 'so long a series . . . each successive term being composed of an even greater number and variety of parts, could not possibly be computed by human faculties'.[24]

The weakness of this 'reduction' of Mill's seems obvious. Even if we should grant Mill's premises and deductions, it still would not follow that the social or historical effect will be significant. Progress might be rendered negligible, say, by losses due to an unmanageable natural environment. Besides, the premises are based on only one side of 'human nature' without considering other sides such as forgetfulness or indolence. Thus where we observe the precise opposite of the progress described by Mill, there we can equally well 'reduce' these observations to 'human nature'. (Is it not, indeed, one of the most popular devices of so-called historical theories to explain the decline and fall of empires by such traits as idleness and a propensity to over-eat?) In fact we can conceive of very few events which could not be plausibly explained by an appeal to certain propensities of 'human nature'. But a method that can explain everything that might happen explains nothing.

If we wish to replace this surprisingly naïve theory by a more tenable one, we have to take two steps. First, we have to attempt to find *conditions* of progress: we must try to imagine *conditions under which progress would be arrested*. This immediately leads to the realization that a *psychological propensity alone* cannot be sufficient to explain progress, since conditions may be found on which it may depend. Thus we must, next, replace the theory of psychological propensities by something better; I suggest, by an *institutional* (and technological) analysis of the conditions of progress.

How could we arrest scientific and industrial progress? By closing down, or by controlling, laboratories for research, by suppressing or controlling scientific periodicals and other means of discussion, by suppressing scientific congresses and conferences, by suppressing universities and other schools, by suppressing books, the printing press, writing, and, in the end, speaking. All these things which indeed might be suppressed (or controlled) are social institutions. Language is a social institution without which scientific progress is unthinkable, since without it there can be neither science nor a growing

---

[23] Comte, *loc. cit.*, p. 345.
[24] Mill, *loc. cit.*, section 4.

and progressive tradition. Writing is a social institution, and so are the organizations for printing and publishing and all the other institutional instruments of scientific method. Scientific method itself has social aspects. Science, and more especially scientific progress, are the results not of isolated efforts but of the *free competition of thought*. For science needs ever more competition between hypotheses and ever more rigorous tests. And the competing hypotheses need personal representation, as it were: they need advocates, they need a jury, and even a public. This personal representation must be institutionally organized if we wish to ensure that it works. And these institutions have to be paid for, and protected by law. Ultimately, progress depends very largely on political factors; on political institutions that safeguard the freedom of thought: on democracy.

It is of some interest that what is usually called '*scientific objectivity*' is based, to some extent, on social institutions. The naïve view that scientific objectivity rests on the mental or psychological attitude of the individual scientist, on his training, care, and scientific detachment, generates as a reaction the sceptical view that scientists can never be objective. On this view their lack of objectivity may be negligible in the natural sciences where their passions are not excited, but for the social sciences where social prejudices, class bias, and personal interests are involved, it may be fatal. This doctrine, developed in detail by the so-called '*sociology of knowledge*', entirely overlooks the social or institutional character of scientific knowledge, because it is based on the naïve view that objectivity depends on the psychology of the individual scientist. It overlooks the fact that neither the dryness nor the remoteness of a topic of natural science prevents partiality and self-interest from interfering with the individual scientist's beliefs, and that if we had to depend on his detachment, science, even natural science, would be quite impossible. *What the 'sociology of knowledge' overlooks is just the sociology of knowledge*—the social or public character of science. It overlooks the fact that it is the public character of science and of its institutions which imposes a mental discipline upon the individual scientist, and which preserves the objectivity of science and its tradition of critically discussing new ideas.[25]

In this connection, I may perhaps touch upon another of the doctrines (*Objectivity and Valuation*). There it was argued that, since scientific research in social problems must itself influence social life, it is impossible for the social scientist who is aware of this influence to

---

[25] A fuller criticism of the so-called 'Sociology of Knowledge' will be found in ch. 23 of my *Open Society and Its Enemies*. The problem of scientific objectivity, and its dependence upon rational criticism and inter-subjective testability, is also discussed there in ch. 24, and, from a somewhat different point of view, in my *Logic of Scientific Discovery*.

retain the proper scientific attitude of disinterested objectivity. But there is nothing peculiar to social science in this situation. A physicist or a physical engineer is in the same position. Without being a social scientist he can realize that the invention of a new aircraft or rocket may have a tremendous influence on society.

I have just sketched some of the institutional conditions on whose realization scientific and industrial progress depends. Now it is important to realize that most of these conditions cannot be called necessary, and that all of them taken together are not sufficient.

The conditions are not necessary, since without these institutions (language perhaps excepted) scientific progress would not be strictly impossible. 'Progress', after all, *has* been made from the spoken to the written word, and even further (although this early development was perhaps not, properly speaking, *scientific* progress).

On the other hand, and this is more important, we must realize that with the best institutional organization in the world, scientific progress may one day stop. There may, for example, be an epidemic of mysticism. This is certainly possible, for since some intellectuals *do* react to scientific progress (or to the demands of an open society) by withdrawing into mysticism, everyone *might* react in this way. Such a possibility may perhaps be counteracted by devising a further set of social institutions, such as educational institutions, to discourage uniformity of outlook and encourage diversity. Also, the idea of progress and its enthusiastic propagation may have some effect. But all this cannot make progress certain. For we cannot exclude the logical possibility, say, of a bacterium or virus that spreads a wish for Nirvana.

We thus find that even the best institutions can never be foolproof. As I have said before, 'Institutions are like fortresses. They must be well designed *and* properly manned'. But we can never make sure that the right man will be attracted by scientific research. Nor can we make sure that there will be men of imagination who have the knack of inventing new hypotheses. And ultimately, much depends on sheer luck in these matters. For truth is *not manifest*, and it is a mistake to believe—as did Comte and Mill—that once the 'obstacles' (the allusion is to the Church) are removed, truth will be visible to all who genuinely want to see it.

I believe that the result of this analysis can be generalized. The human or personal factor will remain *the* irrational element in most, or all, institutional social theories. The opposite doctrine which teaches the reduction of social theories to psychology, in the same way as we try to reduce chemistry to physics, is, I believe, based on a misunderstanding. It arises from the false belief that this 'methodological psychologism' is a necessary corollary of a methodological individualism —of the quite unassailable doctrine that we must try to understand all collective phenomena as due to the actions, interactions, aims, hopes, and thoughts of individual men, and as due to traditions created and preserved by individual men. But we can be individualists without accepting psychologism. The 'zero method' of constructing rational models is *not* a psychological but rather a logical method.

In fact, psychology cannot be the basis of social science. First, because it is itself just one of the social sciences: 'human nature' varies considerably with the social institutions, and its study therefore presupposes an understanding of these institutions. Secondly, because the social sciences are largely concerned with the unintended consequences, or repercussions, of human actions. And 'unintended' in this context does not perhaps mean 'not *consciously* intended'; rather it characterizes repercussions which may violate *all* interests of the social agent, whether conscious or unconscious: although some people may claim that a liking for mountains and solitude may be explained psychologically, the fact that, if too many people like the mountains, they cannot enjoy solitude there, is not a psychological fact; but this kind of problem is at the very root of social theory.

With this, we reach a result which contrasts startlingly with the still fashionable method of Comte and Mill. Instead of reducing sociological considerations to the apparently firm basis of the psychology of human nature, we might say that the human factor is *the* ultimately uncertain and wayward element in social life and in all social institutions. Indeed this is the element which ultimately *cannot* be completely controlled by institutions (as Spinoza first saw);[26] for every attempt at controlling it completely must lead to tyranny; which means, to the omnipotence of the human factor—the whims of a few men, or even of one.

But is it not possible to control the human factor by *science*—the opposite of whim? No doubt, biology and psychology can solve, or will soon be able to solve, the 'problem of transforming man'. Yet those who attempt to do this are bound to destroy the objectivity of science, and so science itself, since these are both based upon free competition of thought; that is, upon freedom. If the growth of reason is to continue, and human rationality to survive, then the diversity of individuals and their opinions, aims, and purposes must never be interfered with (except in extreme cases where political freedom is endangered). Even the emotionally satisfying appeal for a *common purpose*, however excellent, is an appeal to abandon all rival moral opinions and the cross-criticisms and arguments to which they give rise. It is an appeal to abandon rational thought.

The evolutionist who demands the 'scientific' control of human nature does not realize how suicidal this demand is. The mainspring

---

[26] See note 2 on p. 90, *The Poverty of Historicism.*

of evolution and progress is the variety of the material which may become subject to selection. So far as human evolution is concerned it is the 'freedom to be odd and unlike one's neighbour'—'to disagree with the majority, and go one's own way'.[27] Holistic control, which must lead to the equalization not of human rights but of human minds, would mean the end of progress.

[27] See Waddington (*The Scientific Attitude*, 1941, pp. 111 and 112), who is prevented neither by his evolutionism nor by his scientific ethics from denying that this freedom has any 'scientific value'. This passage is criticized in Hayek's *The Road to Serfdom*, p. 143.

Part 2

Scientism and the Philosophy of the Social Sciences

MAY BRODBECK

On the Philosophy of the Social Sciences

When, in recent years, philosophers of science attend to the physical sciences, their activity centres on the analysis and clarification of the methods and theories of these sciences. Thus philosophers have made remarkable contributions to our understanding of mechanics, the relativity theory, the quantum theory, probability, and geometry, as well as to the foundations of mathematics. More general discussions about theory construction, explanation, and concept formation always are illustrated and illuminated by reference to specific theories within science. In our generation, most philosophers of science have taken for granted that physical science is descriptive, empirical, functional, and —leaving aside controversial interpretations of quanta—deterministic.

With Galileo's research on falling bodies as our paradigm, we may say that science is descriptive because the body's behaviour is explained by giving the mathematical formula for the process, not in looking for its purpose; it is empirical because the variables that enter into these formulae denote observables or are defined in terms of the observable, unlike such an element as the soul or other entelechy. It is functional, in the mathematical sense, for no distinction is made between the 'accidental' and the 'essential'; the variables are interdependent in determinate ways and the relations between all of them must be taken into account in order to describe accurately what happens. That in principle the future is completely predictable from the present follows as a corollary, no leeway being left for accident or for purpose from the point of view of the observer. Such is the frame of reference in terms of which special theories are analysed by philosophers of science and about which, elementary text-book writing apart, they say little. In the social sciences, however, philosophers still argue about the frame of reference.

Contemporary theory of the social sciences follows four major patterns. I shall simplify to make them stand out clearly. *First*, there are the self-conscious continuers of the Galilean-Newtonian tradition who insist upon essential identity in method between the social and the physical sciences. These thinkers incline to the view that social theory is, in some sense, reducible to psychology which in turn, through physiology, is reducible to physics. Armed with the laws of physics and the state of the universe at any moment, Laplace's demon extends his purview from the physical world to the fate of all mankind. From Mill to the logical positivists, these are the objectivists and reductionists. *Second,* from the early nineteenth century until our own time, the Romantics insist upon the unique character of what later came to be called *Geisteswissenschaften,* the sciences of man. Organicist, holist, and emergentist, this school deplores the Laplacean vision as radically mistaken, if not viciously demeaning to the dignity of man and his works. It counters the objectivists' fervour for the empirical methods of science with an equally ardent belief in the superiority of *verstehen.* These are the two extreme views. The other two combine, in different proportions, ingredients of these extremes.

The *third* view, represented by Marxists and pragmatists, unites— or attempts to unite—the empiricist, scientific tradition with anti-analytical holism and historicism. The study of society they claim can and must be objective and scientific. But its laws are held to be unique in kind, unlike those of either psychology or physics. The *fourth* conception of the social sciences is reductionist in one sense, anti-reductionist in another. The behaviour of groups must be explained in terms of the behaviour of individuals; but the psychology of individuals cannot be reduced to anything else. Although it opposes organicism, it too rejects the so-called unity of the sciences, insists like the holists on a unique and, perhaps, subjective method in the social sciences. The most articulate contemporary proponent of this position is the economist, F. A. Hayek.[1]

These four views all share a common feature. Each of them asserts something about the nature of man and society. For the proponents of physical reduction, human and social characteristics 'are'—in some sense of 'are'—ultimately atoms and electrons. For the organicist, society is a unique whole. The Marxists and the pragmatists fuse these visions. But for Professor Hayek, neither organic wholes nor electrons take honours—the uniqueness resides in man.

Which, if any, of these four views is true, which false, is a matter of fact. There is, of course, nothing new or remarkable about philosophers, or social scientists turned philosophers, speculating about matters of fact. Abhorring a vacuum, philosophers rush in where scientists fear to tread. What is remarkable is that, with the exception of the idealistic holists who believed they were enunciating special metaphysical truths,

---

[1] A generation ago a very similar view was held by the social psychologist, William McDougall. Both advocate the reduction to psychology of all other social sciences; both are ardently anti-reductionist in psychology. But Professor Hayek is not, as was McDougall, a vitalist. Again, McDougall thought of psychology as the science of behaviour, while Professor Hayek most emphatically does not.

these philosophers do not recognize their speculations for what they are.

They do not realize that they are anticipating the results of future scientific research, making guesses about what would be shown in an ideally completed science. If we knew everything and also if—though I am not sure what this means—if we *knew* that we knew everything, we should be able to say whether or not there was a deductive relationship between our physics, our psychology, and our sociology. It would depend upon the facts. But our philosophers, reductionist and anti-reductionist alike, make assertions about what *must* be the case, not about what merely happens, as a matter of fact, to be the case. There is also a related error. Some philosophical scientists restrict reality to those areas illuminated by their particular method. Watson, for instance, denied the existence of images in thought or even of any reflective processes at all because of his bias against the method of introspection. His research interest in learning phenomena rather than in genetic factors led him to his equally notorious denial of individual differences. It is no longer novel in the history of ideas to discover values being accorded the dignity of fact or logic for ulterior ideological motives.[2] Ironically, F. A. Hayek, the latest and most provocative to reveal hidden rationalizations in the thought of others, himself commits an error of the same kind.

As is well known, Professor Hayek's ideological motive is his horror of the planned economy. The reasons for this reaction cannot and should not be dismissed lightly. However, it is not my purpose to evaluate those reasons here; this requires reflection on our value system, the relative weights we give to specific values within this system, and, also, factual considerations about what various types of economy can be expected to achieve. The issue is moral, not one in the philosophy of science. So, taking my cues from Professor Hayek's recent book,[3] I shall here consider some issues pertinent to our field.

The three aspects of Professor Hayek's argument that I shall discuss here are his contentions, first, that the social sciences are 'systematically subjective'; secondly, that the use of macroscopic, collective, non-psychological concepts is always illegitimate; and, thirdly, that explanation in social science must be in terms of individual motivation and behaviour. The last two points are, of course, intimately related,

[2] For an illuminating analysis of the nature of social and scientific ideologies, see Gustav Bergmann, 'Ideology', *Ethics*, 51, 1951. Also, valuable discussions relevant to the issues treated below may be found in the same author's 'Theoretical Psychology', *Annual Review of Psychology*, Vol. 4, Stanford University Press, 1953, and 'Holism, Historicism, and Emergence', *Philosophy of Science*, 11, 1944.

[3] *The Counter-Revolution of Science: studies on the abuse of reason*, The Free Press, Glencoe, Illinois, 1952. Unless otherwise noted, all page references are to this book. *Ed.* For the most part Brodbeck's discussion may be referred to the selection from Hayek in the present volume.

but they are not quite the same point. All three issues are, independently of Professor Hayek, still unduly controversial in the philosophy of the social sciences. Professor Hayek gives the old arguments a new turn whose analysis may, I hope, cast fresh light on the issues themselves.

THE 'SYSTEMATIC SUBJECTIVISM' OF SOCIAL SCIENCE

Professor Hayek has three reasons for his belief that social science is irredeemably subjective. (1) Its subject matter is human opinions and attitudes; (2) this subject matter can be adequately known only by a subjective method, namely, introspection; (3) mental categories are indispensable for explanation of social phenomena and this, allegedly, implies subjectivism.

(1) Is the subject matter of social science solely human attitudes and opinions? Natural science, as Professor Hayek says, studies things independently of what men do or think about them, while for social science what people think of the world makes a difference. Professor Hayek usefully distinguishes between the natural sciences of man, like the problem of the spread of contagious diseases or the study of nutrition, in which human volition and motivation do not play a role, and the social sciences proper in which they do. The latter 'must start from what men think and mean to do. . . . Not only man's actions towards external objects but also all the relations between men and all the social institutions can be understood only in terms of what men think about them.' Professor Hayek goes on, 'So far as human actions are concerned the things *are* what the acting people think they are. . . . Our data must be man and the physical world as they appear to the men whose actions we try to explain.'[4] To drive home his point, he elsewhere makes what he calls the 'general and obvious statement' that 'no superior knowledge the observer may possess about the object, but which is not possessed by the acting person, can help us in understanding the motives of their actions'.[5] Thus, according to Professor Hayek, social science is concerned with, and only with, the world as it appears to men, and with men's beliefs about what they can do in the world as they see it. To what extent this picture of the world fits the facts is wholly irrelevant. In terms of these varying opinions and beliefs social science explains its phenomena; they are not themselves to be explained by social science.

If the 'objectivism' of natural science, for Professor Hayek, rests on the dispensability of human beliefs and attitudes, then social science

---

[4] Pp. 33, 27, 35.
[5] *Individualism and the Economic Order*, p. 60, University of Chicago Press, Chicago, 1948. Also cf. *The Counter-Revolution of Science*, p. 30.

is clearly not 'objectivist'. The most ardent advocate of an objective science of behaviour would surely agree. People's beliefs and attitudes do indeed make a difference. But it is simply not true that the social scientist can, with impunity, wholly ignore the difference between what people think of the world and what the world is like. A gulf frequently yawns between what a man thinks he can do and what in matter of fact the circumstances will permit him to achieve. Unless this gulf is taken into account, the social scientist will be at a loss to account for much in the individual's behaviour. It may not be necessary for him to explain the genesis of a delusion—he may well leave that to the psychologist— but that it is a delusion he will need to know. We may predict certain purchases on the basis of a man's beliefs about what he can afford. Only by knowing that he is mistaken can we predict his subsequent trips to the money lender or the bankruptcy courts. The motive power of a belief is not a function of its truth or falsity, but the consequences of acting on a belief will differ as the belief is in fact either true or false.

People are full of foolish fancies about the world and their station in it. These fancies are, as Professor Hayek insists, as real as the true state of affairs, but unless the social scientist is able to compare one with the other, unless he does have 'superior knowledge', much of what happens in the social structure must remain a mystery to him. Apropos the necessity for superior knowledge by the observer, can anyone, at this stage of the game, really believe that to explain people's actions we need to know no more than they do, not only about the external world, but about themselves? Is it still possible to say that only people's conscious beliefs and attitudes determine their behaviour? I suppose that an affirmative answer is not quite like holding that the earth is flat, yet surely even the most conservative student of human personality would hazard that we are at least not certain that what people say and believe are their motives really are their motives. Professor Hayek is not prepared to concede even this much to the psychology of the past half-century. So far as he is concerned the science of psychology, either normal or abnormal, might never have existed—and this despite Professor Hayek's insistence that social science is rooted in psychology.

(2) Suppose we grant that people's opinions, attitudes, and beliefs and only these are the subject matter of social science. From the observer's point of view these are observable facts like any other, like the facts of the natural sciences, not opinions. Professor Hayek agrees. Human attitudes, organic processes, the stars in their courses—all, in a narrow sense, are different subject matters. In a broader sense, as 'facts given to the observation',[6] they are one subject matter. Why then does Professor Hayek maintain that there is an unbridgeable gap between the method of natural and of social science?

[6] *The Counter-Revolution of Science*, p. 28.

M.I.C.—4*

The two besetting sins of what Professor Hayek calls 'scientism', the aping of the method of the natural sciences by the social sciences, are 'objectivism' and 'collectivism'. Of 'collectivism' later. 'Objectivism' Professor Hayek defines as 'the various attempts to dispense with our subjective knowledge of the working of the human mind', that is, all attempts 'to do without the knowledge derived from "introspection".' The difference between natural and social science is thus a difference in the kind of observation by which we know natural and social phenomena. Social science is subjective, according to Professor Hayek, not only in the odd sense that its data happen to be, among other things, opinions, but also in the usual sense that the observer's knowledge of this data is private, based on examination of his own mind. Only by 'such inside knowledge of human affairs' can we understand what is meant by 'tools, commodities or money, crimes or punishments, words or sentences'. Since other people's mental states are never directly data for us, we must therefore interpret things wholly 'in the light of our own mind'.[7] This, and not some naïve notion of a 'rational man'— Professor Hayek is too human and too wise to be caught in that trap— is why all motivation must be conscious. We must have access to it in ourselves in order to understand others. In other words, social science is irremediably subjective because our knowledge of psychology in terms of which it is to be explained is irremediably subjective.

The key to Professor Hayek's position is his rejection of the fond fiction of a Martian observer deposited on our planet to study human society as we study bees and ants. This, Professor Hayek reiterates, is in principle impossible. The Martian could not study human behaviour, not because he would for a time be at a loss, like an anthropologist studying a primitive culture, but because, not being human, he could not understand human nature. Only one with the mind of a man can understand the intentions and motives of men. The familiar retort has not lost its sting: need I be an atom in order to understand one? That Professor Hayek thinks so or, at least, that he thinks there is a crucial difference between these cases is, of course, his link with romanticism, with *Geisteswissenschaften* and *verstehende* social science. This fits queerly with his otherwise toughminded anti-holism and anti-historicism. What his view amounts to is that a science of psychology is not so much impossible as unnecessary. We already know it for it is about men, which we are. One might also add that we already know sociology and economics for they are about society, in which we live. But, of course, Professor Hayek does not make this extension. A science of psychology is unnecessary because we already know it by knowing ourselves, the only channel to knowledge of others. One patent

[7] Pp. 44–45, 59, 77.

absurdity of this position has been pointed out: 'Only a war-like historian can tackle a Genghis Khan or a Hitler!'[8]

I suspect that one reason for Professor Hayek's belief that social science is subjective is that he has succumbed to the temptation to make a metaphysical position out of some unexamined commonplaces. I refer to the prevailing quips that social science is nothing but documentation of the obvious, the mere statisticalization of common sense.[9] The state of mind reflected by these stereotypes is shared by all who endorse the view that social science, unlike natural science, explains the familiar in terms of the familiar. The explanations of natural science are 'surprising', we are told, while those of social science are not.[10] Maybe what the psychologists tell us isn't surprising any more, but once it was. As careful experimentation proceeds in the social sciences, many more surprising things may turn up, not only about the lower depths. It is even possible that a good case could be made for the Martian on practical as well as logical grounds. He might be the best equipped to study human society, simply because he does not share the preconceptions that limit us, the hopes that blind us, and the tendencies to overgeneralize from our possibly eccentric family, friends, and colleagues.[11]

(3) Professor Hayek's belief that the indispensability of mental categories makes inevitable the subjectivity of social science raises a more complex issue. Three separate questions are involved: (a) Is a physical explanation of mental processes possible? (b) If it were possible would we still need mental concepts for an adequate description of social facts? (c) If we still needed them, with or without physical

---

[8] J. W. N. Watkins, 'Ideal Types and Historical Explanation', in *Readings in the Philosophy of Science*, eds. H. Feigl and M. Brodbeck, Appleton Century Crofts, New York, 1953, p. 740 fn. 45. I shall discuss an issue raised in Mr Watkins' excellent paper in my last section. [*Ed.* See Watkins below, p. 162.]

[9] Of such stuff is the jealous 'Hostile Highbrow' reaction by humanistic intellectuals to serious social science. Our inevitable empathy with this reaction should be tempered by the fact that its stereotypes are hardly distinguishable from those of the 'Hostile Lowbrow'. There is criticism and criticism, after all. For an amusing and enlightening analysis of Friendly and Hostile reactions to social science see the essay by D. Lerner in *Continuities in Social Research*, R. K. Merton and P. F. Lazarsfeld (eds.), Free Press, Illinois, 1950.

[10] See, for instance, Watkins, *loc. cit.*, p. 735 [p. 156 below].

[11] *An American Dilemma* impressively attests to the success of one attempt to approximate the man-from-Mars condition. The Trustees of the Carnegie Corporation who initiated and financed this elaborately detailed study of the American Negro deliberately 'imported' a general director, Dr Gunnar Myrdal, who would be as free as possible from traditional attitudes both specifically American and imperialistic. True, Dr Myrdal is human, but by simple extension of Professor Hayek's thesis, the best man for the job would have been a southern American, perhaps one Negro and one White. Would they not know most intimately American attitudes on this subject?

explanation, does this imply subjectivism? Professor Hayek denies that
a physical explanation is possible, asserts that even if it were we would
still need mental categories and, therefore, we would still have to appeal
to introspection. Professor Hayek's intricate defence of these views
makes some valid and important points. Nevertheless, I do not believe
that they imply what he thinks they imply.

The 'Paradox' of Complete Explanation
Professor Hayek's belief that a complete physical explanation of
mental processes cannot be given draws upon a very useful distinction
he makes between an 'explanation of the principle' on which a process
operates and an explanation of a particular state of affairs.[12] The latter
permits precise prediction of, say, a particular price change, while the
explanation of the principle tells only the general direction that prices
will take under certain conditions. Because of the large number of
variables involved in any concrete social phenomenon, precise explanation and prediction cannot be made. Professor Hayek applies this
distinction between types of explanation to the mental processes of
classification. People often classify things similarly even when these
things have no recognizable physical properties in common. The
variety of objects or actions people call tools, money, or threatening
acts may, within each group, be physically wholly different. We
understand why different things mean the same to other people because,
according to Professor Hayek, we too in our subjective experience
classify them together. Even if a physiological explanation were found
for the *general* principle on which the mind classifies different phenomena, such an explanation of the *particular* ways external stimuli are
classified cannot be realized. To account for this impossibility, Professor
Hayek invokes a paradox or contradiction that he discovers to be
inherent in any attempt at explaining our own knowledge.

He maintains that 'if we knew how our present knowledge is conditioned or determined, it would no longer be our present knowledge.
To assert that we can explain our own knowledge is to assert that we
know more than we do know, a statement which is nonsense in the
strict meaning of that term.' The paradox prohibits us from knowledge
of 'why we hold the particular views we hold, of how our actual
knowledge is determined by specific conditions'. From this alleged
paradox, Professor Hayek infers the logical impossibility that all 'the
particular circumstances of time or place . . . of the particular, of the
fleeting circumstances of the moment and of local conditions'[13] can
ever be known except in fragmentary form, dispersed among many

[12] Pp. 42, 49, 89.
[13] Pp. 89, 98.

people. And no apparatus of classification could ever know how each particular act or thing would be classified. Therefore, Professor Hayek concludes, we would have to fall back upon our own subjective experience.

It is true that explanations of particular events are hard to come by, while we abound in generalizations, or explanations of the principle of a process. The situation in social science, however, is no different from that in physics. The physicist may know all the principles involved yet be quite at a loss to predict, say, how many leaves will blow off a tree in the next storm. The poignant difference is, of course, that in social matters, we desperately want explanation in detail, while in physical changes we are frequently indifferent. Laws in social science, if we had them, would contain many more variables than those of physics. Yet we berate the social scientist for not being able to do what even the model science cannot do. The multiplicity and complexity of factors in social phenomena impose limitations upon what we can reasonably expect to achieve. These limitations are only a practical, though perhaps practically insuperable, difficulty and we simply do the best we can.

Professor Hayek disposes in masterly fashion of the historicist's argument from uniqueness against the possibility of social science. Yet, there are overtones of the same appeal to uniqueness in his discussion of the complexity of classification by 'meaning' in contrast with classification by physical properties. Since two tools, like a can-opener and a telephone, or two crimes, like murder and income-tax evasion, have in each case no physical properties in common, Professor Hayek appears to speak as if they had nothing at all in common by virtue of which we call them both tools or both crimes. He speaks as if the meaning in each case was not itself an instance of a type and therefore classifiable. Hence, the infinite complexity that makes it impossible for our brain ever to explain completely the way it classifies particulars. Hence, the indispensability of mental categories derived from intro-spection. But meanings are no more unique than colours; or, perhaps with better analogy, no more unique than complex events like those particular historical eras which Professor Hayek correctly calls unique patterns of many nonunique elements. If we classify colours, wars, or economic structures, then we can classify meanings.

But what of Professor Hayek's 'paradox'? Professor Hayek has many telling criticisms to make of the sociologists of knowledge. But this particular one will not do. Why can we not know the causes for our beliefs? It is, of course, tautological that we cannot explain our most general hypotheses or theories. They are most general because they explain everything else while not themselves being explained. But Professor Hayek does not dispute the possibility of high-order theories.

The 'paradox', as he sees it, lies not in the derivation of one theory from another, as Newton's from Einstein's, but in the possibility of such derivation for all the particulars of time and place. Actually to achieve this, we just saw, is only a practical problem. Where is the contradiction in knowing 'why we hold the particular views we hold'? Professor Hayek seems to say that we cannot, without paradox, know the causes for our true beliefs. But such knowledge merely adds to the sum of present knowledge. It does not mean that I know more than I do know which, of course, is nonsense. As Professor Hayek himself incisively insists, the reasons why my beliefs are true may be quite independent of their causes. There is therefore no reason why one cannot know both. Professor Hayek sees paradox where none exists for reasons quite extraneous to the methods of social science.

For consider, why is he so pleased, as he is, with this allegedly necessary limitation on the scope of knowledge? If true, would it not rather be a ground for regret? That, of course, depends. Men are no longer so sanguine as once they were that the truth will make them free. For, of course, in social science, manipulating the factors may mean controlling society, controlling the variables means manipulating men. If one man or group of men knew everything that is now known only in fragments in highly dispersed form, then a master plan for society could be drawn up and put into execution. If we knew the conditions that determine our knowledge and beliefs, if we had a complete sociology of knowledge, then the human mind could be consciously controlled. As Professor Hayek says, 'Central economic planning is nothing but [the] application of engineering principles to the whole of society based on the assumption that such a complete concentration of all relevant knowledge is possible'.[14] Now, I share his horror at these future 'engineers of the soul', as he tells us the Soviet Union honorifically calls its artists. What sane and humane person does not? I share too his apprehensions about the uses to which our growing behavioural science may be put. But will self-delusion help? Professor Hayek grasps at the impossibility of knowledge as the straw to preserve us from those who would misuse it if we had it. From 'planning is dangerous' to 'planning is impossible' is a broad but familiar leap. Unfortunately, Professor Hayek's ingenious twentieth-century arguments narrow that gap no more than did Spencer's less sophisticated nineteenth-century ones.

The Implications of Reductionism
Perhaps Professor Hayek is uneasy about his derivation of the in-

[14] P. 97.

dispensability of mental categories from the logical impossibility of complete knowledge. At any rate, he explores the implications of complete reductionism, a physical explanation for each of our mental states. He concludes that even if this were both possible and accomplished we would still have to use mental concepts. The logic of his case is particularly worth examining, since, for the sake of the argument, it assumes the frame of reference of many social scientists today, namely, physiological reductionism. And there is considerable general confusion about what reductionism would mean for social science if we had it.

To play the game, then, Professor Hayek postulates complete correlation between mental and physical states. In this case he asserts

> We should thus have 'unified' science, but we should be in no better position with respect to the specific task of the social sciences than we are now. We should still have to use the old categories, though we should be able to explain their formation and though we should know the physical facts 'behind' them.[15]

Not only do I agree with Professor Hayek when he says that the problem of physiological psychology is not the problem of social science. In some sense I also agree that whether the former problem is 'solved or not, for the social sciences the given mental entities must provide the starting point, whether their formation has been explained or not'. But what kind of a 'must' is this? Under what conditions must we use mental entities? Under what conditions, if any, are they dispensable?

The point at issue is the same whether one speaks of reducing behaviour to physiology and physics or of such reduction for the contents of consciousness. Behaviourism, after all, is merely a method for getting at the latter. The issue essentially is whether, given complete reduction, the science of psychology becomes unnecessary. The notion, referred to and repudiated by Professor Hayek,[16] that we have to wait on developments in physical science before we can hope for progress in social science militates equally against the methods of behaviourism and the methods of introspection. In either case, though my reasons are not Professor Hayek's, this notion seems to me clearly mistaken.

If we had reduction of the kind Professor Hayek postulates, then the concepts of psychology would be related to but *not identified* with the concepts of physics or neurology in some specific way, just as the properties of a gas are related to but not identified with the mechanical properties of particles. And the laws of psychology become derivable from neurology, just as the laws of thermodynamics are derived from

[15] P. 49.
[16] P. 50.

mechanics. The assertion that the occurrence of a particular psychological state or disposition is always accompanied by a particular bodily state is an empirical law. This law is not derivable from laws mentioning either *only* psychological or *only* bodily states. If ϕ_1 and ϕ_2 are physiological correlates of behavioural (or mental) states ψ_1 and ψ_2 and we know the causal connection between ϕ_1 and ϕ_2, then given ϕ_1 *and* the empirical law asserting the correlation between ϕ_1 and ψ_2, we may directly predict ψ_2 without recourse to ψ_1. Thus, by means of the reduction each behavioural (or mental) concept at some time for some purposes could be dispensed with. But at no time, if we wish to know what people are doing or thinking, could we dispense with all such concepts together. If psychological concepts are never used, we should have only the physics of human nature, not its psychology. Without psychological categories we could no more assert anything about what people are thinking or doing than we could assert anything about the temperature of a gas if we used only mechanical concepts, or about what people see under certain circumstances, if we used only electromagnetic concepts and never optical ones. However, just as in the physical cases, although the concepts are not dispensable, if we knew their relation to physical facts, then in all logic we could skip the stage of finding psychological laws, that is, relationships among the psychological concepts themselves. For, given the correlation and the initial physical state, the psychological laws follow deductively from the physical ones in the manner just indicated.

Thus I too insist that to explain the mental in terms of the physical is not to explain the former *away*. Even given complete reduction, there would still be both bodies *and* minds. We would simply know the causal connection between these two kinds of things, that is, between the neurological state and the mental state. Since there are two levels, the scientist may attend to only one of them, as non-physiological psychologists do in fact. Reduction provides an explanation, not a substitute. If someone classifies a set of physical properties as 'money', then we would know the corresponding neurological state. But the individual still has an attitude towards the green paper stuff. Even with reduction, the science of psychology remains what it is. Greed is still greed, not a congeries of atoms and electrons. Psychological concepts are psychological concepts. And psychological laws are psychological laws, since they relate psychological, not physical, concepts.

Incomplete Definition and 'Subjectivity'
But a relation implies at least two terms. In order to know the relation between the physical and the psychological concepts we must therefore recognize each of these two classes. This I believe is why Professor Hayek asserts that we would still have to use the old concepts even

if we had complete reduction. And, in the sense I have just discussed, he is correct. But why does this imply subjectivity? For Professor Hayek, the subjectivity inheres in the way we recognize instances of mental concepts, like a friendly face or a threatening gesture. In kinetic theory, while temperature and its correlate, the kinetic energy of particles, are both objectively given, the mental concepts corresponding in our analogy to temperature are not objectively given. Professor Hayek's ground for this belief is, of course, also the ground for his rejection of behaviourism. The reason he adduces, however, while it does indeed point to a methodological problem is something less than compelling.

Most psychological concepts are complex, referring to a cluster of traits, dispositions, or acts. Psychological laws either correlate one such cluster with another, as in personality tests, or with environmental conditions, as in any stimulus-response situation. Hunger, fear, anger, aggression, friendliness, are typical psychological terms that may be related either to one another or to external conditions evoking them. Let me quote Professor Hayek's statement of the difficulty with these concepts.

> Probably in no single instance has experimental research yet succeeded in precisely determining the range of different phenomena which we unhesitatingly treat as meaning the same thing to us as well as to other people. . . . To say that when we speak about a man being angry we mean that he shows certain physical symptoms helps us very little unless we can exhaustively enumerate all the symptoms by which we ever recognize, and which always when they are present mean, that the man who shows them is angry. Only if we could do this would it be legitimate to say that in using this term we mean no more than *certain* physical phenomena.[17]

There are two remarks to make about this matter. *First*, every science, not psychology alone, must distinguish between (a) the empirical or operational definition of a term by which, independently of any further knowledge, we identify its referent and (b) those traits or dispositions that observation shows to be correlated with the defining characteristics. Thus, if 'Angry men grow red in the face' is not tautological, anger is defined independently of the disposition to alter complexion. And surely Professor Hayek would not wish to assert, after the manner of Hegelian holists, that we must know everything about an entity, like anger, before we can meaningfully use the term. Yet, to demand exhaustive enumeration of all the symptoms is to be bewitched by the holistic magic. Rather than indicating an inherent subjectivity, Pro-

[17] Pp. 47, 213, fn. 39.

fessor Hayek's criticism merely points up a characteristic feature of concept formation.

Secondly, in science as an on-going process, definitions of empirical concepts have what might be called 'open-ends'. If we take a still picture of a cross-section of a science at any given moment, then we may logically distinguish between definitions and laws without ambiguity. This 'horizontal' view, or logical reconstruction of science at any given stage, reveals the structure of laws and theories. It is, therefore, indispensable for understanding how and why the structure changes from one horizontal point to another. But the dialectic of concept-formation in the 'vertical' dimension, in science as it develops in time, is highly fluid. A trait or disposition found to be invariably correlated with the cluster named by the definition may well be added to the latter. Or there may even be a complete interchange between the empirical and definitional content of the concept, if this produces greater precision or ease of identification, as, for example, when a disease first defined in terms of its symptoms is later redefined as the presence of specified bacteria, while the symptoms become part of the empirical content. The less systematic the science, the more likely its definitions will be open-ended. The more highly organized the science, the more prone its definitions to closure. The presence of open-end definitions, or a resistance by the observer to terminological closure, is merely a measure of the fluidity or instability of the theoretical structure at a given time.

The application of the term 'symptom' to a *defining* characteristic or cluster of traits is itself a signal that the definition is tentative, held only until that which its referent symptomizes is uncovered. The presence of alternative definitions of the 'same' concept, as, say, of hunger in a laboratory animal or, for that matter, of electric current, signalizes the scientists' belief that something else is present of which the various definitional properties are symptoms. If and when the characteristics of this something else are uncovered, the hitherto defining traits become empirical correlates within the system. Both psychological concepts and, given reduction, the correlated physiological ones will be, from the point of view of the scientist, relatively open or closed as the case may be. This is a practical matter, signifying no inherent difference between the two levels. Professor Hayek's contention that it signifies an ineradicable subjectivity, for we must 'just know' what we mean without being able to *say* what we mean, is therefore without foundation.

Professor Hayek's arguments for the subjectivism of social science have carried us over a fairly wide range of topics. Fortunately, after combing this tangled terrain, the other two main aspects of his position may be more briefly considered.

CONCEPT FORMATION AND 'METHODOLOGICAL INDIVIDUALISM'

Professor Hayek's doctrine, it will be recalled, represents the fourth pattern in contemporary theory of the social sciences; although the psychology of the individual cannot be reduced to anything else, the behaviour of groups must be explained in terms of the behaviour of individuals. This is the 'methodological individualism' that, together with 'systematic subjectivism', Professor Hayek believes defines the unique character of social science. Objectivism, the denial of systematic subjectivism, is the first abuse of reason in social science; collectivism, the denial of methodological individualism, is the second.

I shall not linger over Professor Hayek's contention that while the method of natural science is analytic that of social science is synthetic or 'compositive'. He himself mentions the exception of astronomy, whose laws are composed from the elements, rather than by working backwards from the whole to these constituents. And elsewhere he hints that he is perhaps not wedded to the distinction. Physical science of course uses both methods, resolution or analysis, and recomposition or synthesis. Therefore, I shall just consider the claim that for social science only the synthetic method is possible, that the wholes must be constituted from their familiar component parts.

Professor Hayek carefully distinguishes between ideas which are *constitutive* of social phenomena and ideas which are *about* these phenomena, between ideas that cause and ideas that explain the social structure.[18] (The latter may, of course, also play a causal role, but the distinction still remains.) Only the motivating or constitutive opinions are data for social science. The speculative theories which people form about the whole must not be taken as data, but must be revised and replaced by more appropriate ones. According to Professor Hayek, vague popular theories are reflected in our language by macroscopic or collective terms like 'capitalism', 'society', 'imperialism' and the like. Whoever adopts such concepts treats as facts what are merely inchoate theories. For he believes that no collective term ever designates 'definite things in the sense of stable collections of sense attributes', but is always a name for a theory about the connection of the components. Apart from a true theory there is no whole, for a whole is always a nonperceptible pattern of equally nonperceptible relations. Hence, collective terms cannot themselves enter into theories as components of laws, since they are themselves theories. Who thinks other-

---

[18] Pp. 36 f.

wise, says Professor Hayek, commits the fallacy of conceptual realism or 'essentialism'.[19]

It is in fact frequently true that the more macroscopic concepts do name a poorly articulated structure of laws or a theory. But this is neither true of all collective concepts nor does it, when true, distinguish such concepts in social science from those of the physical sciences. Our conception of a physical object includes dispositional properties, like solubility, which are interesting because of low-order laws into which they enter; for example, salt is soluble. This does not preclude these concepts from entering into further laws. Nor are all the relations forming a complex whole causal, nonperceptible relations. Some patterns or relations among things are as directly given as the things themselves. Professor Hayek confuses observable relations of fact, like gives or receives, on the one hand, with what Hume called philosophical relations, like cause or effect, on the other.

This confusion reveals a curiously materialistic, almost kinesthetic, notion of fact no more appropriate to physical science than it is to social science. Group concepts like family, firm or opera can be defined in terms of empirical, non-causal relations among individuals. Professor Hayek's illustration of the 'market' as an arrangement for regular contacts between potential buyers and sellers is not itself a theory, but a name for cluster of properties and relations which may enter into a theory. Since it is such a cluster, the group concept may of course be decomposed into its elements and the relations among them. It is one thing to hold that for every name there must be a corresponding individual thing, for example, that the state is literally a superperson, or, perhaps, a person among persons. It is quite another thing to believe that such terms refer to nothing at all. Planets may be conglomerations of atoms but no one would deny reality to planets. Likewise, crowds may be groups of individuals, but there are also crowds. Universities exist just as much as professors, students, and administrators, although the university is not a separable fourth thing but a name for relations among the other three. Only one who makes such a separation hypostatizes the concept.

In sum, what is true for psychological concepts is, to a certain extent, true also for sociological or otherwise collective rather than individual concepts. Reduction of one to the other may well be possible. But if we wish to speak of group phenomena, then we *may* use macroscopic concepts to do so. The permissive 'may' in this context contrasts sharply with the obligatory 'must' for psychological concepts. The difference touches the heart of the matter. Reduction of the psychological to the physiological level means something different from reduction of collec-

[19] Pp. 55, 54.

tive to individual concepts. In the former case, 'reduction' means finding an empirical correlation between two sorts of things, mental and physical. Reduction of group concepts, on the other hand, means defining them in terms of statements about individuals and relations among them. This complex, 'microscopic', definition could be substituted for the macroscopic concept, while such substitution is not possible for psychological concepts. The difference is, I believe, the incontrovertible core of Professor Hayek's argument against 'collectivism'. Nevertheless—and this is the meaningful core of the holistic insight—since a group concept refers to a complex pattern of descriptive, empirical relations among individuals, there is no reason why the behaviour of this complex should not itself be studied. Psychological laws may be ubiquitous, but social laws may be formulated without taking them into account. Psychological laws may have mass effects, making the behaviour of institutions or crowds different from that of individuals. The behaviour of a substance subject to the laws of chemistry differs from the behaviour of its particles subject to the laws of mechanics. A crowd, a club, or a family may just as well be a unit of observation as a planet. There need be no similarity between the behaviour of a complex and the behaviour of elements of the complex. Professor Hayek points out that the unintended consequences of the actions of many men constitute the subject matter of social science. But these undesigned resultants are precisely those structures of relationships whose behaviour differs from that of individuals. All that is required for reductionism is that the complex phenomena be composed of individuals and the relations among them. The use of collective concepts does not in itself commit one to conceptual realism nor to mistaking theories about facts for facts.

Professor Hayek's analysis of the motives inspiring holistic philosophers unfortunately does not frustrate his own equally illicit transitions from the logical to the moral. Arguments for or against methodological individualism draw their strength from our criteria of the meaningful. Arguments for or against political individualism draw their strength from our moral convictions. The bridges linking these disparate issues are purely verbal, their sustaining structure wholly ideological.

EXPLANATION AND 'METHODOLOGICAL INDIVIDUALISM'

In a recent interesting and clarifying paper, influenced by Professor Hayek but less extreme and wholly free of ideological special pleading, J. W. N. Watkins lucidly elaborates a 'Principle of Methodological Individualism'. Although I basically agree with most of what Mr

Watkins says, in some respects he too rather overstates the case for
methodological individualism. Although Mr Watkins approvingly
quotes Professor Hayek on the necessity for psychological reduction
of collective concepts, he concedes that there are overt characteristics
of a complex social situation that may be empirically ascertained
without referring to people's dispositions. He asserts that 'overt characteristics may be *established* empirically, but they are only *explained*
by being shown to be the resultants of individual activities'.[20] Thus,
while permitting the use of macroscopic concepts in laws, he prohibits
their use in explanation.

Mr Watkins presents the alternatives between methodological individualism and methodological holism as those between deducing social
processes either from 'principles governing the behaviour of participating individuals' or from 'macroscopic laws which are *sui generis*
and which apply to the social system as a whole'.[21] His principle of
methodological individualism asserts, with Professor Hayek, that only
the former is permissible. I suggest, however, that this is a false disjunction. The belief that, since human beings are concerned, social
processes are mediated through psychology is indeed the frame of
reference of modern science. Mr Watkins cites a non-human social
system, a beehive, whose activities, on present knowledge, cannot be
explained in accordance with the Principle of Methodological Individualism.[22] A human situation for which the principle fails is also
conceivable. Suppose that Jones behaves in a certain way only if he is
a member of a group—in the same hall or under the same jurisdiction
—of N, say 1,000, people. Suppose further that the law expressing
Jones' behaviour in this situation is not derivable from laws concerning
his behaviour in groups of less than N together with the composition
rules based on these laws. This circumstance then exhibits empirical
emergence at a certain level of complexity, namely groups of size N, and
methodological individualism breaks down as an explanatory principle.
Though such an eventuality is rather implausible, Mr Watkins agrees
that there is nothing *a priori* about the principle; the fact that prices
and tools are human creations does not *entail* methodological individualism. But he implies that unless one holds that social groups are
organisms, that is groups whose properties cannot be derived from
those of individuals, one must repudiate macroscopic laws or theories
in favour of individualistic ones.

Mr Watkins' reference to sociological laws as 'holistic' suggests that,
despite his concession that some overt characteristics may be established empirically, he views all macroscopic concepts as suspect. How-

[20] Watkins, *op. cit.*, p. 732 [p. 153 below].
[21] *Ibid.*, p. 729 [p. 150 below].
[22] *Ibid.*, pp. 730–731 [pp. 151–152 below].

ever, my previous discussion of collective concepts implies a distinction between macroscopic and holistic concepts. 'Macroscopic', or collective, and 'microscopic', or individual, are relative terms. Social concepts are macroscopic relative to psychological ones; these in turn are macroscopic relative to physiological terms, and so on down to the level of quanta of energy. Identification of 'macroscopic' with 'holistic' obscures the fact that one can be holistic on any level. Professor Hayek, we have seen, is holistic with respect to psychological categories, since they may not be reduced to anything else. Some biologists are so with respect to physiological categories. Once chemists were holistic about their laws, because they believed them underivable from physics.

I agree with Mr Watkins that neither society nor any of its subgroups are organisms in the sense he explains. The denial that there are such organisms amounts to denying that there are *sui generis* sociological laws, that is, laws irreducibly macroscopic or sociological. But macroscopic laws may be, as I pointed out before, different from individualistic laws, yet not *sui generis* in the sense of underivable. We frequently have information, statistical or otherwise, concerning groups rather than individuals. The Keynesian hypothesis that the consumption of a community is an increasing function of its total income is, of course, about a group and not about individuals. The same is true of a great many other hypotheses in economics and other social sciences. Contemporary experimental social psychologists find that empirically defined, measurable, macroscopic concepts, making no direct reference to individuals—e.g., 'group climate' or 'cohesiveness'—permit prediction (and explanation) of group behaviour unattainable in practice, if they restrict themselves to seeking the composition rules based on the myriad complex of individual dispositions involved. Insistence upon the indispensability of reduction to the microscopic level in the search for laws and explanatory theories in social science is analogous to the insistence by some that psychologists of the abnormal refrain from using clinical concepts until their physiological correlates have been established! It is true that Keynes, for example, states certain psychological factors or propensities possibly permitting deduction of the aggregate phenomena. Yet in all the mathematical formulations of the theory by Keynesians, the functional relations are among magnitudes not identifiable with the behaviour of any individual. And at one point Watkins in effect admits that for any actual economic system the number of factors at work renders methodological individualism an impossible task.[23]

The growing interest by economists in collective rather than individualistic models is an index of their sensitivity to the tremendous

[23] Note, on p. 724, his quotation to this effect from Walter Eucken [fn. 4, p. 144 below].

difficulties in deducing group behaviour from guesses about individuals. Watkins' assertion that not only should social processes be explained by reference to individuals but that, indeed, they can *only* be so explained sounds very much like a persuasive definition of 'explanation'. Explanation in any field is not absolute, but relative to a set of premises. Drawing on one of his illustrations, an election result may be explained *either* in terms of individual dispositions *or* in terms of macroscopic laws about the history and fate of political parties in power for a given time, the relation to world crises, prosperity, and so forth. The latter alternative would be a perfectly good and even enlightening explanation, but it would be macroscopic. I suggest that elusive as even such macroscopic explanations may be, they are infinitely simpler to both formulate and test than explanations in terms of the multitude of individuals involved. Of course this is merely a guess or hunch, but it is not altogether impertinent, in either sense of that word.

What, then, of the principle of methodological individualism as a heuristic device? As a caveat against hypostatization, it is not only wholly unobjectionable but, in the light of the scientifically disreputable past of social science—its closet cluttered with 'group minds' and other suspect entities—the principle probably should be conditioned into every social scientist's consciousness or, better, his unconscious. But what of the principle as a general, everyday working rule in research and theory construction? It is doubtless true, in science as elsewhere, that a man's reach should exceed his grasp, yet it seems to me that any rule merits a jaundiced eye if it reduces a science either to impotence or to triviality. And given the admitted tremendous complexity of the social factors, I suspect that undeviating adherence to this rule would do just that.

In some instances, laws are closer at hand if the scientist sticks to the macroscopic level of the complex concept. From these laws he may construct theories. In other instances, the microscopic or psychological approach might be more fruitful; in still others, a combination of these approaches. Certainly given the still rudimentary condition of social theory, a crusade for the variable which insists that the scientist wait upon developments in psychology, or, what is worse, act on his own psychological hunches, can only cripple research by restricting it to the trivial. This is not to recommend methodological licence, only methodological liberty for the social scientist to find his laws and explanations where he may.

Ed. In response to Brodbeck's criticisms see below, J. W. N. Watkins, 'Methodological Individualism: A Reply'.

ALAN GEWIRTH

Subjectivism and Objectivism in the Social Sciences

Philosophizing about the social sciences involves an initial problem of denotation. Although the natural sciences are the scene of intramural disputes like those between proponents of quantum mechanics and relativity theory, no one doubts either what the natural sciences are or that they are sciences; and all of them may be said to use, broadly speaking, the same scientific method. But the case of the social sciences is different. It resembles somewhat the situation in mathematics where the intuitionists deny that non-constructible concepts or problems belong to mathematics; and even more the situation in philosophy where groups like the analysts and the existentialists not only do not speak the same language but do not even recognize one another's right to be called 'philosophers'. Similarly, the disciplines which comprise the social sciences today differ from one another in basic ways, involving long-standing disputes over which ones have a right to the names of the several social sciences and what their proper methods are. Familiar examples of these disputes are the controversies between the classicists and institutionalists in economics, and between the analytical and sociological schools in jurisprudence. Consequently, it is impossible for philosophers, or social scientists philosophizing about their general field, to proceed to discuss 'the' subject matter or 'the' method of 'the' social sciences as if the phrases containing these definite articles were definite descriptions on whose objects there was general agreement.

From the initial recognition of this diversity, however, philosophers of social science may proceed in one of two different ways. They may make an inductive study of the specific methods used in these various disciplines, and compare and contrast them with one another. Or—and this is the more usual course—they may begin with a general conception of scientific method taken from the natural sciences, especially physics, and use this as the criterion for selecting the aspects of the social sciences which are to be studied. This latter course usually has the result that most of what are commonly called the 'social sciences' are denied the name of science, being called merely descriptive, or merely theoretical, or merely statistical, and so on, and the discussion proceeds largely in the optative rather than the indicative mood —social science becomes largely something hoped for rather than presently possessed and analysed. Consequently, just as the former approach involves the problem of denotation whereby widely different actual disciplines go by the name of the same social science, so the latter approach involves a different though related problem of denotation whereby the potential rather than the actual state of a discipline is regarded as the proper referent of the names of each of the social sciences.

Now I am not saying that these two approaches—the specific and indicative and the generalized and optative—cannot consistently be combined in some way. Inconsistencies appear, however, when the two approaches are combined simultaneously in application to the same questions. The results of such combination take the form of two contradictions. The first may be called the *permissive-prescriptive contradiction*. On the one hand, the philosopher says that the social sciences must be left free to develop their own methods and doctrines, without the intrusion of the philosopher's own predilections. But on the other hand, the philosopher also insists that the social sciences must conform to a set of methodological and ontological requirements which he lays down—for example, they must be objectivistic, deterministic, and so on. The permissive pole of this contradiction obviously reflects the specific, indicative approach sketched above, while the prescriptive pole just as obviously reflects the generalized, optative approach. I do not think that this contradiction can be removed by distinguishing, for example, between the social scientists' ultimate frame of reference and his specific procedures within that frame, for both the insistences here described are applied to the frame of reference. The philosopher's implicit awareness of this contradiction generates a second contradiction, concerning the way in which his approach to the social sciences is to be interpreted. This may be described as the *metaphysical-scientific contradiction*. On the one hand, the philosopher, attempting to be permissive, describes as 'metaphysical' the prescriptive approach of other philosophers when they say that the method of the social sciences must be objective or subjective (as the case may be), and that the subject matter of the social sciences is or is not reducible to that of the physical sciences. But on the other hand, the same philosopher, becoming himself prescriptive, insists that the method of the social sciences must be objective and not subjective, and that the subject matter of the social sciences must be viewed as in some sense irreducible either to individuals as units or to non-psychological entities. This insistence, however, is now characterized not as 'metaphysical' or as an attempt to anticipate the results of future research but rather as emerging from a clear-eyed awareness of the requirements of scientific method and of the characteristics of the social-scientific subject matter.

How, then, should the philosopher of the social sciences proceed? None of the currently recognized conceptions of the philosopher's function or method seems to be of much help here. We cannot proceed by an appeal to ordinary language, for the question of the proper subject matter and method of the social sciences is a normative question which is not to be answered in terms of how people ordinarily use language. If we proceed in terms of an ideal language we shall tend to be prescriptive and normative; but the developers of ideal languages, like the exponents of ordinary language, seem frequently to regard their constructions as expressing and clarifying what is already known to common sense; and the philosophic problems of the social sciences are not of that kind. Carnap's theory of frameworks is somewhat more helpful here; for in so far as he conceives philosophy as being concerned with external questions of the existence of frameworks, he recognizes that philosophy deals with alternative formulations on issues which are basic to science in the sense that, while they cannot themselves be settled by scientific or empirical evidence, they nevertheless determine how we are to interpret science. The philosophy of the social sciences is concerned with such basic issues. But Carnap tends to hold that because such issues cannot, *ex hypothesi*, be settled by scientific or empirical evidence, they therefore involve merely the choice of one language as against another;[1] so that here he is one with the other two linguistic schools just considered. Now I too think that some at least of the issues in the philosophy of the social sciences are purely linguistic. But others are not; and on the method of resolving them most of the current conceptions of philosophy offer no guidance. The reason for this is that such issues are normative; they involve the questions of the proper method and subject matter of a science; and most of current philosophy is still unable to deal with normative questions in a satisfactory way, except in so far as they are reducible to recognized canons of deductive and inductive logic. The whole contemporary development of philosophy in terms of meta-languages, with such of its recent applications as meta-ethics, seems to suffer from a similar disability in this regard. For such meta-linguistic devices seem to confine themselves to analysing the meanings of linguistic formulations which they take as given, whereas the problems in the philosophy of the social and other sciences include also the questions of what *should* be given—for example, by what methods should social research proceed.

Where angels such as these fear to tread, it would be foolhardy to rush in with a claim to have a complete solution. I should like, however,

[1] R. Carnap, 'Empiricism, Semantics, and Ontology', *Revue Internationale de Philosophie*, IV, 1950, pp. 23 ff.

to suggest what seem to me to be three minimal aspects of the method to be used by philosophers in dealing with such normative problems of the social sciences. In the first place, as already mentioned, purely linguistic problems, which turn on different ways of formulating the same point, should be separated from those which are non-linguistic. In the second place, each science, or each pretender to the name of a science, should be studied in its own terms, and one should be wary of the claim to apply the same method in precisely the same way to all sciences. In the third place, when alternative interpretations of the subject matter and method of a science are set forth, and the issue among these alternatives cannot be decided in either of the first two ways, it seems to me that some such conception as Dewey's doctrine of the continuum of inquiry furnishes at least the basis for a satisfactory criterion of decision. We may put this criterion negatively as follows: If an interpretation of subject matter or method is such as to make continued inquiry fruitless or impossible, then it is not to be accepted. The various recent formulations of criteria of meaning—empiricist, pragmatic, operationalist, and so on—are examples of attempts at such criteria of decision. Where they fall short is precisely where they are interpreted in such a rigid way as to block further inquiry. A familiar example of this in the social sciences is found where both the presence and the absence of quantitative statistical data are variously regarded as the indispensable hallmarks of science.

In the remainder of this paper I shall attempt to apply this approach to the problem of the cleavage between so-called 'subjectivist' and 'objectivist' approaches to social science.

Stated most simply, the subjectivist-objectivist controversy involves two questions: First, are the facts or subject matters dealt with by the social sciences subjective or objective? Second, is the method of obtaining knowledge of these facts subjective or objective?

It is at once apparent that, as thus formulated, the questions are very vague. When they are subjected to analysis, it turns out that while some of the issues they involve are important, most of them are not. This is because, depending on how the terms 'subjective' and 'objective' are understood, any one of three answers to the general questions is admissible: the subject matter and methods of the social sciences are *both* subjective and objective, they are *neither* subjective nor objective, and they are *either* subjective or objective. The reason why any one of these three answers is admissible is that the 'subjective-objective' dualism has variously been interpreted in the dispute as having the meaning of such other dualisms as phenomenalist-realist, idealist-materialist, introspectionist-behaviourist, rationalist-empiricist, deductive-inductive, theoretical-statistical, and so on. If, now, the subjectivist-objectivist dispute is over whether the subject matter of the social sciences consists in mental ideas or material institutions, and is to be known by methods which are introspectionist or behaviourist, deductive or inductive, involving theory or data, then my answer is that obviously *both* poles are needed. If, on the other hand, the two sides of the dispute respectively contend that one pole alone is sufficient, then just as obviously *neither* side is right. And if, finally, the dispute is like the phenomenalist-realist controversy, in that the subjectivists claim that only a phenomenalist interpretation of social science facts and methods is admissible while the objectivists make the same claim for a realist interpretation, then my answer is that this is merely a dispute over the choice of a language, and *either* side is right, although not both at the same time.

We might dismiss the whole question right here, were it not for the exclusivist claims made on each side. Let us therefore deal more specifically with some of the issues raised. And first as to the *subject matter* of the social sciences. The subjectivist-objectivist issue is here frequently put in the following way: do the facts of the social sciences consist solely in how things *appear* to men, or do they also include how things *really* are? This seems like the old appearance-reality debate, and therefore, if due precautions are taken, it can be answered in either way. If it is said that the facts of the social sciences are only what men believe they are, or how things appear to men, this is perfectly acceptable if we stipulate that the men in question must include the social scientists, and that provision must therefore be made for distinguishing between varying degrees of adequacy of belief, and for future as well as present beliefs. This was pointed out as long ago as Plato.[2] On the other hand, if such degrees of adequacy and references to future beliefs are excluded, then we get the obviously absurd result, as Plato also pointed out, that the lunatic's and the dreamer's beliefs must be taken not only as data but also as conclusions beyond which our social science cannot go. But this of course makes impossible the distinction between knowledge and opinion, including the distinction between social science and ignorance, and puts a prompt stoppage to our science and inquiry. Hence it is unacceptable.

On the other hand, it is also possible to view the subject matter of the social sciences in terms of a dual language of appearance and reality. Here we would distinguish between what men think is the case and what really is the case, such as the contrast between my subjective belief that I can afford a Cadillac and the objective fact that I cannot.[3]

[2] Plato, *Theaetectus*, 171D–172B, 178A–179C.

[3] For a fuller treatment of this point as applied to political science, cf. my paper, 'The Psychological Approach to Politics', *Ethics*, LIX, 1949, pp. 211–220.

But it seems to me that the difference between putting it in this way and in the former, purely phenomenalist way is merely one of language. For, as any amateur epistemologist would be quick to point out, what I call the objective fact that I cannot afford a Cadillac can be an item of knowledge only through someone's consulting such things as my income and my bank account—and such consultation comes down ultimately to the beliefs of the consultants about the documents they see and the inferences they draw therefrom.

In the light of this purely linguistic character of the dispute as so far considered, how are we to view the relation between the subject matters of the social and the natural sciences? Subjectivists sometimes seem to hold that there is an absolute contrast between these on the ground that the facts of the natural sciences are hard objects out there like rocks and trees while the facts of the social sciences, like dollar bills and national flags, depend uniquely on the subjective or symbolic interpretations of human beings in certain social contexts. I think that this view is unobjectionable in so far as it emphasizes the unique dependence of social phenomena on the existence, habits, and institutions of human beings, as against the independent existence of natural objects. In this case, it will be noted, we use a 'realist' language for both social and natural entities. But there are two correlative ways in which this contrast can be mitigated. In the first place, if we view natural entities in the context of the natural sciences or of knowledge in general, then they involve an important 'subjective' element. For example, to view a thing as a rock is to make a certain kind of interpretation and classification of an entity, which depends not only on what is out there but also on our categorization of it. Consequently the distinction between the objectivity of natural facts and the subjectivity of social ones cannot consist in the difference between completely uninterpreted or unsymbolized entities and entities involving human interpretation or symbolization. In the second place, social entities like national flags and dollar bills are not so subjective but that there are objective consequences of acting in respect of them. If I attempt to pass a piece of paper which I subjectively view as a dollar bill but which lacks certain physical properties, my act will probably have certain objective consequences. Hence, while social facts do involve certain kinds of interpretation which we can, if we like, call 'subjective', that interpretation must be as intersubjectively confirmable as the interpretations we attach to natural objects if the thing in question is really to be a social fact and not a mere delusion.

Let us turn now to the subjective-objective issue as to the *methods* of the social sciences. Here the issue, although still vague, has a more recognizable relation to options with which social scientists consider themselves to be actually faced. The chief issue is between the advocates of the so-called *verstehen*, consisting primarily in some sort of intro-spection, and the advocates of behaviourism. Now it is admitted, to begin with, that there are two kinds of events which figure in some way in social science research—on the one hand, overt acts to which the behaviourists appeal, and on the other hand the implicit acts, thoughts and feelings, to which the introspectionists appeal. The issue is whether both of these are to be admitted as data. The chief behaviourist argument against the latter is of course that of intersubjective con-firmability. The chief introspectionist argument is that the overt acts fail to reveal all the wealth of nuance involved in social phenomena like loyalty, desire for prestige, and so on, which constitute the beliefs and attitudes distinguishing social objects from natural ones.

The introspectionists sometimes go on, however, to argue that the acts of other men can be understood only through the investigator's introspective awareness that these acts emerge from the same feelings he experiences in himself. It is at this point that the behaviourists make their familiar rejoinder in the form of the rhetorical question: 'Must I experience Hitler's rages in order to understand Hitler?' On this question, however, two considerations are relevant.

In the first place, the question must obviously be answered in the negative if by 'rage' is meant the external manifestations and their antecedents and consequents. But on the other hand, who will say that a man who has never to some degree experienced rage in himself can know what is meant by 'rage' as an internal phenomenon, as against its external manifestations? The major premiss of this query is not that like knows like—for it is not being said that a man must himself be enraged at the very time that he is studying rage—but rather that, since I cannot experience your rage, the only way in which I can know what your rage is phenomenally—i.e., how it is experienced by you—is by my recalling how my own rage felt to me. It seems to me that this can be denied only by those who deny that we can have any knowledge whatsoever of how men's feelings feel to them. But such phenomena as sympathy would seem to refute this denial.

In the second place, there is a difference between attributing to another person an emotion one actually feels in oneself, or actually reduplicating in oneself the emotion one attributes to another, and having the ability to imagine all the wealth of subjective experiences which may underlie and cause overt action. Even if we insist that only what is objectively ascertainable can be data for social science—and I think that the motivation of this insistence deserves respect—the fact remains that the investigator's subjective experience of his own feelings and thoughts can play an important part in his devising and expanding the kinds of objective behaviouristic tests which enable him to obtain what he recognizes as his data. In a recent discussion of social research, a social scientist writes as follows: 'never . . . have we had, on such a large scale, such brilliant and brilliantly-validated use of "diagnostic" questions arranged in scales to test underlying attitudes, nor such grasp of nuances of verbal expression as clues to character. . . .'[4] Here the answers to the test questions and the observed nuances of verbal expression may be said to be behaviouristic and objective; but what led to the recognition that the underlying attitudes and the nuances were there to be looked for was in good part not itself behaviouristic but rather a result of the investigator's sensitive awareness of the introspective acts of which the overt ones were signs, deriving in part at least from his own inner experience, including experiments in imagination. It is the lack of such awarenesses as stimuli to research that has led too many social scientists to think that the only way in which they can be objective and scientific is to count plumbing fixtures and television sets. This kind of objectivism has operated as a block to social inquiry.

[4] D. Riesman, 'Some Observations on Social Science Research', *Antioch Review*, Fall, 1951, p. 271.

RICHARD S. RUDNER

Philosophy and Social Science

I wish, for the sake of the vivacity of any discussion which might ensue, that I could find myself more in disagreement with Dr Brodbeck than I do. As a matter of fact, however, I find myself in substantial agreement with her on practically all of the points upon which she takes issue with Hayek. There are, to be sure, a few questions of relatively minor import that I should like to ask Dr Brodbeck, but in the main I have confined my own discussion to an elaboration and supplementation of some of the points considered in her paper, and some related considerations raised in Hayek's book but which Dr Brodbeck did not have the time, perhaps, to treat.

Hayek argues[1] that the social and non-social sciences are essentially different. He attacks a view which he labels 'scientism'. Sometimes he seems to construe his opponents as being correct in their notions concerning the methodology of the *non-social* sciences, sometimes as being incorrect in this area too. But there is no doubt about his feeling that those who take the scientistic view with regard to *social* science are perniciously mistaken. It is certainly safe to say that Hayek is claiming a radical distinction to obtain between the social and the non-social sciences but it is not always so clear that the distinction to which Hayek's important arguments apply is a distinction in *methodology*.

It is, of course, possible to distinguish the social from the non-social sciences on, e.g., the basis of their respective results or on the basis of efficacious attitudes which the respective groups of scientists may have, as well as on the basis of differences in methodology; and I think it will help illuminate the actual import of some of Hayek's arguments if we keep these possibilities in mind.

I think that Dr Brodbeck's division of Hayek's thesis, concerning the radical distinction between social and non-social sciences, into arguments that 'systematic subjectivism' and arguments that 'methodological individualism' uniquely characterize social science is a helpful one; and my remarks will be directed primarily to the first of these arguments.

---

[1] F. A. Hayek, *The Counter-Revolution of Science: studies on the abuse of reason*, Glencoe, Illinois, The Free Press, 1952.

Dr Brodbeck points out that Hayek has three reasons for believing that social science is irremediably subjective; first, 'its subject matter is human opinions and attitudes'; second, 'this subject matter can be adequately known only by . . . introspection'; third, 'mental categories are indispensable in explanation of social phenomena'.

Suppose we begin by considering the first of these. Hayek argues that the sole concern of social science is people's opinions, beliefs and attitudes. Dr Brodbeck replies that the social scientist is not only interested in these but in certain relationships which obtain between what, e.g., an individual may believe and what is actually the case.

This does not appear to be a wholly satisfactory reply because Hayek may be construing 'social science' so narrowly as to have the term apply only to those areas or parts of areas in which (as in certain aspects of public opinion and attitude research) our interest *is* just what are the opinions and attitudes of a set of individuals.

But even if we agree with Hayek (as indeed we must) that 'social science' *thus* construed is solely concerned with subjective phenomena, this does *not* demonstrate the subjectivity of social science. If Social Science is subjective because its subject matter is, then by the same argument Ornithology would have to be considered a bird-like science and Archaeology an archaic one. At most, what such considerations seem to show is that the *results* of social science thus construed are distinguishable from the results of any other science. This is hardly a unique property of social science.

The second of Hayek's reasons for holding social science to be subjective appears to have more *prima facie* relevance to the issue of the cogency of a methodological distinction.

Hayek maintains that introspection is an indispensable resource of the social scientist because *the only way in which we can come to understand* other minds is by assuming that they work like ours and examining our own—since these are the only accessible ones. Now an immense amount of refutational literature exists relevant to this thesis; but I suppose it is a perennial duty of philosophers to consider the thesis anew whenever anyone reputable or interesting brings it up. Dr Brodbeck points out that one absurdity of this position is that Genghis Khan or Hitler could be 'tackled' only by a war-like historian. But the crucial point of her reply seems to be that Hayek in some sense proves too much; for (she maintains) if his arguments were correct we would already know everything about human psychology and hence *that* science would be unnecessary.

Now, I think Dr Brodbeck's reply is an impressive one, nevertheless I do not find it decisive against the challenge Hayek raises. First, with respect to the counter-example of the historian, it seems to me Hayek could accept the consequences of the alleged absurdity and still unruffledly maintain that it was quite sensible to hold that *ceteris paribus* war-like historians *are* best equipped to 'tackle' war-like historial figures; that to assume this as absurd is to beg the question. Moreover, with respect to Dr Brodbeck's main point here, I do not think it follows from the indispensability of introspection for psychology as a science, that all of that introspection has already taken place. The claim that a certain condition is a necessary one does not imply that that condition has been instituted, and it seems to me that Dr Brodbeck is making just such an inference when she claims that a consequence of Hayek's stand is that human psychology is already known to us. Hayek I think would insist that much pertinent introspection (hence much of psychology) still remains to be done.

Dr Brodbeck in one place also seems to argue that if social science were based on introspection its results wouldn't be surprising—and since they obviously sometimes are, it is unlikely that they are so based. But there is no reason why the results of introspection should not be as surprising as the results of what we ordinarily take to be the method of scientific inquiry. Some of my own introspection leaves me not only surprised—but appalled.

Despite these remarks, however, I would contend with Dr Brodbeck that Hayek is wrong in asserting that introspection is necessary for social science, even narrowly construed. For Hayek to establish his point concerning the *methodological* subjectivity of the social sciences he would have to prove more than the indispensability of introspection as an associated activity; for introspection might well be a necessary activity for social scientists *vis-à-vis* what Reichenbach calls 'the context of discovery' without being methodologically necessary. I am assuming, of course, that considerations of method apply to the context of justification. Hence, even if we were to grant the indispensability of introspection, and, in fact, even if we granted (the more dubious assumption) that this indispensability uniquely characterized the activities of social scientists, we might be granting merely the heuristic necessity of introspection in social science and Hayek would still not have established his point that social science is methodologically distinguished from non-social science. For Hayek to establish his point he would (at least) have to present an example in which introspection serves more than a heuristic function. I do not find that any of the examples he gives does this.

Indeed, if Hayek *is* making a serious proposal then are we not confronted by our old friend the method of intuition. Hayek does not even come to grips with Peirce's invincible arguments (for so they seem to me) against the adequacy of intuition as the method of science, let alone conquer those arguments.

Perhaps, however, Hayek may be construed as accepting Peirce's arguments and hence holding the thesis that the admittedly unsatisfactory method of intuition is the only one open to the social scientist. If this is the case then he must prove that what we ordinarily call the method of science is not a viable method for social research. It seems to me he makes his strongest bid to accomplish this in connection with the third of his reasons for contending that social science is irremediably subjective. This reason, it will be remembered was constituted by the alleged fact that 'mental' concepts were indispensable for explanation in social science.

There is much that is obscure in Hayek's discussion of this contention. We are given no definitive statement of what constitutes a 'mental' concept, but Hayek does give a number of interesting examples that lead me to believe that his intentions might be illuminated if we examine them in the light of a convenient framework which in its present form is due to C. W. Churchman and R. L. Ackoff.[2] Churchman and Ackoff distinguish among a number of ways of classifying activities. I over-simplify, but substantially the following are three of the ways they distinguish: first, a set of objects is said to belong to the same *physical* class if they share a specified physical property (e.g., the set of things which has a temperature of 72° F.); second, a set of things would be said to belong to the same morphological class if they share a set of properties within a specified range (e.g., everything which has a temperature of between 70° and 80° F.); a set of things are said to belong to the same functional class if they share a common teleological property (e.g., a watch, a sundial, a piece of radium, and a water clock all belong to the same functional class for they all serve a common end).

Now, what Hayek seems to be saying is that social science explanation must include mental concepts in the sense of the functional concepts outlined above. Social science studies purposeful behaviour, purposeful behaviour entails functional classification and hence (he appears to maintain) explanations of it must include functional concepts. We can, Hayek asserts, look at a set of disparate objects from now to doomsday but unless we take into account that they are related to a set of individuals by virtue of the fact that the individuals are classifying them functionally, and that they are hence in interesting social science relationships to those individuals, we are missing something essential.

Now, even if we grant the truth of this assertion it is difficult to see how Hayek can thereby establish the point of methodological uniqueness for social science. One can see how, on the basis of the assertion, Hayek might argue that we would *probably* not discover men classified

---

[2] C. W. Churchman and R. L. Ackoff, *Psychologistics* (mimeographed), Philadelphia: University of Pennsylvania, 1946.

functionally unless we had introspected. This, however, is a phenomenon of the context of discovery. Moreover, if the statement that men
characteristically classify functionally were true, explanations and
predictions in social science might well *mention* functional (i.e., mental)
concepts, but they would not therefore necessarily be *using* mental
concepts any more than explanations of radioactive objects would
necessarily be using radioactive concepts.

Finally, even if explanations in social science *used* (rather than
mentioned) these 'subjective' concepts, social science would be no more
subjective than, say, physics; and I am thinking in particular of
relativity theory. The fact is that any science might make a functional
classification of its concepts or of its phenomena whenever this proves
fruitful; such a procedure, however, is dictated by *pragmatic considerations* and not by the peculiar necessity to functionally classify functional
concepts as Hayek appears to argue.

Dr Brodbeck construes Hayek's argument as being to the effect that
we cannot classify 'by [such mental entities as] meanings'. And her
reply is that meanings or functional criteria are as much instances of
types and hence as much classifiable as physical entities. It seems to
me, however, that Hayek's position is not so much that meanings and
the like are unclassifiable—or even that we can't classify 'by meanings'
(whatever that might mean)—as it is that we always need meanings or
something equally 'mental' when we explain or predict in social science.
Moreover his position is that this assertion follows from the assumption
(which we've granted for the sake of argument) that social science
studies subjective phenomena. Such a position could only be assailed
by showing, as has been attempted above, that the assertion does not
follow from the assumption.

Hayek's first major thesis is that the social sciences are characterized
by systematic subjectivism. I have endeavoured to supplement and
elaborate Dr Brodbeck's arguments against that thesis by pointing out
that Hayek doesn't prove his case. His second contention is that the
social sciences are also uniquely characterized by 'methodological
individualism'. The behaviour of groups is held to be explainable only
in terms of individuals. Here, I think Dr Brodbeck's reply *is* decisive
and requires no supplementation. Her argument in brief, is that the
possibility of *reduction* when this process is properly clarified does not
entail the *eliminability* of macro-concepts.

I am, however, somewhat puzzled about one aspect of Dr Brodbeck's
discussion. Some of her remarks suggest that though she disagrees with
Hayek concerning what follows from the statement, she nevertheless
does accept the dictum that group phenomena *are* always reducible to

individual phenomena—at least in the refined sense *she* has explicated.

If indeed this is the import of some of her remarks, then I think she makes an erroneous concession to what (considering the methodological portentiousness of quantum physics) must in these days be called a foolish conceit on the part of Hayek. Surely one should no longer insist that designata for ensembles *must* be reducible in the theoretical structure of any science in the light of the fruitfulness of quantum theory. We must hold open the *possibility* of a similar revolution in social science even while we guard against evils of hypostatization as Dr Brodbeck warns. To close the door, however, once and for all by adopting individualism as a sacred methodological precept is to do precisely what Dr Brodbeck inveighed against earlier: settle *a priori* a matter which must await a great deal of further scientific research.

ALAN GEWIRTH

Can Men Change Laws of Social Science ?

Some Preliminary Distinctions
The relation between the natural and the social sciences, as it bears on their respective subject matters, methods, and propositions, has long been a source of problems for the philosophy of science. The title of this paper is intended to indicate one of the most basic of these problems. Before developing my point, however, I wish to guard against a possible misinterpretation. I am not questioning the accepted fact that as knowledge in any field advances men may come to recognize the incorrectness of what they had previously regarded as 'laws' in that field, and may consequently 'change' these laws to take account of such increased knowledge. Let me call this kind of change of laws *doctrinal change*. The kind of change about which I am asking is rather a change in the subject matter itself in so far as it is subject to laws—i.e., a change in the causal relations among the facts, objects, properties, events, or whatever they may be called, with which the science deals. Let me call this kind of change of laws *factual change*. Now, without inquiring more fully at the moment into the nature of scientific laws as such, we may say that the history of science shows that men can and do effect doctrinal changes in the laws of any science, natural as well as social, and formal as well as empirical. And it is recognized also, with minor exceptions to be noted later, that men cannot effect factual changes in the laws of the natural sciences, since these are independent of human volition or decision. The question I am asking, then, is whether men can effect factual changes in the laws of the social sciences.

One further terminological point by way of preliminary. Since we have distinguished two kinds of changes in scientific laws, we may likewise distinguish two different kinds or aspects of the laws themselves. 'Law' is obviously a double-barrelled word; entirely apart from the ambiguities introduced by treating scientific laws as if they were political laws (of which more later), the term 'law' may refer either to the cause-effect relations which actually obtain in the world, or to men's attempted knowledge and formulation of such relations. Let us, in keeping with our previous distinction, call the former *factual laws* and the latter *doctrinal laws*. Now for the most part I shall be dealing in this paper with men's factual change of factual laws of social science; and in this sense I shall use the terms 'natural laws' and 'social laws' as abbreviations for 'the laws of the natural and the social sciences', respectively. Nevertheless, I wish to retain the title of this paper in its present form, for at least two reasons: (a) one of my main aims is to compare the degree of necessity or probability attainable in the natural and the social sciences; (b) I shall be wanting to refer to both natural and social laws in terms of the kinds of selectivity or discrimination involved in the scientific formulation of laws. This aspect, it is to be noted, is different from the aspect involving increased knowledge which led us to distinguish doctrinal from factual changes in scientific laws.

Social Laws and Men's Reactions on Them

Now the general position I wish to present is the following. In dealing with social phenomena, social science deals largely if not entirely with things which impinge directly on men's values—wealth, power, various kinds of interpersonal relations, and so on. The aim of social science may be said to be to attain knowledge of the laws of these matters— that is, of their cause-effect relations. Since, however, man as conscious voluntary agent is in large part both the knower and the subject matter of these laws, his knowledge of their impact on his values may lead him to react on the laws reflexively in order to change them. Consequently, the laws of the social sciences cannot have the same fixity or permanence as the laws of the natural sciences.

This reflexive reaction of men on social laws has interesting logical as well as social consequences. One of its familiar aspects is found in such reflexive situations as the 'self-destroying prophecy'';[1] for example, if there is wide acceptance of a prediction that because of its superior wealth a nation will win a war in which it is presently engaged, this may lead to a complacency which results in losing the war. Here men's knowledge of a social 'law'—the correlation, other things being equal, between superior wealth and military success—leads to action which removes the effective operation of the law.[2] Similar to this is the 'self-

---

[1] Merton's interpretation of this concept and of the 'self-fulfilling prophecy', however, is more restrictive than that which is presented here. [R. K. Merton, *Social Theory and Social Structure*, Glencoe, Illinois, 1949, pp. 121–122; 197 ff.]

[2] The self-destroying prophecy may be symbolized in either of the following two ways:

(1) $$(\exists x)\ (Px[A \rightarrow C]) \rightarrow \{(\exists y)\ (=Ay \rightarrow (\exists z)\ (=Cz)\}.$$

'If there is a prediction P that a certain kind of action A will result in a certain consequence C, then this prediction has the result that the contrary [symbolized by the two negations placed one under the other] of action A occurs and that it results in the occurrence of the contary of consequence C.'

(2) $$(\exists x)\ (Px[A^1 \rightarrow C]) \rightarrow \{[(\exists y)\ (A^1 y)\cdot(\exists z)\ (A^2 z)] \rightarrow (\exists w)\ (=Cw)\}.$$

'If there is a prediction P that a certain kind of action A^1 will result in a certain fulfilling prophecy'; for example, the Keynesian economists' predictions that if certain policies are followed there will be no depression have resulted in demands for various kinds of governmental regulation and direct governmental concern with the prevention of depression. Here men's knowledge of a prediction based on social knowledge leads to action aimed at fulfilling the prediction.[3] Both these kinds of prophecy may be viewed as forms of 'pragmatic implication', but in a more dynamic sense than is usually found in discussions of the relation between linguistic expressions and the users of those expressions. These modes of the influence of knowledge of social laws or propositions on their empirical effectuation must be sharply differentiated from Heisenberg's principle of indeterminacy according to which the attempt to observe an electron changes the characteristics of the electron. For an electron, unlike a social group, does not change its characteristics because of its own knowledge of those characteristics as disclosed by the observation of it.

A further consequence of this social reflexivity is that while at any given stage we may distinguish the linguistic discourse of a social group from the discourse of the social scientists studying that group, calling the latter 'meta-linguistic' in relation to the former, this distinction collapses when the users of the primary discourse become aware of the meta-linguistic discourse and use it to change their own discourse. As a familiar case in point I may cite the fact that the discourse of sociologists and social psychologists concerning the effects of the use of pejorative expressions to refer to various ethnic groups has led in many cases to the disuse of those expressions—i.e., to a change in the primary language about which the sociologists were talking.

This reflexive characteristic of social laws, and the consequent contrast which I have drawn between them and natural laws in respect of fixity or permanence, involve many complex problems. The situation is by no means so simple as my discussion of it so far may have suggested. To unravel some of its complexities, let us consider two basic arguments against the position here presented. I shall call them 'the argument from the pervasiveness of laws' and 'the argument from the social determination of knowledge and action'.

---

consequence C, then this prediction has the result that action A^1 and also other action A^2 occur, and that these actions have the result that the contrary of consequence C occurs.'

[3] The self-fulfilling prophecy may be symbolized as follows:

$$(\exists x) \ (Px[A \to C]) \to \{(\exists y) \ (Ay) \to (\exists z) \ (Cz)\}.$$

'If there is a prediction P that a certain kind of action A will result in a certain consequence C, then this prediction has the result that action A does occur and that it does result in the occurrence of consequence C.'

The Argument from the Pervasiveness of Laws

Let us agree that every social law, like natural laws, aims to state a correlation of selected and discriminated kinds of entity, and that it states this correlation, moreover, with the implicit or explicit recognition of the conditions under which the correlation holds. On this view, social laws are different both from so-called laws of history concerning the developmental relations among whole civilizations or historical epochs, and from inductive generalizations stated without recognition of qualifying conditions. Let us take as an example the following simplified version of an anthropological 'law': 'All matrilineal and patrilocal societies tend to develop certain kinds of stresses within their family units', where 'matrilineal' means that the wealth is inherited through the females and 'patrilocal' means that the married offspring live in or near the home of the husband's parents. Let us call this *Law A*; and let us assume that the specific characteristics of the stresses which I have vaguely called 'certain kinds of stresses' have been made explicit enough to be objectively measurable: they may include, for example, a certain rate of desertions by the fathers, a certain proportion of quarrels resulting in legal or some similar kind of action, and so on. But now suppose further that all or many of the members of such a society become aware of this law, and realize therefore the cause of the stresses in their society. Obviously they may react in many different ways. Let us assume that one way in which they react is to change from a matrilineal to a patrilineal system. Now this does not of course invalidate Law A, any more than the traditional laws of supply and demand are invalidated by a change from a competitive economy, in which those laws hold, to a monopolistic economy, in which they do not. Rather, what has happened is that the conditions of Law A no longer exist, and instead there is a new set of conditions. But this new set has its own law, such as, for example, that 'A patrilineal and patrilocal society will not tend to develop stresses of the kind generated when the society is matrilineal'. Let us call this *Law B*. The argument from the pervasiveness of laws, then, asserts that men cannot change social laws, but can only exchange the conditions of one law for those of another; and that for each set of conditions there are laws, i.e., relatively constant correlations, which exist among the different characteristics of men's social acts and institutions.

In addition to this exchange of conditions, there are two other ways in which the argument from the pervasiveness of laws asserts that men's intervention does not change social laws. One way is by specification the other by generalization. Let us take Law A again, and let us suppose that the society reacts to its knowledge of this law not by changing from a matrilineal to a patrilineal society but rather by instituting special symbols of respect for the fathers. And let us assume that this experiment works: the society remains matrilineal and patri-local, but the addition of the special symbols of respect is followed by a sharp diminution and ultimately a cessation of the kinds of stresses previously experienced. Has this development invalidated Law A? Obviously not; instead we now have *Law C*: 'A matrilineal and patri-local society in which there are special symbols of respect for the father will not tend to develop stresses of the kind generated when there are not such symbols.' Here, as in Law B, we have exchanged one set of conditions for another, but this new set is related to the old set not as contraries but rather as specific to general, since we have added a new determinant. But this in turn means that Law A must now be stated with a corresponding specifying condition: 'A matrilineal and patrilocal society *in which there are no special symbols of respect for the father* will tend to develop stresses within its family units.' In this way men's intervention through their knowledge of Law A does not change that law but rather leads to a knowledge of one of its specifying conditions.

The other way in which the argument from the pervasiveness of laws makes its point is by generalization. Suppose that, imbued with the cultural relativism of which anthropologists have made so much, we conduct sufficient empirical research to find some societies which are matrilineal and patrilocal and yet develop no stresses of the kinds asserted in Law A. Here, obviously, we would look for the conditions which differentiate the two kinds of society; let us assume that a social myth of maternal divinity is found among the societies which do not develop the kinds of stresses in question, and is not found among the societies that do. This, then, could lead to a specification of Law A, as above in Law C. But in addition it could lead us to look for the more general law or rule governing the occurrence of stresses in all societies, both matrilineal and patrilineal. Such a general law might be, for example, that 'All societies in which authority and prestige are separated from responsibility tend to develop internal frictions'. Let us call this *Law D*. Such a law would not be changed by human inter-vention, for both its conditions and its terms would be general enough to subsume the specific kinds of changes which men's intervention might bring about. This generalizing technique is similar to that used by proponents of 'natural laws' and 'natural rights' in the ethical and political senses when they wish to show that such laws and rights are not invalidated by apparent exceptions.

Nor is this all. For the argument from the pervasiveness of laws goes on to point out that all three ways of answering the assertion that men's intervention can change social laws apply to the laws of the natural as well as the social sciences. Of specification and generalization this is too obviously the case to require discussion. But it also applies to the first way, that of the exchange of conditions. An invention like the elevator or the aeroplane does not invalidate Galileo's law of falling bodies, but rather embodies the results of conditions different from the free fall in a perfect vacuum which is the condition of Galileo's law. And man can at least to some extent control these conditions, just as he can control the conditions which will determine whether one social law empirically obtains or another. Hence, just as inventions like the aeroplane involve not the disproof but rather the application of physical laws through men's intervention, so too with men's intervention in relation to social laws.

Another Statement of the Argument

The points which have been made so far may also be put in another way as follows. In the case of any factual law, natural or social, we may distinguish two different aspects, which may be called the *conditional* and the *existential*. The *conditional* aspect consists in the law viewed as a hypothetical correlation of variables, of the form: *if x, then y*; where '*x*' represents certain conditions and '*y*' represents what occurs when those conditions occur. As the discussion of counterfactual conditionals has made clear, such conditional laws may be true even when the antecedent is false, i.e., does not actually obtain; and the reason for such truth is different from that found in the comparatively trivial case of material implication. Examples of such conditional antecedents are the unhindered operation of gravity in the natural sphere, and the operation of supply and demand in the social sphere. The *existential* aspect of factual laws, on the other hand, consists in the conditions and correlations which actually obtain at any given time. In their existential aspect, then, factual laws are true only when their antecedent conditions are true.[4] Now the argument from the pervasiveness of laws holds that natural and social laws, so far as their being changed by men is concerned, are similar in both their conditional and their existential aspects: in their conditional aspect neither kind of law can be factually changed by men, and in their existential aspect both kinds can be factually changed by men, since men can control the conditions which result in the actual occurrence or operation of one correlation as against another. For example, if we take Newton's law of gravitation and the economic laws of supply and demand in their conditional aspect, then these laws are eternally true in the sense that each sets forth a correlation of variables which remains true regardless

---

[4] This distinction between the conditional and existential aspects of laws is not the same as Dewey's distinction between 'universal' and 'generic' propositions (John Dewey, *Logic*, The Theory of Inquiry, New York, 1938, pp. 264 ff.). As here viewed, a law in its conditional aspect does not 'present the analysis of a conception into its integral and exhaustive contents' (*ibid.*, p. 272).

of what men may do. And if we take these laws in their existential aspect, then each can be changed by men in that men can bring it about that the conditions which function as antecedents in these laws do not actually obtain (e.g., the aeroplane removes the free operation of gravity, and monopoly removes the free operation of the market). Moreover, this argument from the pervasiveness of laws goes on to hold that in so far as there is a difference at all between natural and social laws in respect of their being changed by men, this difference is at most one of degree only, not of kind, and is to be found only in the existential aspect of laws. For since men can effect fewer changes in their natural than in their social environment, it follows that among the laws which actually obtain natural ones reflect human operational changes to a lesser degree than do social laws. But this does not alter the fact that in principle both kinds of laws bear the same relation to human change.

Reply to the Argument
It is now time to see whether these considerations completely negate our initial assertion that man's knowledge of social laws may lead him to change these laws, and that consequently they cannot have the same fixity or permanence as natural laws. That our assertion requires many qualifications in the light of these considerations must certainly be admitted. But with these qualifications understood, it is still true and important.[5] The point which remains amid the objections we have considered may be put in this way. Let us consider three different relations which man may bear to scientific laws: namely, that he can *exchange* the laws, *apply* the laws, and *create* the laws. Man *exchanges* laws when he replaces the conditions under which one set of laws— i.e., one correlation of variables—obtains, for another set of conditions under which a different correlation obtains. Man *applies* laws when he uses a correlation which exists independently of his decisions to produce an effect which would not have occurred if he had not made that use of the correlation. Man *creates* laws, finally, when, by means of his free decision and consequent action, he causes a correlation to exist which did not exist before.

Now there have been many philosophies, like those of the Marxists, the operationalists, and the pragmatists, which have tended to identify

---

[5] I shall not dwell on the far greater difficulties involved in applying experimental methods to confirm or disconfirm the correlations among the highly discriminated characteristics with which we said initially that social laws must deal. When one reads a book like F. S. Chapin, *Experimental Designs in Sociological Research*, New York, 1947, one becomes aware once more of how crude the attempts to isolate the relevant variables still are; and these difficulties are still found in the contemporary attempts to apply mathematical techniques to ascertain the relations among these variables.

the relations which human action bears to natural laws, to social laws, and to technological inventions or artefacts. But all the analogies apart, the following important difference remains. In so far as social laws follow from men's free decisions, men may create social laws. But men cannot create natural laws. In producing new artefacts, men apply natural laws which pre-exist independently of human decisions to effect consequences which would not have occurred without human action.

The crucial issue on this question, of course, is whether men can create new social laws. Is it not rather, as was urged by the argument from the pervasiveness of laws, that men can only exchange the conditions under which one law holds for another set of conditions under which another law holds? The difficulty with this formulation, however, is that it seems to give to social laws the status of eternal correlations which exist apart from all creative activity on the part of men. Now I think that it is not too implausible to describe natural laws in this way, such that even the entities which emerge from operations of the kind typified by atom-smashing machines are nevertheless discovered in nature rather than being artefacts, just as the telescope may be said to find rather than make stars. But if man can to any extent make his own history, then his social laws cannot be characterized in the same way, for the very correlations in which such laws consist may be changed by men's decisions.

Let us analyse this point a little more closely in the following way. We may grant that, given precisely the same conditions, precisely the same effect will follow, so that if a different effect follows, there must have been different conditions. Consequently, if to change a law means to make a different effect follow from precisely the same conditions, then for men to change social laws is impossible. In this sense the argument from the pervasiveness of laws is unanswerable. Nevertheless, there are two interrelated considerations which mitigate this conclusion in so far as it is interpreted as applying against the possibility of men's creating new social laws. In the first place, human volitions or decisions may be among the conditions of social laws. Consequently, by changing the decisions one changes the effect, and therefore a new correlation is created. In this case one has indeed exchanged the conditions of one law for those of another, but the decisions in which those conditions partly consist are made by men, and consequently in this sense the new law or correlation is also made or created by men, and is not merely found by men in the sense in which they find the laws of natural objects which cannot be affected by human decision. It might be held, in accordance with the principle of generalization mentioned above, that all such laws are but applications of some more general and fundamental law which cannot be affected by human decision, just as technological inventions may be said to be applications of general physical laws which are independent of human volition. And it must indeed be admitted that there are rigidities as well as plasticities in the social sphere. To say that men can create new social laws is by no means to say that the possibilities of such creation are limitless. Entirely apart from the limitations imposed by the natural context of such laws, including man's physical environment, it may well be the case that there are limitations set by psychological and specifically social factors. However, the attempts of social scientists to find and state such overarching social laws or rigidities have not been promising. And even if they do exist, it seems safe to say, in view of the variety of human institutions, that the rigidities imposed by these psychological and social factors operate at a very high level of generality, within which there is a great deal of plasticity making possible the kinds of changes in social laws discussed above.

This brings me to my second consideration. As I have said, it is admitted that from precisely the same condition or cause the same effect always follows. But, as the debate over the plurality of causes has shown, all depends on what is meant by the 'same cause' and the 'same effect'. In the social sphere, viewed as it actually exists, there never is exactly the same cause because man's history, including his learning from the past, makes a difference.[6] This does not, of course, mean, as it is sometimes taken to mean, that laws of social science are impossible; for such laws, like natural laws, abstract from these differences. But it does mean that man may create new laws of social science, because by setting up causes which are new in that they embody what he has learned from the past, he can control how these causes will operate—i.e., what effects they will produce. Hence we cannot say that he simply substitutes one pre-existing nexus of cause and effect for another, since what the nexus will be can itself be determined by man's knowledge and will.

Another Statement of the Reply

In terms of the distinction set forth above between the conditional and the existential aspects of laws, the considerations which have just been presented may be put as follows. (a) In their *conditional* aspect social laws can be changed by men in a sense in which natural ones cannot. This sense is that men can generate or create new correlations of social variables by making new decisions which function as antecedent conditions from which new consequences follow. In the natural sphere, on

[6] Of course, there never is 'exactly the same cause' in the natural sphere either. But the point of the contrast being drawn is that the spatio-temporal difference between what may otherwise be regarded as two instances of the 'same' natural cause are not historical differences, since they do not involve learning from the past or other such forms of genetic relations.

the other hand, men cannot generate such new antecedent conditions but can only exchange one set of conditions for another. Now it may be urged in reply that this difference is illusory, since in both the natural and the social sphere there are various possibilities, which ones are actualized being in both spheres partly dependent on human decision; and it may be urged further that such decision is itself the effect of antecedent conditions rather than a purely spontaneous act such as would differentiate it from the events which operate according to natural laws. The latter part of this objection will be dealt with below. Assuming for now that human decisions may occur in a way which is different from that which is operative in the natural sphere, it follows that social correlations may be changed by, just as they arise from, such decisions; while with natural correlations this is not the case. (b) In their *existential* aspect both natural and social laws can be changed by men, but in different senses. Men can exchange one set of conditions for another in both the natural and the social spheres, and can therefore determine which correlations will actually obtain. But in the natural sphere such correlations represent possibilities into which, as such, human decisions do not enter. For human decisions are external to the subject matter of natural science; this is why we describe the substitution of the airplane for a free gravitational fall as a substitution of 'art' for 'nature', and not as a substitution of one natural correlation for another. This point is more than a merely terminological one precisely in so far as it serves to make a real differentiation, namely, between what does and what does not exist independently of human volition. But when men exchange one set of social conditions for another, and thereby change social laws in their existential aspect, human decisions are internal to such changes, because human decisions may be the antecedents of social correlations and not merely forces externally imposed on them as in the case of artificial changes in the natural sphere.

I may briefly sum up the point we have reached so far in another way as follows. It is recognized that the relations of implication which hold between antecedent and consequent in natural laws are different from those which hold in the case of purely logical relations like those of mathematics. My point then is that the relations of implication in social laws are different from both of these. For both within the antecedent and between the antecedent and the consequent in social laws, human decisions do or may enter. Therefore, even the kind or degree of eternal truth found in natural laws which may be said to hold only for our present cosmic epoch, is not found in social laws.

There still remain, however, some important difficulties in this conception. I turn to consider some of them now in connection with the second argument against the possibility of men's changing social laws.

The Argument from the Social Determination of Knowledge and Action
Our discussion of the first argument led us to emphasize the possibility
of man's playing a creative role in effecting social laws through his
knowledge of those laws. But it may well be argued that this way of
differentiating social from natural laws is completely illusory.

In the first place, we must beware of overemphasizing the relation
of conscious human purposiveness to social institutions. Those institutions are products of habit, custom, tradition, history, environment,
far more than of deliberate human decision or contrivance. Consequently, man's conscious reaction on social laws in the light of his
knowledge of them must be viewed as a possibility rather than as an
actuality, although the stated purpose of much of social science research
is to make such reaction possible.

In the second place, even where we can trace an explicit working of
individual or collective decision, it is often possible to predict that
decision by correlating it with causes which determine it to one object
rather than another. The whole theory of the psychology of advertising
rests on this principle, and so too do many of the attempts to predict
how people will vote. Samuel Lubell in his book *The Future of American
Politics* has shown how the will of the voter is determined by—or, if
you prefer, correlated with—such factors as his economic, social, and
religious background. Consequently, social knowledge and choice, so
far from being independent causes of social change, are themselves
rather the effects of social forces. The 'sociology of knowledge', of
course, is but a further development of this point.

In the third place, recent history has shown to what a large extent
the sphere of indeterminacy which still remains in human choice may
be cut down by political institutions. Orwell's book *1984* portrays how
a dictatorship by building certain attitudes into its subjects could make
their reactions to stimuli almost as predictable as the reactions of iron
filings to a magnet. Something similar to this was suggested with
approval a few years ago by Bertrand Russell when he wrote that what
was needed was a science of mass psychology which would show how
the people could be persuaded to follow the urgings of their leaders
without question.[7] Russell conceived these leaders as completely
benevolent social scientists, and their device of persuasion as a temporary one, but obviously its potentialities go far beyond such a context.

What such considerations suggest is that the factor of man's knowledge of social laws and his consequent creation of new laws can be
used only in an extremely limited fashion, if at all, to differentiate
social from natural laws. If man's very knowledge and intervention

[7] Bertrand Russell, 'The Science to Save Us from Science', *New York Times
Magazine*, 19 March, 1950.

themselves follow social laws, then is it not illusory to hold that man through his knowledge can intervene to change social laws?

Three Questions Distinguished

This question involves at least three subordinate questions which must be carefully distinguished:

(a) Can men's knowledge lead to action which exerts a causal influence on the operation of social laws or which creates new social laws?

(b) Is that knowledge itself subject to causal laws?

(c) Are these latter laws always non-cognitive and non-rational, of the kinds mentioned above?

From confusing these three questions, and the respective answers to them, stem many of the perennial confusions of social philosophy and social science.

Let us take question (b) first; and let us assume an affirmative answer to it, in accordance with one interpretation of the principle of causality. Now even if men's actual knowledge is subject to causal laws, it does not follow that that knowledge cannot lead to changes in social laws or in the conditions under which those laws operate. All that follows is that one force or agency operating in society in accordance with its own causal laws acts on other forces having their own laws. Hence an affirmative answer to question (b) does not, as such, entail a negative answer to question (a). But what if the laws determining men's knowledge are themselves social laws? This of course brings us to question (c). If the operation of human knowledge is itself determined by social laws, then how can human knowledge react on those laws? In this case, would not social laws be all-inclusive and unchangeable by action based on knowledge, since that knowledge would have to step outside its causal framework in order to change the laws?

The error underlying this question is that of viewing social laws as so all-inclusive that from a small number of them there follow *en bloc* all social phenomena, including knowledge. But if we view social laws as specific correlations of distinct phenomena, then the causal laws determining men's knowledge may well be different from those determining other social phenomena, and thus there is no impossibility in knowledge leading to action which reacts on and changes the latter phenomena.

Up to this point we have been unduly patient with question (c). But actually there are important arguments against the causal determination of knowledge by social factors. I shall not go into the familiar ones revolving around the sociology of knowledge, but rather shall make a different though related point; one which brings out again in another way the contrast I have drawn between natural and social laws. For which social laws do in fact hold depends upon man's social institutions. Hence, the answers both to the question of whether man's knowledge can be an independent cause leading him to intervene in the social laws actually operating in his society, and to the question of what kinds of causes lead to that knowledge and intervention, depend upon the character of that society. In a totalitarian state the possibilities both of acquiring the relevant knowledge apart from determination by prevailing social forces, and of acting on that knowledge, are extremely limited if not non-existent for all but a very small group of men; and the tendency of such a state is to perpetuate a closed society in the sense that new knowledge and new forms of action have no means of acting on the social laws or correlations which actually prevail. On the other hand, many contemporary social scientists hold that the same thing is true of all societies, including democratic ones. For they assert that men's knowledge is itself relative to, because caused by, various non-rational factors of the kinds mentioned above, and consequently they strongly question whether men in democratic societies do or can act from knowledge as contrasted with various prejudices deriving from their economic, racial, religious backgrounds and so on. I wish to devote the remainder of this paper to pointing out four confusions which result from the way in which many contemporary scientists, taking off from the view just noted, interpret social scientific laws and their relation to social knowledge and social change.

Four Confusions
The first confusion is the assumption that for a social cause to be scientifically ascertainable is for it to be non-rational. This confusion results from the interpretation which many contemporary social scientists make of their aim of using methods and attaining laws like those of the natural sciences. This aim, as such, need not be criticized in so far as it stems from a praiseworthy desire for objectivity and rigour, for, if correctly interpreted, it is too general to account by itself for the confusion I am talking about. But many contemporary social scientists interpret this aim in such a way that only non-rational factors of the kind mentioned above are viewed as scientifically ascertainable causes of men's attitudes and actions, on the analogy of physical and biological forces whose causal operation is independent of man's knowledge or reason. This interpretation, however, is by no means a result solely of empirical observation of how men actually think and act. It is rather the result of confusing scientific determinism with the view that it is impossible for such factors as reason and knowledge to play an independent causal role in social action, and hence with the view that

these factors, if admitted at all, are to be regarded as passive effects of non-rational and non-cognitive causes.

I might point out parenthetically that this consideration, while relevant to current meta-ethical issues of the relation of reason and knowledge to values and choice, does not presume any one answer on those issues if such answer is interpreted sufficiently broadly. In other words, the point I am making could be fitted into Hume's doctrine as well as Aristotle's or Kant's.

Closely related to this first confusion is a second—the confusion between the operation of social laws and the absence of conscious social action based on knowledge. This confusion usually takes the form of the plea that men not interfere through legislation or other means with the operation of social or economic laws. It is based on the view, derived variously from the natural-law, social-Darwinian, and other schools of social thought, that all social laws operate in some kind of automatic fashion akin to laws of physical or biological nature, so that all conscious attempts by men to effect changes in the operation of these laws are simply ill-conceived modes of interference with the inevitable. Now it is important not to deny one of the insights on which this view is based—the important influence of custom and tradition both in the shaping of social uniformities and, on the side of value, in the achievement of social stability. But to recognize this is not to deny that conscious human action based on knowledge of past social uniformities can effect different uniformities, so that such action involves not the substitution of non-law for law, but rather the substitution of one law for another, the latter being created by men's knowledge and consequent action.

This second confusion, however, leads directly to a third—the confusion of social scientific laws and the knowledge of such laws both with the absence of political freedom and with political laws. This confusion leads men to fear the acquisition of knowledge of social scientific laws because they fear that such knowledge will lead to political laws curtailing their freedom. Now I would certainly not want to deny this possibility. But it is only one of the possibilities; it is not logically entailed by the acquisition of social knowledge. On the contrary, to know the conditions and consequences of freedom is itself to know social scientific laws, in the sense of causal correlations between freedom and other variables. The contrast between a free political society and an enslaved one is quite different from the contrast between an ignorant and a knowing society; on the contrary, it may well be argued that the preservation of freedom in the modern world requires much knowledge of its conditions and consequences. As Dewey has said, the problem of democracy is in this sense an intellectual problem.[8] Whether such values as political freedom will or will not

[8] John Dewey, *The Public and its Problems*, New York, 1927.

be better preserved if men attain knowledge of social scientific laws and use that knowledge to substitute one set of social uniformities for another, is obviously an empirical question. But this question is not to be answered by confusing social scientific laws and the knowledge of such laws with the absence of political freedom.

Finally, there is a fourth confusion to which one aspect of the two preceding confusions frequently leads—namely, the confusion between the need for social knowledge and the political hegemony of the social scientists. This confusion sometimes takes the form of the insistence that since the social scientists or 'social psychiatrists' know social laws, including the conditions of the preservation and extension of democracy, they must therefore be the sole rulers, manipulating the masses for their own good. I shall not comment on the ancient problem of the relation between knowledge and virtue on which this confusion partly rests. But it is obviously illegitimate to conclude that because some men have most knowledge of the conditions of freedom, they must therefore have most political power to effectuate those conditions. On the contrary, one of the propositions which such knowledge might well be held to establish is that freedom requires individual responsibility and government responsible to the governed.

In summary, I have tried in this paper to present considerations upholding two main points. (1) Man through his awareness of the impact of the laws of social science on his values may intervene, in a way which is impossible in the natural sciences, to remove some of those laws from actual operation and to create new laws of social science. In this sense man can effect a factual change in the laws. (2) The knowledge from which this interventional activity emerges need not itself be uniquely or completely determined by social laws or uniformities in so far as these are viewed as non-rational or non-cognitive.

Part 3
Methodological Individualism

J. W. N. WATKINS

Ideal Types and Historical Explanation

INTRODUCTION

In this paper I shall consider: first, what sort of creatures ideal types should be if they are to be used in the construction of social theories; and secondly, what we do when we try to explain historical events by applying such theories to them.[1]

[1] It has been established by Professor K. R. Popper that the formal structure of a prediction is the same as that of a full-fledged explanation. In both cases we have: (a) initial conditions; (b) universal statements; and (c) deductive consequences of (a) plus (b). We explain a given event (c) by detecting (a) and by postulating and applying (b); and we predict a future event (c) by inferring it from some given (a) and postulated (b). Nevertheless, I think that in social science explanation and prediction should be considered separately, for two reasons. First, as Professor G. C. Hempel has pointed out in a most illuminating discussion of this problem (see his 'The Function of General Laws in History' in *Readings in Philosophical Analysis*, ed. H. Feigl and W. Sellars, New York, 1949, pp. 462–465) in history we often have to be content (and in fact *are* content) with what he calls an explanation *sketch*, i.e., a somewhat vague and incomplete indication of (a) and (b) from which (c) is not *strictly* deducible. And if we go back to a time when (a) but not (c) has occurred, this partial sketch of (a) and (b) will not allow us to predict (c). For example, we may be satisfied by the explanation that Smith insulted Jones because Jones had angered him, although we should *not* be prepared to admit that if Jones angers Smith in the future, Smith will necessarily react by insulting Jones.

Secondly, even the social scientist who can provide a *full-fledged* explanation of a past event will run into difficulties if he tries to predict similar events, because they will occur in a system which is not isolated from the influence of factors which he cannot ascertain beforehand. The Astronomer Royal can prepare a Nautical Almanac for 1953 because he is predicting the movements of bodies in a system isolated from extraneous influences, but the Chancellor of the Exchequer cannot prepare an Economic Almanac for 1953 because, even if he possessed sufficient knowledge to explain completely the 1951 levels of prices, production, investment, exports, etc., his predictions of future levels would undoubtedly be upset by unforeseeable, world-wide disturbing factors, the effects of any of which might be cumulative.

Hence, the problem of social prediction raises questions not raised by the problem of historical explanation, and this paper is not concerned with the former.

HOLISTIC AND INDIVIDUALISTIC IDEAL TYPES

It is only decent to begin a discussion of ideal types by considering Weber's views; but he held two successive conceptions of what an ideal type should be and do, without, I think, realizing what important differences lay between them.

His earlier version is set out in an article translated under the title ' "Objectivity" in Social Science and Social Policy'.[2] At this time (1904) Weber believed that the social scientist should not try to imitate the natural scientist's procedure of systematically subsuming observation-statements and low order theories under more comprehensive laws. The social scientist should first decide from what point of view to approach history. Having decided, say, to treat its economic aspect he should then select from this some unique configuration of activities and institutions, such as 'the rise of capitalism'. Then he should pin down and describe its components. His final task is to draw in the causal lines between these components, imputing 'concrete effects to concrete causes'.[3]

This programme could never be carried out; 'in any actual economic system so many factors are at work simultaneously that the effect of a single factor by itself can never be known, for its traces are soon lost sight of'.[4] And separate facts cannot be linked together as causes and effects with no reference to general laws. However, I will not press these criticisms of a methodological position which Weber tacitly abandoned later.

To assist the social scientist in this task of explaining particular events by relating them to their particular antecedents, Weber proposed his first version of the ideal type. This was to be constructed by abstracting the outstanding features from some (more or less clearly demarcated) historical complex, and by organizing these into a coherent word-picture. The ideality of such a type lies in its simplification and aloofness from detail: it will be free from the detailed complexity of the actuality to be analysed with its aid. As this kind of ideal type emphasizes the 'essential' traits of a situation considered *as a whole*, I call it 'holistic', in contrast with the 'individualistic' ideal type described by Weber in Part I of his posthumous *Wirtschaft und Gesellschaft*.[5]

[2] Max Weber, *The Methodology of the Social Sciences*, translated and edited by E. A. Shils and H. A. Finch, Illinois, 1949, ch. 2.
[3] *Op. cit.*, p. 79.
[4] Walter Eucken, *The Foundations of Economics*, translated by T. W. Hutchison, London, 1950, p. 39.
[5] Translated by A. R. Henderson and Talcott Parsons as *The Theory of Social and Economic Organisation*, Introduction by Talcott Parsons, London, 1947.

In this work he held that the social scientist's first task was to build up a generally applicable theoretical system; and for arriving at this he proposed the use of ideal types similar to the models used in deductive economics. These are constructed, not by withdrawing from the detail of social life, but by formalizing the results of a close analysis of some of its significant details considered in isolation. The holistic ideal type was supposed to give a bird's eye view of the broad characteristics of a whole social situation, whereas the individualistic ideal type is constructed by inspecting the situations of actual individuals, and by abstracting from these: (a) general schemes of personal preferences; (b) the different kinds of knowledge of his own situation which the individual may possess; and (c) various typical relationships between individuals and between the individual and his resources. An individualistic ideal type places hypothetical actors in some simplified situation. Its premises are: the form (but not the specific content) of the actors' dispositions, the state of their information, and their relationships. And the deductive consequences of these premises demonstrate some principle of social behaviour, e.g., oligopolistic behaviour. The ideality of *this* kind of ideal type lies: (i) in the simplification of the initial situation and in its isolation from disturbing factors; (ii) in the abstract and formal, and yet explicit and precise character of the actors' schemes of preferences and states of information; and (iii) in the actors' rational behaviour in the light of (ii). It is not claimed that a principle of social behaviour demonstrated by an individualistic ideal type will often have an exact empirical counterpart (though the principle of perfect competition has been precisely manifested, for instance in commodity-markets). But economists do claim that there is a limited number of basic economic principles, and that any economic phenomenon is a particular configuration of some of these, occurring at a particular place and time, which can be explained by a synthesis of the relevant ideal types, and by specifying the content of their formal premisses.[6]

[6] 'This morphological study of economic history reveals a *limited* number of pure forms out of which *all* economic systems past and present are made up.' Eucken, *op. cit.*, p. 10 (my italics). The 'de-idealization' of the pure principles of economic theory which occurs when they are combined into a particular configuration which is applied to an empirical counterpart, is exactly paralleled in the natural sciences. For example, Galileo combined the Law of Inertia (which describes the motion of a body not acted upon by any force—a condition which can never be realized), and the Law of Gravity (which describes the motion of a body in a vacuum which the experimenter cannot obtain), and the principles of air resistance, into a theoretical configuration which allows complete prediction of the trajectories of e.g., cannon-balls, if the initial conditions are known. 'All universal physical concepts and laws . . . are arrived at by idealisation. They thereby assume that simple . . . form which makes it possible to reconstruct any

Weber was no Platonist; he proposed both kinds of ideal type as heuristic aids which, by themselves, tell you nothing about the real world, but which throw into relief its deviations from themselves. The individualistic ideal type was to assist in the detection of disturbing factors, such as habit and tradition, which deflect actual individuals from a rational course of action—a proposal I shall examine later. Now I shall examine the assumptions underlying Weber's earlier proposal to use holistic ideal types.

One might improve one's appreciation of the shape of a roughly circular object by placing over it an accurate tracing of a circle. This analogy brings out Weber's conception of the purpose, and manner of employing, holistic ideal types in three respects. (i) By comparing an impure object with an ideal construction the deviations of the former from the latter are thrown into relief; and Weber did regard this kind of ideal type as a 'purely ideal *limiting* concept with which the real situation . . . is *compared* and surveyed for the explication of certain of its significant components'.[7] (ii) Both the object and the construct are considered *as a whole*. (iii) The analogy involves what is presupposed by the idea of comparison, namely, a simultaneous awareness of the characteristics of both things being compared. And in 1904 Weber did assume that the social scientist can place his knowledge of a real situation alongside his knowledge of an ideal type he has himself constructed, and compare the two.[8] It is the simultaneous knowability of the features of both which enables holistic ideal types to be 'used as conceptual instruments for *comparison* with and *measurement* of reality'.[9]

At this point an awkward question arises: If the characteristics of a historical situation have already been charted *before* the ideal type is brought into play, why bother with ideal types? They are not hypotheses[10] which guide the social scientist in his search for facts, for they are not supposed to be realistic, or empirical. A holistic ideal type is not a guess about reality, but an *a priori* word-picture—in other words, a definition. What Weber's earlier proposal amounts to is that holistic

---

facts, however complicated, by synthetic combination of these concepts and laws, thus making it possible to understand them.' (Ernst Mach, quoted by F. Kaufmann, *Methodology of the Social Sciences*, New York, 1944, p. 87.)

[7] *Methodology*, p. 93.

[8] Thus he speaks of the 'relationship between the logical structure of the conceptual system . . . and what is immediately given in empirical reality' (*op. cit.*, p. 96). The term 'immediately given' should not, I think, be taken too seriously. What this phrase does imply is that the social scientist's knowledge of ideal type and corresponding reality are on an equal footing.

[9] *Op. cit.*, p. 97.

[10] *Op. cit.*, p. 90.

ideal types should be used as explicit definitions of those 'hundreds of words in the historian's vocabulary [which] are ambiguous constructs created to meet the unconsciously felt need for adequate expression and the meaning of which is only concretely felt but not clearly thought out'.[11]

Thus the holistic ideal type transpires to be something of a mouse, a mere demand for definitions;[12] and I shudder when I imagine each of those 'hundreds of words' being replaced by lengthy verbal definitions, though such defining *may* be helpful in particular circumstances. For instance, to order and classify a collection of variegated instances it may be necessary to construct a scale with limiting ideal types at either end. The survey of the constitutions of 158 Greek states was probably tidier and more systematic than it would have been if Aristotle's 'Monarchy-Aristocracy-Polity' and 'Tyranny-Oligarchy-Democracy' scales, or some equivalent, had not been used.

But such scales are for classifying facts already analysed, not for analysing raw material; and the real weakness of Weber's earlier proposal lies in the method of historical analysis which was to accompany the use of holistic ideal types. With *individualistic* ideal types, it will be remembered, we *start* with individuals' dispositions, information and relationships, and work outwards to the unintended consequences of their interaction (deducing a price-level, for example, from demand and supply schedules). But with *holistic* ideal types the analysis is supposed to proceed in the opposite direction. Here, the historian is supposed to start with the broad (or 'essential') characteristics of an entire historical situation, and then to *descend* to an ever closer definition of its deviations from the ideal type with which it is being compared. In principle, this descent from overall traits to detailed ingredients might continue until, *at the end of the analysis*, the relevant dispositions, information, and relationships of the people concerned had been established.

The idea that we can apprehend the overall characteristics of a social situation *before* learning something of the individual situations of the actors in it *appears* to be borne out by a statement such as, 'The British economy in 1850 was competitive'. This statement apparently attributes an overall characteristic to a demarcated whole, while saying nothing about individuals (just as 'The lake's surface was calm' says nothing about water-particles). Now the unintended merit of the holistic ideal type is that its use forces us to recognize the falsity of this idea. If, in order to assess the competitiveness of the British economy in 1850, we try to establish an ideal type of 'perfect competition' we shall at once

[11] *Op. cit.*, pp. 92–93.
[12] For a criticism of such demands, see K. R. Popper, *The Open Society and Its Enemies*, London, 1945, Vol. 2, Ch. 11, Sect. ii.

find that we can only define it in terms of the preferences, information and relationships of individuals—an assertion which can be confirmed by turning to any economics text-book. In other words, we shall have established an *individualistic* ideal type.[13] But if knowledge of the general characteristics of a social situation is always derivative knowledge, pieced together from what is known of individuals' situations, then it is not possible for historical analysis to proceed *from* overall characteristics *towards* individuals' situations. The former is logically derivative from the latter. Weber's earlier conception of an ideal type presupposed that one can detect the essential traits of some historic 'whole' while remaining aloof from the detail of personal behaviour; but this belief is shown to be false when we actually construct such a type. It was probably this experience which later led Weber tacitly to abandon holistic ideal types and the impossible method associated with them, in favour of individualistic ideal types and the method of reconstructing historical phenomena with their aid.[14]

The assertion that knowledge of social phenomena can only be derived from knowledge about individuals requires one qualification. For there are certain overt features[15] which can be established without knowledge of psychological facts, such as the level of prices, or the death-rate (but *not* the suicide-rate). And if we detect more or less regular changes in such overt features we have something eminently suitable for analysis. But some people, over-impressed by the quasi-

---

[13] Similarly, if we try to construct an ideal type for 'feudalism', say, we shall at once find ourselves speaking of people's obligations and privileges towards their superiors, inferiors, the land, and so on.

[14] What I call a 'holistic ideal type' roughly corresponds to what Eucken called a 'real type', a name he used to denote the 'stages', such as 'city economy', 'early capitalism', 'mature capitalism', through which, according to the Historical School of economists, any economic system develops. He also rejected such types in favour of individualistic ideal types (which he simply called 'ideal types') and he criticized Weber for confusing the two, but from a somewhat different viewpoint to my own. His fascinating book, *The Foundations of Economics*, contains a sustained plea for the fertile marriage of abstract theory and concrete fact, and a powerful criticism of the Historical School for blurring the distinction between the two; whereas I am arguing against methodological holism, and for methodological individualism. Our arguments tend to coincide because 'historicism' is closely related to 'holism': the belief in laws of development presupposes a 'whole' which undergoes the development. See K. R. Popper, 'The Poverty of Historicism', *Economica*, XI, 1944, pp. 91–92. For Eucken's discussion of real and ideal types, see especially pp. 347–349.

[15] By 'overt feature' I do not mean something which can necessarily be directly perceived—it may be a highly theoretical construct. But whether it be the price of a marked article in a shop-window, or the average level of prices in 1815, an overt feature is something which can be ascertained without referring to people's dispositions, etc. See R. Stone, *The Role of Measurement in Economics*, Cambridge, 1951, p. 9.

regularity of, for example, a long-term 'wave' in economic life, have supposed that such a thing possesses a sort of internal dynamic, and obeys its own laws; and that while *it* must therefore be taken as a datum, many other phenomena (such as bursts of inventiveness, emigration movements, outbreaks of war) can be explained as consequences of it.[16]

This is a sort of blasphemy. The Israelites also imputed their fortunes and misfortunes to a superior entity immune from their own activities; but they rightly called this 'God'. But economic cycles do not possess a quasi-divine autonomy. They are mere human creations—not deliberate creations, of course, but the unintended product of the behaviour of interacting people.

For the last few paragraphs a basic methodological principle has been struggling to emerge and the time has come to bring it into the open in order to clarify its meaning and status.

THE PRINCIPLE OF METHODOLOGICAL INDIVIDUALISM

This principle states that social processes and events should be explained by being deduced from (a) principles governing the behaviour of participating individuals and (b) descriptions of their situations.[17]

---

[16] I have written the above with the Russian economist Kondratieff in mind. He asserts that the view that long waves 'are conditioned by casual, extra-economic circumstances and events, such as (1) changes in technique, (2) wars and revolutions, (3) the assimilation of new countries into the world economy, and (4) fluctuations in gold production . . . reverse[s] the causal connections and take[s] the consequence to be the causal (N. D. Kondratieff, 'The Long Waves in Economic Life', *Readings in Business Cycle Theory*, Blakiston Series, London, 1950, ch. 2, p. 35). In other words, the long wave is *the* fundamental datum, in terms of which even such a strictly individual and psychological matter as human inventiveness is to be explained.

[17] This principle does not apply to the study of purely physical, biological or behaviouristic properties of human groups. Professor Hayek has drawn a very useful distinction between the 'natural sciences of society', such as vital statistics and the study of contagious diseases, and the study of the 'social sciences proper'. (*Individualism and Economic Order*, London, 1949, p. 57.) Typical problems of the social sciences are war, unemployment, political instability, the clash of cultures. Professor M. Ginsberg has asserted that principles of historical interpretation 'are not necessarily exclusively psychological or even teleological: there may well be social laws *sui generis* . . .' (*Aristotelian Society, Supplementary Volume* XXI, 1947, 'Symposium: The Character of a Historical Explanation', p. 77). The only example he gives of something determined by such laws is phonetic change. But phonetic change is either an unconscious, behaviouristic process to be studied by a natural science of society, or a deliberate process, in which case it can be explained individualistically, e.g., in terms of a man's desire to raise his social status by acquiring a superior accent.

The contrary principle of methodological holism states that the behaviour of individuals should be explained by being deduced from (a) macroscopic laws which are *sui generis* and which apply to the social system as a whole, and (b) descriptions of the positions (or functions) of the individuals within the whole.

There is clearly an important difference between these two principles. What are my grounds for accepting the individualistic, and rejecting the holistic, method?

(1) Whereas physical things can exist unperceived, social 'things' like laws, prices, prime ministers and ration-books, are created by personal attitudes. (Remove the attitudes of food officials, shop-keepers, housewives, etc., towards ration-books and they shrivel into bits of cardboard.) But if social objects are formed by individual attitudes, an explanation of their formation must be an individualistic explanation.

(2) The social scientist and the historian have no 'direct access' to the overall structure and behaviour of a system of interacting individuals (in the sense that a chemist does have 'direct access' to such overall properties of a gas as its volume and pressure and temperature, which he can measure and relate without any knowledge of gas-molecules). But the social scientist and the historian can often arrive at fairly reliable opinions about the dispositions and situations of individuals. These two facts suggest that a theoretical understanding of an abstract social structure should be derived from more empirical beliefs about concrete individuals.[18]

But neither (1) the truism that social objects are created by personal attitudes, nor (2) the 'invisibility' of social structures, *entail* methodological individualism; they only support it.

(1) The fact that prices, for instance, are charged and paid by people, the fact that they are human creations, does not, by itself, entail that the whole price-system may not be governed by some overall law which is underivable from propositions about individuals. (2) A holist who denied that 'the English State, for example, is a logical construction out of individual people',[19] and who asserted that it is an organism which develops, and responds to challenges, according to underivable holistic laws, might also admit that only its individual components were visible and that any operational definition of the laws it obeyed would be in terms of individual behaviour.

---

[18] 'The social sciences . . . do not deal with "given" wholes but their task is to *constitute* these wholes by constructing models from the familiar elements. . . .' 'The whole is never directly perceived but always reconstructed by an effort of our imagination.' F. A. Hayek, *The Counter-Revolution of Science: studies on the abuse of reason*, The Free Press, Glencoe, Illinois, 1952, p. 56 and p. 214.

[19] A. J. Ayer, *Language, Truth and Logic*, 2nd ed., London, 1948, p. 63.

Moreover, an extremely unlikely circumstance is conceivable in which methodological individualism would have to be demoted from a rule to an aspiration; for it apparently suffers this humiliation in the study of certain non-human societies.

One can see what upsets methodological individualism by considering three different systems of interacting components: (a) the solar system as conceived by classical mechanics; (b) the economic system as conceived by classical economics; and (c) a bee-hive.

(a) Here, methodological individualism is altogether adequate. The behaviour of the whole system can be explained by applying the inverse square law and the law of inertia to the system's components, if their relative positions, masses and momenta are known. Indeed, methodological individualism in the social sciences is analogous to the method of resolution and re-composition which characterizes Galilean and Newtonian physics: the method, namely, of analysing a complex whole into its atomic constituents, and into the simplest principles which they obey, and of deductively reconstructing the behaviour of the whole from these.

(b) Adam Smith stated that the individual

generally, indeed, neither intends to promote the public interest, nor knows how much he is promoting it . . . ; by directing [his] industry in such a manner as its produce may be of the greatest value, he intends only his own gain, and he is in this, as in many other cases, led by an invisible hand to promote an end which was no part of his intention. (*The Wealth of Nations*, Bk. 4, Ch. 2.)

But the invisible hand is, strictly, gratuitous and misleading. What Smith actually showed was that individuals in competitive economic situations are led by nothing but their *personal dispositions* to promote unintentionally the public interest. Here again, methodological individualism is altogether adequate.

(c) Mr E. S. Russell, basing himself on experiments by Rösch, has reported the following strange fact[20] (strange, that is, to the methodological individualist). If young worker-bees (whose normal function is to feed the larvae from their salivary glands) are segregated into one half of a hive sealed off from the other half, in which have been segregated the older worker-bees (whose salivary glands have atrophied and whose normal function is to produce wax from their newly developed wax-glands, and later, to forage), then the following will occur: after two days' dislocation and near-starvation some of the young workers will start foraging and their salivary glands will atrophy prematurely; while the atrophied salivary glands of some of the older workers will revive and continue functioning long after the normal

[20] See *The British Journal for the Philosophy of Science*, 1950, I, pp. 113–114.

period, enabling them to feed the larvae in their half of the hive. The bees' functions will be increasingly differentiated until the division of labour in both halves approximates to that of a whole hive. Here it really is as if individual bees were led by an invisible hand, not merely to promote the interest of the whole half-hive, but to adapt drastically their biological structure in order to do so. It seems extremely difficult to believe that the emergence of these two new systems of specialized functions could be explained individualistically, in terms of the situations and principles of behaviour of each bee, because all the bees in each half-hive were of a similar type and in approximately the same situation, yet only the requisite number adapted themselves to new functions. Thus each half of the bifurcated bee-hive appears to be an organism in the sense that its components' behaviour is determined by teleological principles which apply to the whole half-hive and which cannot be derived from a knowledge of individual bees—though one hopes that this appearance is misleading and that the re-emergence of specialization will eventually be explained individualistically.

The principle whose status I have been trying to elucidate is a methodological rule which presupposes the factual assertion that human social systems are not organisms in the above sense. There is no evidence to suggest that this presupposition is false; but one cannot assert *a priori* that it is true. What one *can* assert is that *if* any social system were such an organic entity then it would be something utterly different from anything so far imagined. For the only sorts of organism so far imagined are (a) physical or biological; (b) mental; and (c) social; and it will be shown that social systems are none of these.

(a) It is at any rate plausible to say that the personalities of a mating couple are sometimes submerged beneath the biological laws of their physical union. But it would be stretching terms to call this a 'social system'; and in the case of such social organizations as the Comintern or the International Red Cross, it is clear that what holds these bodies together is not physical ties but the ideals, discipline and beliefs of their dispersed members.

(b) Is the behaviour of a number of individuals ever regulated by some super-individual *mental* entity? It is just possible that this is so in the case of a panicking crowd or of an ecstatic revivalist meeting. But in general, 'group-minds' are very rightly out of fashion; for to impute a big social phenomenon (such as war) to a big mental counterpart (such as a 'nation's' aggressive spirit) is not to explain but to duplicate.[21] Moreover, social phenomena which nobody wants are precisely those whose occurrence most needs explaining; and it would

---

[21] This criticism is parallel to Aristotle's chief criticism of Plato's theory of Forms, to the effect that instead of accounting for their perceptible likenesses the Forms merely divert attention to transcendent duplicates. *Met.* 992a.27.

obviously be absurd to impute mass unemployment, for instance, to some mental counterpart such as a 'nation's' laziness.

(c) When a sociologist proffers a holistic law the entity whose behaviour it is supposed to determine is usually thought of as a special sort of organism, neither physical nor biological nor mental, but *social*. Alleged social entities such as 'The State', 'Capitalism', etc., however, are only hypostatizations of sociological terms. As we have seen, whenever we try to make these terms precise we find ourselves speaking individualistically.

Hence society is not an organism in any existing sense of the term. The ontological basis of methodological individualism is the assumption that society is not some unimagined sort of organism, but really consists only of people who behave fairly intelligibly and who influence each other, directly and mediately, in fairly comprehensible ways.

This section was intended to clarify and justify methodological individualism. We can now revert to the construction and use of ideal types.

CONCLUDING REMARKS ON IDEAL TYPES

The preceding argument can be summarized thus: An understanding of a complex social situation is always derived from a knowledge of the dispositions, beliefs, and relationships of individuals. Its overt characteristics may be *established* empirically, but they are only *explained* by being shown to be the resultants of individual activities.[22]

All this was recognized by the later Weber. In *The Theory of Social and Economic Organization* ideal type construction means, not detecting and abstracting the overall characteristics of a whole situation, and organizing these into a coherent scheme, but placing hypothetical, rational actors in some simplified situation, and deducing the consequences of their interaction.

Such intellectual experimenting *may* be fruitful even if some of the premisses are very unrealistic. For instance, the concept of a static economy in equilibrium aids the analysis of the changes and disequilibria of actual economies. And gross exaggeration of one factor may show up an influence which would otherwise have been overlooked. This is particularly important in social science where the influence of

[22] An explanation may be in terms of the *typical* dispositions of more or less anonymous individuals, or in terms of the peculiar dispositions of specific individuals. (This is the basis of my distinction between 'explanation in principle' and 'explanation in detail'. See p. 154.) Thus, you might try to explain an election result in terms of how 'the Lancashire shop-keeper' and 'the non-party professional man', etc., felt; or, if you had an unlikely amount of knowledge, in terms of the dispositions of each elector.

different factors can seldom be accurately calculated. If E is the *sort* of effect produced by F_1, and if F_1 and E are both present, the social scientist tends to assume that F_1 is *the* cause of E, whereas F_1 may have caused only a *part* of E, and an undetected factor F_2 may have caused the rest of E. For example, the domestic economic policy of country A will be a major influence on its own economy; but this may also be influenced by the domestic economic policy of country B. In order to show up this secondary influence, we might assume provisionally that A exports *all* its production to, and imports *all* its consumption from B, and then deduce the effect on A of a change of policy in B.[23]

But that would be a preliminary intellectual experiment. The premises of a finished ideal type should be sufficiently realistic for it to be applicable to historical situations. I now turn to the problem of application.

HISTORICAL EXPLANATION

I shall consider three levels of historical explanation: (I) colligation (where ideal types play no significant role); (II) explanation in principle (which is the field *par excellence* for ideal types); and (III) explanation in detail (where ideal types are mostly constructed *ad hoc*, and rendered increasingly realistic until they become empirical reconstructions.)[24]

(I) *Colligation*. The term 'colligation' has been revived by Mr Walsh[25] to denote a procedure which is important, not because it is methodologically powerful, but because most 'literary' historians do in fact use it when they write, for example, constitutional history. It means 'explaining an event by tracing its intrinsic relations to other events and locating it in its historical context'.[26] Thus we begin to understand why a bill was enacted in May 1640 condemning Strafford to death when we learn of such matters as: his autocratic power in Ireland: Parliament's fear of the Irish army and Pym's ruthlessness as a parliamentary leader; the King's dependence on Parliament to pay indemnities to the Scottish army in the north; and the angry anti-royalist mob which beset Westminster during the bill's passage. It may

---

[23] I owe this example to Professor J. E. Meade.
[24] Professor F. A. Hayek also draws a distinction between explaining in principle and explaining in detail, but he wishes to distinguish an explanation of why, say, a price will rise under certain conditions, from a quantitative prediction of the amount by which it will rise (*The Counter-Revolution of Science*, pp. 42–43); whereas I wish to distinguish between explanations in terms of *typical* dispositions, etc., and explanations in terms of the characteristics and personal idiosyncrasies of the principal actors concerned.
[25] See W. H. Walsh, *An Introduction to Philosophy of History*, London, 1951, ch. 3, section 3.
[26] *Op. cit.*, p. 59.

also be better understood by being colligated with *subsequent* events. Thus the Long Parliament's later treatment of Laud and Charles suggests that its treatment of Strafford was not eccentric, but part of a campaign against extra-parliamentary power.

However, as Mr Walsh admits, colligation yields only what he calls a 'significant narrative', which is more than a chronicle, but less than a full explanation, of the events colligated.

(II) *Explanation in Principle.* The principle of the automatic governor can be demonstrated in a simple model which shows that a fall in some temperature, voltage, speed, pressure, etc., below a certain level will move a lever which will increase the supply of heat, etc.; and vice versa. Understanding this, you can explain the constant temperature of your car's circulating water *in principle* if you know that an automatic governor controls it, although you do not understand its detailed operation.[27]

Analogous explanations are used in applied economics. Consider the bargaining process. The principle of this is demonstrated in the following ideal type. Two rational agents are postulated. Each possesses one homogeneous, divisible good, and each knows the schedule of those combinations of various portions of his own and the other's good which he would exchange differently for the whole of his present good. These premisses are highly precise, and also highly formal. Call them α and β. From these it is deduced that only the limits within which a bargain will be struck are determined, and that within those limits the outcome will be arbitrary. Call this consequence ω. Now consider post-war Anglo-Argentinian trade negotiations. Here, we can, I think, detect factors A, B, c, d . . . Z where: A and B are the resources and policies of the trade delegations, and are concrete examples of α and β; c, d . . . are minor factors whose small influences on Z may partly cancel out; and Z is the outcome of the negotiations, the actual instability of Anglo-Argentinian trade relations, which is a rough empirical counterpart of ω. The 'α, β, ω' ideal type explains in principle the 'A, B, c, d . . . Z' situation.[28]

In this example I have assumed that only one main economic principle, demonstrable in a single ideal type, was at work in the historical situation. But the situation will usually be more complex. Consider a wage-bargain. Perhaps there is a closed shop and limited entry into the trade union. The firm, a centrally planned organization, buys its raw materials, which are rationed, through a government agency, and its machinery at the best price it can get from oligopolistic suppliers. By

---

[27] It is the principle of an invention rather than its physical detail which is usually described in patents. See M. Polanyi, *The Logic of Liberty*, London, 1951, p. 21.

[28] I owe this example to Professor Lionel Robbins.

law it must export a proportion of its produce, and the export market is highly competitive. Its home prices are fixed by a cartel agreement.[29] The general situation is inflationary.

Here, the outcome of the bargaining process will be shaped by a number of economic principles besides that illustrated in the previous example. And in order to understand the whole situation in principle it would be necessary to build up a complex model from the relevant simple ideal types. Here, an '(α, β), (λ, μ), (σ, τ) . . . ω' model would be used to explain in principle an 'A, B, c . . .L, M, n . . . S, T, u . . .Z' situation (where c . . n . . u . . represent comparatively uninfluential factors).

The social scientist's explanations in principle lack the quantitative precision of explanations in mathematical physics. But he may claim that his explanations are at any rate 'intelligible' and 'satisfying', whereas those of the natural scientist are not. The most universal laws which the latter applies in his explanations and predictions contain terms (e.g., 'elementary quantum of action') whose connotation the layman cannot 'picture' or 'grasp'. Moreover, the status of these most universal laws is probably only temporary: they will probably come to be subsumed under higher order laws.

But the ultimate premises of social science are human dispositions, i.e., something familiar and understandable (though not introspectable since they are not mental events). They 'are so much the stuff of our everyday experience that they have only to be stated to be recognized as obvious'.[30] And while psychology may try to explain these dispositions, they do provide social science with a natural stopping-place in the search for explanations of overt social phenomena. The social scientist might claim more. The natural scientist cannot, strictly speaking, *verify* valid hypotheses; he can only *refute* false ones.[31] He can say, 'If H, then E. But not-E. Therefore not-H.' But if he says, 'If H, then E. Moreover E. Therefore H' he commits the fallacy of affirming the consequent.[32] But a social scientist might claim that a

---

[29] The definitions of perfect competition, oligopoly and monopoly provide, incidentally, good illustrations of the principle of methodological individualism. An entrepreneur faces: (a) perfect competition if the price at which he sells is determined for him; (b) oligopoly, if he can alter his price, but if this alteration may lead to price changes by his competitors which may force him to make further, undesired alterations to his own price; and (c) monopoly, if he can alter his price without causing undesired repercussions. Competition, oligopoly and monopoly are nothing but the outcome of the behaviour of interacting individuals in certain relationships.

[30] Lionel Robbins, *The Nature and Significance of Economic Science*, London, 1935, p. 79.

[31] See K. R. Popper, *Logik der Forschung*, Vienna, 1935, *passim*.

[32] See F. S. C. Northrop, *The Logic of the Sciences and the Humanities*, New York, 1948, pp. 108–109; and, e.g., H. W. B. Joseph, *An Introduction to Logic*, Oxford, 1916, pp. 522–523.

valid social theory *can* be verified because both its conclusions *and* its premisses can be confirmed—'you assent to the former because they correspond with recognized social facts; and you assent to the latter because they correspond with your ideas of how people behave'. An example of the belief that a social theory can be wholly verified by being confirmed at both ends is to be found in Keynes' *General Theory*. There he asserts 'the fundamental psychological law, upon which we are entitled to depend with great confidence . . . from our knowledge of human nature . . . that men are disposed, as a rule and on the average, to increase their consumption as their income increases, but not by as much as the increase in their income'; and vice versa.[33] He then shows that the empirical fact that no depression has worsened until 'no one at all was employed' is a deductive consequence of this law.[34] The theory is thus doubly confirmed, and therefore verified: 'it is *certain* that experience would be extremely different from what it is if the law did not hold'.[35] No natural scientist could claim so much for *his* laws. His explanations are 'surprising' in the sense that he explains the familiar in terms of the unconfirmable unfamiliar. But the social scientist explains the familiar in terms of the familiar. The element of surprise in *his* explanations lies in the logical demonstration of connections which had not been seen before between facts which are *prima facie* discrete.

But a double caution must be entered against the idea of double confirmation in social science: (i) The same conclusion can, of course, be deduced from different sets of premisses, and we cannot be certain that our set of psychological assumptions is the correct set. (ii) Even if our psychological assumptions *are* correct, and even if we *do* find that their deductive consequences correspond to recognized facts, we may nevertheless be mistaken if we explain these facts as a consequence of those psychological factors. This is because we can seldom calculate the relative influence of different psychological factors.[36] Thus Keynes' belief that people are disposed to save a smaller proportion of their income if their income diminishes may well be correct; his demonstration that this general disposition would not allow depressions to worsen indefinitely is immaculate; and the fact that depressions do not worsen indefinitely is undoubted. It is nevertheless conceivable that *no* depression has been halted because of this disposition. One may have been halted by an outbreak of war, another by an upsurge of confidence, another by a public works policy, and so on. In explaining social

[33] *The General Theory of Employment, Interest and Money*, London, 1936, p. 96.
[34] *Op. cit.*, p. 252.
[35] *Op. cit.*, p. 251 (my italics).
[36] I was myself inclined to accept the idea of double confirmation until Professor Popper pointed out to me the relevance of this consideration.

phenomena we must not be content with the detection of one factor which, singly, would have produced, after an unstated period, an unstated amount of an effect which may, in any particular situation, have been caused mainly by quite different factors.

If I am right in supposing that social theories derive sociological conclusions from dispositional premisses, we should expect to find that major theoretical advances in social science consist in the perception of some typical feature of our mental make-up which had previously been disregarded, and in its formulation in a way which is more deductively fertile and which goes to explain a wider range of facts, than the psychological generalizations relied on hitherto. And this is precisely what we do find. I think that it would be generally conceded that economics is the most mature social science, and that the two most striking advances made in economics during the last century are: (i) the 'revolution' which occurred in the early 1870s when Jevons, Menger and Walras introduced the concept of marginal utility; and (ii) the Keynesian 'revolution'.

(i) The classical economists saw that the price of a good must be partly determined by the demand for it, and that that demand must reflect the buyers' estimates of the good's utility—and yet diamonds, whose utility is low, fetch a far higher price than water, whose utility is high. So they tried to escape from their dilemma by saying that the price of a good is determined by the cost of its production, though this would obviously be untrue of an unwanted good which had been expensively produced. This difficulty dissolved with the introduction of the idea of the utility, not of a whole good, but of its least important, or 'marginal', unit. For—and this is the recognition of a psychological contour-line which had not been clearly mapped before—it is in terms of that unit that we tend to value a whole good; and the more we have of the same good, the more its marginal utility diminishes. Hence, if diamonds became abundant and water very scarce, their subjectively determined values would be reversed. F. H. Knight has given a vivid description of the elegance and power of the concept of marginal unility:

> To its admirers it comes near to being the fulfilment of the eighteenth-century craving for a principle which would do for human conduct and society what Newton's mechanics had done for the solar system. It introduces simplicity and order, even to the extent of making it possible to state the problems in the form of mathematical functions dealt with by the methods of infinitesimal calculus.[37]

(ii) The reader who is unfamiliar with Keynes' contribution to the theory of employment must take its value on trust, for it is impossible

---

[37] F. H. Knight, *The Ethics of Competition*, London, 1935, p. 158.

to describe it briefly. But here again we find that what it rests on is the perception and precise formulation of certain human dispositions which Keynes regarded as 'ultimate independent variables',[38] and from which he could deduce such dependent variables (or overt phenomena, as I have called them previously) as the amount of employment and the general level of prices. At the heart of his *General Theory* Keynes placed 'three fundamental psychological factors, namely, the psychological propensity to consume, the psychological attitude to liquidity and the psychological expectation of future yield from capital-assets'.[39]

(III) *Explanation in Detail.* The mark of an explanation in principle is its reliance on typical dispositions and its disregard of personal differences. But it is often impossible to disregard these, for instance, in diplomatic history. Here, the premisses of a historical explanation must be the specific dispositions, beliefs and relationships of actual people. This is what I call 'explanation in detail'.

So far, I have allowed two questions to lie dormant: (i) What is the status of these dispositions, and wherein lies their explanatory power? (ii) What assumptions concerning people's rationality are we obliged to make when we explain something in terms of their dispositions and beliefs? These questions were not acute so long as explanations in principle were being considered. An explanation requires a general statement as its major premiss; and when we postulate a typical disposition we assert that all men (with trivial exceptions and minor deviations, and, perhaps, within a limited historico-geographical area) are prone to behave in a certain kind of way; and this gives us the generality we required. And we explain in principle by combining types which are, after all, ideal, and which may therefore be expected to contain idealized simplifications of real life, such as the assumption of fully rational behaviour in the light of preferences and beliefs.

But when we turn to explanations in detail these two questions do become acute. For we are here concerned with the variegated dispositions of actual people, and these appear to lack the generality which the major premiss of an explanation needs. And actual people do not behave altogether rationally, which suggests that we cannot go on assuming that they do. I shall discuss the first question under the head of 'Personality', and the second under the head of 'Rationality and Purposefulness'.

(i) *Personality.* A series of occurrences constitutes a person's life, and a complex and evolving system of dispositions constitutes his per-

---

[38] *Op. cit.*, p. 246. Of course, the variables are only 'independent' from the social scientist's point of view. The psychologist would probably consider them 'dependent'.

[39] *Op. cit.*, pp. 246–247.

sonality.[40] Dispositions 'are not laws, for they mention particular things or persons. On the other hand, they resemble laws in being partly "variable" or "open".'[41] The dispositions which comprise a unique personality are, so to speak, 'laws' which apply to only one man over a limited period of time. It is as if the laws of chemistry concerning, say, mercury, applied only to a period in the life of one solitary bottle of mercury which has come into existence, matured, and will dissolve, and whose twin, we may confidently assume, never has existed, and never will.

All this presupposes that men do have personalities, i.e., that their behaviour is fairly consistent over a period of time if their personalities are not subjected to dissolvent shocks. This assumption of the quasi-permanence of personalities corresponds roughly—very roughly—to the natural scientist's belief in the permanence of the natural order.

The generalizations of psychology fit into this scheme in the following ways: (a) Some attribute a certain disposition to all men. The theory of the association of ideas is an example. (b) Others attribute certain dispositions to a certain type of man, e.g., the 'introvert'. (c) Yet others attempt to describe the dynamics of personality-development, deriving later dispositions from prior determining conditions in the light of psychological theory. (It is this search for the primitive determining conditions which leads back to the 'formative years' of early childhood.) An example is the theory of the 'incest-complex', which asserts that a man who idealized his sister as a child will be prone to hypo-aesthesia on marriage.

A disposition attributed to one man is no weaker than the same disposition attributed to all men in explaining and predicting that one man's behaviour. 'X will accept office' can be deduced from the minor premiss, 'X believes that if he refuses the office he has been offered he will find himself in the wilderness' in conjunction with *either* (a) the

---

[40] I have adopted the terminology of Professor G. Ryle's *Concept of Mind* (London, 1949; see especially ch. 5), but not that book's famous denial that a man has 'privileged access' to his own mind. Sitting beside the driver of a car who turns white and wrenches the steering-wheel over, I may perceive instantaneously *that* he fears an accident, but I do not *feel* his fear. Moreover, the historian is usually in the position of the policeman who tries to reconstruct what happened from skid-marks and reports of witnesses; and for him the dualism between uninterpreted overt behaviour (e.g., Jan Masaryk's fall from a Prague window) and its interpretation in psychological terms is very real.

But the following characteristic remarks suggest that Professor Ryle has now modified his original anti-dualism: 'We have . . . a sort of (graduatedly) privileged access to such things as palpitations of the heart, cramps, and creaks in the joints.' 'I have elsewhere argued for the idea that a tickle just *is* a thwarted impulse to scratch . . . But I do not think now that this will do.' ('Feelings', *The Philosophical Quarterly*, April 1951, 1, 198–199).

[41] Ryle, *Concept of Mind*, p. 123.

major premiss, 'All men seek power', *or* (b) the major premiss, 'X is a power-seeker'; but whereas (b) may be true, (a) is the sort of statement which is likely to be false because men are not uniform.[42]

Similarly, a detailed description of one man's chess-playing dispositions (his knowledge of the rules, evaluations of the different pieces, and ability to see a certain number of moves ahead) together with his present beliefs about his opponent's intentions and the positions of the pieces, imply his next move, which could not be deduced from propositions about chess-players in general in conjunction with a description of the present state of the game.

Thus the idea that the historian's interpretative principles are simply generalizations about human nature, into which he must have special insight, is inadequate.[43] His knowledge of human nature in general has to be supplemented by a knowledge of the peculiar personalities of the principal actors concerned in the situation he is trying to understand, whether his problem be X's behaviour, or the chess-player's next move, or the rise of Christianity, or the Congress of Vienna.

The dispositions which the historian attributes to a personality he is trying to reconstruct resemble scientific laws in two further ways.

(a) They are postulated hypotheses which correspond to nothing observable, although observable behaviour can be inferred from them in conjunction with factual minor premisses. Consequently, in judging their validity we want to know, not the mental process by which the historian arrived at them, but their degree of success in accounting for what is known of the man's behaviour. The hypothetical dispositions postulated by the historian who has 'sympathetically identified himself with his hero' may be richer than those of the historian who has not done so, but it is not this which gives them a certificate of reliability. Professor Hempel has put the matter very clearly:

> The method of empathy is, no doubt, frequently applied by laymen and by experts in history. But it does not in itself constitute an explanation; it is rather essentially a heuristic device; its function is to suggest certain psychological hypotheses which might serve as explanatory principles in the case under consideration.[44]

---

[42] On law-like dispositions of very limited generality, see R. Peters, 'Cure, Cause and Motive', *Analysis*, April 1950, 10, No. 5, p. 106.

[43] This idea underlies Mr Walsh's contribution to the symposium on 'The Character of a Historical Explanation' (*Aristotelian Society, Supplementary Volume* XXI, 1947). From it he infers that, since 'men's notions of human nature change from age to age' we must recognize 'the subjective element which history undoubtedly contains' (p. 66). The point is, do historians' notions of, say, Napoleon's personality change from age to age, not because of the discovery of fresh evidence, etc., but arbitrarily?

[44] *Op. cit.*, p. 467. Failure to realize this is, I think, the weakness of R. G. Collingwood's *The Idea of History* (ed. T. M. Knox, Oxford, 1946).

And the historian is no more precluded from reconstructing a strange and unsympathetic personality than is the scientist from reconstructing the behaviour of an atom which does things he would not dream of doing himself.[45]

(b) The dispositions which constitute a personality also resemble scientific laws in that they form a hierarchical system; and this is of considerable methodological importance. It is, of course, essential that the dispositions which a historian attributes to a historical figure should not be mere *ad hoc* translations of known occurrences into dispositional terms. It is no explanation of Brutus' behaviour to say that he was disposed to assassinate Caesar, though it would be a ground for an explanation to say that Brutus was disposed to place his loyalty to the State above his loyalties to his friends, if independent evidence were found to support this hypothesis. Moreover—and it is here that the idea of a hierarchy of dispositions is important—the historian who can explain some aspect of a person's behaviour *up to a certain time* in terms of a certain disposition, although his *subsequent* behaviour conflicts with this disposition, must not merely say that at that time the earlier disposition gave way to another. He should find a *higher order* disposition which helps to explain both earlier and later lower order dispositions, and hence the whole range of the person's behaviour. For example: suppose that Russian foreign policy is controlled by a consistent, integrated personality. Before 1939 Russia was disposed to pursue an anti-fascist foreign policy. But in 1939 came the Russo-German Pact. In order to explain this aberration it is not enough for the historian to say that the anti-fascist disposition was replaced. He must find a higher order disposition (e.g., 'Russian foreign policy is determined by considerations of national expediency, not by ideological factors') from which, in conjunction with factual premises, the change in policy is derivable. In doing this it is clear that the historian will *not*

---

[45] Failure to recognize this vitiates, I think, some of the argument in Professor F. A. Hayek's 'Scientism and the Study of Society', *The Counter-Revolution of Science*, Part One [see excerpts above]. There, despite all the work done in abnormal psychology, he asserts: 'When we speak of mind what we mean is that certain phenomena can be successfully interpreted on the analogy of our own mind. . . . To recognise mind cannot mean anything but to recognise something as operating in the same way as our own thinking.' From this false premiss he correctly infers the false conclusion that 'history can never carry us beyond the stage where we can understand the working of the minds of the acting people because they are similar to our own' [pp. 65–67]. Only a war-like historian can tackle a Genghis Khan or a Hitler! Moreover, if it were true that people, young and old, do not recognize as mind what they cannot interpret on the analogy of their own mind they would never learn to speak. For children must unconsciously realize that adult noises differ importantly from their own gibberish in being meaningful before they can begin to understand adult talk.

I hasten to add that I owe much to other parts of Professor Hayek's argument.

be translating an occurrence (the signing of the pact) into dispositional terms, but deriving both the occurrence and the change in lower order dispositions from a more permanent and fundamental disposition.

In conclusion it should be said that the personality of a man in society comprises dispositions both of a more private and temperamental kind, and of a more public and institutional kind. Only certain individuals are disposed to weep during the death-scene in *Othello*, but all policemen are disposed to blow their whistles under certain circumstances and any Speaker in the House of Commons is disposed to disallow parliamentary criticism of exercises of the Prerogative. And these more public and institutional dispositions, which may vary very little when one man undertakes another's role, can be abstracted from the total, variegated flux of dispositions, and so provide the social scientist with a fairly stable subject matter.[46]

(ii) *Rationality and Purposefulness.* Before asking what assumptions the historian is obliged to make about the rationality of those whose behaviour he is trying to interpret, we must establish a satisfactory 'definition in use' of the term 'rational behaviour'. Weber defined it, very austerely, as the deliberate and logical choice of means to attain explicit goals, in the light of existing factual knowledge. This is unsatisfactory for two reasons. (a) Whitehead said somewhere that 'civilization advances by extending the number of important operations we can perform without thinking about them'. This morning's toothbrushing was not irrational because done from habit and not from deliberations on dental hygiene. Our pursuit of goals need not be conscious in order to be rational. (b) Behaviour often does not conform to the end-means pattern. I may tell the truth, or go fishing, simply from a desire to do so, with no further end in mind.[47]

We escape these difficulties by saying that a person has behaved rationally if he *would* have behaved in the same way if, with the same *factual* information, he had seen the full *logical* implications of his behaviour, whether he actually saw them or not. And if we define purposeful behaviour as trying (consciously or otherwise) to do or achieve something wanted, it follows that fully rational behaviour is a limiting case of purposeful behaviour.

The historian who tries to interpret overt behaviour must assume that it is purposeful but not necessarily fully rational.[48] Consider a *crime passionnel* committed by an enraged husband. A judge who

[46] See Hayek, *Counter-Revolution*, p. 34.

[47] 'We invest our capital reluctantly in the hope of getting dividends. . . . But the angler would not accept or understand an offer of the pleasures without the activities of angling. It is angling that he enjoys, not something that angling engenders.' Ryle, *op. cit.*, p. 132. See also H. A. Pritchard, *Moral Obligation*, Oxford, 1949, pp. 10–11.

[48] See Robbins, *op. cit.*, ch. 4, section 5.

assumed that the husband had behaved purposelessly could reconstruct the event in a number of quite arbitrary ways—perhaps cramp caused his finger to contract round the trigger of a gun which happened to be pointing at his wife's lover. But while the judge must not assume purposelessness he need not assume full rationality. The husband would probably have confined himself to threats and remonstrances if he had paused to consider the less immediate consequences of a violent course of action.

The assumption of purposefulness is constantly made by those who attempt the most intensive analysis of human behaviour, i.e., practising psycho-analysts. It has often been pointed out that the psycho-analyst is on the side of rationality in that he tries to cure his patients. More interesting from our point of view is his assumption that the behaviour of an *uncured* patient is thoroughly purposeful. Suppose a patient forgets to wind his watch, and so arrives late at his father's funeral. Unlike the layman, the psycho-analyst will not attribute the stopped watch to accidental forgetfulness, to a purposeless psychic aberration. He will ask his patient *why* he *wanted* his watch to stop—maybe he felt guilty on having a death-wish fulfilled and so created an excuse for avoiding the funeral. This would certainly be purposeful behaviour, and might even be regarded as rational behaviour based on misinformation.[49]

(iii) *Conclusion*. Having considered the status of dispositions and the problem of rationality, we can now return to explanations in detail.

Weber advocated using individualistic ideal types, which depict rational behaviour, to show up the partial irrationality of actual behaviour. But this is unacceptable. Suppose that a historian wishes to interpret a general's behaviour during a battle. He has reconstructed, as best he can, both the dispositions which constitute that aspect of the general's personality with which he is concerned, and the general's information about the military situation. Suppose that, in conjunction, these dictate retreat as the rational course of action, but that the general is known to have given the signal to advance. Now the historian, like the psycho-analyst, will not want to leave puzzling overt behaviour uninterpreted; but according to Weber he should simply call this a deviation from the ideally rational course of action implied by the premises of his theoretical reconstruction of the situation. But since an irrational aberration can be attributed to anything from boredom to panic, this procedure would result in thoroughly arbitrary reconstructions. Rather, the historian must discover the most satisfactory amendment to the premises of his ideal type (constructed more or less

---

[49] The mixture of rationality and misinformation due to childhood associations which psycho-analysis brings to the surface was pointed out to me by Professor Popper.

ad hoc to depict the main features of the general's personality and situation) which will remove the discrepancy between what it implies and what happened. Perhaps there is independent evidence to suggest that the general was more lion-hearted than the historian had supposed; or perhaps he had underestimated the enemy's strength, or, in estimating the immediate consequences of an advance, he had overlooked a more distant undesirable repercussion. When *ad hoc* ideal types are used in detailed historical explanations, they have to be amended and amended until they cease being ideal constructs and become empirical reconstructions. The historian who claims to have interpreted a historical situation should be able to show: (a) that the behaviour of the actors in it flows from their personalities and situational beliefs; and (b) that significant events which no one intended are resultants of the behaviour of interacting individuals.

SUMMARY

An individual's personality is a system of unobservable dispositions which, together with his factual beliefs, determine his observable behaviour. Society is a system of unobservable relationships between individuals whose interaction produces certain measurable sociological phenomena. We can apprehend an unobservable social system only by reconstructing it theoretically from what is known of individual dispositions, beliefs and relationships. Hence holistic ideal types, which would abstract essential traits from a social whole while ignoring individuals, are impossible: they always turn into individualistic ideal types. Individualistic ideal types of explanatory power are constructed by first discerning the form of typical, socially significant, dispositions, and then by demonstrating how, in various typical situations, these lead to certain principles of social behaviour.

If such a principle, or a number of such principles, is at work in a historical situation, the outcome of that situation can be explained anonymously, or in principle, by an application to it of the relevant ideal type, or combination of ideal types. If the idiosyncrasies of the actors concerned significantly influenced the outcome, it must be explained in terms of their peculiar dispositions and beliefs. In either case, the hypothetico-deductive method is used. The hypotheses consist of postulated dispositions, beliefs and relationships of (anonymous or specific) individuals; and their test lies in the correspondence or otherwise between their deductive consequences and what is known of the overt characteristics of the situation being reconstructed. How the historian establishes the overt characteristics of a vanished situation is another story.

J. W. N. WATKINS

Historical Explanation in the Social Sciences

INTRODUCTION

The hope which originally inspired methodology was the hope of finding a method of inquiry which would be both necessary and sufficient to guide the scientist unerringly to truth. This hope has died a natural death. Today, methodology has the more modest task of establishing certain rules and requirements which are necessary to prohibit some wrong-headed moves but insufficient to guarantee success. These rules and requirements, which circumscribe scientific inquiries without steering them in any specific direction, are of the two main kinds, formal and material. So far as I can see, the formal rules of scientific method (which comprise both logical rules and certain realistic and fruitful stipulations) are equally applicable to all the empirical sciences. You cannot, for example, deduce a universal law from a finite number of observations whether you are a physicist, a biologist, or an anthropologist. Again, a single comprehensive explanation of a whole range of phenomena is preferable to isolated explanations of each of those phenomena, whatever your field of inquiry. I shall therefore confine myself to the more disputable (I had nearly said 'more disreputable') and metaphysically impregnated part of methodology which tries to establish the appropriate *material* requirements which the *contents* of the premises of an explanatory theory in a particular field ought to satisfy. These requirements may be called regulative principles. Fundamental differences in the subject matters of different sciences—differences to which formal methodological rules are impervious—ought, presumably, to be reflected in the regulative principles appropriate to each science. It is here that the student of the methods of the social sciences may be expected to have something distinctive to say.

An example of a regulative principle is mechanism, a metaphysical theory which governed thinking in the physical sciences from the seventeenth century until it was largely superseded by a wave or field world-view. According to mechanism, the ultimate constituents of the physical world are impenetrable particles which obey simple mechanical laws. The existence of these particles cannot be explained—at any rate by science. On the other hand, every complex physical thing or event is the result of a particular configuration of particles and can be explained in terms of the laws governing their behaviour in conjunction with a description of their relative positions, masses, momenta, etc. There may be what might be described as unfinished or half-way explanations of large-scale phenomena (say, the pressure inside a gas-container) in terms of other large-scale factors (the volume and temperature of the gas); but we shall not have arrived at rock-bottom explanations of such large-scale phenomena until we have deduced their behaviour from statements about the properties and relations of particles.

This is a typically metaphysical idea (by which I intend nothing derogatory). True, it is confirmed, even massively confirmed, by the huge success of mechanical theories which conform to its requirements. On the other hand, it is untestable. No experiment could overthrow it. If certain phenomena—say, electromagnetic phenomena—seem refractory to this mechanistic sort of explanation, this refractoriness can always (and perhaps rightly) be attributed to our inability to find a successful mechanical model rather than to an error in our metaphysical intuition about the ultimate constitution of the physical world. But while mechanism is weak enough to be compatible with any *observation* whatever, while it is an untestable and unempirical principle, it is strong enough to be incompatible with various conceivable physical *theories*. It is this which makes it a *regulative*, non-vacuous metaphysical principle. If it were compatible with everything it would regulate nothing. Some people complain that regulative principles discourage research in certain directions, but that is a part of their purpose. You cannot encourage research in one direction without discouraging research in rival directions.

I am not an advocate of mechanism but I have mentioned it because I am an advocate of an analogous principle in social science, the principle of methodological individualism.[1] According to this principle, the ultimate constituents of the social world are individual people who act more or less appropriately in the light of their dispositions and under-

[1] Both of these analogous principles go back at least to Epicurus. In recent times methodological individualism has been powerfully defended by Professor F. A. Hayek in his *Individualism and Economic Order* and *The Counter-Revolution of Science*, and by Professor K. R. Popper in his *The Open Society and its Enemies* and 'The Poverty of Historicism', *Economica*, 1944–1945, **11–12**. Following in their footsteps I have also attempted to defend methodological individualism in 'Ideal Types and Historical Explanation', *British Journal for the Philosophy of Science*, 1952, **3**, 22, reprinted in *Readings in the Philosophy of Science*, ed. Feigl and Brodbeck, New York, 1953 [see above]. This article has come in for a good deal of criticism, the chief items of which I shall try to rebut in what follows.

standing of their situation. Every complex social situation, institution, or event is the result of a particular configuration of individuals, their dispositions, situations, beliefs, and physical resources and environment. There may be unfinished or half-way explanations of large-scale social phenomena (say, inflation) in terms of other large-scale phenomena (say, full employment); but we shall not have arrived at rock-bottom explanations of such large-scale phenomena until we have deduced an account of them from statements about the dispositions, beliefs, resources, and interrelations of individuals. (The individuals may remain anonymous and only typical dispositions, etc., may be attributed to them.) And just as mechanism is contrasted with the organicist idea of physical fields, so methodological individualism is contrasted with sociological holism or organicism. On this latter view, social systems constitute 'wholes' at least in the sense that some of their large-scale behaviour is governed by macro-laws which are essentially *sociological* in the sense that they are *sui generis* and not to be explained as mere regularities or tendencies resulting from the behaviour of interacting individuals. On the contrary, the behaviour of individuals should (according to sociological holism) be explained at least partly in terms of such laws (perhaps in conjunction with an account, first of individuals' roles within institutions and secondly of the functions of institutions within the whole social system). If methodological individualism means that human beings are supposed to be the only moving agents in history, and if sociological holism means that some superhuman agents or factors are supposed to be at work in history, then these two alternatives are exhaustive. An example of such a superhuman, sociological factor is the alleged long-term cyclical wave in economic life which is supposed to be self-propelling, uncontrollable, and inexplicable in terms of human activity, but in terms of the fluctuations of which such large-scale phenomena as wars, revolutions, and mass emigration, and such psychological factors as scientific and technological inventiveness can, it is claimed, be explained and predicted.

I say 'and predicted' because the irreducible sociological laws postulated by holists are usually regarded by them as laws of social development, as laws governing the dynamics of a society. This makes holism well-nigh equivalent to historicism, to the idea that a society is impelled along a predetermined route by historical laws which cannot be resisted but which can be discerned by the sociologist. The holist-historicist position has, in my view, been irretrievably damaged by Popper's attacks on it. I shall criticize this position only in so far as this will help me to elucidate and defend the individualistic alternative to it. The central assumption of the individualistic position—an assumption which is admittedly counter-factual and metaphysical—is that no social tendency exists which could not be altered *if* the individuals concerned both wanted to alter it and possessed the appropriate information. (They might want to alter the tendency but, through ignorance of the facts and/or failure to work out some of the implications of their action, fail to alter it, or perhaps even intensify it.) This assumption could also be expressed by saying that no social tendency is somehow imposed on human beings 'from above' (or 'from below')—social tendencies are the product (usually undesigned) of human characteristics and activities and situations, of people's ignorance and laziness as well as of their knowledge and ambition. (An example of a social tendency is the tendency of industrial units to grow larger. I do not call 'social' those tendencies which are determined by uncontrollable physical factors, such as the alleged tendency for more male babies to be born in times of disease or war.)[2]

My procedure will be: first, to delimit the sphere in which methodological individualism works in two directions; secondly, to clear

[2] The issue of holism *versus* individualism in social science has recently been presented as though it were a question of the existence or non-existence of irreducibly social *facts* rather than of irreducibly sociological *laws*. (See M. Mandelbaum, 'Societal Facts', *The British Journal of Sociology*, 1955, **6**, and E. A. Gellner, 'Explanations in History', *Aristotelian Society*, Supplementary Volume **30**, 1956. [See below pp. 221–234 and 248–263.] This way of presenting the issue seems to me to empty it of most of its interest. If a new kind of beast is discovered, what we want to know is not so much whether it falls outside existing zoological categories, but how it behaves. People who insist on the existence of social facts but who do not say whether they are governed by sociological laws, are like people who claim to have discovered an unclassified kind of animal but who do not tell us whether it is tame or dangerous, whether it can be domesticated or is unmanageable. If an answer to the question of social facts could throw light on the serious and interesting question of sociological laws, then the question of social facts would also be serious and interesting. But this is not so. On the one hand, a holist may readily admit (as I pointed out in my 'Ideal Types' paper, which Gellner criticizes) that all observable social facts *are* reducible to individual facts and yet hold that the latter are invisibly governed by irreducibly sociological laws. On the other hand, an individualist may readily admit (as Gellner himself says) that some large social facts are simply too complex for a full reduction of them to be feasible, and yet hold that individualistic explanations of them are in principle possible, just as a physicist may readily admit that some physical facts (for instance, the precise blast-effects of a bomb-explosion in a built-up area) are just too complex for accurate prediction or explanation of them to be feasible and yet hold that precise explanations and predictions of them in terms of existing scientific laws are in principle possible.

This revised way of presenting the holism *versus* individualism issue does not only divert attention from the important question. It also tends to turn the dispute into a purely verbal issue. Thus Mandelbaum is able to prove the existence of what he calls 'societal facts' because he defines psychological facts very narrowly as 'facts concerning the thoughts and actions of specific human beings' (*op. cit.*, p. 223). Consequently, the *dispositions of anonymous* individuals which play such an important role in individualistic explanations in social science are 'societal facts' merely by definition.

methodological individualism of certain misunderstandings; thirdly, to indicate how fruitful and surprising individualistic explanations can be and how individualistic social theories can lead to sociological discoveries; and fourthly, to consider in somewhat more detail how, according to methodological individualism, we should frame explanations, first for social regularities or repeatable processes, and secondly for unique historical constellations of events.

WHERE METHODOLOGICAL INDIVIDUALISM DOES NOT WORK

There are two areas in which methodological individualism does not work.

The first is a probability situation where accidental and unpredictable irregularities in human behaviour have a fairly regular and predictable overall result.[3] Suppose I successively place 1,000 individuals facing north in the centre of a symmetrical room with two exits, one east, the other west. If about 500 leave by one exit and about 500 by the other I would not try to explain this in terms of tiny undetectable west-inclining and east-inclining differences in the individuals, for the same reason that Popper would not try to explain the fact that about 500 balls will topple over to the west and about 500 to the east, if 1,000 balls are dropped from immediately above a north-south blade, in terms of tiny, undetectable west-inclining and east-inclining differences in the balls. For in both cases such an 'explanation' would merely raise the further problem: why should these west-inclining and east-inclining differences be distributed approximately *equally* among the individuals and among the balls?

Those statistical regularities in social life which are inexplicable in individualistic terms for the sort of reason I have quoted here are, in a sense, inhuman, the outcome of a large number of sheer *accidents*. The outcome of a large number of decisions is usually much less regular and predictable because variable human factors (changes of taste, new ideas, swings from optimism to pessimism) which have little or no influence on accident-rates are influential here. Thus Stock Exchange prices fluctuate widely from year to year, whereas the number of road-accidents does not fluctuate widely. But the existence of these actuarial regularities does not, as has often been alleged, support the historicist idea that defenceless individuals like you and me are at the chance mercy of the inhuman and uncontrollable tendencies of our society. It

[3] Failure to exclude probability-situations from the ambit of methodological individualism was an important defect of my 'Ideal Types' paper. Here, Gellner's criticism [pp. 252–253 below] does hit the nail on the head.

does not support a secularized version of the Calvinist idea of an Almighty Providence who picks people at random to fill His fixed damnation-quota. For we can control these statistical regularities in so far as we can alter the conditions on which they depend. For example, we could obviously abolish road-accidents if we were prepared to prohibit motor-traffic.

The second kind of social phenomenon to which methodological individualism is inapplicable is where some kind of physical connection between people's nervous systems short-circuits their intelligent control and causes automatic, and perhaps in some sense appropriate, bodily responses. I think that a man may more or less literally smell danger and instinctively back away from unseen ambushers; and individuality seems to be temporarily submerged beneath a collective physical *rapport* at jive-sessions and revivalist meetings and among panicking crowds. But I do not think that these spasmodic mob-organisms lend much support to holism or constitute a very serious exception to methodological individualism. They have a fleeting existence which ends when their members put on their mufflers and catch the bus or otherwise disperse, whereas holists have conceived of a social whole as something which endures through generations of men; and whatever holds together typical long-lived institutions, like a bank or a legal system or a church, it certainly is not the physical proximity of their members.

MISUNDERSTANDINGS OF METHODOLOGICAL INDIVIDUALISM

I will now clear methodological individualism of two rather widespread misunderstandings.

It has been objected that in making individual dispositions and beliefs and situations the terminus of an explanation in social science, methodological individualism implies that a person's psychological make up is, so to speak, God-given, whereas it is in fact conditioned by, and ought to be explained in terms of, his social inheritance and environment.[4] Now methodological individualism certainly does not prohibit attempts to explain the formation of psychological characteristics; it only requires that such explanations should in turn be

---

[4] Thus Gellner writes: 'The real oddity of the reductionist [i.e., the methodological individualist's] case is that it seems to preclude *a priori* the possibility of human dispositions being the dependent variable in an historical explanation—when in fact they often or always are' [p. 254 below]. And Mr Leon J. Goldstein says that in making human dispositions methodologically primary I ignore their cultural conditioning. (*The Journal of Philosophy*, 1956, **53**, 807.) [See p. 269 below.]

individualistic, explaining the formation as the result of a series of conscious or unconscious responses by an individual to his changing situation. For example, I have heard Professor Paul Sweezey, the Harvard economist, explain that he became a Marxist because his father, a Wall Street broker, sent him in the 1930s to the London School of Economics to study under those staunch liberal economists, Professors Hayek and Robbins. This explanation is perfectly compatible with methodological individualism (though hardly compatible, I should have thought, with the Marxist idea that ideologies reflect class-positions) because it interprets his ideological development as a human response to his situation. It is, I suppose, psycho-analysts who have most systematically worked the idea of a thorough individualist and historical explanation of the formation of dispositions, unconscious fears and beliefs, and subsequent defence-mechanisms, in terms of responses to emotionally charged, and especially childhood, situations.

My point could be put by saying that methodological individualism encourages *innocent* explanations but forbids *sinister* explanations of the widespread existence of a disposition among the members of a social group. Let me illustrate this by quoting from a reply I made to Goldstein's criticisms.

> Suppose that it is established that Huguenot traders were relatively prosperous in 17th-century France and that this is explained in terms of a wide-spread disposition among them (a disposition for which there is independent evidence) to plough back into their businesses a larger proportion of their profits than was customary among their Catholic competitors. Now this explanatory disposition might very well be explained in its turn—perhaps in terms of the general thriftiness which Calvinism is said to encourage, and/or in terms of the fewer alternative outlets for the cash resources of people whose religious disabilities prevented them from buying landed estates or political offices. (I cannot vouch for the historical accuracy of this example.)
>
> I agree that methodological individualism allows the formation, or 'cultural conditioning', of a widespread disposition to be explained only in terms of other human factors and not in terms of something *in*human, such as an alleged historicist law which impels people willy-nilly along some pre-determined course. But this is just the anti-historicist point of methodological individualism.

Unfortunately, it is typically a part of the programme of Marxist and other historicist sociologies to try to account for the formation of ideologies and other psychological characteristics in strictly sociological and non-psychological terms. Marx, for instance, professed to believe that feudal ideas and *bourgeois* ideas are more or less literally generated by the water-mill and the steam-engine. But no description, however complete, of the productive apparatus of a society, or of any other non-psychological factors, will enable you to deduce a single psychological conclusion from it, because psychological statements logically cannot be deduced from wholly non-psychological statements. Thus whereas the mechanistic idea that explanations in physics cannot go behind the impenetrable particles is a prejudice (though a very understandable prejudice), the analogous idea that an explanation which begins by imputing some social phenomenon to human factors cannot go on to explain those factors in terms of some inhuman determinant of them is a necessary truth. That the human mind develops under various influences the methodological individualist does not, of course, deny. He only insists that such development must be explained 'innocently' as a series of responses by the individual to situations and not 'sinisterly' and illogically as a direct causal outcome of non-psychological factors, whether these are neurological factors, or impersonal sociological factors alleged to be at work in history.

Another cause of complaint against methodological individualism is that it has been confused with a narrow species of itself (Popper calls it 'psychologism') and even, on occasion, with a still narrower sub-species of this (Popper calls it the 'Conspiracy Theory of Society').[5] Psychologism says that all large-scale social characteristics are not merely the intended or unintended result of, but a *reflection* of, individual characteristics.[6] Thus Plato said that the character and make-up of a *polis* is a reflection of the character and make-up of the kind of soul

[5] See K. R. Popper, *The Open Society and its Enemies*, 2nd edn., 1952, ch. 14.

[6] I am at a loss to understand how Gellner came to make the following strange assertion: '. . . Popper refers to both "psychologism" which he condemns, and "methodological individualism", which he commends. When in the articles discussed [i.e., my "Ideal Types" paper] "methodological individualism" is worked out more fully than is the case in Popper's book, it seems to me to be indistinguishable from "Psychologism".' Finding no difference between methodological individualism and a caricature of methodological individualism, Gellner has no difficulty in poking fun at the whole idea: 'Certain tribes I know have what anthropologists call a segmentary patrilineal structure, which moreover maintains itself very well over time. I could "explain" this by saying that the tribesmen have, all or most of them, dispositions whose effect is to maintain the system. But, of course, not only have they never given the matter much thought, but it also might very well be impossible to isolate anything in the characters and conduct of the individual tribesmen which *explains* how they come to maintain the system [p. 262 below]. Yet this example actually suggests the lines along which an individualistic explanation might be found. The very fact that the tribesmen *have never given the matter much thought*, the fact that they accept their inherited system uncritically, may constitute an important part of an explanation of its stability. The explanation might go on to pin-point certain rules—that is firm and widespread dispositions—about marriage, inheritance, etc., which help to regularize the tribesmen's behaviour towards their kinsmen. How they come to share these common dispositions could also be explained individualistically in the same sort of way that I can explain why my young children are already developing a typically English attitude towards policemen.

predominant in it. The conspiracy theory says that all large-scale social phenomena do not merely reflect individual characteristics but are deliberately brought about by individuals or groups of individuals.

Now there are social phenomena, like mass unemployment, which it would not have been in anyone's interest deliberately to bring about and which do not appear to be large-scale social reflections or magnified duplicates of some individual characteristic. The practical or technological or therapeutic importance of social science largely consists in explaining, and thereby perhaps rendering politically manageable, the unintended and unfortunate consequences of the behaviour of interacting individuals. From this pragmatic point of view, psychologism and the conspiracy theory are unrewarding doctrines. Psychologism says that only a change of heart can put a stop to, for example, war (I think that this is Bertrand Russell's view). The conspiracy theory, faced with a big bad social event, leads to a hunt for scapegoats. But methodological individualism, by imputing unwanted social phenomena to individuals' responses to their situations, in the light of their dispositions and beliefs, suggests that we may be able to make the phenomena disappear, not by recruiting good men to fill the posts hitherto occupied by bad men, nor by trying to destroy men's socially unfortunate dispositions while fostering their socially beneficial dispositions, but simply by altering the situations they confront. To give a current example, by confronting individuals with dearer money and reduced credit the Government may (I do not say will) succeed in halting inflation without requiring a new self-denying attitude on the part of consumers and without sending anyone to prison.

FACTUAL DISCOVERIES IN SOCIAL SCIENCE

To explain the unintended but *beneficial* consequences of individual activities—by 'beneficial consequences' I mean social consequences which the individuals affected *would* endorse *if* they were called on to choose between their continuation or discontinuation—is usually a task of less practical urgency than the explanation of undesirable consequences. On the other hand, this task may be of greater theoretical interest. I say this because people who are painfully aware of the existence of unwanted social phenomena may be oblivious of the unintended but beneficial consequences of men's actions, rather as a man may be oblivious of the good health to which the smooth functioning of his digestion, nervous system, circulation, etc., give rise. Here, an explanatory social theory may surprise and enlighten us not only with regard to the connections between causes and effect but with regard to the existence of the effect itself. By showing that a certain economic system contains positive feed-back leading to increasingly violent oscillations and crises an economist may explain a range of well-advertised phenomena which have long been the subject of strenuous political agitation. But the economists who first showed that a certain kind of economic system contains negative feed-back which tends to iron out disturbances and restore equilibrium, not only explained, but also revealed the existence of, phenomena which had hardly been remarked upon before.[7]

I will speak of organic-like social behaviour where members of some social system (that is, a collection of people whose activities disturb and influence each other) mutually adjust themselves to the situations created by the others in a way which, without direction from above, conduces to the equilibrium or preservation or development of the system. (These are again evaluative notions, but they can also be given a 'would-be-endorsed-if' definition.) Now such far-flung organic-like behaviour, involving people widely separated in space and largely ignorant of each other, cannot be simply observed. It can only be theoretically reconstructed—by deducing the distant social consequences of the typical responses of a large number of interacting people to certain repetitive situations. This explains why individualistic-minded economists and anthropologists, who deny that societies really are organisms, have succeeded in piecing together a good deal of unsuspected organic-like social behaviour, from an examination of individual dispositions and situations, whereas sociological holists, who insist that societies really are organisms, have been noticeably unsuccessful in convincingly displaying any organic-like social behaviour—they cannot observe it and they do not try to reconstruct it individualistically.

There is a parallel between holism and psychologism which explains their common failure to make surprising discoveries. A large-scale social characteristic should be explained, according to psychologism, as the manifestation of analogous small-scale psychological tendencies in individuals, and according to holism as the manifestation of a large-scale tendency in the social whole. In both cases, the *explicans* does

---

[7] This sentence, as I have since learnt from Dr A. W. Phillips, is unduly complacent, for it is very doubtful whether an economist can ever *show* that an economic system containing negative feed-back will be stable. For negative feed-back may produce either a tendency towards equilibrium, or increasing oscillations, according to the numerical values of the parameters of the system. But numerical values are just what economic measurements, which are usually ordinal rather than cardinal, seldom yield. The belief that a system which contains negative feed-back, but whose variables cannot be described quantitatively, is stable may be based on faith or experience, but it cannot be shown mathematically. See A. W. Phillips, 'Stabilisation Policy and the Time-Forms of Lagged Responses', *The Economic Journal*, 1957, 67.

little more than duplicate the *explicandum*. The methodological individualist, on the other hand, will try to explain the large-scale effect as the *indirect*, unexpected, complex product of individual factors none of which, singly, may bear any resemblance to it at all. To use hackneyed examples, he may show that a longing for peace led, in a certain international situation, to war, or that a government's desire to improve a bad economic situation by balancing its budget only worsened the situation. Since Mandeville's *Fable of the Bees* was published in 1714, individualistic social science, with its emphasis on unintended consequences, has largely been a sophisticated elaboration on the simple theme that, in certain situations, selfish private motives may have good social consequences and good political intentions bad social consequences.[8]

Holists draw comfort from the example of biology, but I think that the parallel is really between the biologist and the methodological individualist. The biologist does not, I take it, explain the large changes which occur during, say, pregnancy, in terms of corresponding large teleological tendencies in the organism, but physically, in terms of small chemical, cellular, neurological, etc., changes, none of which bears any resemblance to their joint and seemingly planful outcome.

HOW SOCIAL EXPLANATIONS SHOULD BE FRAMED

I will now consider how regularities in social life, such as the trade cycle, should be explained according to methodological individualism. The explanation should be in terms of individuals and their situations; and since the process to be explained is repeatable, liable to recur at various times and in various parts of the world, it follows that only very general assumptions about human dispositions can be employed in its explanation. It is no use looking to abnormal psychology for an explanation of the structure of interest-rates—everyday experience

---

[8] A good deal of unmerited opposition to methodological individualism seems to spring from the recognition of the undoubted fact that individuals often run into social obstacles. Thus the conclusion at which Mandelbaum arrives is 'that there are societal facts which exercise external constraints over individuals' [p. 234 below]. This conclusion is perfectly harmonious with the methodological individualist's insistence that plans often miscarry (and that even when they do succeed, they almost invariably have other important and unanticipated effects). The methodological individualist only insists that the social environment by which any particular individual is confronted and frustrated and sometimes manipulated and occasionally destroyed is, if we ignore its physical ingredients, made up of other *people*, their habits, inertia, loyalties, rivalries, and so on. What the methodological individualist denies is that an individual is ever frustrated, manipulated or destroyed or borne along by irreducible sociological or historical *laws*.

must contain the raw material for the dispositional (as opposed to the situational) assumptions required by such an explanation. It may require a stroke of genius to detect, isolate, and formulate precisely the dispositional premisses of an explanation of a social regularity. These premisses may state what no one had noticed before, or give a sharp articulation to what had hitherto been loosely described. But once stated they will seem obvious enough. It took years of groping by brilliant minds before a precise formulation was found for the principle of diminishing marginal utility. But once stated, the principle—that the less, relatively, a man has of one divisible commodity the more compensation he will be disposed to require for foregoing a small fixed amount of it—is a principle to which pretty well everyone will give his consent. Yet this simple and almost platitudinous principle is the magic key to the economics of distribution and exchange.

The social scientist is, here, in a position analogous to that of the Cartesian mechanist.[9] The latter never set out to discover new and unheard-of physical principles because he believed that his own principle of action-by-contact was self-evidently ultimate. His problem was to discover the typical physical configurations, the mechanisms, which, operating according to this principle, produce the observed regularities of nature. His theories took the form of models which exhibited such regularities as the outcome of 'self-evident' physical principles operating in some hypothetical physical situation. Similarly, the social scientist does not make daring innovations in psychology but relies on familiar, almost 'self-evident' psychological material. His skill consists, first in spotting the relevant dispositions, and secondly in inventing a simple but realistic model which shows how, in a precise type of situation, those dispositions generate some typical regularity or process. (His model, by the way, will also show that in this situation certain things cannot happen. His negative predictions of the form, 'If you've got this you can't have that as well' may be of great practical importance.) The social scientist can now explain in principle historical examples of this regular process, provided his model does in fact fit the historical situation.

This view of the explanation of social regularities incidentally clears up the old question on which so much ink has been spilt about whether the so-called 'laws' of economics apply universally or only to a particular 'stage' of economic development. The simple answer is that the economic principles displayed by economists' models apply only to those situations which correspond with their models; but a single model may very well correspond with a very large number of historical situations widely separated in space and time.

[9] I owe this analogy to Professor Popper.

In the explanation of regularities the same situational scheme or model is used to reconstruct a number of historical situations with a similar structure in a way which reveals how typical dispositions and beliefs of anonymous individuals generated, on each occasion, the same regularity.[10] In the explanation of a unique constellation of events the individualistic method is again to reconstruct the historical situation, or connected sequence of situations, in a way which reveals how (usually both named and anonymous) individuals, with their beliefs and dispositions (which may include peculiar personal dispositions as well as typical human dispositions), generated, in this particular situation, the joint product to be explained. I emphasize *dispositions*, which are open and law-like, as opposed to *decisions*, which are occurrences, for this reason. A person's set of dispositions ought, under varying conditions, to give rise to appropriately varying decisions. The subsequent occurrence of an appropriate decision will both confirm, and be explained by, the existence of the dispositions. Suppose that a historical explanation (of, say, the growth of the early Catholic Church) largely relies on a particular decision (say, the decision of Emperor Constantine to give Pope Silvester extensive temporal rights in Italy). The explanation is, so far, rather *ad hoc*: an apparently arbitrary *fiat* plays a key role in it. But if this decision can in turn be explained as the offspring of a marriage of a set of dispositions (for instance, the Emperor's disposition to subordinate all rival power to himself) to a set of circumstances (for instance, the Emperor's recognition that Christianity could not be crushed but could be tamed if it became the official religion of the Empire), and if the existence of these dispositions and circumstances is convincingly supported by independent evidence, then the area of the arbitrarily given, of sheer brute fact in history, although it can never be made to vanish, will have been significantly reduced.

[10] This should rebut Gellner's conclusion that methodological individualism would transform social scientists into 'biographers *en grande série*' [p. 263 below].

J. W. N. WATKINS

Methodological Individualism: A Reply

In this paper I shall try to meet Professor May Brodbeck's criticisms of methodological individualism.[1]

I will begin by restating the principle. It is based on the metaphysical commonplace that social events are brought about by *people*. Speaking loosely, one can say that climate, famine, the location of minerals, and other physical factors help to determine history, just as one can say that alcohol causes road accidents. But speaking strictly, one should say that alcohol induces changes in people who drink it, and that it is the behaviour of alcohol-affected people, rather than alcohol itself, which results in road accidents. Alcohol may indirectly affect society in another way, through the ideas which people entertain about alcohol. People who believe that it is evil, or profitable to manufacture, or that it can bear a heavy tax, may behave very differently because of their different ideas; and their behaviour may, as Prohibition showed, have all sorts of unintended consequences.

Thus the fact that physical causes operate in society does not invalidate the assumption on which the principle of methodological individualism rests. For they operate either by affecting people, or through people's ideas about them. In either case it is *people* who determine history, however people themselves are determined.

This factual or metaphysical claim has the methodological implication that large-scale social phenomena like inflation, political revolutions, etc., should be explained in terms of the situations, dispositions and beliefs of *individuals*. This is what is called methodological individualism.

Many people would regard this as a truism. Bur some philosophers of history have taken an opposite view, equally metaphysical but recondite and exciting, perhaps because it is a piece of theology in disguise. A providential theory of history asserts that individuals act under their own volition, but that their desires and circumstances have been so cunningly arranged that the overall result of their individual activities is the continuous achievement of further stages in the

[1] In *Philosophy of Science*, 21, **2**, April 1954.

Ed. See above pp. 91–110. I have altered all original references to the pagination in this volume.

unfolding of a divine plan. In the secularized version of this theory it is the social whole which so determines matters for the individual that he cannot avoid (or can hardly avoid: the determinism may be a little loose) fulfilling his function within the whole system. On this view, the social behaviour of individuals should be explained in terms of their positions within its cultural-institutional structure, together with the laws which govern the system. These laws are supposed to be *sui generis*, applying to the whole as such and not derivable from statements about individuals and their interrelations. This is what is called methodological holism.

I admitted in my paper that we cannot know *a priori* that methodological individualism is true, but I pointed out that we have good reasons for accepting it, whereas methodological holism involves a claim which seems rather extraordinary.[2] I now turn to Professor Brodbeck's criticisms.

First, she says that it has been asserted (by me) that explanations in social science are not *surprising*. She relates this to her more general complaint that *methodological individualism* somehow trivializes social science. Now I did not quite say that explanations in social science are not surprising. What I did say was that they were not surprising *in the same way* that explanations in natural science, which explain the familiar in terms of the unfamiliar, are surprising. Explanations in social science, I said, explain the familiar in terms of the familiar; but the *connection* may be surprising (as it is when the rise of capitalism is connected with Protestantism, for example).

Professor Brodbeck next attempts to refute methodological individualism with the help of an intellectual experiment:

> Suppose that Jones behaves in a certain way only if he is a member of a group—in the same hall or under the same jurisdiction—of N, say 1,000 people. Suppose further that the law expressing Jones' behaviour in this situation is not derivable from laws concerning his behaviour in groups of less than N together with the composition rules based on these laws. This circumstance then exhibits empirical emergence at a certain level of complexity, namely groups of size N, and methodological individualism breaks down as an explanatory principle [p. 108].

Now there are two *kinds* of reason why Jones' behaviour might change in groups of a certain size. His response to the situation might be an understandable personal response, in keeping with his character. (Perhaps he becomes prone to claustrophobia when the hall gets too crowded.) This would be in accord with methodological individualism.

---

[2] See J. W. N. Watkins, 'Ideal Types and Historical Explanation', in *Readings in the Philosophy of Science*, eds. H. Feigl and M. Brodbeck, Appleton-Century Crofts, New York, 1953 [see above]. As its references indicate, this paper is very indebted to the work of Professors Hayek and Popper.

But there is another kind of reason for Jones' behaviour, strange but not inconceivable. He *might* come under a new and weird sort of control when a group to which he belongs reaches a certain critical size. When it reaches this size, he and other members of the group may cease acting under their own steam and become like iron-filings in something analogous to a magnetic field which organized him and them into a holistic pattern of behaviour. As Professor Brodbeck was trying to refute methodological individualism she presumably meant to exemplify this second kind of reason for Jones' behaviour, and not the first. But her imaginary example proves only that holism is conceivable, which I have not denied. I only said that it was unbelievable, for various reasons. Moreover, Professor Brodbeck herself, only a few sentences later, rejects the holistic alternative:

> I agree with Mr Watkins that neither society nor any of its subgroups are organisms in the sense he explains. The denial that there are such organisms amounts to denying that there are *sui generis* sociological laws [p. 109].

So I am not quite clear what is supposed to have been established.

Before I turn to her next criticisms I must explain something which I did not make sufficiently clear in my paper. I said there that an individualistic explanation of a social event need not refer to *specific* individuals; it may be what I called an 'anonymous explanation'. If I ask my stock-broker why De Beers shares have been rising and am told, 'Because an increase is anticipated', I shall have been given an individualistic explanation although I have not been told anything about any particular share-holder. The explanation gave a brief summary or general characterization of the anticipations of anonymous individuals. It did not, of course, refer to some impersonal, unattached, anticipation. If I doubt the explanation I can only test it by polling individual share-holders.

Let me illustrate the distinction between an anonymous individualistic explanation and a holistic explanation with another example. Suppose an election-result is explained in terms of a 'swing of the pendulum'. According to the principle of methodological individualism, such an explanation is permissible if it is no more than a short-hand way of saying that more and more (anonymous) electors grow more and more dissatisfied with any party the longer it remains in office. But it is, according to methodological individualism, an impermissible holistic explanation if it really intends to assert that there is a *social* law which requires the electorate to display a periodically oscillating pattern of electoral behaviour.

Now I am afraid that Professor Brodbeck has not fully appreciated the difference between an impermissible, holistic explanation and a permissible, anonymous, short-hand individualistic explanation. She writes: 'Drawing on one of [Watkins'] illustrations, an election result may be explained *either* in terms of individual dispositions *or* in terms of macroscopic laws about the history and fate of political parties in power for a given time, the relation to world crises, prosperity, and so forth. The latter alternative would be a perfectly good and even enlightening explanation, but it would be macroscopic' [p. 110]. She appears to identify an anonymous explanation with 'macroscopic' explanation. If 'The Great Depression caused the defeat of the Labour Government in 1931' is short-hand for something like 'Most electors blamed the Government for the unemployment and poverty and voted anti-Labour' then it is permissible; but if it were really meant to suggest that the behaviour of voters is *controlled* by an economic cycle, then it is, according to methodological individualism, impermissible. (In my paper I criticized Kondratieff's version of this latter kind of neo-Marxist explanation.)

Professor Brodbeck's subsequent criticisms are all vitiated by her failure to recognize the covertly individualistic character of explanations which refer only to anonymous individuals. Thus she puts forward as an objection to methodological individualism:

> The Keynesian hypothesis that the consumption of a community is an increasing [*sic*] function of its total income is, of course, about a group *and not about individuals* [p. 155, my italics].

This seems plainly belied by Keynes' own words:

> The amount that the community spends on consumption obviously depends (i) partly on the amount of its income, (ii) partly on the other objective attendant circumstances, and (iii) partly on the subjective needs and *the psychological propensities and habits of the individuals composing it* . . . (*The General Theory*, pp. 90–91, my italics).

In my paper I argued that if the individualistic interpretation of social science is sound we should expect to find that important advances in social theory consist in detecting and delineating a typical human disposition which had been overlooked but which helps to explain hitherto unexplained phenomena; and I went on to instantiate this with examples, one of which was Keynes' theory. I quoted a passage in which Keynes says that he bases his theory on three fundamental psychological dispositions. Why, then, does Professor Brodbeck advance Keynes' theory as a counter-example to my thesis? The only explanation I can offer is that Keynes did not say that *all* individuals *always* save proportionately more when their incomes rise, but that 'by and large and on the average' individuals do this. But a *statistical* statement about people is still a statement *about people*. She next claims that

Contemporary experimental social psychologists find that empirically defined, measurable, macroscopic concepts, making no direct reference to individuals—e.g., 'group climate' or 'cohesiveness'—permit prediction (and explanation) of group behaviour . . . [p. 109].

If by 'no direct reference to individuals' she means no *explicit* reference, then I agree of course. But she presumably means more than this. And I do not see how such concepts can 'permit prediction' without making at least a tacit reference to individuals. If 'The Jewish race is cohesive' does *not* mean that, for instance, Jews usually marry Jews, live in close communities, share religious rituals, etc., if it does not refer to Jewish people (whose behaviour can be observed) but only to the Jewish race (which cannot be observed), then I do not see how it can be tested or have any empirical content. In my paper I claimed that one unintended benefit of Max Weber's early insistence on the need to use and define holistic concepts in historical investigations was that, when we obey his injunction and try to define them, we invariably find that we have transformed them into individualistic concepts.

Finally, Professor Brodbeck claims that I have myself admitted that methodological individualism is defeated by the sheer complexity of economic life:

And at one point Watkins in effect admits that for any actual economic system the number of factors at work renders methodological individualism an impossible task [p. 109].

I wish that I had made the long section I devoted to anonymous explanations, or, as I (following Hayek) called them, 'explanations in principle', clearer. Her footnote refers to a passage where, drawing on Walter Eucken, I was saying that it is often impossible in practice to trace all the factors which led to a certain event. Let me revert to my De Beers example: it would be practically impossible to explain in detail the fact that they have risen 10s. during the last month, by detecting and describing all the anticipations and decisions of all the individuals whose market operations have led to this result; but we know that it is quite possible to explain the rise in the price in the shares in principle, or anonymously. Overlooking my discussion and illustrations of anonymous explanations and erroneously assuming that methodological individualism permits only *detailed* explanations in terms of the peculiar dispositions and beliefs of *specific* individuals, Miss Brodbeck understandably fears that methodological individualism will reduce social science 'to impotence or to triviality' [p. 110]. But her fears are groundless.

The general impression her paper gives is that methodological individualism is not so much valid as too narrow: the antithesis between methodological individualism and methodological holism is, she says,

M.I.C.—7

'a false disjunction' [p. 108]. She rather suggests that methodological individualism is appropriate in some circumstances, and methodological holism in others.

Now if, as I suspect, she is confusing methodological individualism with detailed individualistic explaining and methodological holism with explaining anonymously or in principle, then what she says is perfectly correct. A lengthy part of my paper was devoted to indicating where detailed explanations are possible and appropriate and where explanations in principle are adequate, or the best we can hope for.

But if 'methodological individualism' and 'methodological holism' are given the meanings I gave them in my paper, then an eclectic belief in both becomes hardly possible. If you became persuaded that the metaphysical assumption on which methodological holism is based is true, then your whole view of yourself and other people, of the social world in which you live, would be transformed. You would believe that the things we do because we want to do them are really done because our society requires us to do them. This is not the sort of idea with which an individualist can come to a comfortable compromise.

JOSEPH AGASSI

Methodological Individualism[1]

My aim in the present essay is to argue that individualism need not be psychologistic, and to defend institutionalistic individualism, which I consider to be Popper's great contribution to the philosophy of the social sciences.

I

When the individualist contends that only individuals are responsible actors on the social and historical stage, the holist retorts that society is more than merely a collection of individuals. To this retort the individualist answers that there is no mysterious additional entity which turns a collection of individuals into a society; a collection of individuals is a society if there is strong interaction between them; this interaction is due to the fact that when any one individual acts (rationally) on the basis of his own aims and interests, he takes into account the existence of other individuals with aims and interests. To this the holist retorts that the individualist misses the point; that people's aims do not constitute a society but rather depend on society; so that members of different societies have different aims and interests. The individualist in turn answers that the holist misses the point, by taking the social setting as God-given rather than as explicable in terms of human action. The holist in turn argues that human action does not determine but is rather constrained by, or directed by, the social setting (perhaps because social forces are much stronger than any single individual).

[1] An earlier version of sections III and V of the present essay was read to the seminar of E. Gellner and T. Bottomore at the London School of Economics early in 1958. An earlier version of section I of the present essay was read to the London School of Economics' Sociology Club in a debate with E. Gellner, on December 4, 1958; and a subsequent version was also read to the Theoretical and Comparative Sociology Study Group of the British Sociological Association on December 16, 1958. I am grateful to my wife, Mr P. Cohen, Mr E. Gellner, Mr E. Goodman, Mr K. Klappholz, Mr D. G. MacRae and Mr J. W. N. Watkins for reading the MS. in its various stages and for valuable suggestions.

This argument may be schematized in the following manner in an attempt to characterize the two traditional views.

(a) *Holism*	(b) *Individualism*
1. Society is the 'whole' which is more than its parts (holism).	Only individuals have aims and interests (individualism).
2. 'Society' affects the individual's aims (collectivism).	The individual behaves in a way adequate to his aim, given his circumstances (rationality principle).
3. The social set-up influences and constrains the individual's behaviour (institutional analysis).	The social set-up is changeable as a result of individuals' action (institutional reform).

It is obvious that here we have a characterization of two different positions. Yet, so far the characterization is not sufficient to bring out the fact that these two positions are mutually incompatible. Traditionally, many individualists have refused to assume the existence of any social entity *because* they assumed that only individuals can have aims and interests. They viewed 'the national interest', 'public policy', and such-like expressions either as empty or as mere shorthand expressions for sum-totals of many individuals' interests and policies. The holists, however, have traditionally insisted that national aims, class-interests, and *destinies of social groups* do exist. Logically this amounts to altering our schema in the following way: we add to *both* views, holism *and* individualism, the following proposition, and reinterpret the other propositions in its light.

4. If 'wholes' exist *then* they have distinct aims and interests of their own.

This additional proposition 4 renders 1 (a) inconsistent with 1 (b); it also enables us to reinterpret 2 (a) and 2 (b), as well as 3 (a) and 3 (b), in a manner which renders them inconsistent with each other. The individualist does not deny 2 (a) (collectivism) unless it is reinterpreted in accord with 4. He does not deny that one's aims can be affected by others' aims, and he can explain rationally such phenomena. He merely denies that one's aims can be explained by reference to the social aim. Similarly, the holist does not deny 2(b) (rationality principle) unless it is reinterpreted in accord with 4. He does not deny that the individual acts purposefully (rationally). He merely denies that individuals' aims and physical circumstances alone determine action. He insists that the aims of the social group constitute a major factor in determining the actions of its members. Again, the individualist does not deny 3 (a) (institutional analysis) unless it is reinterpreted according to 4. He does not deny that the behaviour of an individual is constrained and influenced by social factors provided that we can explain such constraints and influences as results of choices of other individuals. Only when the holist attributes these social constraints and influences to the aim of the social group does the individualist disagree with him. Similarly as to 3 (b) (institutional reform): the holist denies it only when the set-up which the individual supposedly changes is the 'society' or the social group—that is to say society's aims and destinies; he will not deny that the individual can alter his material environment, or other individuals' tastes, and similar 'superficial' factors.

Thus, proposition 4 renders the previous propositions more definite by interpreting holism as the view according to which the individual's interest is bound to the existing social interest, and individualism as the view that *only* individuals exist and have interests. This form of individualism is known as *psychologistic* individualism, or as individualistic psychologism.

Proposition 4 is not explicitly stated by writers on the present controversy, and it is not the only proposition which renders the two sides of our schema incompatible with each other. However, in my view, it is often implicit in many works on the controversy, old and new. Indeed it is sometimes so obviously implicit in these works that I find it a little puzzling that so few people have noticed it and have found it worthy of a comment. Whether proposition 4 is acceptable or not, refraining from stating it explicitly may easily lead to confusion. It is one thing to state explicitly that all individualism is psychologistic and quite another thing to confuse individualism with psychologism.

Psychologism is the programme of explaining all social phenomena solely with the aid of psychological theory. If the psychological theory which is to explain social phenomena is individual psychology, then our psychologism is of the individualist brand, while if it is collective psychology, then our psychologism is of the collectivist or holist brand. Thus, while Freud's attempt at a psychological explanation of some social phenomena (religion, leadership) is individualist, Jung's similar attempt is collectivist or holist, since he assumes the existence of group-subconsciousness. Similarly, Plato's theory of the state is an attempt to explain class structure, not institutionally, but psychologically—as reflecting the mental structure of the state. We thus have two divisions—psychologism versus institutionalism, and individualism versus holism—which yield four possible programmes: (a) psychologism-cum-individualism (the main stream of the individualist tradition); (b) institutionalism-cum-holism (the main stream of holism or collectivism); (c) psychologism-cum-holism (in rare examples like Plato's and Jung's theories); and perhaps (d) institutionalism-cum-individualism. (It should be added, perhaps, that these are by no means all the possibilities; cybernetics, for instance, falls into none of the four categories mentioned here.) The fourth possibility (d) is precisely what is denied by proposition 4. It is the central thesis of the present essay that proposition 4 is false.

	Individualism	Holism
Psychologism	a	c
Institutionalism	d	b

Admittedly proposition 4 is *prima facie* very convincing. It entails that either *all* statements about societies and social institutions should be taken at their face value or *all* of them should be viewed as shorthand assertions about many individuals. It sounds rather *ad hoc* to claim, as institutionalist-individualists have to claim, that *some* of these statements (say about the state of war between Britain and Germany) have to be taken at their face value, and some of these statements (about Germany's desire to win the war or its fight against Britain) have to be viewed as shorthand assertions about individuals. This may partly explain the fact that traditionally social philosophers accepted proposition 4 without discussing it.

And yet, in spite of this *prima facie* argument in favour of proposition 4, Popper rejects it. He asserts that 'wholes' do exist (though, of course, not in the same sense in which people exist), but they have no (distinct) interests. These 'wholes' are social groups as well as social institutions —in the widest sense of the word, and covering a wide variety, from customs to constitutions, and from neighbourhoods to states. An institution may have aims and interests only when people *give it an aim*, or act in accord with what *they consider should be its interest*; a society or an institution cannot have aims and interests of its own.

It is obvious that Popper can incorporate both 1 (a) and 1(b) into a consistent view which is incompatible with both holism and psychologistic individualism provided that this view contains the negation of proposition 4. And he can incorporate into this view all the other propositions in the above schema provided that they are interpreted not in accordance with proposition 4 but rather in opposition to it. Thus, in 2 (a), not the aims of institutions but rather their existence affects the individual's behaviour: the existing institutions constitute a part of the individual's circumstances which together with his aims determine his behaviour in accordance with 2 (b). While according to psychologistic individualism only material conditions may be considered as relevant circumstances, according to Popper the existence of institutions may be considered as relevant circumstances too. This addition enriches 2 (b) and turns it from the psychologistic rationality principle into what Popper calls 'situational logic'. Similarly, 3 (a) is admitted as institutional analysis not by admitting that the aims of institutions constrain the individual's behaviour, but by admitting that the existence and characteristics of institutions (as well as people's adoption of definite attitudes towards them) constrain the individual's behaviour, according to the logic of his situation. 3 (b) is the theory of institutional reform, of the way people may alter an institutional situation so as to abolish or enforce social constraints, and alter other people's attitudes (by resorting to violence or by democratic means—according to the logic of their situation).

Both 3 (a) and 3 (b) relate to an important aspect of human behaviour —the unintended social consequences of individual actions. The institutional analysis (3 (a)) will show how people act under certain circumstances in a way to forward their own aims, and in so doing affect the social system. In particular this will be so when their action is a reform of institutions (3 (b)). It is the very combination of 3 (a) and 3 (b) which renders the unintended consequences so important and which amounts to a theory of social change. It would be deserving of the title 'social dynamics' had not this title been used differently by some sociologists. The holist social dynamics is but a historicist assertion of the goal or destiny of the social whole; it has no explanatory power. The psychologistic individualist social dynamics is but an idea about the interaction of many individuals; it is far too complicated to be capable of development in any detail. None of these views of social dynamics accord with the following sketch of a simple example of social change. Consider the institutional circumstances (3 (a)) under which some workers find it profitable to organize a trade union for collective bargaining (3 (b)). In these new institutional circumstances following the formation of a trade union (3 (a)), other workers will find it profitable to organize as well (3 (b)). This subsequent situation in which most workers are organized (3 (a)) makes it desirable for the employers to organize (3 (b)). The existence of both workers' and employers' organizations will profoundly influence the relations between worker and employer (3 (a)); and it may even bring about the government's intervention, perhaps in the form of new legislation (3 (b)). Thus, unintentionally, the first trade union organizers have started a social avalanche.

I should add, in parenthesis, that many thinkers seem to have felt the need for a *via media* between the two traditional views, and even for a consistent synthesis between the reasonable elements in them. I maintain that Popper has succeeded in carrying out this intuitively felt programme, thus rendering explicit the approach which in fact underlies the fruitful and reasonable part of existing social studies, while retaining the central thesis of individualism, namely the thesis that only individuals have aims and responsibilities.

In the rest of this essay I shall try to elaborate points stated in the first section. I shall entirely ignore psychologistic holism, and discuss, from the methodological aspect, institutionalist holism, psychologistic individualism, and institutionalist individualism. I shall then conclude with a comment on the metaphysical views behind these approaches.

II

In this section I shall try to criticize holism from a methodological rather than from a metaphysical viewpoint. I shall not discuss the existence or non-existence of group-interests (or of group-minds), but stress the metaphysical character[2] of any assumption concerning group interests, and the danger involved in not recognizing this metaphysical character, or in regarding holism as 'scientific'.

The major question to which holism gives rise concerns the relation between the distinct interests of the group and those of the individuals belonging to it. Logically, these two kinds of interest may be in harmony or in conflict. The diversity of individuals' interests forces one to admit that the group's interest may be in conflict with some individuals' interests. One has to decide then, in case of a conflict of individual and the group's interest, which of these is, or should be, dominant. (1) One may assert that in case of conflict the group's interests should be dominant. In this case one merely advocates a collectivist morality. (2) One may assert that the group's interest is dominant, if not now, then at least 'in the long run', even without being imposed on its individual members who may all act against it. In this case, one expresses a fatalist view or a prophecy about things to come; Popper has tried to show (in his *Poverty of Historicism*) the barrenness and unscientific character of such prophecies. (3) One may assert that in case of conflict the group's interest is latent, and comes into play only when the group's members' interests alter so as to coincide with the group's interest. This is the pattern of many widespread popular beliefs. As a naïve example we may take the myth that when all Jews keep the Sabbath the Messiah will come. The newest theory which follows this pattern is that the leader discovers the destiny of his group; this is but a variation on the book of *Exodus*. All the variants which follow this pattern are obviously metaphysical; its main interest, I think, lies in its relation to a specific moral philosophy of the individual's responsibility to the collective. (This kind of morality falls neither under the heading of collectivist morality nor under the heading of individualistic morality—the two kinds of morality

---

[2] The term 'metaphysical character' is here used in Popper's sense, namely to denote irrefutability and lack of explanatory power. The proposal to attribute aims to societies is labelled by Popper 'methodological collectivism'. In this paper, however, I prefer to use Gellner's terminology: his term 'holism' is synonymous with Popper's '(methodological) collectivism'.

discussed in Popper's *Open Society*.[3]) (4) The only other alternative seems to be this: the group's interest always and necessarily manifests itself in, and acts through, some individuals' aims and interests. One may state a scientific theory while following this pattern, by specifying the individuals whose aims are identical with the group's interests and by specifying these individuals' aims and circumstances. But then the assertion about the identity of these individuals' and the group's interests which that theory would contain, will be redundant in the sense that the testability of the explanatory power of that theory will not diminish with the omission of this assertion. If this assertion is omitted the theory will accord with the pattern of institutionalistic individualism, but if this assertion is not omitted one may be tempted to stick to it when the scientific part of the theory is refuted. For, being unscientific, this assertion is irrefutable and can be safely upheld, though this amounts to dogmatism. I shall now discuss two examples of this kind of holism, Marxism and Functionalism.

What Marx said about class interest is hardly open to rational argument and is thus metaphysical, while his assertions concerning the way class interest manifests itself in the individual's action are open to criticism and are scientific. For example, one can criticize Marx by pointing out that a worker's interest does not always coincide with that of his fellow worker, and adduce empirical examples to this effect. Of course, one may dismiss such criticism as irrelevant on the grounds that only the workers' 'short-run' interests can conflict, but not their 'long-run' interests.[4] This is the attitude of those who are determined to uphold the metaphysical part of Marx's view dogmatically, even at the expense of ignoring the scientific part of Marx's view. Yet, obviously, it is the scientific part which is more interesting and more important.

Furthermore this attitude may easily lead to a collectivist morality. For, by admitting that the class interest may clash with the ('short-run') interest upon which its members act, one's views come very close to collectivist morality, and they become completely so when priority is explicitly given to the class interest itself. Thus, Marxist collectivist

---

[3] For the Jewish tradition of individual responsibility towards the collective see my 'Jacob Katz on Jewish Social History', *The Jewish Journal of Sociology*, Vol. I, No. 2, December 1959, especially p. 264. The existence of such a tradition refutes the views that there exist only two kinds of morality and that a collectivist social philosophy invariably leads to a collectivist morality.

[4] If 'long-run' here means what is usually meant by this term in economic literature, one can obviously find conflicts between the 'long-run' interests of different workers. When the 'long-run' interest, however, is simply the (distinct) interest of the class as a whole the theory of the identity of workers' interests becomes metaphysical as well as trite. The vacillation between the two meanings is, of course, an irrational part of contemporary Marxism.

morality begins with blaming workers for not behaving in accord with Marx's predictions.

My second example is from current social anthropology. I mention it diffidently, because I am not sufficiently familiar with modern anthropological studies. I understand that in some interpretations functionalism is viewed as the attempt to show how the social-group's interest of self-preservation is manifest in the compatibility of different social roles, when these coincide either in any one person or in any one situation. The scientific part of this approach consists of a variety of specific assumptions of the compatibility between specific social roles and of the critical examination of these assumptions, and is quite independent of any views concerning the group's interest. In particular it is independent of the metaphysical view that a group's interest is manifest in the compatibility of social roles. This metaphysical view leads to the dogma that compatibility must exist and to the corollary that there can never be any ('endogenous') social causes of social change, so that only 'alien' bodies or factors can cause social change. Gellner's excellent criticism of this dogma[5] seems to me to be quite unanswerable. My point here is that

---

[5] E. Gellner, 'Time and Theory in Social Anthropology', *Mind*, LXVII, April 1958, pp. 182–202. I should make it quite clear that my sketch of functionalism is greatly over-simplified. A slightly more adequate formulation allows for conflicts which can be resolved by institutional means (by ceremony, resignation, etc.). Yet this formulation in turn raises many problems which I cannot enter into. I should only like to mention that it renders functionalism yet more metaphysical, for we can always hope to find the method of resolution of a conflict—even if it does not exist. Moreover, in a sense it renders functionalism entirely trivial. For its claims that any institutional and repeated conflict (others will be hardly noticed by the members of the society in question, much less by the anthropologist) will sooner or later lead to the institutionalization of some remedies for it, at least in the same sense that people will get used to living with it (or else perish).

Gellner has made the same criticism somewhat differently: to assert that *some* method of co-ordination exists in a society is trivial, and even follows from the meaning of the word 'society'; while to assert that *full* co-ordination exists leads to the untenable view which excludes any ('endogenous') change. Thus, functionalism is either trivial or dogmatic.

There exist conflicts which are institutionalized, e.g., feuds, or relations between in-laws. Functionalism forces its adherents to view institutionalized conflicts as means of social co-ordination and as means of resolving conflicts. This led Evans-Pritchard to his ingenious view of feuds as means of co-ordination or cohesion between the different lineages or clans or tribes. Yet this view sounds dangerously apologetic, and, indeed, for some philsophers it seems to have become a mystical dogma. It is by far preferable, I think, to view feuds merely as means of protection, and to view the rest of what anthropologists may call their function as their unintended consequences. For such consequences may be *un*desirable and lead to reform. Alternatively, the feud system may become unnecessary when some reform leads to a better method of protection, and the undesired consequences of that reform may be the vanishing of the desirable consequences of the feud system which Evans-Pritchard and Gluckman have discovered.

this dogma stems from holism and is quite redundant: the parts of functionalism which are reasonable and interesting are entirely independent of it.

The same may be said about Gellner's criticism of the functionalist doctrine of survival. According to this doctrine social relics do not exist: no social institution survives its function: if it exists today it must have a function today, and this function will explain and justify its existence independently of its history. In my own view there are two strong methodological points behind the functionalist doctrine of survival. The first is a methodological criticism of the approach which was widespread before the rise of functionalism ('historism', about which see below, p. 198): the assumption that an institution once existed is not an explanation of its existence now, that is to say, of its survival. The second is the methodological rule of attempting to explain a seeming social relic by assuming it to be something of contemporary significance. We do not know which institution is a social relic and which is functioning, and we should investigate such questions with open minds. Yet these two sound rules concerning survivals can easily be exaggerated and turned into the claim that social relics never exist and that history does not matter at all. This is almost identical with the view that all institutions operate with perfect harmony, and withstand any external disturbances by quick and efficient adaptation at the expense of the quick elimination of institutions whose services are no longer required.

The metaphysical and arch-conservative character of this holistic view are quite obvious, and the exaggerations it contains well deserve Gellner's criticism. This criticism led Gellner to pose the problems of the explanation of survivals and of the place of history in social explanation, problems which, I suggest, are capable of solution in terms of Popper's situational logic. First, situational logic allows for the existence of social relics, as well as for the explanation of their survival. For instance, we may explain the survival of an obsolete law as being due to the legislative body's being overworked, or due to respect for the printed letter. (Obsolete laws sometimes become significant just because they were never formally abolished and because some people discover them and use them according to the logic of their situations.) Secondly, though it is clearly unsatisfactory to explain the existence of an institution merely by assuming its existence in the past, this assumption may be an ingredient in a satisfactory explanation. Situational logic brings into the explanation of the existence of an institution its immediate history, which constitutes the circumstances of individuals. Given the institutional arrangement of any one period, we can try to explain its preservation, or reform, or abolition, in the next period, in terms of rational or purposeful behaviour. Thus, by eliminating group-interest, we have all that is reasonable in functionalism without being confined to 'static' models only.

To conclude, a holistic theory either has no explanatory power, or else it has explanatory power which it would retain when the holistic element in it is eliminated. Yet if the holistic element of the theory is retained, particularly after its scientific element is empirically refuted, then the holistic element leads its adherents to obscurantism and perhaps to collectivist morality. This (as I understand it) is Popper's argument against holism—against attributing (distinct) interests to societies or to social institutions—quite apart from his metaphysical conviction that societies and social institutions, though they do exist, have no (distinct) interests.

III

In this section I shall criticize psychologistic individualism or individualistic psychologism or simply psychologism (since I shall not discuss holistic psychologism this abbreviation can hardly cause any confusion). As in the previous section, my criticism will be methodological rather than metaphysical.

The metaphysical differences between institutionalism and psychologism somewhat resembles the difference between a drawing and a pointillist painting which contains only coloured dots but looks *as if* it contains lines. Psychologism admits institutions into the picture of society in the same manner in which the pointillist admits lines into his painting—as mere illusions created by oversight of details. In this section I shall discuss not this metaphysical view, but the methodology based on it.

Before coming to that I should point out, in fairness to some adherents of psychologism, that originally psychologism was not a programme to explain social phenomena but an attempt to design the ideal rational society.

The origin of psychologism seems to me to be the application of Bacon's theory of knowledge to social and political problems.[6] Bacon explained the ability to contribute to scientific progress purely psychologically: an individual possesses this ability only if his mind is in its natural state—only if his mind is free from superstition. And superstition is the result of impatience and self-flattery: impatience leads to guessing and self-flattery leads to self-deception which makes it impossible to get rid of one's original guess however false it may be and in spite of all refutations. This being so, he said, science can develop *only*

---

[6] The origin of Bacon's theory of knowledge seems to be rooted in political theory. See Popper's *Open Society*, ch. 9, on 'canvas cleaning'.

if we forget all past superstitions and start by observing facts as they are. Bacon thus explained social phenomena psychologically: ancient science was due to man's natural open-mindedness; the Mediaeval darkness was due to man's self-deception; and modern science is due to forgetting Mediaeval superstitions. Obviously the application of these views to social, political, and legal problems is highly radicalist (especially since they contain the demand that we should start afresh). Being conscious of this, and being a conservative, Bacon repeatedly dissuaded his readers from attempting to apply his views to social and legal studies. Yet as soon as his views were accepted as the explanation of Newton's incredible success, they led to the radicalism of the eighteenth century. All past institutions were dismissed as irrational together with all past views on which they rested; these views were declared to be sheer superstitions. The institution known as modern science was viewed not as an institution but as the result of the abolition of the previous (institutionalized) learning (especially the teaching in Church institutions) and reversion to man's natural capacity to learn.[7] Similarly, the hope for social reform was the hope not that institutions would be replaced by better ones but that they be abolished and give rise to an institutionless society of (enlightened) natural men who are able to forward their natural interests in the best manner.

Practically all the leading thinkers of the eighteenth century agreed that the existence of bad institutions vitally depended on people's irrational and even superstitious acceptance of them. 'Nothing appears more surprising', says Hume (in his Essay on *The First Principles of Government*), 'to those who consider human affairs with a philosophic eye, than the easiness with which the many are governed by the few, and the implicit submission with which men resign their own sentiments and passions to those of their rulers. When we inquire by what means this wonder is effected, we shall find that as force is always on the side of the governed, the governors have nothing to support them but opinion.' Hume emphasized that the opinion of the governed, by which tyranny is maintained, is quite irrational. Although he opposed the use of the myth of the social contract as a justification of existing institutions (in his essay on *The Original Contract*), he himself endorsed a less rose-coloured version of it (in his essay on *The Origin of Government*) in order to explain the existence of irrational institutions like tyranny. He attributed some (military) rationality to the act of instituting a government, and explained its survival (in peace time) after it had lost its original function by the subjects' irrational force of habit. Rousseau

[7] Psychologism is still taken for granted by most writers on the problem of knowledge. Popper's institutionalism stems from his theory of knowledge in a strange parallel to psychologism. See his *Logic of Scientific Discovery*, sections 8 and 27.

had a similar view of tyranny. 'The strongest is never strong enough to be always the master unless he transfers his strength into right, and obedience into duty', he wrote in his *Social Contract* (Bk. I, ch. III). Yet he was more concerned to stress the irrationality of accepting the right of the strongest 'whose sole result is a mass of inexplicable nonsense', than to explain existing social circumstances. Similarly, Adam Smith had no intention to explain slavery on rational lines; he considered it to be 'absurd' and the most inefficient and expensive form of labour; at most he was willing to explain it as rooted in people's ignorance and prejudice.

Thus, the original view behind modern psychologism is the eighteenth-century theory according to which almost all previous institutions were 'a mass of inexplicable nonsense'. 'The humanist thinkers of the Enlightenment', writes Watkins,[8] 'regarded history as a long record of unnecessary suffering; but they repudiated the doctrine of original sin and attributed the suffering partly to physical causes which might be revealed by science and controlled by technology, and partly to superstition and ignorance, products of bad education which, they said, had rendered man's natural goodness impotent'. Existing institutions are rooted in 'bad education'; 'human nature' is at the root of the perfectly rational future society. The idea that most existing institutions are inexplicable with the aid of the rationality principle 2 (b) led to the condemnation of these institutions, not of the principle. Only the ideal liberal Utopia can be fully explained by the rationality principle, for this society is perfectly rational as in it human nature operates unimpeded by institutions, or by the 'mass of inexplicable nonsense' on which institutions are based.

According to the humanist thinkers of the Enlightenment, not only the ideal society but also its rise can be explained purely psychologically —by reference to human nature alone: once people see that the existing order is superstitious they will cease to accept it, by which very act they will have created the ideal society. This naïve view was attacked from two sides, the traditionalist and the extreme radicalist. The traditionalists defended society's need for some blind obedience ('superstition' is the individualists' name for the same). The extreme radicalists demanded that the state (or some other institution) should use radical means to eradicate bad institutions and the superstitious education on which they rest. The traditionalists naturally moved towards holism as did those extreme radicalists who noticed that what they demanded was no longer the abolition of all institutions but rather the establishment of some new institutions in order to destroy some older ones: they

---

[8] 'The Strange Face of Evil', *The Listener*, September 30, 1954, Vol. 52, pp. 522–523.

started to view the scene as a battlefield in which old and new institutions (or classes, or social forces) were struggling. (L. Pearce Williams' very interesting paper concerning the debate about the reform of education immediately after the French Revolution[9] presents a detailed historical example of such a development.) The eighteenth-century psychologistic programme of planning a future liberal Utopia ended with its failure to produce this Utopia after the French Revolution. It has two intellectual heirs, however: the anarchist movement, and the nineteenth-century psychologistic programme of explaining existing social phenomena, whose chief promoters were Comte and Mill.

It is a most interesting fact that there is no other difference between the eighteenth-century psychologism and the nineteenth-century psychologism but that the one was a programme to design the perfectly rational society and the other was a programme to explain the existing societies. Both had at their disposal nothing but physical circumstances and the psychology which is equally applicable to *all* individuals—namely, human nature.

The nineteenth-century psychologistic programme reflects a compromise between the desire to explain social entities which could no longer be explained away and the traditional (mistaken) individualistic aversion from the admission of social entities (or 'holistic entities' as Gellner calls them).[10] But this in itself does not explain the persistence of the idea that only human nature should be used in the explanation of social phenomena. The persistence of this idea can be explained by reference to other opinions which were common to both the eighteenth- and the nineteenth-century individualists. Common to both groups is the view that a satisfactory theory must be an assertion about the essence of the phenomena explained by that theory; and the essence of all human phenomena is human nature. Common to both groups (especially with regard to Mill) is also the idea that explaining a social set-up rationally (2 (b)) is tantamount to justifying it. I shall not discuss these two ideas, since there is a stronger argument for allowing only human nature to enter our explanation of social phenomena: including the psychology of people as we know them would seem to make our explanation too easy, *ad hoc*, and uninteresting. It would enable us to explain monogamy by the monogamous tendencies of the individual members of a monogamous society, and polygamy by the polygamous

[9] L. Pearce Williams, 'The Politics of Science in the French Revolution', Paper Ten, *Critical Problems in the History of Science*, ed. Marshall Clagett, University of Wisconsin Press, Madison, 1959.

[10] 'Explanations in History', *Proceedings of the Aristotelian Society*, Supp. Vol. 30, 1956. Reprinted in *Theories of History*, ed. Patrick Gardiner, 1959 [see below]. See also his *Reply* to Mr Watkins printed at the very end of that volume.

tendencies of the individual members of the polygamous society. This unsatisfactory mode of explanation will be ruled out if we allow only human nature to be used as the psychological element in our explanation. For, by definition, human nature is common to all members of mankind. For the sake of clarity I shall call the kind of psychologism which has only human nature at its disposal 'traditional psychologism' and the opposite kind of psychologism 'vulgar psychologism'.

Traditional psychologism is a daring programme. It is the suggestion that we should not be satisfied with any explanation of social phenomena unless this explanation is an assertion about human nature and material circumstances. Hence, it is the suggestion that we should explain the variety of social phenomena by assuming a variety of material circumstances (since human nature is unalterable). But many social phenomena and their varieties hardly depend on material circumstances—take language as an obvious example. Hence traditional psychologism seems to be untenable. The only way out of this difficulty is the suggestion that we should explain today's variety of social phenomena not by reference to the varieties of today's material circumstances, but by reference to the varieties of material circumstances of today as well as of yesterday. (This renders the psychologistic programme a version of historism,[11] namely of the programme to explain phenomena by relating their history.)

But this would not help either. If we want to explain a child's adaptation to an institution without taking as given the fact that its parents are adapted to it, we have to explain the parents' being adapted to it by reference to their childhood. This regress will be an unsuccessful attempt to eliminate statements about institutions from our own explanation, unless we assume that there was at least one moment in the society's history in which only material environment and human nature determined rational action. Hence traditional psychologism is pushed to the unintended view that every society had a definite historical beginning. This view is dismissed by Popper as 'the methodological myth of the social contract' (*Open Society*, ii, 93).

The methodological myth of the social contract seems to be employed in the creation of various kinds of historical myths. Sometimes these are stories about collective events which left their impressions on the further developments of the societies in which they occurred. A famous example of such a myth is Freud's description of the beginning of

---

[11] Historism should not be confused with its near relative historicism: historism explains a phenomenon as a result of a chain of events in the past and historicism as a link between past and future events, as taking its place in the present according to History's timetable. Historism should not be viewed as wholly or mainly a part of psychologistic individualism: its main exponents belong to the Platonic (holistic) tradition.

society and the creation of the Oedipus complex as the outcome of a specific event of a collective father-killing. Other myths are stories about strong individuals who left their impact on posterity. A famous example of this is Carlyle's *Heroes and Hero-Worship*. For my part, I view Carlyle's effort as an attempt to solve a problem within the framework of individualism but in a manner designed to render it as indistinguishable from holism as possible; his solution was intended to be a bridge along which one could easily pass from the individualists' to the holists' camp. Stripped of its holistic hero-worship, however, Carlyle's mythology would be a part of a more general discussion of the contribution of past events to the shaping of our present societies. And the unheroic impression which Cleopatra's nose is alleged to have made on poor Antony is as good an instance of such an event as the heroic entry of Carlyle's Odin on to the historical and social stage.

I do not wish to challenge the prominence of Cleopatra's nose in the historiographic literature, but rather to claim that it is too far-fetched as a part of an explanation of today's social set-up. If the psychologistic programme is to be carried out successfully, we have not only to trace the historical origin of a specific social characteristic, but also to explain how the effect of a historical event has persisted through the ages.[12] Hence, the explanation of today's set-up must contain a description of yesterday's set-up and an assumption which explains the emergence of today's set-up from yesterday's set-up. But these two assumptions are quite sufficient, and we should therefore start with them, although, of course, having provided an explanation of today's set-up, we may try to explain yesterday's set-up (and its roots in that of the day before yesterday).

And yet it should be noticed, perhaps, that unlike holism, traditional psychologism sometimes does lead to theories which are open to criticism and even to empirical criticism. Thus, psychologistic attempts to explain some social events by stressing the roles of certain individuals

---

[12] It should be noted that Freud's famous theory of mass-psyche (end of *Totem and Taboo*) is an attempt to explain the persistence of the (Oedipus) guilt-feeling which he explains historically by assuming an event of a collective father-killing. It is remarkable that Freud was fully conscious of the methodological problems present at each stage of the development of his views, but had never fully worked out his methodology as such. Thus one can see in his *Totem and Taboo* how his psychologism drives him to the methodological myth of the social contract —which he consciously accepts—and how, as soon as he relates the myth, he becomes more and more aware of the emergent problem of the persistence of the contract. And yet, on the whole, as his individualism drove him to psychologism and as his psychologism drove him to collectivism, ultimately he was left with an inconsistent methodology. As to his mass-psyche theory, its metaphysical character was made manifest by the development, through his own teachings, of social (educational) reforms which led to the rise of societies much less guilt-ridden than his own.

(rather than of the institutional set-up) in history, has provoked admirable criticisms such as Tolstoy's (in *War and Peace*). Similarly, Mill's contention that economics is based only on the universal disposition to get rich, though uninteresting is at least criticizable. Indeed it was criticized by pointing out that the competitive system does not follow from the disposition to get rich, and that economic competition is not universal. This criticism led to the psychologistic claim that primitive people, who do not have competition (and are therefore primitive), do not compete because of climatic conditions which make people lazy or contented, etc. Yet competition has been found even among some primitive people, though not the competition Mill knew.

Difficulties of this kind are not due to some specific errors but due to the poverty of the tools which the traditional psychologistic programme offers to its adherents. This can be seen more intuitively, perhaps, if we look at an imaginary future than if we look at the past. Assume that the future of mankind is going to be better. Since, ultimately, all the tools the adherents of psychologism can use in order to explain (or predict) this future are again the unalterable human nature and physical conditions, they are almost bound to say that, if the future is going to be better *in any sense*, it is going to be better because of some sort of improvement of our physical conditions—the development of science and technology. This is why the Utopianists of the Age of Reason lay such stress on the advancement of learning, as Watkins rightly remarks (see p. 196 above). This is why Robert Owen expressed his optimism by claiming that the improvement of man's material conditions is going to cause improvement of man's general conditions: according to traditional psychologism ultimately there is almost nothing else which can cause any improvement. Nowadays the error of this view is, regrettably perhaps, only too obvious. We know that the future of mankind depends less on technological success and more on our ability or inability to create effective institutional means for preventing the misuse of our technological achievements.

So much about traditional psychologism. Unlike traditional psychologism, which offers too few tools for the explanation of social phenomena, vulgar psychologism offers too many tools. It allows one to attribute to individuals all the characteristics of the society to which they belong. It is not only *ad hoc*, but also untenable, as it allows one to assume conflicting characteristics in order to explain conflicting institutions, institutionalized conflicts, and other undesired social phenomena. For example, adherents of vulgar psychologism would and did explain unemployment by claiming that workers are lazy. This approach, when pushed far enough, becomes plainly ridiculous and ceases to be individualistic, as it would render the rationality principle (2 (b)) inapplicable to messy situations.

Adherents of vulgar psychologism can hardly be expected to have discussed this criticism explicitly. Nonetheless, one may view certain ideas as attempts to mitigate it, as, for instance, the following suggestions. (1) Unemployment is desired by *some* individuals. (2) Unemployment is not yet understood for want of factual information. (3) Unemployment is an *unintended* consequence of rational behaviour.

According to the first suggestion it is not the unemployed who want to have unemployment, but *some* other people. This is a version of what Popper calls 'the conspiracy theory of society':[13] every social evil is desired and brought about by *some* wicked people. This theory is entirely metaphysical. It allegedly explains (evil) social phenomena by attributing (evil) intentions to some people but it does not tell us why these sinister people rather than well-wishers enforce their intentions on others. The statement that those who are engaged in wars are wicked is an unsatisfactory explanation of wars; the statement that the industrial magnates love war (or money or power) is no explanation of wars unless one adds to it assumptions concerning the social circumstances which makes them capable of imposing their wills on others. (This criticism is due to Marx.) Hence, any admissible explanation of social evils by conspiracy assumes the existence of some previous social circumstances, which contained some other social evils. The suggestion that those can be explained by previous conspiracies would lead to a rather funny version of the methodological myth of the social contract.

According to the second suggestion, before we can attempt to explain any social phenomena, we simply have to collect *indiscriminately* all factual information about all individuals involved in the social setting in which the phenomena took place, and when sufficient information about them is known, their social setting will be known and the phenomena in question explained. In order to understand unemployment, it is suggested, we must know much more about the workers, their employers, their organizers, etc., etc. I shall call this view 'inductivist psychologism'.

Inductivist psychologism may be the view that the multitude of facts will array themselves into a picture just like the points in the pointillist painting do. This would only raise the question of *why* do the facts fall into pattern; the increasingly detailed description is not an explanation; on the contrary, the more facts we describe, the more we want explanations. Moreover, the more facts we describe, the less will they fall into pattern by themselves. Those who want to collect more facts in order to explain a given fact usually admit all this, but

---

[13] The conspiracy theory of society has holistic versions; it is, historically, of a holistic origin.

they claim that we can find a good explanation only if we have knowledge of sufficiently many facts to *adduce* this explanation from—according to the Baconian method of *induction*.

According to the Baconian view the proper method of inquiry is to collect many facts, to adduce from them theories, to adduce from these theories more general theories (the *axiomata media*), and to go on increasing the generality of our theories until we arrive at the most general theory—to the essence of things. The general theory will explain the less general theories in succession and, ultimately, it will explain the original fact from which it is adduced. Obviously, then, since the essence of human phenomena is human nature, advocating the application of the Baconian method to human phenomena seems to be advocating traditional psychologism[14]. Moreover, according to Baconian inductivism raising problems is dangerous since it prevents one from observing facts indiscriminately. Hence inductivists should not bother about how the general theory of human nature would explain the less general theories (the *axiomata media*), nor need they bother about how it would explain undesired social institutions. The faith in the possibility of adducing more and more general theories from observed facts reassures one that the most general theory of human nature will ultimately appear and that then all will be quite clear. The only trouble with this faith is that it is based on logical errors.

The third suggestion is Max Weber's individualistic *ideal type* approach. It is the suggestion that we should describe the average or typical member of a given society or social group by attributing to him *some* typical social characteristics and by trying to *explain* (or predict) his having other typical social characteristics (especially the undesired ones) as the *unintended consequences* of his rational or purposeful behaviour in his typical environment.

Weber and his followers have succeeded in applying his approach fruitfully, producing along its lines interesting theories which are open to critical argument. Weber's approach *may* be viewed as a devulgarized version of vulgar psychologism. Hence, at least one version of psychologism is fruitful. However, I wish to stress two points in this connection. First, Weber's own appraisal of his approach seems to be that it is an improved version of traditional psychologism, not of vulgar psychologism. Secondly Weber's approach is defective in its being applicable only to a narrow range of problems.

As to the first point, it explains the function of Weber's repulsive theory of the *charisma*. According to this theory the origin of any ideal

---

[14] Durkheim, who was an inductivist, escaped this conclusion by claiming that social wholes are observable. This was pointed out by F. A. Hayek in his *The Counter-Revolution of Science*.

type is a historical individual who had strong magical hypnotic powers (*'charisma'* is Weber's term for these powers) which he used in order to force his friends and acquaintances to imitate him. Now this theory seems to be a historical explanation of the diversity of societies (or of ideal types) by reference to human nature alone—it is yet another version of the methodological myth of the social contract. But Weber's theory of the *charisma* is not individualistic: according to it the rise of the ideal type is not a result of individuals' rational or purposeful behaviour but of their being hypnotized. Moreover, the *charisma* theory is criticizable in the same way as the conspiracy theory: although *charisma* (like conspiracy) is a (small) part of social life, the *charisma* theory (like the conspiracy theory) is no explanation as yet.

Ignoring Weber's myth of the *charisma*, we remain with two other alternative ways of interpreting Weber's individualistic ideal type approach. The one way is to view it as an improved version of vulgar psychologism and the other is to view it as a version of institutionalism. According to the institutionalist interpretation of Weber's approach only the institutionalized characteristics may be attributed to the ideal type, while according to the psychologistic approach there is no basis for the distinction between the institutionalized and the uninstitutionalized characteristics of the members of the society in question. Since the whole point about the characteristics of the ideal type is that they persist, one can clearly see that the application of Weber's approach will be more successful and interesting if we attribute to the ideal type only institutional characteristics. This is what Watkins makes of Weber's theory. He emphasizes[15]

> that the personality of a man in society comprises dispositions both of a more private and temperamental kind, and of a more public and institutional kind. Only certain individuals are disposed to weep during the death-scene in Othello, but all policemen are disposed to blow their whistles, under certain circumstances, and any Speaker in the House of Commons is disposed to disallow parliamentary criticism of exercises of the Prerogative. And these more public and institutional dispositions, which may vary very little when one man undertakes another's role, can be abstracted from the total, variegated flux of dispositions, and so provide the social scientist with a fairly stable subject-matter.

Now I fully agree with this keen observation of Watkins', but I have to stress that though it is a fair and commonsensical comment on Weber's approach, it is not a part of it. The comment explains why

---

[15] 'Ideal Types in Historical Explanation', *The British Journal for the Philosophy of Science*, **3**, 9, 1952, p. 40, reprinted in *Readings in the Philosophy of Science*, edited by H. Feigel and M. Brodbeck, N.Y., 1953, p. 741 [see p. 163 above].

204   *Joseph Agassi*

this approach was successful; but those who apply this approach need not know why it is successful and therefore they have no need to mention institutions even though the characteristics which they attribute to their ideal types happen to be institutional. The advantage of speaking of (institutional) characteristics of the ideal type, instead of speaking of institutions (and of institutional roles) proper, is rather plain: this mode of speaking evades the problem of whether institutions exist (1 (a)), and, if they exist, whether they have distinct aims and interests of their own (4). In other words, the whole advantage of Weber's approach is that it *can* be viewed as psychologistic *and* it *can* be viewed as institutionalistic. For those who have decided upon these issues, this advantage of Weber's approach disappears, while its disadvantages, the great limitations upon its range of applicability, remain. Briefly, they are these.

As Watkins has pointed out, Weber's approach allows one to attribute to the typical individual only public and institutional characteristics, so that it does not enable us to explain satisfactorily effects of detailed characteristics of one prominent individual and other detailed events of (social) history: Weber's approach ties us too much to the typical. This, it seems quite obvious, leads to further and much more serious limitations. Weber's approach leaves no room for sociologically significant yet untypical characteristics (such as the more abstract institutions which leave no mark on any typical individual) and the untypical cases of specific and unique institutional reforms.[16] At most it allows one to assume (without debate) changes which constitute the emergence of a new society (i.e., of new ideal types). It allows us to explain social evils as unintended consequences of purposeful behaviour, but it does not allow room for purposeful institutional reform. Consequently it is inapplicable even to the case of the typical reformer of institutions. And all this is in exchange for not having to mention institutions explicitly!

Weber's approach is on the borderline between psychologism and institutionalism. At most it can be made to appear psychologistic. But we need not insist on this point. Even if it were psychologistic it would not render psychologism a satisfactory programme. It seems incredible that intended social reform—quite a commonplace in Weber's days—could not in his time be placed satisfactorily in any methodological

---

[16] Mr Watkins has drawn my attention to the following remark of Talcott Parsons, in his edition of Max Weber's *The Theory of Social and Economic Organization* (1947), which is appended to a note by Weber referring to an intended chapter on revolutions (p. 354 n.): 'no systematic account of revolutions is available . . . in Weber's published works'. It seems that Parsons noted that although Weber was very interested in social changes, he rarely discussed them, being methodologically handicapped; cf. *ibid.*, p. 24. Parsons is in favour of using more boldly holistic ideas where Weber's individualistic ideas are inapplicable.

framework. The reason for this, I suggest, is the universal and tacit acceptance of the proposition (4) that if institutions exist, they are things with independent aims, interests and destinies. Weber's approach was certainly the best at the time when the tacit acceptance of this proposition caused a confusion between individualism and psychologism; it is better to evade a confusion than to succumb to it; but it is still better to clear it and to identify the error upon which it is based.

IV

In this section I shall try to defend institutionalist-individualism by showing that it does not suffer from the central difficulties which the two traditional approaches encounter.

The main problems for holists concerns the relations between the social aims and the aims of individuals. Since, according to institutionalist-individualism, social aims do not exist, it does not raise these problems. The main difficulty of psychologism stems from the impossibility of explaining different social set-ups psychologically. Admitting institutions as an element of sociological explanation, institutionalist-individualism does not encounter this difficulty.

I shall now briefly argue that the two traditional approaches do not enable us to explain intended institutional reform, and they do not even enable us to explain the absence of reform.[17]

It is obvious from general considerations that conscious institutional reform cannot be explained along either of the two traditional lines. For, according to holism, any change of an institution is a natural change—be it growth or decay—and according to psychologistic individualism institutional reform is but the unintended consequence of rational or purposeful action (since institutions as such do not exist). No doubt there is much truth in each of these descriptions, or rather in their combinations. 'Only a minority of social institutions are consciously designed,' writes Popper (*Open Society*, ii, 93), 'while the vast majority have just "grown" as the undesigned results of human actions . . . and we can add that even most of the successfully designed . . . do not turn out according to plan . . .' Yet very many institutions are consciously designed, and for certain definite purposes; and this is inexplicable along the traditional lines. Moreover, as almost all institutions may act as a constraint on some persons in some instances, they are always prone to induce these persons to attempt to reform them. In cases in which it is obvious that reform would be costly and lead to

---

[17] This point was first made by Watkins in his 'Historical Explanation in the Social Sciences', *The British Journal for the Philosophy of Science*, **7**, 30, 1957, p. 112 n., reprinted in *Theories of History*, ed. Patrick Gardiner, 1959, pp. 509–510 [see p. 173 n. 6, above].

little benefit, one would hardly raise the question of reform; and yet, obvious as the answer to it may be, as long as the question of reform is not *a priori* ruled out, our discussion is not quite on the traditional lines.

Let us take an example of how an obvious case of the absence of reform leads to mystification because holism leaves no room to discuss even the absence of reform. Let us consider Durkheim's idea that law-breakers serve society by reminding its members of the existence of the laws which they break. This functionalist idea seems to be highly unsatisfactory, because it seems to be the result of a determination to explain any event as one which contributes towards social cohesion in the face of schisms and disintegration. And yet somehow one tends to admit that there is more to Durkheim's idea than just this. To my surprise I found that some students of sociology are still unable to state simply the reasonable element in Durkheim's idea. It is, of course, the truism that punishment *may* be used as a deterrent; and that when it is a successful deterrent it strengthens the law. But this is by no means universally the case. Therefore, a full explanation of a specific case of a crime followed by a punishment which strengthens the law has to be an explanation of the following facts: that the law was broken (rather than universally observed); that the criminal was punished (rather than ignored or rewarded); and that the punishment acted as a deterrent (and was neither ignored nor opposed by the public). Parts of the explanation are often so obvious that they are not stated explicitly; but while the explanation is restated in a holistic fashion these parts are silently omitted.

To take another example, we know that there exist no public telephone directories in Moscow. The following simple explanation of this fact may be true or false but it is quite open to rational argument: the authorities fear that telephone directories will be used by prospective reformers ('counter-revolutionaries') in order to communicate and organize a reform movement. The unintended consequences of the authorities' behaviour are very interesting, especially for those who wish to know under what conditions such highly centralized control will lead to a complete collapse of the social system. Thus, our explanation of this society and its ability or inability to remain unaltered for long necessarily contains a discussion of possible changes and prospective reformers.

The same examples will show the inadequacy of psychologism (in all its versions). Take punishment again. What distinguishes it (at least in democratic societies) from personal revenge is, according to some adherents of psychologism, the consent which the judge's norms receive from many individuals. This explanation is refuted by any case of punishment which comes after public demand for reform of the law upon which that punishment is based but before the reform is implemented. The adherent of psychologism may now try to modify his theory, but he will have to modify it while taking account of the situation in which the refuting instance has occurred, thus risking his psychologism altogether. This point will be more obvious when we take our second example of stringent central control over all the citizens' activities.

The existence of such a central control is the most eloquent evidence, if evidence is wanted, for the view that personally the citizens subject to it are highly disposed to reform, and yet it is the (institutional) control which makes reform less practicable. Thus, although *personally* Hungarians nowadays are by and large more disposed to reform than Britons, *institutionally* Britain is more disposed to reform than Hungary. Admittedly the increase of individual people's discontent will tempt a prospective rebel in Hungary to act, but his action, his attempt to institutionalize this discontent, is psychologistically inexplicable. Psychologism blocks the way to the explanation of the fact that success in creating institutions expressing and co-ordinating the existing discontent constitutes a successful revolution or a major step towards it.

Admitting such criticisms, some adherents of psychologism view institutional reforms not as the spread of new attitudes but as the simultaneous occurrences of many individuals' decisions which are caused by the spread of the new attitudes. This view is nothing but the admission that psychologism leaves no room for the explanation of the fact that individuals choose to act in a co-ordinated fashion.

The adherent of psychologism will claim, perhaps, that the boot is on the other foot. He will admit that co-ordination exists, but he will want to explain this co-ordination (psychologically) and not take it for granted as the institutionalist would. This retort is not void of substance, for institutionalism does allow one to take the existing institutional co-ordinations for granted. Yet ultimately the retort is based on an error. The institutionalist programme is neither to assume the existence of *all* co-ordinations nor to explain *all* of them, but rather to *assume* the existence of *some* co-ordination in order to *explain* the existence of *some* other co-ordinations. It is an error to assume that the only satisfactory explanation of institutions is by assumptions which say nothing about institutions. Admittedly such an explanation, if it were possible, would be highly desirable (as it would be simpler and thus more open to critical argument). But there exists a very obvious reason which makes it impossible to produce such explanation. It is what I would call 'Popper's rational principle of institutional reform', and it is this. However bad the existing institutional co-ordinations are a prospective reformer will try his best to make use of them in his attempt to reform them or to abolish them. Therefore, the existing social co-ordinations will constitute an important factor in determining the rational or purposeful behaviour of the prospective reformer, in determining the likelihood of success, the cost of the reform, and the expected benefit from it.

In my previous two sections I have tried to argue that all reasonable explanations within the holistic and psychologistic frameworks can be formulated within Popper's institutionalist-individualist methodology —situational logic. In the present section I have gone further and stated that almost all reasonable explanations of social phenomena, when fully stated, cannot be fitted into the previous frameworks but can be fitted into situational logic. In brief, almost all serious social thinkers have employed situational logic even though Popper was the first to formulate it. This last assertion of mine may be true or false, but it is certainly no more inconsistent than the widely accepted assertion that Euclid used rules of mathematical logic (like *reductio ad absurdum*) long before mathematical logicians formulated them. I should even stress that adherents of psychologism were often ardent reformers of social institutions, just as Aristotle often used inferences which cannot form part of his logic. Although the employment of situational logic is not new, its formulation is. And it forms a great advance relative to the untenable holistic scheme and the untenable psychologistic scheme, and even relative to Weber's acceptable though narrow scheme of individualistic ideal type.

V

This section concerns the nature of society and social and political institutions as such, and is therefore metaphysical. According to *holism* society is a *super-individual*; according to *psychologistic individualism* society is the *sum-total of individuals' interactions*; according to *institutionalistic-individualism* society is the *conventional means of co-ordination* between individual actions. This last view is known as contractualism or conventionalism.

A defence of any view must constitute an answer to the criticism launched against this view and show that it is preferable to all the existing alternatives to it. More one cannot do, for it is always possible that future criticism will show the unacceptability of that view and future thinking might bring about better alternatives. In accordance with this attitude, I shall now try to discuss the criticism of conventionalism or contractualism and then argue that it is preferable to holism and to psychologism.

There exist two objections to conventionalism or contractualism: the one is that the convention or contract was never signed; the other is that while one may contract out of a convention or a contract one cannot contract out of society. The first object is slight: conventionalism or contractualism need not entail the view that a contract was ever signed; an individual gives his implicit consent to an existing contract every time that he acts in accordance with it, even while attempting to abolish it. No one ever stops any individual from contracting out of any convention. Here proposers of the second objection (like Adam Smith) will point out that such people as policemen and magistrates see to it that no individual contracts out of the existing institutions, and that therefore institutions are not contracts. But this is an error. What an individual cannot do is to force other individuals, policemen or no policemen, to contract out of a convention. The lawbreaker is the person who, by the act of breaking a law, contracts out; if the other individuals in his society do not contract out they will try to catch and punish him in accordance with the laws (namely the conventions) which they adopt; if they contract out as well, he will not be punished, and that is all there is to it.

Undoubtedly, any individual's decision as to whether or not to contract out of any given convention may depend on the question of whether or not he thinks other individuals are tempted to contract out as well. This is how individual actions are co-ordinated, not only when they conform to a given convention but also when (as the unintended consequence of existing convention or as the result of the development of new ideas) they are highly disposed towards accepting a new convention or towards abolishing or reforming an existing convention.

What the critics of conventionalism seem to have missed is that although one person's contracting out of an institution depends on other people's choice, it is, ultimately, his own choice. Moreover, they seem to have missed the point that when one chooses to act one does not necessarily like the conditions under which one acts. Choice is often between evils, and the aim is to choose the lesser evil. Why anti-conventionalists view the abidance by tyranny as stronger an objection to conventionalism than the willingness to die on the barricades I do not know. Both of these kinds of behaviour are—to me at any rate—profoundly puzzling. And yet only conventionalism, I think, allows for both of them; the holistic view *and* the psychologistic view amount to giving up hope ever to understand them.

Totalitarians have often claimed that conventions which they contracted out of were 'mere pieces of paper' or mere customs, while those which suited them were 'real'. The plain fact is that *all* conventions are 'mere pieces of paper'—that without agreement to abide by it any institution is void. (Otherwise these tyrants' propaganda machines would have been quite unnecessary.) This was known already to Hume and Rousseau (see above, p. 196), and was merely smoke-screened by holistic propaganda. And yet this holistic propaganda contains a strong point which is this.

Although any convention may in principle be discarded, people do want to have some conventions; it is better to have almost any law and order (i.e., conventional co-ordination) than to have none. This anti-anarchistic contention can be used in order to explain rationally people's abidance by tyranny without thereby justifying tyranny. For it is a poor justification of a system that it is preferable only to complete disorder. Realizing this, most of those who are subject to tyranny will try to reform it. Admittedly some people accept tyranny because their illusion that it is government by force rather than by convention leads them to expect from it more security or more efficiency. Admittedly, some people accept tyranny because they benefit from it, or hope to benefit from it, and some people accept tyranny just because they admire tyrants. But most people, I contend, abide by tyranny merely because they see no other way of keeping alive and may wait for the first opportunity to organize and overthrow it. And a significant part of this attitude is people's realization of the bitter truth that even tyranny may be preferable to total disorder. This realization may sometimes be the product of revolutions which lead to disorder. Thus we can explain the strange history of battles against tyranny which ended by establishing much worse tyrannies, such as the French and Russian terrors; tyranny is sometimes tolerated because people realize that they have no idea of how to overthrow successfully the tyranny rather than the tyrant. Here people's opinions enter as a major factor in the social situation; but they enter not so much as personal opinion but rather as institutional or public opinion (be it scientific or not). Of course, tyranny is not always better than total disorder. The realization that an existing tyranny is worse than disorder, however, may even lead to suicidal revolts like the Warsaw Ghetto Uprising. And in any case such rare tyrannies lead to states of affairs in which the relation between masters and oppressed is that of government by brute force. Such relations, not being institutional at all, do not enter the present discussion.

The holistic view explains the existence of institutions which no one desires, by the suggestion that these institutions serve society as a whole. But holism misses the problem to be solved, which is not what is the function of these institutions, but rather why do people accept them against their will?[18] Even if an institution is useful to society,

---

[18] In order to explain why people accept an institution against their will one may endorse one of the following two suggestions. First, experience transmitted by tradition shows the danger of abolishing them. This is an individualist solution which makes holism redundant (see Popper's 'Towards a Rational Theory of

even if it is useful to everybody, the puzzle remains: why do people abide by it while desiring to overthrow it? The holistic view cannot be disproved, but one can show that it explains nothing at all, that it may lead to historicism and dogmatism, and that it may lead to an unacceptable moral outlook.

The psychologistic view explains the changes of social organizations by changes in people's situations and attitudes. There is truth in this explanation, but there are two arguments against the view that this is the whole explanation. First, individuals' attitudes concern not only individuals but also their social organization. Society is not a pointillist picture just because people's aims happen to be co-ordinated by nature; society is a picture because people want it to be one, because people are ready to change their attitudes, in a give-and-take fashion or by a civil war, but in order to create or to alter this or that picture. The second argument is this. Institutions are not just the reflection of the psychology of the majority of their participants. (Two identical groups of individuals in identical surroundings, but with somewhat different conventions or rules of behaviour, will develop very differently from each other not only socially but also psychologically.) As Russell said,[19] 'institutions mould character and character transforms institutions. Reform in both must march hand in hand'.

Before concluding this section I wish to draw attention to an interesting scientific theory which incorporates the conventionalist or contractualist assumption which I have described above. It is M. Banton's view concerning the problem of racial prejudices in Britain (*White and Coloured*, 1959). The traditional psychological approach to race relations is inapplicable here where the rapid emergence of a coloured section in British society has created the problem before widespread prejudices and emotional attitudes could emerge. (The uselessness of holism here need hardly be mentioned.) An important ingredient in Banton's explanation is the assumption that this rapid emergence of a coloured section in British society has caused a serious gap in the body of social conventions which had somehow to be closed rather quickly, particularly because the British society is highly conventionalized. I cannot discuss Banton's interesting theory here; I mention it as an example of the application of conventionalism in proposing a specific sociological explanation.

Tradition', *The Rationalist Annual*, 1949). Secondly, one may postulate the existence of social sub-consciousness or mass-psyche or group-spirit. Gellner claims that nowadays nobody takes this view seriously. I, on the contrary, maintain that most holists sooner or later assume implicitly the existence of a group-spirit which embraces both the social interest and the vehicle which carries the wisdom of abiding by the (undesired) institutions which serve it.

[19] *Portraits From Memory*, Reflections on my Eightieth Birthday.

To conclude this section I shall repeat that institutions can be explained as inter-personal means of co-ordination, as attitudes which are accepted conventionally or by agreement. Not that an agreement was signed by those who have the attitude, but the attitude is maintained by one largely because it is maintained by many, and yet everyone is always at liberty to reconsider his attitude and change it. This idea leaves room for the rational principle of institutional reform (see above, p. 207). It accords with the classical individualistic idea that social phenomena are but the interactions between individuals. Yet it does not accord with the classical individualistic-psychologstic idea that this interaction depends on individuals' aims and material circumstances alone; rather it adds to these factors of interaction the existing inter-personal means of co-ordination as well as individuals' ability to use, reform, or abolish them, on their own decision and responsibility.

At this point we have to go over to Popper's programme for moralizing politics rather than politicizing morals, and to his idea that the task of social and political philosophy is the planning not of the ideal society but of the reform of the existing ones. But at this point I shall close my discussion.

Part 4

Critique of Methodological Individualism

K. J. SCOTT

Methodological and Epistemological Individualism

Hayek and Popper have something important to say on methodological individualism. I have been reading more recent writings on this subject, and I wish to report that the game's not worth the candle. The more recent writings I have read comprise eight contributions to the *British Journal for the Philosophical Science*, various contributions to *Philosophy of Science, The British Journal of Sociology*, the *Aristotelian Society Supplementary Volumes*, and *The Journal of Philosophy*, and parts of several books.[1]

Two different principles have the attractive designation 'methodological individualism'. Hayek applies the term to a methodological principle, and Popper applies it to an epistemological principle. Hayek's principle is one about the *methods* that should be employed in gathering information and forming theories: our *data* in the social sciences are 'the relations between individual minds which we directly know'.[2] Popper's principle is a blanket epistemological principle: whatever methods we have used, 'we should never be satisfied by an explanation in terms of so-called "collective" (states, nations, races, etc.)'.[3] Hayek's principle is about how we should start our inquiries, Popper's about how we should finish them: Hayek says that the methodological individualist 'systematically *starts from* the concepts which guide individuals in their actions';[4] Popper says that methodological individualism 'rightly insists that the "behaviour" and the "actions" of collectives, such as states or social groups, must be *reduced* to the behaviour and to the actions of human individuals'.[5] Hayek's principle is synthetic, Popper's analytical: Hayek says that the social sciences 'do not deal with "given" wholes but their task is to *constitute* these wholes by *constructing* models from the familiar elements';[6] Popper says

---

[1] Many of the reference are given in footnotes to J. W. N. Watkins, 'Historical Explanation in the Social Sciences' [see pp. 166–184 above].

[2] F. A. Hayek, *The Counter-Revolution of Science*, Illinois, 1952, p. 57.

[3] K. R. Popper, *The Open Society and its Enemies*, London, 2nd edn., 1952, Vol. 2, 98.

[4] *Op. cit.*, p. 38 (my italics).

[5] *Op. cit.*, p. 91 (my italics).

[6] *Op. cit.*, p. 56 (my italics of second word italicized).

that 'institutions (and traditions) must be *analysed* in individualistic terms'.[7] It is not surprising that there should be this series of related differences between Hayek and Popper, for Hayek is interested only in how theories are formed and says nothing about testing theories, and Popper says:

> The question, 'How did you first *find* your theory?' relates, as it were, to an entirely private matter, as opposed to the question, 'How did you *test* your theory?' which alone is scientifically relevant.[8]

I have read eight articles and notes by Watkins on methodological individualism, five of them in the *British Journal for the Philosophy of Science*. He does not distinguish between methodological individualism properly so called and what I have called epistemological individualism. He writes as though Hayek and Popper mean the same thing by 'methodological individualism'. He advocates a 'methodological individualism' which is a jumble of Hayek's principle and Popper's principle. The jumbling process has distorted both of these principles without producing any new principle.

Hayek says that 'in the social sciences our data or "facts" are themselves ideas or concepts'[9] in the minds of individuals. Even statistics, which one might expect an economist to regard as furnishing important data, are (unless they are 'concerned with the attributes of individuals')[10] quite irrelevant to social theory, since they do no more than 'provide us with the data to which our theoretical generalizations must be applied to be of any practical use'.[11] This may be sound or unsound, but it is at least unqualified methodological individualism.

Watkins distorts Hayek's methodological individualism when he says:

> The assertion that knowledge of social phenomena can only be derived from knowledge about individuals requires one qualification. For there are certain overt features which can be established without knowledge of psychological facts, such as the level of prices, or the death-rate (but *not* the suicide-rate)[12]

He gives a circular definition of 'overt feature' as 'something which can be ascertained without referring to people's dispositions, etc'.[13] In other words, Hayek's universal principle applies to all social phenomena except the ones it does not apply to.

Hereafter in deference to Popper I shall drop the term 'epistemological individualism'. Popper says that methodological individualism is the

---

[7] *Op. cit.*, p. 324 (my italics).
[8] K. R. Popper, *The Poverty of Historicism*, London, 1957 [see p. 71 above].
[9] *Op. cit.*, p. 36.   [10] *Op. cit.*, p. 61.   [11] *Op. cit.*, p. 63.
[12] J. W. N. Watkins, 'Ideal Types and Historical Explanation' [p. 148 below, Watkins's italics].
[13] *Ibid.*

doctrine that 'we must try to understand all collective phenomena as due to the actions, interactions, aims, hopes, and thoughts of individual men, and as due to traditions created and preserved by individual men'.[14] At first sight it is puzzling that Popper should superadd this requirement to what he so often says is his sole requirement, testability. Thus it is not easy to reconcile his methodological individualism with his statement that 'the question, "How did you *test* your theory?" alone is scientifically relevant'. I believe that to solve this puzzle we have to examine Popper's views on the purpose of social science. This purpose is twofold: first, to form 'sociological laws or hypotheses which are analogous to the laws or hypotheses of the natural sciences';[15] second, to give 'the explanation of some regularity or law'.[16] The solution to the puzzle is that in a law all that matters is testability, but an explanation must comply with the principle of methodological individualism. Laws do not need to comply with this principle. Most of Popper's examples of sociological laws[17] contravene the principle of methodological individualism, for instance 'You cannot have a centrally planned society with a price system that fulfils the main functions of competitive prices' and 'You cannot have full employment without inflation'.

Watkins distorts Popper's principle (and shows that he forgets the purpose of science) when he down-grades Popper's 'laws' to 'unfinished or half-way [*sic*] explanations':

> According to this principle, the ultimate constituents of the social world are individual people who act more or less appropriately in the light of their dispositions and understanding of their situation. Every complex social situation, institution, or event is the result of a particular con-figuration of individuals, their dispositions, situations, beliefs, and physical resources and environment. There may be unfinished or half-way explanations of large-scale social phenomena (say, inflation) in terms of other large-scale phenomena (say, full employment); but we shall not have arrived at rock-bottom explanations of such large-scale phenomena until we have deduced an account of them from statements about the dispositions, beliefs, resources, and inter-relations of individuals. (The individuals may remain anonymous and only typical dispositions, etc., may be attributed to them.)[18]

Watkins gives two illustrations of theories that his principle would prohibit. To be satisfactory, these would have to be illustrations of either (a) explanations that do not comply with the principle or (b) 'half-way' explanations that cannot be reduced to explanations that

[14] Popper, *The Poverty of Historicism* [pp. 85–87 above].
[15] *Ibid.*, p. 62.
[16] *Ibid.*, p. 122.
[17] *Ibid.*, pp. 62–63.
[18] Pp. 167–168 above.

comply with the principle. They both prove, on examination, to be illustrations of (c) 'half-way' explanations that can be so reduced. As 'half-way' explanations they are laws and hence acceptable in Popper's view; and, even if Popper required laws to be reducible to individualistic statements (which he does not do), these explanations would still be acceptable to him since they are so reducible. The first illustration is:

> An example of such a superhuman, sociological factor is the alleged long-term cyclical wave in economic life which is supposed to be self-propelling, uncontrollable, and inexplicable in terms of human activity, but in terms of the fluctuations of which such large-scale phenomena as wars, revolutions, and mass emigration, and such psychological factors as scientific and technological inventiveness can, it is claimed, be explained and predicted.[19]

This illustration is unsatisfactory unless Watkins can produce an economist who purports to propound a theory that is inexplicable in terms of human activity. This he does not do. It is worth noting that in a footnote to a very similar passage in his 1952 article Watkins says that he wrote the passage with the Russian economist Kondratieff in mind. As he does not repeat the footnote in his later article, he possibly no longer believes that Kondratieff illustrates his point. In the article referred to by Watkins, Kondratieff does not say that the long-term cyclical wave is 'self-propelling, uncontrollable, and inexplicable in terms of human activity'. What Kondratieff does say is:

> In asserting the existence of long waves and in denying that they arise out of random causes, we are also of the opinion that the long waves arise out of causes which are inherent in the essence of the capitalistic economy. This naturally leads to the question as to the nature of these causes. We are fully aware of the difficulty and great importance of this question; but in the preceding sketch we had no intention of laying the foundations for an appropriate theory of long waves.[20]

The second illustration is: 'Marx, for instance, professed to believe that feudal ideas and *bourgeois* ideas are more or less literally generated by the water-mill and the steam-engine'.[21] But this is a travesty. What Marx says is fully in accord with methodological individualism:

> M. Proudhon the economist understands very well that men make cloth, linen or silk materials in definite relations of production. But what he has not understood is that these definite social relations are just as much produced by men as linen, flax, etc. Social relations are closely bound up with productive forces. In acquiring new productive forces men change their mode of production; and in changing their mode of production, in changing the way of earning their living, they change all their social

---

[19] P. 168 above.
[20] Kondratieff, in source cited by Watkins [p. 149 above].
[21] P. 172 above.

relations. The hand-mill gives you society with the feudal lord; the steam-mill, society with the industrial capitalist.[22]

There are further confusions in what Watkins has to say. Popper clearly distinguishes methodological individualism from methodological psychologism:

> The mistake of psychologism is its presumption that this methodological individualism in the field of social science implies the programme of reducing all social phenomena and all social regularities to psychological phenomena and psychological laws.[23]

Watkins advocates a psychologistic methodological individualism in his 1952 article [pp. 143–165 above], and an anti-psychologistic methodological individualism in his 1957 article [pp. 166–184 above]. In 1952 he gave a classic statement of methodological psychologism:

> From this truism I infer the methodological principle which underlies this paper, namely, that the social scientist can continue searching for explanations of a social phenomenon until he has reduced it to psychological terms.[24]

And in 1957, without any apparent awareness that he had changed his views, he said:

> Another [misunderstanding] of methodological individualism is that it has been confused with a narrow species of itself (Popper calls it 'psychologism'). . . .[25]

There is of course no reason why a writer's views should not change over the years, but when they change he should not confuse his readers by leading them to suppose that his new views are re-statements of his old views.

In the same 1957 article there appears an economic digression which Watkins might have supposed runs counter to any version of methodological individualism:

> . . . it is very doubtful whether an economist can ever *show* that an economic system containing negative feed-back will be stable. For negative feed-back may produce either a tendency towards equilibrium, or increasing oscillations, according to the numerical values of the parameters of the system. But numerical values are just what economic measurements, which are usually ordinal rather than cardinal, seldom yield. The belief that a system which contains negative feed-back, but

[22] Marx, *The Poverty of Philosophy*, London, Martin Lawrence, not dated, p. 92.
[23] Popper, *The Open Society*, Vol. 2, p. 98.
[24] Pp. 149–150 above.
[25] P. 173 above.

whose variables cannot be described quantitatively, is stable may be based on faith or experience, but it cannot be shown mathematically.[26]

Watkins does not appear to have replied to what I consider the most cogent of the criticisms of methodological individualism, Maurice Mandelbaum's 'Societal Laws', which appeared in the *British Journal for the Philosophy of Science* in 1957.[27] This is odd, for Watkins had replied to most of the criticisms levelled against his versions of methodological individualism, and has replied to a criticism which appeared in that journal six months later than Mandelbaum's article. Mandelbaum gives a clear-headed classification of sociological laws into four classes and shows point by point that his fourth class (which he calls 'abstractive-functional societal laws'), though prohibited by the principle of methodological individualism as it is stated by Watkins, are free from the defects that Watkins attributes to the theories his principle prohibits.

It is true that Mandelbaum is non-committal on whether such laws exist:

> Whether such laws have been found, or whether we have reason to believe that they may be found, is not the question which I have proposed for this discussion.[28]

But Mandelbaum also says:

> Among the examples of attempts to formulate such laws we may cite the following: statements concerning relationships between modes of production and marriage systems; between size of population and political organization; between forms of economic organization and political organization; or, to cite a classic study of Tylor's (which has been amplified and elaborated by Murdock in his *Social Structure*) between certain specific aspects of marriage systems, e.g. rules of residence and rules of descent.[29]

Mandelbaum's distinction between 'laws' and 'attempts to formulate such laws' is unsatisfactory in terms of Popper's refusal to accept a distinction between hypotheses and laws.[30] If attempts have been made to formulate laws, then hypotheses have been advanced. But even if Mandelbaum had not in effect stated that hypotheses of his fourth class have in fact been made, Watkins would still need to reply, for the point at issue between Mandelbaum and himself is about a methodological prescription. Watkins says that certain kinds of theory may not legitimately be postulated as they have certain defects, and Mandelbaum says that one class of these theories are free from the defects Watkins attributes to them.

[26] P. 175 n. 7, above.
[27] Societal Laws [pp. 235–247 below].
[28] *Ibid.*, p. 245 below.   [29] *Ibid.*, p. 244 below.
[30] For instance, Popper, *op. cit.*, Vol. 2, pp. 260–261.

MAURICE MANDELBAUM

Societal Facts

INTRODUCTION

If one adopts Broad's distinction between critical and speculative philosophy, the following paper may be regarded as an attempt to deal with one of the major problems of a critical philosophy of the social sciences. Like all such attempts, this paper faces some difficulties which are not encountered in equally acute form by those who deal with the concepts and methods of the natural sciences. In the first place, the concepts and methods utilized in the natural sciences have been more sharply defined than have been those which social scientists employ. In the second place, there is less disagreement among natural scientists than among social scientists as to the purposes which actually do underlie, or which should underlie, their studies. In the third place, the relations among the various branches of natural science seem to be more easily definable and less subject to dispute than is the case among the social sciences. It is with one aspect of the relations among the various social sciences that this paper will be concerned.

There can scarcely be any doubt that there is at present a considerable measure of disagreement among social scientists concerning the relations which obtain among their various disciplines. For example, there is little agreement as to how the province of 'social psychology' is related to general psychology on the one hand or to sociology on the other. There is perhaps even less agreement as to how sociology and history are related, or whether, in fact, history is itself a social science. Even the province of cultural anthropology which, in its earlier stages, seemed to be capable of clear definition, is now in a position in which its relations to the other fields of social science have become extremely fluid. This type of fluidity in the boundaries of the various social sciences, and the ease with which concepts employed in one discipline spread to other disciplines, has been quite generally regarded as a promising augury for the future of the social sciences. One notes the frequency with which 'integration' is held up as an important programmatic goal for social scientists. But such pleas for integration are ambiguous. On the one hand, they may merely signify a recognition of

221

the fact that attempts to understand some concrete problems call for co-operation between persons trained to use the concepts and methods of different social sciences, or that workers in one discipline should be aware of the methods and results of those who work in other fields. On the other hand, what some who plead for 'integration' in social science seem to demand is that the various disciplines should merge into one larger whole. On such a view the goal of integration would be the achievement of a state in which all persons who work in the field of social science would operate with the same set of concepts and would utilize the same methods of inquiry. If I am not mistaken, it is sometimes assumed that the social sciences will have made their greatest advance when the individual social sciences which now exist will have lost their separate identities. In so far as this paper has a practical purpose, its purpose is to indicate that 'integration', taken in this sense, is a mistaken goal for sociologists and psychologists to pursue.[1]

In stating that I wish to argue against what some social scientists believe to be the most promising path which their sciences can follow, it is clear that this paper has what might be termed an injunctive character. I am attempting to rule in advance that certain modes of procedure should or should not be adopted by practising social scientists. To those trained in the critical philosophy of the natural sciences, such a procedure will doubtless seem both foolhardy and perverse. Yet, it is unavoidable. So long as there are fundamental differences among social scientists with respect to the types of concepts and types of method which they actually use, and so long as the criteria by means of which they measure the adequacy of these concepts and methods differ, every attempt to do more than compile a *corpus* of materials for comparison, will involve the analyst of the social sciences in taking his own stand with respect to the matters under debate. Where one can show reasons for the position adopted, the injunctive element in one's analyses cannot be claimed to be wholly arbitrary. It is in proportion to the strength of these reasons that any particular injunctive proposal is to be judged.

However, any proposal as to the relations which ought to obtain between two or more social sciences will presuppose a belief as to what the goal of the social sciences may be. Concerning this topic there is also a considerable amount of debate. However, I believe it possible to formulate a general statement which might be acceptable to all, leaving unprejudiced those specific issues which have divided social scientists into opposed camps. I submit that the following statement would be quite generally acceptable: it is the task of the social sciences to attain a body of knowledge on the basis of which the actions of

---

[1] In this paper I shall not be concerned with the other social sciences.

human beings as members of a society can be understood. This definition of the aim of the social sciences does not rule out the possibility that an understanding of the actions of human beings as members of a society may be instrumental to some further aim, such as that of attaining the means of controlling human behaviour, or of promoting human welfare. (Nor, of course, does it affirm that this is the case.) Furthermore, it is to be noted that in this statement of the aims of the social sciences I have avoided prejudging this issue as to whether the body of knowledge which is sought can be formulated as a system of laws, and whether an understanding of human actions is equivalent to explaining these actions in the sense in which the term 'explanation' is used in the natural sciences. Throughout this paper I wish to avoid raising these questions, and in so far as possible I shall confine my discussion to a neutral terminology which does not prejudge any of these issues. Wherever my language seems to suggest that I am using the model of explanation used in the natural sciences, my point could equally well be phrased in terms which are compatible with the view that the methods and concepts of the social sciences are utterly different from those employed in the natural sciences. And, conversely, where I use the language of 'understanding', my discussion can equally well be rephrased in terms of the language of scientific 'explanation'.

Having now defined what I take to be the task of the social sciences, I can state the aim of this paper. My aim is to show that one cannot understand the actions of human beings as members of a society unless one assumes that there is a group of facts which I shall term 'societal facts' which are as ultimate as are those facts which are 'psychological' in character. In speaking of 'societal facts' I refer to any facts concerning the forms of organization present in a society. In speaking of 'psychological facts' I refer to any facts concerning the thoughts and the actions of specific human beings.

AN EXAMPLE OF THE IRREDUCIBILITY OF SOCIETAL CONCEPTS

If it be the case, as I wish to claim, that societal facts are as ultimate as are psychological facts, then those concepts which are used to refer to the forms of organization of a society cannot be reduced without remainder to concepts which only refer to the thoughts and actions of specific individuals.[2] There are many reasons why the type of claim that

[2] The term 'ultimate' may, of course, have other meanings as well. In the present paper, however, I am taking the irreducibility of a set of concepts to be equivalent to the ultimacy of that set of facts to which these concepts refer.

M.I.C.—8*

I am putting forward has been doubted, and we shall note some of these reasons as we proceed. First, however, it will be well to lend some plausibility to the view by means of an example.

Suppose that I enter a bank, I then take a withdrawal slip and fill it out, I walk to a teller's window, I hand in my slip, he gives me money, I leave the bank and go on my way. Now suppose that you have been observing my actions and that you are accompanied by, let us say, a Trobriand Islander. If you wished to explain my behaviour, how would you proceed? You could explain the filling out of the withdrawal slip as a means which will lead to the teller's behaviour towards me, that is, as a means to his handing me some notes and coins; and you could explain the whole sequence of my action as directed towards this particular end. You could then explain the significance which I attached to the possession of these notes and coins by following me and noting how the possession of them led other persons, such as assistants in shops, to give me goods because I gave them the notes and coins which the bank teller had handed to me. Such would be an explanation of my observed behaviour in terms of the behaviour of other specific individuals towards me. And it might at first appear as if an explanation couched in terms of these interpersonal forms of behaviour would be adequate to cover all of the aspects of the case.

However, it would also be necessary for you to inform the stranger who accompanies you that it does not suffice for a person to fill out such a slip and hand it to just anyone he may happen to meet. It would also be only fair to inform him that before one can expect a bank teller to hand one money in exchange for a slip, one must have 'deposited' money. In short, one must explain at least the rudiments of a banking system to him. In doing so one is, of course, using concepts which refer to one aspect of the institutional organization of our society, and this is precisely the point which I wish to make. (And the same point can be made with reference to how Malinowski has explained to *us* the Trobriand Islanders' system of ceremonial exchanges of gifts.) In all cases of this sort, the actual behaviour of specific individuals towards one another is unintelligible unless one views their behaviour in terms of their status and roles, and the concepts of status and role are devoid of meaning unless one interprets them in terms of the organization of the society to which the individuals belong.

To this it may be objected that any statement concerning the status of an individual is itself analysable in terms of how specific individuals behave towards other individuals, and how these in turn behave towards them. Thus it might be claimed that while the explanation of an individual's behaviour often demands the introduction of concepts referring to 'social status', such concepts are themselves reducible to further statements concerning actual or probable forms of behaviour.

Thus, societal concepts might be held to be heuristic devices, summarizing repeated patterns of behaviour, but they would be nothing more: their real meaning would lie in a conjunction of statements concerning the behaviour of a number of individuals.

However, this view is open to serious objection. We have seen in the foregoing illustration that my own behaviour towards the bank teller is determined by his status. If the attempt is now made to interpret his status in terms of the recurrent patterns of behaviour which others exemplify in dealing with him, then *their* behaviour is left unexplained: each of them—no less than I—will only behave in this way because each recognizes the teller of a bank to have a particular status. Similarly, it is impossible to resolve the bank teller's role into statements concerning his behaviour towards other individuals. If one wished to equate his societal role with his reactions towards those who behave in a particular way towards him, it would be unintelligible that he should hand us money when we present him with a withdrawal slip when he stands in his teller's cage, and yet that he would certainly refuse to do so if we were to present him with such a slip when we met him at a party. Bank tellers as well as depositors behave as they do because they assume certain societally defined roles under specific sets of circumstances. This being the case, it is impossible to escape the use of societal concepts in attempting to understand some aspects of individual behaviour: concepts involving the notions of status and role cannot themselves be reduced to a conjunction of statements in which these or other societal concepts do not appear.

[Precisely the same point may be made with respect to attempts to translate societal concepts into terms of the thoughts of individuals rather than into terms of their overt behaviour. If one should wish to say that I acted as I did towards the teller because I foresaw that through my actions he would be led to give me money, one would still have to admit that my anticipation of his response was based upon my recognition of the fact that he was a bank teller, and that the role of a bank teller demands that he should act as the bank's agent, and the function of a bank (so far as each depositor is concerned) is that of being a custodian of legal tender, etc. Thus, in attempting to analyse societal facts by means of appealing to the thoughts which guide an individual's conduct, some of the thoughts will themselves have societal referents, and societal concepts will therefore not have been expunged from our analysis.]

Now I do not wish to claim that an individual's thoughts or his overt actions are wholly explicable in terms of status and roles. Not only does it seem to be the case that some actions may be explained without introducing these concepts, but it is also the case that two individuals, say two bank tellers, may behave differently towards me in spite of the identity in their roles. Thus, one may be friendly and the other hostile or aloof, and the nature of my own behaviour towards them will then differ. Thus it should be apparent that I am not seeking to explain all facets of individual behaviour by means of statements, which only refer to societal facts. What I wish to contend is (a) that in understanding or explaining an individual's actions we must often refer to facts concerning the organization of the society in which he lives, and (b) that our statements concerning these societal facts are not reducible to a conjunction of statements concerning the actions of individuals. I take it that almost all social scientists and philosophers would grant the first of these contentions, but that many social scientists and most philosophers would reject the second, insisting that societal facts are reducible to a set of facts concerning individual behaviour.

THE CRITERION OF 'IRREDUCIBILITY'

It is now necessary to state the criterion of irreducibility which the foregoing illustration has presupposed.

Let us assume that there is a language, *S*, in which sociological concepts such as 'institutions', 'mores', 'ideologies', 'status', 'class', etc., appear. These concepts all refer to aspects of what we term 'a society'. That there is a language of this type is clear from the works of sociologists, anthropologists, and historians. It is clear also from the fact that we use such terms as 'The President of the United States', or 'the unmarried children of X'. In order to define the meaning of the latter terms we must make reference to the Constitution of the United States, or to the laws which govern our marriage and kinship systems, and in these references we are employing societal concepts.

There is, of course, also another language, *P*, in which we refer to the thoughts and actions and capabilities of individual human beings. In making statements in this language (which, for want of a better name, I have called our 'psychological language')[3] we are not using societal concepts. The differences between these two languages may be illustrated by the fact that the connotation of the term 'The present

---

[3] It will be noted that what I have termed our psychological language does not include terms such as 'neural paths', 'brain traces', etc. My argument aims to show that societal facts are not reducible to facts concerning the thoughts and actions of specific individuals; the problem of whether both societal facts and facts concerning an individual's thoughts and actions are explicable in terms of (or, are in some sense 'reducible' to) a set of physical or physiological correlates is not my present concern. It will readily be seen that this is not the point at issue. Those who seek to reduce societal facts to facts concerning individual behaviour are not attempting to speak in physical and physiological terms.

President of the United States' carries implications which do not follow from the personal name 'Dwight D. Eisenhower', and statements concerning the personality of Dwight D. Eisenhower carry no implications for our understanding of his societal role. This remains true even though we admit that in this case, as in most others, the status of an individual is often causally connected with the nature of his personality, and even though we also admit that an individual's personality is often connected with the fact that he occupies a particular status, or that he functions within this status as he does.

Put in these terms, my thesis that societal facts are irreducible to psychological facts may be reformulated as holding that sociological concepts cannot be translated into psychological concepts *without remainder*. What is signified by the stipulation 'without remainder' must now be made clear.

It would seem to be the case that all statements in the sociological language, S, are translatable into statements concerning the behaviour of specific individuals, and thus would be translatable into the language P. For example, a statement such as 'The institution of monogamous marriage supplanted the polygamous marriage system of the Mormons' could presumably be translated into statements concerning the actions of certain aggregates of individuals. However, it is by no means certain that such translations could be effected without using other concepts which appear in the sociological language. These concepts too might have their translations into P, but the translation of the concepts of S into P would not be complete if such translations still had to employ other concepts which appear in S. It is with respect to incomplete translations of this type that I speak of translations which cannot be effected 'without remainder'.

An analogue of this situation was pointed out by Chisholm in his criticism of C. I. Lewis's theory of knowledge.[4] According to Chisholm, thing-statements cannot be completely reduced to statements concerning sense-data because one must specify the conditions of the appearance of these sense-data, and in doing so one must again use thing-statements. And this is precisely the situation which we found to obtain in our illustration of the behaviour of a person withdrawing money from a bank.

Now, it might be argued (as it has sometimes been argued with respect to Chisholm's contention) that our inability to carry out such translations, without remainder, represents a practical and not a theoretical inability. According to those who take this view, the practical difficulty which is present arises from the indefinitely long

---

[4] Cf. Chisholm, 'The Problem of Empiricism' in *Journal of Philosophy*, V, 45 (1948), pp. 512 ff. (I am indebted to Roderick Firth for calling my attention to this analogue.)

conjunction of statements which we should have to make in carrying out our analyses, and to the fact that some of these statements would involve a foreknowledge of future events. But it is claimed that no theoretically important consequences follow from our inability to complete a detailed analysis of a particular statement: such partial analyses as we can actually make may not have omitted any theoretically significant aspects of the statements which we wish to analyse. Such a rejoinder would be open to two objections, so far as our present discussion is concerned.

First, we are here concerned with the problem of the relations between two empirical disciplines. Therefore, if it be admitted that it is impossible in practice to reduce statements which contain societal terms to a conjunction of statements which only include terms referring to the thoughts and actions of specific individuals, the rejoinder in question might conceivably be significant from the point of view of a general ontology, but it would not affect my argument regarding the autonomy of the societal sciences.

Second, it is to be noted that whatever may be the case regarding Chisholm's argument concerning the relation of sense-data statements to thing-statements, the problem of reducing statements which include societal terms to statements which only concern specific individuals is not merely a question of how we may *analyse* action statements, but how we may *explain* certain facts. It has been my contention that if we are to explain an individual's behaviour when, say, he enters a bank, we must have recourse to societal concepts and cannot merely employ terms which refer to the fact that this individual makes marks on paper, approaches a specific point, hands the marked paper to another individual, etc., etc. He who knew all of this, and who also knew all of the other actions performed by the members of a society, would possess a series of protocol statements, or biographical 'logs'. Even though this set of logs included reference to all of the actions performed by all of the members of the society, no societal concepts would appear in it. However, this information would not make it possible for our omniscient collector of data to explain why the depositor fills out a slip in order to withdraw money, or why the teller will exchange notes and coins for such a slip. Such a transaction only becomes explicable when we employ the concept of 'a bank', and what it means to speak of 'a bank' will involve the use of concepts such as 'legal tender', and 'contract'. Further, what it means to speak of 'a contract' will involve reference to our legal system, and the legal system itself cannot be defined in terms of individual behaviour—even the legal realist must distinguish between the behaviour of judges and policemen and the behaviour of 'just anyone'. Thus, if we are to explain certain forms of individual behaviour we must use societal concepts, and these concepts are not

(I have argued) translatable without remainder into terms which only refer to the behaviour of individuals.

Yet it is important to insist that even though societal concepts cannot be translated into psychological concepts without leaving this societal remainder, it is not only possible but is indeed necessary to make the *partial* translation. It is always necessary for us to translate terms such as 'ideologies' or 'banks' or 'a monogamous marriage system' into the language of individual thought and action, for unless we do so we have no means of verifying any statements which we may make concerning these societal facts. Ideologies and banks and marriage systems do not exist unless there are aggregates of individuals who think and act in specific ways, and it is only by means of establishing the forms of their thoughts and their actions that we can apprehend the nature of the societal organization in which they live, or that we can corroborate or disallow statements concerning this organization. Yet, the necessity for this translation of specific sociological concepts into terms of individual behaviour in order that we may verify and refine our sociological statements does not alter the fact that the possibility of making such a translation always involves the necessity for using other societal concepts to define the conditions under which this behaviour takes place. Thus, the translation can never obviate the use of societal concepts and reduce the study of society to a branch of the study of the actions of individuals.

OBJECTIONS

In the foregoing discussion I have been at pains to state my position in such a way as to avoid the most usual objections to the general type of view which I hold. However, it will be useful to comment on three objections which have frequently been raised against the view that societal facts are irreducible to psychological facts.[5]

[5] When we consider the type of 'irreducibility' which has here been claimed to characterize societal facts, we must be prepared to allow that it may not be the only type of irreducibility to be found among 'existential emergents'. (On the meaning of this term, which has been borrowed from Lovejoy, cf. my 'Note on Emergence', in *Freedom and Reason*, edited by Baron, Nagel, and Pinson; Free Press, Glencoe, Ill., 1951.) I am in fact inclined to believe that there is a stronger form of irreducibility than is here in question. This stronger form may be said to exist between, say, the colour 'red' and brain events or light frequencies. In such cases it might be true that even a *partial* translation cannot be effected. All that I have wished to show is that while it is undeniable that we can and do make partial translations of societal concepts by using psychological concepts, these translations cannot be complete: we must always use further societal concepts to specify the conditions under which the observed forms of societally oriented behaviour take place.

The first of these objections may be termed the ontological objection. It consists in holding that societal facts cannot be said to have any status of their own since no such facts would exist if there were not individuals who thought and acted in specific ways. Now, to hold the view which I hold, one need not deny that the existence of a society presupposes the existence of individuals, and that these individuals must possess certain capacities for thought and for action if what we term a society is to exist. Yet, this admission does not entail the conclusion which is thought to follow from it: one need not hold that a society is an entity independent of all human beings in order to hold that societal facts are not reducible to the facts of individual behaviour. The warrant for the latter position is merely this: all human beings are born into a society, and much of their thought and their action is influenced by the nature of the societies in which they live; therefore, those facts which concern the nature of their societies must be regarded as being independent of them. To be sure, these facts are not independent of the existence of *other* individuals, and it will be from the forms of behaviour of these other individuals that any specific individual will have acquired his own societally oriented patterns of behaviour. But these individuals, too, were born into an already functioning societal organization which was independent of them. Thus, their societally oriented behaviour was also conditioned by an already existing set of societal facts, etc., etc.

To be sure, those who wish to press the ontological objection may insist that at some remote time in the history of the human race there were individuals who were not born into an already existing society, and that these individuals must have formed a societal organization by virtue of certain patterns of repeated interpersonal actions. Thus, they would seek to insist that all societal facts have their origins in individual behaviour, and that it is mistaken to argue, as I have argued, that societal facts are irreducible to the facts of individual behaviour. However, this rejoinder is clearly fallacious. Whatever may have been the origin of the first forms of societal organization (a question which no present knowledge puts us in a position to answer), the issue with which we are here concerned is one which involves the nature of societies as they exist at present. To argue that the nature of present societal facts is reducible to the facts of individual behaviour because the origins of a particular social system grew up out of certain repeated forms of behaviour is a clear example of the genetic fallacy. One might as well argue on the basis of our knowledge of the origins of the Greek drama and of the modern drama that every current Broadway play is really to be understood as a religious festival.

However, the above answer to the ontological type of objection is clearly not sufficient.[6] It is, I hope, adequate to show that one usual form of countering my position is untenable; yet, the essential paradox remains. One can still legitimately ask what sort of ontological status societal facts can conceivably possess if it is affirmed that they depend for their existence on the activities of human beings and yet are claimed not to be identical with these activities. There are, it seems to me, two types of answer which might be given to this question. In the first type of answer one might contend that a whole is not equal to the sum of its parts, and a society is not equal to the sum of those individual activities which go to form it. This familiar holistic answer is not the one which I should be inclined to propose. In the first place, it is by no means certain that the principle of holism (as thus stated) is philosophically defensible. In the second place, such an answer assumes that what may be termed the 'parts' of a society are to be taken to be individual human beings, and this is an assumption which I should be unwilling to make. All of the preceding argument entails the proposition that the 'parts' of a society are specific societal facts, not individuals. If this were not the case, societal concepts could be translated into terms referring to individual behaviour if we had sufficient knowledge of all the interrelations among these individuals. Instead, we have found that an analysis of a statement which concerns a societal fact will involve us in using other societal concepts: for example, that what it means to be a depositor in a bank will involve statements concerning our legal system and our monetary economy. Similarly, what it means to be a college student cannot be defined without recourse to statements concerning our educational system, and such statements cannot be analysed without utilizing concepts which refer to statutory laws as well as to many other aspects of our societal organization. Thus, from the arguments which have been given, it follows that the 'parts' of a society are not individual human beings, but are the specific institutions, and other forms of organization, which characterize that society. Once this is recognized, it remains an open question as to the extent to which any specific society (or all societies) are to be conceived holistically or pluralistically.

The second method of dealing with the ontological objection is the one which I should myself be inclined to adopt. It consists in holding that one set of facts may depend for its existence upon another set of facts and yet not be identical with the latter. An example of such a relationship would be that which a traditional epiphenomenalist would regard as existing between brain events and the contents of consciousness. Whatever objections one may raise against the epiphenomenalist

---

[6] In what follows I shall only be discussing human societies. The differences between 'animal societies' and human societies are far more striking than their similarities.

view of the mind-body relationship, one would scarcely be justified in holding that the position must be false because the content of consciousness could not be different from the nature of brain-states and yet be dependent upon the latter. If one has reasons for holding that the content of consciousness *is* different from brain states, and if one also has reason for holding that it *does* depend upon the latter, one's ontology must be accommodated to these facts: the facts cannot be rejected because of a prior ontological commitment. And, without wishing to press my analogy further than is warranted, I can point out that my statement concerning 'the parts' of a society has its analogue in what those who hold to the epiphenomenalist position would say concerning the proper analysis of any statement referring to the content of an individual's field of consciousness. Just as I have claimed that the component parts of a society are the elements of its organization and are not the individuals without whom it would not exist, so the epiphenomenalist would (I assume) say that the parts of the individual's field of consciousness are to be found within the specific data of consciousness and not in the brain events upon which consciousness depends.

These remarks are, I hope, sufficient to dispel the ontological objection to the position which I wish to defend. To be sure, I have not attempted to say what position should be assigned to societal facts when one is constructing a general ontology. To do so, I should have to say much more concerning the nature of societal facts, and I should of course also have to discuss the nature of other types of entity. Here it has only been my concern to suggest that what I have termed the ontological objection to my thesis is by no means as strong as it may at first glance appear to be: the admission that all societal facts depend upon the existence of human beings who possess certain capacities for thought and for action by no means precludes the contention that these facts are irreducible to facts concerning those individuals.

The second of the most usual objections to the thesis that societal facts cannot be reduced to psychological facts is an epistemological objection. This objection may take many forms, depending upon the theory of knowledge which is held by the objector. However, the common core of all such objections is the indubitable fact that societal concepts are not capable of being 'pointed to', in the sense in which we can point to material objects, or to the qualities or activities of these objects. Whenever we wish to point to any fact concerning societal organization we can only point to a sequence of interpersonal actions. Therefore, any theory of knowledge which demands that all empirically meaningful concepts must ultimately be reducible to data which can be directly inspected will lead to the insistence that all societal concepts are reducible to the patterns of individual behaviour.

I shall not, of course, seek to disprove this general theory of knowledge. Yet it is possible to indicate in very brief compass that it is inadequate to deal with societal facts. Since those who would hold this theory of knowledge would presumably wish to show that we can be said to know something of the nature of human societies, and since they would also wish to hold that our means of gaining this knowledge is through the observation of the repeated patterns of activities of individuals, a proof that their theory of knowledge cannot account for our apprehension of the nature of individual action is, in the present context, a sufficient disproof of the epistemological type of objection.

In order to offer such a disproof, let us revert to our illustration of a depositor withdrawing money from a bank. In order to understand his overt actions in entering a bank, filling out a slip, handing it to a teller, receiving notes and coins, and leaving the bank, we must view this sequence of actions as one internally connected series. Yet what connects the elements within the series is the person's intention to withdraw money from his account, and this intention is not itself a directly observable element within the series. Thus, unless it be admitted that we can have knowledge of aspects of human behaviour which are not directly presented to the senses, we cannot understand his behaviour and therefore cannot understand that which we seek to understand; i.e., those societal facts which supposedly are the summations of instances of behaviour of this type. To this, it may of course be objected that we have learned to attribute certain intentions to agents on the basis of our own experienced intentions, and when this introspective experience is combined with our observation of overt behaviour we learn to interpret human actions. Yet if this enlargement of our modes of knowing is allowed, there is no reason to stop with the facts of individual behaviour as the building-blocks of a knowledge of societal facts. Within our own experience we are no less directly aware of our own names, of our belonging to a particular family, of our status as youngsters or elders, etc., than we are of our own intentions. To be sure, our societal status must, originally, have been learned by us in a sense in which our intentions need not presumably have been learned. Yet, once again, we must avoid the genetic fallacy: the origin of our knowledge is not identical with that knowledge itself. Just as the concept of number has a meaning which need not be identical with the experiences through which it was learned, so the concept of a family, or of differentiated status due to age or sex, need not (even for a child) be identical with the experiences through which this concept was first made manifest. And to these remarks it should be added that once we have grasped the idea of status, or of family, or of authority, we can transfer this concept to situations which are initially alien to our own experience (e.g., to new forms of family organization) no less readily than we can apply a knowledge of our own intentions to the under-standing of the intentions of those who act in ways which are initially strange to us. The problem of extending our knowledge from our own experience of others is not, I submit, more impossible in principle in the one case than in the other. And if this be so, there is no epistemo-logical reason why we should seek to reduce societal facts to the facts of individual behaviour. Only if it were true that individual behaviour could itself be understood in terms of the supposedly 'hard data' of direct sensory inspection would there be any saving in the reduction of societal facts to facts concerning this behaviour. But, as I have indicated, this is not the case.

The third type of objection to the view which I have been espousing is the objection that such a view interprets individual men as the pawns of society, devoid of initiative, devoid even of a common and socially-unconditioned nature, conceiving of them as mere parts of a self-existing social organism.[7] However, such a view I have in fact already rejected. To hold, as I have held, that societal facts are not reducible without remainder to facts concerning the thoughts and actions of specific individuals, is not to deny that the latter class of facts also exists, and that the two classes may interact. Those who have in the past held to the irreducibility of societal facts have, to be sure, often gone to the extreme of denying that there are any facts concerning individual behaviour which are dependent of societal facts. Such has not been my thesis. And it is perhaps worth suggesting that if we wish to understand many of the dilemmas by which individuals are faced, we can do no better than to hold to the view that there are societal facts which exercise external constraints over individuals no less than there are facts concerning individual volition which often come into conflict with these constraints.

[7] It is to be noted that some societally oriented behaviour is only intelligible when interpreted with respect to *both* a societal concept and an individual's intention (e.g., in our case of a person withdrawing money from a bank). However, other instances of societally oriented behaviour (e.g., customary observances of age and sex differences) do not involve a consideration of the agent's intentions.

MAURICE MANDELBAUM

Societal Laws

In an earlier paper I argued that societal facts are not reducible, without remainder, to facts concerning individual behaviour.[1] In short, I argued against one of the basic theses of 'methodological individualism'. However, the issue of whether there are irreducible societal *facts* is not the main problem with which methodological individualism has been concerned. The main problem has been whether or not there are societal *laws* which are irreducible to laws concerning the behaviour of individuals. I would uphold the view that there are, and thus would reject a second thesis of methodological individualism.[2] However, before arguing this point it is necessary to disentangle the problem from some of the misleading issues which have become associated with it. In my opinion, these misleading issues have arisen because it is widely and erroneously assumed that those who reject methodological individualism must accept a position which is termed 'methodological holism'. It is the primary purpose of the present paper to show that there are in fact several alternatives to methodological individualism, and that not all of these alternatives entail an acceptance of 'holism'.[3]

I

Let us briefly review the issue between what has been designated as 'methodological individualism' and what has been designated as 'methodological holism'.[4]

---

[1] 'Societal Facts' [pp. 221–234 above].

[2] It will be noted that my view is therefore more radical than that adopted by May Brodbeck in her attack on methodological individualism ('On the Philosophy of the Social Sciences' [pp. 91–110 above]. She rejects the view that there are irreducible societal laws [*loc. cit.*, p. 109].)

[3] In a further paper I hope to show how societal laws are to be distinguished from psychological laws, and to argue on the basis of that distinction for the irreducibility of societal laws.

[4] The most important recent formulations of methodological individualism probably are: the articles of Hayek which have been collected in his book *The Counter-Revolution of Science*, Glencoe, 1952; K. R. Popper, 'The Poverty of Historicism', *Economica*, N.S., 1944, **11**, pp. 86–103 and pp. 119–137; **12**, pp. 69–

The term 'methodological individualism' seems to have been derived from Schumpeter[5] and two of its chief exponents are Popper and Hayek. As is well known, the writings in which both of the latter have discussed the methodology of the social sciences have been works which have had a special polemical character: they were not merely discussions of methodology but were attacks on historicism, organicism, and social holism. For this reason, Popper and Hayek have tended to equate a rejection of methodological individualism with the acceptance of methodological holism. This over-simplified classification of alternative theories has now unfortunately become standard.

To illustrate the usual view of the dichotomy between methodological individualism and holism I shall quote a passage from W. J. N. Watkins' defence of methodological individualism:

> If social events like inflation, political revolution, 'the disappearance of the middle classes', etc., are brought about by people, then they must be explained in terms of people; in terms of the situations people confront and the ambitions, fears and ideas which activate them. In short, large-scale *social* phenomena must be accounted for by the situations, dispositions and beliefs of *individuals*. This I call methodological individualism.
>
> You may complain that this is commonsensical and hardly needed saying. The trouble is that some philosophers of history have made the opposite assumption . . . In the secularized version of [their] theory it is the social whole which so determines matters for the individual that he cannot avoid (or would be foolish to try to avoid; the determinism may be a little loose) fulfilling his function within the whole system. On this view, the social behaviour of individuals should be explained in terms of the position or functions of these individuals and of the law which govern the system. These laws must be regarded as *sui generis*, applying to the whole as such and not derivable from individualistic principles. This I call methodological holism.[6]

---

89 (cf. especially p. 80 and p. 88) and his *Open Society and Its Enemies*, London, 1945, Vol. II, Chap. 14; J. W. N. Watkins, 'Ideal Types and Historical Explanation', *British Journal for the Philosophy of Science*, **3**, pp. 22–43, and 'Methodological Individualism: A Reply', *Philosophy of Science*, **22**, pp. 58–62 [see above pp. 143–165 and 179–184]. Also relevant is Isaiah Berlin, *Historical Inevitability*, Oxford, 1954.

Perhaps the most important recent attacks on the principle of methodological individualism are those of Brodbeck [as cited in note 2, p. 235], M. Ginsberg, 'The Individual and Society', in his essays *On the Diversity of Morals*, London, 1957, and 'Factors in Social Change', in *Transactions of the Third World Congress of Sociology*, **1**, pp. 10–19; E. A. Gellner, 'Explanations in History', *Aristotelian Society*, 1956, Suppl. Vol. 30, pp. 157–176 [see pp. 248–263 below]; L. J. Goldstein, 'The Inadequacy of the Principle of Methodological Individualism', *Journal of Philosophy*, 1956, **53**, pp. 801–813 [see pp. 264–278 below].

[5] Cf. note 50 of Machlup, 'Schumpeter's Economic Methodology', *Review of Economics and Statistics*, 1951, **33**, pp. 145–151.

[6] Methodological Individualism' [p. 179 f.].

In this passage it is to be noted that a denial of what is defined as methodological individualism is assumed to imply methodological holism. Further, methodological holism is identified with certain forms of the philosophy of history; it is not treated as a methodological principle which might be used by economists, political scientists, anthropologists, or empirical sociologists. Thus it is perhaps not unfair to say that in this passage there is a tendency to assume that the dichotomy between methodological individualism and methodological holism is equivalent to the dichotomy between an empirical explanation of social phenomena and the sort of philosophic interpretation which is characteristic of material philosophies of history.[7] What is more important, however, is that it is assumed that all so-called 'methodological holists' view a social system as an organic whole, the component parts of which are individual human beings. This is not necessarily the case. Some who reject methodological individualism would regard the component parts of a social system as being the institutions which comprise that system.[8] Therefore, *if* they hold that the whole determines the actions of the parts, they are not necessarily arguing that individual human beings are determined by the society as a whole—though they may of course also claim this. And, finally, this passage clearly involves the assumption that if one regards societal laws as being *sui generis* (i.e., as not being in principle reducible to laws concerning individual behaviour) then one must hold that such laws concern the society as a whole. In other words, a rejection of the principle defined as methodological individualism has been assumed to involve an acceptance of the thesis that, whatever societal laws there may be, these laws will concern the functioning of a society treated as an organic whole. It would therefore seem that anyone who wished to reject the *metaphysical* theses of holism in general (e.g., 'the whole is greater than the sum of its parts') would be committed to accepting the *methodological* principle which has been defined as 'methodological individualism'.

The root error in all this is, I believe, the assumption that all who deny methodological individualism are committed to exactly the same positions as were those nineteenth-century philosophers who attacked the individualistic approach of the eighteenth century. More specifically, the tenets used to characterize 'methodological holism' are precisely those which were held in common by Comte, Hegel, and Marx. This is

[7] This impression is strengthened by the passage omitted in the second paragraph of the above quotation, and by much of the argument used by Hayek. (For a discussion of the nature of material philosophies of history, cf. my article 'Some Heglected Philosophic Problems Regarding History', *Journal of Philosophy*, 1952, **49**, pp. 317–329.)

[8] This is also the view that I would hold. (Cf. 'Societal Facts' [pp. 231–233 above].)

perhaps understandable in the light of the polemical purposes which we have noted in Popper and Hayek, but it is important to see that a rejection of methodological individualism does not entail an acceptance of an organismic or historicist view of society. This will become apparent in what follows.

I shall proceed by drawing two sets of distinctions concerning law-like statements. By combining these two sets of distinctions into a four-celled table it will be seen that those who accept the belief that there are (or may be) irreducible societal laws can be holding quite diverse views regarding these laws. Leaving aside those law-like statements which seek to reduce societal facts to facts concerning individual behaviour, a societal law could belong to any of the four classes which I shall distinguish. (At certain points it will become apparent that even these classes can be further divided into sub-classes.) It so happens, however, that the theories most frequently discussed by methodological individualists usually fall into only one of these classes. Thus it will be shown that the dichotomy which is usually drawn between methodological individualism and methodological holism is an over-simplified and misleading classification of types of social theory.

II

The first of the distinctions that I wish to draw is between 'a law of functional relation' and 'a law of directional change'. (I shall usually refer to these as 'functional' and as 'directional' laws.) The distinction between these two types of laws, which are sometimes referred to as synchronic and diachronic laws,[9] can perhaps most easily be illustrated through reference to the physical sciences. Boyle's law or Newton's inverse square law would be examples of *functional* laws, while the second law of thermodynamics would be the outstanding

[9] Cf. Goldstein's discussion [p. 271 ff.]. (It is to be noted that Goldstein does not deny the applicability of methodological individualism in synchronic studies, though I would do so.)

In an earlier article Edgar Zilsel referred to these as 'temporal laws' and 'simultaneity laws' and attempted to establish that both types are to be found in history (cf. 'Physics and the Problem of Historico-sociological Laws', *Philosophy of Science*, 1941, **8**, pp. 567–579). It would seem that Zilsel's position with respect to methodological individualism is essentially similar to that held by Brodbeck.

In his *Philosophy of Science*, Madison, 1957, G. Bergmann draws a distinction between 'process laws' and 'laws of development' which, I believe, corresponds in many respects to the distinction which I have attempted to draw between functional and directional laws. (He also discriminates between these two types of law and two other types: 'cross-sectional laws' and 'historical laws'. The first of these is not relevant to our present problem; the second, as Bergmann shows, is in many cases reducible to a process law.)

example of a *directional* law. In the field of history the distinction would be between what I have elsewhere called 'laws *concerning* history' and 'laws *of* history'.[10] Marx's theory of the relation between the economic organization of a society and other institutions in that society (his doctrine of 'the superstructure') would be a functional law, i.e., a law *concerning* history. On the other hand, one may interpret his view of dialectical development as an attempt to formulate a law stating a necessary pattern of directional change in history, i.e., as a law *of* history.[11]

These two types of law are obviously different. While either would make prediction possible if we possessed adequate knowledge of the initial and boundary conditions of the state of affairs to which the law was to be applied, the first type of law (a functional law) would only enable us to predict immediately subsequent events, and each further prediction would have to rest upon knowledge of the initial and boundary conditions obtaining at that time. The second type of law (a directional law) would not demand a knowledge of subsequent initial conditions (though it would assume stability of boundary conditions), for if there were a law of directional change which could be discovered in any segment of history we could extrapolate to the past and to the future without needing to gather knowledge of the initial

---

[10] 'A Critique of Philosophies of History', *Journal of Philosophy*, 1948, **45**, pp. 365–378.

[11] It appears to me that Marx failed to see the difference between these two types of explanation, and that the second type constitutes a survival of Hegelianism in his social theory. To be sure, there are passages in Marx which would make it appear that the pattern of directional change is merely the result of the forces which he attempts to analyse in terms of his economic theory and of his doctrine of 'the superstructure'. Nevertheless, it does seem equally plausible (at the very least) to maintain that he regarded the pattern which he traced in the history of mankind as having an inherent necessity in it, i.e., that it was 'inevitable', and was not merely the actual outcome of forces operating from moment to moment. (Even on the latter interpretation of Marx, there are two possible alternative interpretations: (a) that the inevitability rests on the necessary pattern of development in the means of production, particularly the technology; (b) that the inevitability of the pattern is an expression of the ultimate dialectical process in all reality.)

A somewhat similar confusion between laws of history and laws *concerning* history is present in Toynbee. His concept of 'challenge and response' purports to throw light on the forces at work at each stage in the course of a civilization's history, but the pattern of change which he traces seems to assume the shape of a quasi-inevitable directional tendency. In other words, the concept of 'challenge and response' performs the same sort of function as a law *concerning* history would perform in a scientifically oriented theory, while his construction of the histories of civilization in terms of their stages is an attempt to show that there is an inherent tendency for the course of history to follow a definite pattern of development.

conditions obtaining at each successive point in the historical process.[12]

We now come to the second distinction which I wish to draw: a distinction between what I shall designate as *'abstractive* laws' and what I shall designate as *'global* laws'.

In an abstractive law the attempt is made to state a relation between specific aspects or components which are present in a state of affairs, and to state this relation in such a way that it will be applicable in all cases in which these particular aspects or components are present. In formulating such a law, the specific nature of the state of affairs in which these elements are to be found does not enter into the law itself, but is only considered with respect to the initial and boundary conditions which must be taken into account in applying the law.

On the other hand, it is possible to regard some entities in terms of their global properties, to consider them as unitary systems, or wholes. And it may be possible that when we so regard them we can formulate law-like statements concerning changes in their global properties, or concerning relationships between the nature of the system as a whole and the manner in which its component parts behave. In stating such a law we are considering the system as a system, and a reference to the properties of the system is included in the law which we formulate.

Now, in order to avoid an unnecessary misunderstanding, it must immediately be pointed out that the acceptance of a global law (or of the possibility that there are global laws) does not commit one to the position of 'emergence', or to any form of 'holism'. Such laws might be held to be derivative from laws concerning the component aspects of the system, and thus be reducible to abstractive laws. To be sure, one might not so regard them, and in that case one would in all likelihood be accepting the position usually designated as 'holism'. Yet even this is not necessary. For example, if one were to hold that there are laws concerning the relations between one component in a certain type of system, and the nature of any such system considered as a whole, and if one were also to hold that it is this component which determines the properties of the whole, then one would be formulating a law concerning the global properties of a system, and yet not be a 'holist' in the most usual sense of that term: it would be a part which determines the nature of the whole, not the whole which determines the nature of its parts.

This last warning may help to elucidate the distinction which I

---

[12] Cf. the method of Henry Adams. It is to be noted that in those cases in which a directional law is derived from metaphysical principles (rather than being empirically derived), it is not even thought to be necessary to assume stability in the boundary conditions for a society.

have sought to draw between abstractive and global laws. The distinction is not one between non-holism and holism, but between laws which are formulated in terms of particular aspects or components which have been abstracted from a concrete state of affairs, and laws which are formulated in terms of the nature of particular types of system. In other words, there is a difference in what the laws are *about*. Abstractive laws are about the relationships between two aspects or components that occur in a variety of different concrete situations; the nature of the situations in which these aspects are embedded constitute the initial and boundary conditions which must be taken into account in applying the law. Global laws, on the other hand, are about the properties of systems, attempting to show how these systems change over time, or how the system as a whole is related to its component parts.

III

We have now drawn two distinctions: first, a distinction between laws concerning functional relations and laws concerning directional change; second, a distinction between abstractive laws and global laws. These distinctions engender four possibilities concerning law-like statements, and if we now examine the theories of those who have rejected the principle of methodological individualism we shall find that social theorists have attempted to formulate law-like statements of each of the four types. However, methodological individualism has been almost solely concerned with a criticism of the attempt to find *global laws of directional change*. It has in fact tended to identify the view that there are irreducible societal laws with a belief in laws of this type. If we now briefly examine each of the four types we shall be in a position to see to what extent, if at all, each may properly be regarded as holistic.

(i) Let us first examine the view that there are law-like statements which are both functional and global. Such laws would relate the global properties of a social system as a whole to one or more of its component parts, i.e., to its specific institutions or sanctioned usages.

As we have already noted, there are two main ways of proceeding in attempting to establish laws of this general type. On the one hand, we may regard the global properties as determinants of the properties possessed by component parts of the system. This is the case in Ruth Benedict's descriptive analysis of particular patterns of culture; it is also the case in Radcliffe-Brown's form of Functionalism in which the need for self-maintenance in a society considered as a whole determines specific usages, such as the punishment of criminals or funeral ceremonies.[13] Marx, on the other hand, would derive at least certain of the global properties of a social system (e.g., the defining characteristics of 'feudalism' or 'capitalism') from one specific component within that system, viz. the means of production. Others might seek to find a composition law by means of which, given the properties of two or more component parts of the system, the global properties of the system as a whole could be derived. All of these types of law would be instances of an attempt to state global laws of the functional type, i.e., laws which involve the relation of its components to the concrete nature of a system considered as a whole. I believe that it is obvious that not all of these attempts would be 'holistic' in the same sense.

(ii) It would also be possible to attempt to establish laws of directional change concerning global properties. Such laws would not be seeking to relate the properties of a system as a whole to the nature of one or more of its component parts, but would attempt to formulate a law-like statement concerning the successive states of a system. In other words, a law of this type would be a statement concerning a pattern of directional change in a social system considered as a whole, e.g., that there exists a specific sort of uni-directional development, or a cyclic flow, in the over-all aspects of a society. Such a law, of course, would not be intended to be merely a description of what has taken place in one social system during a restricted time interval, but would be held to be applicable at all times and with respect to all societies,[14] or with respect to all segments of one all-embracing historical process, viz. to the history of mankind as a whole.

A theory of history which is based on the belief in a law of this type would regard the over-all changes which took place as being 'inevitable'. Furthermore, such theories usually regard the directional law which they seek to establish as being an ultimate law, i.e., one not deducible from functional laws concerning the components of the systems. Where this is the case, we may legitimately speak of 'holism'. However, we must note that such a law might *not* be treated as ultimate. For example, it might not be wholly misleading[15] to re-phrase Marx's doctrine concerning historical inevitability to make it

---

[13] Cf. Radcliffe-Brown, 'On the Concept of Function in Social Science', *American Anthropologist*, 1935, **37,** pp. 394–402. (The specific illustration used is to be found on p. 396.) Also, 'On Social Structure', *Journal of the Royal Anthropological Institute*, 1940, **70,** pp. 1–12.

It is to be noted that Radcliffe-Brown's form of Functionalism is to be distinguished from that held by Malinowski (after 1926). On this distinction, cf. Radcliffe-Brown, 'A Note on Functional Anthropology', *Man*, 1946, **46,** section 30, and 'Functionalism: A Protest', *American Anthropologist*, 1949, **51,** pp. 320–323.

[14] Of course, this may be limited to societies of a given type, e.g., to 'civilisations' but not to 'primitive societies'.

[15] Cf. [note 11, p. 239 above].

appear that the law of directional change in history is a consequence of two other laws: a functional law asserting that the global properties of a social system are determined by the means of production, and a directional law concerning changes in this specific component. Such a position would still maintain the thesis that there is a law descriptive of the direction of social change in all social systems, and it would therefore espouse the doctrine of historical inevitability, but it would not be an example of 'holism'.

The above suggestion is not intended to be a contribution to the exegesis of Marx, but is included for two other reasons. First, it should serve to suggest that not all doctrines of historical inevitability are 'holistic', or (at least) equally 'holistic'.[16] Second, it serves to introduce the third general type of law with which we are concerned: the attempt to find a directional law which is abstractive in the sense that it is concerned with changes occurring in one component of a social system, and not with the social system considered as a whole.

(iii) Attempts to formulate laws of directional change concerning specific institutions, regardless of the societies in which they are embedded, have been very prevalent in anthropological and sociological theory. Among the many examples it is only necessary to call to mind theories of the necessary stages in religious development, or in marriage systems; attempts to formulate a law concerning the tendency of language to change from a more complex to a simpler structure, or of the arts to develop from the abstract-decorative towards the representational role (or vice versa). There have, of course, also been attempts to trace cyclical changes (and to formulate laws concerning the sequence of such changes) in political forms or in styles of art. Whether these directional laws regarding specific institutions have been unidirectional or cyclic, those who have formulated them have not usually viewed them as derivative from abstractive functional laws.[17] Rather, they have generally (but not always) regarded them as derivative from other laws of directional change. These more basic directional laws have usually been of either two kinds: laws concerning the direction of change in the total social system (i.e., directional laws

---

[16] It should also be noted that not all examples of holism in the philosophy of history accept the thesis of historical inevitability, if by 'inevitability' is meant that each stage in the development follows necessarily from the preceding stage. In Herder's philosophy of history, for example, the element of necessity is strongly stressed in each part of the process, but the process as a whole is not viewed as proceeding through an over-riding necessity. (For example, cf. *Ideen zur Philosophie der Geschichte der Menschheit*, 13th Book, 7th Chapter.)

[17] This is to be expected, since the attempt to formulate such a directional law of change with respect to a specific institution involves an isolation of that component from the other societal components which are contemporaneous with it.

of the global type) or laws concerning the changes in the nature of the human mind. By holding that there is a necessary direction of change in a society as a whole, and by holding that form of global law which states that the whole is so related to its parts that the parts are determined by the whole, a law of change concerning a specific institution follows. Or by holding that there is a particular pattern of growth in the capacities of the human mind, and by making the assumption that each institution will go through stages which reflect this growth, a law of change in a specific institution could be derived. These two alternative ways of deriving a law of directional change in a specific institution from some more ultimate law of change are not incompatible. They are not incompatible since it is possible to hold (and has often been held, e.g., by Comte and, in a sense, by Hegel) that the law of development which applies to the properties of society considered as one systematic whole, is a reflection of the development of the human mind or spirit. This should be recalled by those who tend to regard holist views of the structure of society as being primarily due to the tendency to regard societal facts as different from facts concerning human thought and action.

(iv) The fourth possible type of societal law which follows from our distinctions would consist in the attempt to state functional laws of the abstractive type. Among the examples of attempts to formulate such laws we may cite the following: statements concerning relationships between modes of production and marriage systems; between size of population and political organization; between forms of economic organization and political organization; or, to cite a classic study of Tylor's[18] (which has been amplified and elaborated by Murdock in his *Social Structure*) between certain specific aspects of marriage systems, e.g., rules of residence and rules of descent.

It is to be noted that laws of this abstractive-functional type are different in aim from the laws of the other three types.[19] In being functional laws, they do not assume that there is any necessary direction of historical change, either within specific institutions or within a society considered as a whole. Furthermore, in being abstractive they seek to explain such changes as do occur in terms of the successive initial and boundary conditions which obtain at specific points in time,

---

[18] 'On a Method of Investigating the Development of Institutions; Applied to Laws of Marriage and Descent', *Journal of the Royal Anthropological Institute*, 1889, **18**, pp. 245–269.

[19] To be sure, the purpose for which Tylor, as a social evolutionist, used his data concerning functional relations was primarily for the reconstruction of the evolution of marriage systems. It is also to be admitted that his explanations of *why* 'adhesions' took place were often couched in psychological terms. However, he does not appear to have believed that such psychological explanations were alone sufficient to account for the facts (cf. *loc. cit.*, p. 248).

and do not assume that these conditions must be identical in all societies. In being abstractive they also remain uncommitted on the question of whether any particular society (or every society) can be regarded as a single organic whole; it becomes the task of empirical investigation to determine to what extent the various aspects of a given state of affairs *are* interrelated. Thus, those who hold that there are (or may be) abstractive-functional societal laws are neither committed to historicism nor to organicism, both of which have usually been held to be consequences of the rejection of methodological individualism.

IV

Without entering into the empirical and methodological issues which are involved, I should like to state that I believe there are important reasons for doubting that we shall find irreducible societal laws of the first three types.[20] Therefore I venture the suggestion that *if* there are empirically derivable laws concerning social phenomena, and if these cannot all be reduced to laws concerning individual behaviour, those which cannot be so reduced will be abstractive laws concerning functional relations between specific types of societal facts. Whether such laws have been found, or whether we have reason to believe that they may be found, is not the question which I have proposed for this discussion. However, before closing, I should like briefly to indicate the various possible relationships which might obtain between psychological laws concerning the behaviour of individuals and laws which attempt to state functional relationships between specific aspects of social structures.

If one assumes that there are (or may be) laws which accurately express the functional relations between two or more specific types of fact in all societies (or in all societies of a specific type), it could be the case that these laws follow deductively from laws of individual behaviour when one takes into account the conditions obtaining in the societies in question. This is the view held by methodological individualism which rejects *irreducible* societal laws.

If, however, one believes that there are irreducible societal laws, two positions still remain open to one. One *might* hold that such laws are themselves sufficient (granted the initial and boundary conditions) to explain all that occurs in societies. To this position methodological individualists would doubtless be no less opposed than they are to a holistic view, since this view would also render human choice and

---

[20] Some reasons for doubting each of these three types are implicit in my earlier article, 'A Critique of Philosophies of History', *Journal of Philosophy*, 1948, **45**, pp. 365–378. I shall discuss the issue in detail in a future article.

human action nugatory in the realm of social affairs. On the other hand, one might hold that an adequate explanation of social phenomena would have to use *both* psychological laws and societal laws, and that neither of these types of law is reducible to the other.

There would, I submit, be nothing mysterious in such a claim.[21] When, for example, we wish to explain a concrete phenomenon of social history such as the failure of a particular soil conservation programme, we need to employ psychological generalizations concerning human behaviour, but we also need to employ generalizations drawn from the physical sciences concerning the effects of the conservation steps which were taken. In such cases of interaction between men and their physical environment no one, I should suppose, would challenge the belief that an adequate explanation of the series of events would demand the use of laws belonging to different sciences, as well as demanding a knowledge of the initial conditions relevant to the application of each set of laws. Further, no one, I should suppose, would argue that one set of these laws must be reducible to the other in order that we should be able to use both in explaining this concrete event. And I see no reason why an analogous situation could not obtain with respect to the explanation of social phenomena, i.e., that in such explanations we may need to employ both psychological and societal laws. A belief of this type would not entail the acceptance of historical inevitability, nor would it entail any form of holism. Finally we may note that such a view would not necessarily entail a rejection of the thesis that psychological laws are *always* relevant to the explanation of social phenomena. It could accept this thesis and yet hold that *in some cases*[22] a knowledge of the initial conditions under which individuals act, and a knowledge of the laws of individual behaviour, is not adequate to explain the outcome of their actions: for this one must also employ abstractive-functional generalizations concerning societal facts.

The purpose of this paper has been limited to pointing out that a rejection of methodological individualism is compatible with a number of diverse views concerning the nature of societal laws. Therefore the simple dichotomy of methodological individualism *or* methodological holism stands in need of drastic revision. It seems to me that the classification which I have offered may also help to point out frequently unnoticed similarities and diversities among social theorists, thus making an analysis of their theories somewhat more manageable. And

---

[21] I believe that Gellner is correct in thinking that many methodological individualists *would* think this 'mysterious'. [Cf. Gellner, pp. 256–257 below.]

[22] I should not myself be inclined to accept the more radical form of the doctrine here under considerations, viz. that in *all* cases this is true.

if, as I believe, there are good empirical and methodological reasons to doubt the feasibility of establishing either abstractive or global laws of directional change, or global laws of a functional sort,[23] then the issue of whether there are irreducible societal laws can be confined to one set of claims: that there are (or are not) some irreducible laws governing the functional relationships of specific aspects or components in societal life. The establishment of such laws would not demand that we accept the thesis of historical inevitability, nor the political and moral implications of either historicism or organicism. Nor would it commit us to either the metaphysics, or the explanatory methods, of holism.

[23] I am here only referring to laws of this type which are claimed to be 'ultimate', i.e., not reducible to abstractive-functional laws.

E. A. GELLNER

Explanations in History

The problem of explanation in history is also the problem of the nature of sociology. The views adopted in this field are held to have profound moral and political implications. We have recently often been reminded of this. The simplest argument connecting a premiss about the nature of historical explanation with political or ethical consequences runs as follows: if rigid, unchangeable, and wide-ranging generalizations are attainable with regard to historical processes, then an outlook which presupposes individual responsibility is basically misguided. Having pointed out this implication, philosophers hostile to the conclusion then devote themselves to undermining the premiss. They may do so either by pointing out that the required historical laws have not been found, or by arguing that they could not be.

I shall not directly concern myself with this matter of the existence or possibility of historical *laws*, but attempt to isolate the issues which arise here that can be stated without at any rate explicit reference to the law-like nature of history. I shall concern myself with the kind of concept or term characteristically employed when we talk of history or of societies. Notoriously the grammatical subject of sentences written or uttered by social scientists is often not a man, or enumerated or characterized men, but groups, institutions, 'cultures', etc. The proper study of mankind is human groups and institutions.

Thus the alleged argument leading to the elimination of individual autonomy and responsibility may be stated without at least explicit and obvious presupposition of the attainment of causal generalizations in history. Those concerned with defending humanity against historicist or other mythologies—I shall call these defenders ' Individualists'— notice this fact. This gives rise to an attempt to 'eliminate' so-called 'holistic' concepts, or rather to show that these are in principle eliminable. That such an elimination should be possible seems strongly suggested by the fact that, after all, groups consist of people, and institutions are what people do, etc. A state cannot exist without citizens, nor a legal system without judges, litigants, etc. The

248

worst obstacle such elimination could encounter, it seems would be complexity.[1]

The matter, however, is not so simple. Arguments have been put forward to the effect that the elimination is in principle impossible.[2] Moreover, it is a weighty fact that at least some explanations in social sciences would in practice not be stated or be at all easily statable in individualist terms.[3]

To each side in this dispute, its own position appears very nearly self-evident, and the opponents' position something that can be *said*, but not seriously practised. To the Individualist, his own position appears so true that it barely needs the confirmation of actually carried out eliminations, whilst he gleefully points out that in practice the holist can and does only approach his institutions, etc., through what concrete people do, which seems to the Individualist a practical demonstration and implicit confession of the absurdity of holism. By contrast (and with neat symmetry) the holist sees in the fact that the individualist continues to talk in holistic term a practical demonstration of the unworkability of individualism, and he certainly does not consider the fact that he can only approach groups and institutions through the doings of individuals to be something which he had implicitly denied and which could count against him. Both sides find comfort in the actual practice of the opponent.

One should add here that the possibility of political implications cuts both ways. Individualists who attempt to save us, in the name of logic and liberty, from misconstruing our situation, are not wholly free at all

---

[1] There is one foreseeable objection to both my arguments and those I criticize, namely, that a 'naming' theory of meaning underlies both the approaches contemplated. For instance, Mr R. Wollheim in his review of Mr Weldon's 'Vocabulary of Politics' in *Mind*, 1955, makes a point of this kind in a similar context. Now this type of currently fashionable general appeal to the heterogeneity of meaning does not seem to me to cut much ice; perhaps because the 'naming theory' of meaning has not been adequately exorcized from my mind, but perhaps for better reasons. These might be along the following lines: not all reductions are impossible, but on the contrary some are both possible and salutary. The general acceptance of the great variety of ways in which words have meaning does indeed leave us with the baby, but also with much undesirable bath water. It does not by itself give us any insight into how various concepts are used. We gain that, amongst other ways, by trying to reduce some concepts to others. For instance, the Individualist is quite right in insisting that a rising marriage rate is not the kind of thing which could be the cause of an individual marriage. It only records the fact that more such marriages occur. At the same time when reductions fail, the fact that they do and the reasons they do, give us some understanding of the nature of the unreduced concepts.

[2] Cf. Maurice Mandelbaum, 'Societal Facts' [pp. 221–234 above].

[3] Cf. M. Ginsberg, 'The Individual and Society' in *The Diversity of Morals*, 1956.

times from the suspicion that a little propaganda for *laissez faire* is being hitched on to those very general issues.[4]

What is at issue is the ontological status of the entities referred to by the holistic terms. As the notion of ontological status is not as clear as it might be, I shall at some stages shift provisionally to something which is as important to the reductionist and which to him is an index of existence—namely, causation. He does not wish to allow that the Whole could ever be a cause, and to insist that explanations which make it appear that it is can be translated into others. That which is a mere construct cannot causally affect that which 'really exist'; this is, I suspect, the feeling of the Individualist, the reductionist. This in conjunction with the truism that a whole is made up of its parts, that nothing can happen to a whole without something happening to either some at least of its parts or to their mutual relations—leads him to to the misleading conclusion that explanation in history and in social studies must ultimately be in terms of individual dispositions. The holistic counter-argument works in reverse; if something (a) is a causal factor (b) cannot be reduced, then in some sense it 'really and independently exists'.

When we face a problem of 'reduction' in philosophy we are often confronted with a dilemma; on the one hand forceful formal arguments tend to show that a reduction must be possible, on the other hand all attempted reductions fail or are incomplete, and features can be found which suggest or prove that they cannot succeed or be complete. For instance, phenomenalism is supported not by the plausibility or success of actual reductions but by the force of the arguments to the effect that there must be a reduction, whilst at the same time the interesting arguments against it as cogently indicate that phenomenalist translation can never be completed.

The situation is similar with regard to the present problem. I consider, for instance, one particular, rather ambitious attempt to demonstrate that a reduction must be possible.

'All social phenomena are, directly or indirectly, human creations. A lump of matter may exist which no one has perceived but not a price which no one has charged, or a disciplinary code to which no one refers, or a tool which no one would dream of using. From this truism I infer

---

[4] As Ginsberg says: 'Similarly those who refuse to accept methodological individualism . . . are not committed . . . to a totalitarian view of political action. They are well aware . . . of the dangers of concentrated power. But they deny that the only choice open to us is between a spontaneous competitive order on one hand, and a system of all-pervading control on the other. It is odd that those who attack what they call scientism should feel able to predict with certainty that any form of socialism must necessarily lead to cultural and political totalitarianism . . . In any event, "logicism" is no improvement on "scientism".' *Op. cit.*, pp. 161–162.

the methodological principle . . . that the social scientist can continue searching for explanations of a social phenomenon until he has reduced it to psychological terms.'

The conclusion reached in the end is:

'Individualistic ideal types of explanatory power are constructed by first discerning the form of typical . . . dispositions, and then by demonstration how these lead to certain principles of social behaviour'.[5]

As the argument also maintains that 'individualistic ideal types' are alone possible, what the conclusion amounts to is something like this: to explain a social or historical situation is to deduce it from what the individuals involved in it are disposed to do.

This contention can be broken up into two claims; that an explanation specifies *individual* dispositions, and that it specifies individual *dispositions*. In other words: (1) Statements about things other than individuals are excluded from a final explanation; (2) Statements which are not about dispositions are similarly excluded. By 'disposition' here is meant something 'intelligible', a conceivable reaction of human beings to circumstances; not necessarily one we share, still less necessarily one we can 'introspect'; but still something opposed to what we would call 'dead' physical causation where 'anything could cause anything'.

Having broken up the requirements of reduction into two parts, we get four possibilities, of which three are excluded. Let us consider these excluded ones in turn.

(1) Holistic subject plus intelligible disposition. This is equivalent to a 'group mind' theory. I take it no one is advocating this seriously.

(2) Holistic subject without *intelligible* dispositions—i.e., attributions of regularity or pattern to wholes, without any suggestion that these patterns express conscious or purposive reactions.

(3) Individualistic subjects without *intelligible* dispositions.

Let it be said that events explicable along the lines of alternative (3) can be excluded from history or sociology only by an inconvenient and arbitrary fiat. The destruction of Pompeii or the Black Death are historical events. It is true that the *reaction* of survivors to these 'blindly causal' events calls for explanation not in terms of 'dead' causation but possibly in terms of aims, dispositions, expectations, convictions. So be it; but the very fact that semi-deliberate and blindly causal events are so often and intimately fused in life brings out the inconvenience of excluding one kind.

[5] J. W. N. Watkins, 'Ideal Types and Historical Explanation' in *The British Journal for the Philosophy of Science*, Vol. iii, No. 9, 1952 [see pp. 143–165 above]. See also Discussion of this paper by the same author in the following issue of the same *Journal*.

When in this paper I say 'Individualism' I mean 'methodological individualism', roughly along the lines outlined in these two articles.

Consider now exclusion of kind (2). When an historian speaks of the maintenance or growth of an institution, or a linguist about phonetic change, or an anthropologist about the maintenance of a system of kinship structure, they do not in fact always or often mention individual dispositions. The question is, *could* they?

The first step towards such a translation is easy. 'The monarchy is strong' can be translated into a disposition of subjects to have a certain set of attitudes to the monarch. Note: not necessarily all subjects or all the time, but a sufficient number of them sufficiently often, and above all at crucial times. Neither 'sufficient number' nor 'sufficiently often' nor 'crucial times' can be defined with precision, nor ultimately without referring back to the holist term 'monarchy'. The same applies to the 'set of attitudes'.

By and large, institutions and social structures and climates of opinion are not the results of what people want and believe, but of what they take for granted. Let us allow the reductionist to class tacit acceptance amongst dispositions, though I suspect we shall find the same circularity here as occurs above. Such translations would, however, be clumsy, nebulous, long and vague, where the original statements about an institution or feature of the social scene was clear, brief and intelligible.

If, however, we grant that 'in principle' this translation is possible, it in no way follows that these tacit and irregularly diffused dispositions are in turn explicable in terms of familiar, intelligible human responses. The existence of a diffused monarchical disposition was inferred logically from the truth of 'The monarchy is strong'; the dependence of the latter on the former, if it obtains at all, does so in virtue of logic or the truism that an institution is what people do. The dependence of the perhaps validly inferred disposition on a piece of intuitively obvious psychology would be a casual matter, and there are no reasons in logic or fact for supposing it to hold. On the contrary, in as far as such a procedure seems to assume the possibility of isolating more elementary dispositions 'as they are prior to their manifestations in a social context', formal doubts may be raised concerning the realizability of such a programme.

There are two specific points, possibly inconclusive by themselves but worth noting, which influence the holist at this stage.

First, very small differences in individual conduct distributed irregularly over a large population, may have important consequences for the society at large without being detectable individually. The argument in favour of 'social facts' is historically connected with the presence of statistical regularities where none can be found at the molecular, individual level. The statistical regularity can be explained in terms of features of the social situation as a whole, but in practice it is seldom possible to trace the nexus in individual cases. To insist that it is always 'in principle' possible is to prejudge the issue under discussion. Moreover, something like a Principle of Indeterminacy may very well operate here, for the amount of disturbance involved in observing the individual case may very often be much larger than the small difference which accounts for the statistical result and may, so to speak, 'drown it'.

Secondly, individuals do have holistic concepts and often act in terms of them. For instance, a number of reviewers of the recently published Memoirs of Général de Gaulle have commented on the fact that de Gaulle's actions were inspired by his *idea* of France—which may perhaps have had little relation to actual Frenchmen. When the holistic ideas of many individuals are co-ordinated and reinforced by public behaviour and physical objects—by ceremonials, rituals, symbols, public buildings, etc.—it is difficult for the social scientist, though he observes the scene from the outside, not to use the holistic concept. It is quite true that the fact that X acts and thinks in terms of an holistic idea—e.g., he treats the totem as if it were his tribe, and the tribe as if it were more than the tribesmen—is itself a fact about an individual. On the other hand, though the holistic term as used by the observer may be eliminable, as used by the participant it is not. Are we to say that a logical impeccable explanation of a social situation is committed to crediting its subjects with nonsensical thought? Perhaps we are. On the other hand, the fact that holistic terms are ineliminable from the thought of participants may well be a clue to their ineliminability from that of observers.

It is perhaps unnecessary at this stage to insist on the fact that very little is gained by having individual dispositions as the bedrock of a historical or social explanation. Their 'intelligibility' is either familiarity, or, as often, springs from the fact that dispositional terms come in clusters each of which is a more or less exhaustive crude taxonomy: such as, perhaps, for instance: 'Knowing-believing-considering-tacitly accepting-disregarding', or 'wanting-being indifferent to-not wanting'. If with the help of such terms we characterize someone's conduct, on the analogy of the parallelogram of forces, do we thereby really approach the actual causal sequences?

It is true that this kind of diagnosis fits fairly well in the case of one social science, namely, economics. This, however, is presumably due to the fact that this science restricts itself to behaviour with regard to which aims and relevant convictions and explanations are reasonably avowable and specifiable; to some extent it may be said that economic theory applies to people who have been taught to act in accordance with it. Also, the words most frequently used by economists happen to be *ceteris paribus*. Moreover, whilst an economist may explain a man's behaviour in a market situation, it takes a non-economist to explain how he ever comes to be economically rational. If, for instance, one comes to explain that in terms of the mundane application of a religious notion of 'vocation', is that transition an 'intelligible disposition?' Yes, in the sense that I see, roughly, what happens, know that it could happen to me, and if I believe it to be a regular occurrence may use it to explain particular incidents. But by those criteria any disposition can become 'intelligible'.[6]

The real oddity of the reductionist case is that it seems to preclude *a priori* the possibility of human dispositions being the dependent variable in an historical explanation—when in fact they often or always are—and secondly to preclude the possibility of causes, in the sense of initial conditions, being a complex fact which is not desirable in terms of the characteristics of its constituent parts alone—which in turn seems often to be the case.

Let it be added that in as far as the original argument is valid, it is equally valid for the non-human sciences. The fact that the natural sciences seem to be free from restrictions with regard to the kind of explanation they use does not derive from the fact that there are unobserved pieces of matter.[7] Moreover, in natural science as much as any-

---

[6] Having criticized the notion of 'intelligibility' of human dispositions and in particular the accompanying suggestion that it gives us double access or confirmation of human reality, once through social appearance and secondly through dispositions as psychological things-in-themselves I do not wish to be interpreted as denying the importance of *Einfühlung*, of sympathetic understanding. But the nature and value of this method or heuristic device seems to me the very opposite to what is supposed by the reductionist. It lies in the familiarization with alien reactions and dispositions, not in forcing on them interpretations making them into variants of what is familiar anyway. This last may perhaps be the practice of economic theorists—but just that may help to explain the unreality of that discipline outside certain limits.

Collingwood's celebrated doctrines concerning this matter seem to amount perhaps to not much more than this: history like other disciplines uses the hypothetico-deductive method, and in history the hypotheses are usually about what people attempted to do. Stated thus, the doctrine becomes less startling. It also ceases to be open to the two criticisms normally levelled against it, namely that Collingwood took the ghost in the machine too seriously, and secondly, that he misinterpreted an heuristic device as an essential characteristic of historical knowledge.

Further, 'hypothetico-deductive method' is a misnomer. One can only speak of *method* where there is an alternative. But the only alternative to *this* way of studying things is not another way, but not studying them at all. For this 'method' really means only thinking about things and then seeing whether what one had thought is true.

[7] Evidently Watkins himself no longer holds this proof valid. He explains in the discussion note in the following number that he considers a counter-example to the principle of methodological individualism to be conceivable; so that the principle can hardly be susceptible of formal proof. But the counter-example

where else, wholes are composed of their constituent parts. Nothing follows from this truism concerning the general nature of initial conditions in dependence statements; but physicists could, no doubt, use animist language if they wished—they could speak of intelligible dispositions instead of the behaviour of particles.

The present paper is essentially an attempt to separate an indisputably true—because tautologous—proposition (roughly 'Assertions about people are assertions about people'), from its alleged implications which are at the very least questionable and hence not tautologous, and (hence) not its implications. One might equally have proceeded in the opposite direction and tried to separate the truism 'Assertions about societies *are* assertions about society' from an alleged and mistaken consequence that societies 'exist' in the same sense as individuals, or independently of them. But the contemporary climate of opinion makes this latter exercise less necessary.

A full clarification of these issues would probably be possible only if we were clearer about what is meant by causation in social contexts. A related matter which I have not pursued is the probability that what counts as 'explanation' in history and in the social sciences is far from homogeneous in kind, any more than what counts as a 'problem'. This, over and above the particular difficulties discussed in this paper, may be a very serious objection to formal methodological arguments providing an *a priori* recipe for 'explanation'.

So far I have in this paper indicated what seem to me flaws in an attempted reduction. I have little doubt that actual procedure in historical and social explanation often is holistic, and that over and above this appeal to actual procedure, general reasons can be found, and probably stated more forcefully than I have stated them, to support the contention that this must be so. But it is equally obvious to me that this will not shake the determined individualist. Not only does he see important ethical issues hingeing on his doctrine, but also some deep logical intuition which many of us can empathize would have to be repressed by him before he could abandon his position. Indisputably, 'history is about chaps'; hence 'historical events must be explained in terms of what chaps do'. Now we all agree that repression is a bad thing; hence it is desirable to diagnose and render harmless the compulsive insight, rather than merely argue against it.

Let us try to call up this intuition in ourselves by attending to the

---

envisaged by him is of the 'group mind' type—dispositional interpretation predicated of social wholes, in my scheme—such as he thinks might be suggested by some facts from the social life of insects. My arguments against the Principle are quite independent of any such possibility. I am more than willing to concede that no phenomena calling for a 'group mind' occur.

argument of one trying to demonstrate the *im*possibility of reducing holistic social concepts to individual ones.

Mandelbaum's recent argument restating an old point in 'language' —language starts from the premiss that an action such as drawing money from the bank cannot be explained without the use of holistic concepts such as 'banking system'. It must be (at least tacitly) understood by the agent, and must be understood by the observer if he is to understand the action. When Mandelbaum says 'explain' he might perhaps say 'describe', for the rules of deposit banking are all somehow implicit in the concept of cashing a cheque. (A causal explanation *might* actually be simpler and not involve any understanding of the rules of banking.)

So far, there is nothing that need upset the individualist. Individuals act guided by nebulous holistic concepts—so far so good. As far as the object connoted by the concept is concerned the Individualist is sure that it can be 'translated' in terms of what various individuals involved in banking institutions are doing. (Mandelbaum does not agree, on the grounds that the description of their activity in turn will involve use of the concept of 'banking': but let us leave that aside for the moment.)

Let us just agree—as is indeed true—that drawing a cheque is internally related to the whole banking system, that what is meant by cashing a cheque involves by its very meaning the general features of banking; that, tacitly or otherwise, the concept 'bank' is being employed by anyone describing or understanding the cashing of a cheque. I am stressing this, for the Individualist cannot but come with us this far.

It is the next step that he will refuse to take. This step emerges at the end of Mandelbaum's article, when he speaks of individuals and what he calls 'societal facts' (e.g., banking systems) *interacting*; in other words, implying that it makes sense for the object of a holistic concept to have an effect on a concrete individual. What the Individualist will here object to is the inference from an holistic concept, somehow abstracted from the concrete behaviour of concrete individuals, being then able to figure in the antecedent of a causal sentence. He will refuse to admit this even if he concedes the ineliminability of the holistic concept in description. This seems indeed, he feels, to endow an abstraction with flesh and power; and we can easily feel this with him.

Of course, he isn't denying that causal statements of this kind are meaningfully and truthfully uttered. He only wishes to insist that the antecedent must in such cases be translatable into individualistic terms. Surely the insubstantial cannot constrain the substantial? I think we can provisionally agree to this principle; (though earlier we *seemed* to have contradicted it when uttering the truism that a cause may be as complex an event as we wish—as indeed it can). At the same time

Mandelbaum's central point, that holistic concepts cannot be eliminated, stands. Here is a dilemma indeed.

Attempted Diagnosis
Consider the following two series:

(1) Jones is going to Germany. All members of the platoon are going, etc. All members of the company are going, etc. All members of the battalion are going, etc.
(2) Jones. The Platoon. The Company. The Battalion.

The first series begins with a singular proposition, and continues with general ones of increasing generality. The second series is one of terms or concepts, in which the preceding is at each stage a part of the subsequent one.

Concerning series (1) it is obvious that each subsequent proposition can only be true in virtue of a set of propositions of the earlier kind being true. Propositions of the latter kind can, unless their subjects are open classes, be 'reduced' or translated into conjunctions of propositions of the preceding kind. To talk of the more general propositions causing, constraining, etc., those of lesser generality subsumed under them is nonsense.

Series (2) lists parts and wholes in such a manner that an earlier member of the series is always a part of a latter member. Latter members depend for their existence on the existence of earlier members, though not necessarily on any definite list of them. *But:* there is no reason in logic or fact why causal sentences should in their antecedent clauses (or consequent clauses, for that matter) be restricted in their subjects to items of the kind that would only appear at the beginning of the series. If 'complexity of causes' obtains, which it often seems to, causal sentences in ordinary language if they are to be expressed in subject-predicate grammatical form will have to have later members of the series as their subjects.

The cause, or at any rate one of the central causes, of the general dilemma under discussion is the attribution of obvious features of series (1) to the series (2), concerning which they are certainly not obvious and probably not true.

For when we speak of societies we mean partly (a) generalizations about classes of human individuals which indeed are true only in virtue of propositions about those individuals, and can be 'reduced' to them, but also (b) groups, complexes, constellations of facts. These latter can indeed exist only if their parts exist—that is indeed the predicament of all wholes—but their fates *qua* fates of complexes can nevertheless be the initial conditions or indeed final conditions of a causal consequence.

The powerful disinclination to allow social or general causes arises from the confusion of (a) and (b). Jones is not caused to go to Germany by the general fact that all other members of the battalion are going; the general proposition merely *says*, amongst other things, that Jones is going. But there is no reason whatever for excluding *a priori* the possibility of unanimity of his comrades, *qua* unanimity, influencing Jones to volunteer to go. That all members of the unit feel the *esprit de corps* is a generalization (which is seldom true); but to say that *esprit de corps* has influenced an individual is not to say that he has been influenced by isolable individuals or their acts.

It should now be clear that the following three propositions are not incompatible:

A generalization is true only in virtue of the truth of singular propositions.

A whole is made up of its parts.

No *a priori* legislation is possible concerning the complexity of links in causal chains.

The error of the Individualist is to conclude from the first two propositions, which are analytic, the falsity of the third, through the confused identification of the hierarchy of propositions in terms of generality with the hierarchy of things in terms of complexity and inclusiveness.

Let us illustrate this with another example. If I say 'All the men in the square were excited' I may simply mean a generalization to the effect that each of the men there was excited; in such a case it would make no sense to speak of the generalization being an independent fact, less still a causal factor.

If, on the other hand, I say 'There was an atmosphere of tension in the square', though this cannot be true without some of a nebulously defined and large set of propositions about the men in the square being true, and *a fortiori* it cannot be true unless there are men in the square, there is yet no way of interpreting this as a mere conjunction. We cannot even describe the state of mind of typical individual participants in the situation without referring back to the situation as a whole. This to some extent throws light on a fact mentioned earlier, namely that whatever the logical rights and wrongs of the case, individuals do think in holistic terms. What this amounts to—amongst other things— is the kind of patterns they are capable of isolating in their environment and react to. The pattern isolated, however, is not 'merely abstracted' but is, as I am somewhat sheepishly tempted to say, 'really there'.

For any individual, the *mores*, institutions, tacit presupposition, etc., of his society are an independent and external fact, as much so as the physical environment and usually more important. And if this is so for each individual, it *does* follow that it is so for the totality of individuals composing a society. Of course, societies not being endowed with group minds, the question doesn't arise for 'the totality'; *just because* the Individualist is in one sense right and 'there is no such *thing*' as the 'totality', the question of the externality and independence of social facts does not arise for it. But it can and does arise for the observer, who may of course be simultaneously a member of the society in question. And though he may in some cases account in some way for the social facts in terms of the interaction of individual decisions with prior 'social facts', any attempt to eliminate these altogether will only lead to a regress and possibly to an irrelevant genetic question of the hen-and-egg kind. The important thing about 'hen-and-egg' is not that we do not know, but that if we did know it would not throw much light on either hens or eggs.

It might be objected that too much is being made of this matter of causation. Complexity of causes is a familiar phenomenon; it does not follow from its occurrence that the constituents of a complex cause make up a 'whole'. My suggestion is that if perceived as a whole, referred to as such, etc., they do. It might again be objected that this merely shows that there are Social *Gestalten* incorporated in the perception by individuals of their social environment. But these *Gestalten* are so to speak veridical; their objects, individual ways of behaving, conform to them and often act as their sanctions, as reminders to the perceiver of the *Gestalt* that its object is there and must be reckoned with. There re-inforcing acts are indeed acts of individuals; but they in turn are led to behave along the suitable lines by their perception of the same or similar 'social fact'.

The existence of a complex concept parts of which are logically inseparable is after all a familiar thing. For example, a mountain summit *entails* a slope, and so on. The complications which arise with regard to the present problem are two; first, that of the two constituents which appear to be so connected, i.e., individual men and their social context, one is tangible, the other not. (Of course, it is not 'man' and *any* social contact that is so connected, but individual acts and their contexts.) This leads to the desire to 'reduce'the latter to the former, on the misguided assumption that unless this is done one would have to concede that the latter is similarly tangible. The reductionist indeed points both to the intangibility and necessary connection ('Without men and their doings, no society, institutions, etc.'), and then mistakenly infers that a reduction must be possible. The second complication arises through the fact that in these subjects we are dealing with conscious men, in other words objects aware of things in the same way as the observer. Hence the complex concepts are met with twice over—once in the minds of men, and once *in re* as the dealings of the observer with things, if you prefer.

The confusion of the hierarchy of propositions graded by generality and of groups graded by size and inclusiveness leads to what might be called the picture or mirror theory or explanation.[8] The merits and otherwise of the picture theory of meaning and propositions is a familiar story, but the reappearance of this tempting model with regard to explanation deserves special treatment.

What seems to happen is something along the following lines. Take as an example a generalization such as 'The committee decided to appoint Jones'. This means, amongst other things, that each of the members of the committee came in the end to accept a certain conclusion, and if this were an important or interesting event, the historian or sociologist concerned with explaining it might be very happy if he could give an account of the ways by which each of the committee members came to reach his conclusion. This is indeed the paradigm of explanation as conceived by the Individualist—the feared Whole has evaporated in a series of partial biographies and character studies.

It is of course perfectly true that generalizations and abstractions do not give us additional facts; but it does not follow that all propositions whose subjects seem to include the 'atoms'—whatever they may happen to be—of a particular discourse, are therefore necessarily generalizations, abstractions or somehow constructs. A failure to see this is the defect often attributed to 'atomism' in other spheres, and sociological reductionism seems to be a related species.

In as far as the proposition used as an example is only a generalization of the form 'All members of the committee . . .' the alleged explanation, the paradigm of all explanations, is merely a verification and not an explanation at all. If this were all that could be done, explanation in history and the social sciences would be identical with the gathering of confirming evidence. To explain would be to illustrate; to illustrate

---

[8] 'Its overt characteristics (i.e., those of a "complex social situation") may be *established* empirically, but they are only to be *explained* by being shown to be the resultants of individual activities'. Watkins, *op. cit.* (italics his). This might be called the stock-exchange theory. The opposite could easily be maintained though I prefer merely to delay the second part of the statement. The temptation to believe that overt general features can be observed but must then be explained by something individual may spring from the fact that, for instance, the economist gets his empirical material pre-digested by the statistician. An index or a price level looks like a general fact. The field-worker is less tempted to believe that it is the overt feature of the social situation which he *observes*, whilst he only concludes about the individual. On the contrary, he is in close contact with the individuals with whom he passes the time of day, and if the explanations were *there*, he'd have his explanation as soon as he'd gathered his material, or at worst as soon as he had explored the characters of the individual. But this is not what happens. It cannot even be said that his task is the exploration of long-term and unforeseen consequences of individual dispositions. It is the consequences of social features that he is after.

fully, to provide the complete picture, would be to give the best explanation. But is this so?

Of course, the Individualist feels that something more should be involved in explanation than illustration, but he seeks it in broader generalizations about each of the committee-men involved; 'broader' meaning either more persistent, or 'simpler' in a sense to be indicated. There are what might be called simple disposition-types—sloth, pursuit of gain, of power, or security, etc. of which the more idiosyncratic dispositions of individual men may perhaps be interpreted as variants or combinations.

An example of this kind of approach would be, for instance, the eighteenth century attempt to explain moral feelings as combinations of sympathy and vengefulness: vengefulness on behalf of sufferers other than oneself, whose sufferings had been imaginatively relived, produces, say, a sense of justice. (This kind of approach, incidentally, is not *always* unfruitful; I am only arguing against the contention that historical or social explanation must always employ it.)

It is difficult to see how this attempt to bring in explanation which is more than illustration differs from what has sometimes been called psychologism.[9] The objection to it is that there is no way in general of isolating these pure or more persistent dispositions from the social context in which they occur. We have indeed two impossibilities here, one causal and one logical. Popper's argument against psychologism makes use of the former, Mandelbaum's of the latter. As a matter of causal fact, our dispositions are not independent of the social context in which they occur; but they are not even independent logically, for they cannot be described without reference to their social context.

What the Individualist is demanding might be described as the translation from the Active into the Passive Voice; the translation of statements such as 'such and such a kind of family organization tends to perpetuate itself' into statements such as 'As a result of such and such aims, convictions, dispositions, etc., of individuals this kind of family organization continues.' (To the Individualist it seems, of course, that the translation is *into* a 'really' Active Voice, on the general ground that institutions, etc., being constructs from individual behaviour, they *must* 'really' be passive.) But the undesirability of such a translation in some cases follows partly from various considerations already stated such as the diffused, individually imperceptible nature of some of these dispositions, or the fact that they refer back to the institutional

[9] Cf. K. Popper, *The Open Society and Its Enemies*, chap. 14. In this chapter Popper refers to both 'psychologism', which he condemns, and 'methodological individualism', which he commends. When, in the articles discussed, 'methodological individualism' is worked out more fully than is the case in Popper's book, it seems to me indistinguishable from 'Psychologism'.

context, and also from the fact that they may be utterly uninteresting because obvious. The only relevant dispositions may be, to take the example of the permanence of a kind of family organization, the normal sexual, security and reproductive aspirations which do not distinguish people in that social context from others. The *differentia* which as the distinctive component in a complex set of conditions will be worthy of the investigator's attention may well be something institutional and not psychological. It is perfectly possible, for instance, that there are no psychological differences of any importance between two European countries of widely divergent institutions, and that to explain the differentiation is only possible in sociological, not in psychological terms. Of course, psychological differences *may* be significant. The harm done by the kind of Individualism discussed, if taken seriously by investigators, is that it leads to a conviction that such differences must always be present and be significant. The danger of this pre-conception seems to me graver at present than the one which worries the Individualist, namely that of 'reifying' abstraction.

In fact, some historical or sociological explanations—as when, for instance, an historian explains the growth of an institution, or an anthropologist the self-maintenance of a social structure—will do this in terms of features of the relevant institution or structure without explicit mention of any individual dispositions.

At this point the Individualist will no doubt protest that despite the absence of explicit mention of individual dispositions, implicitly they are present; ultimately, every social event must have its habitat in the individual psyche. Now this must be conceded: if Individualism is to degenerate into what could be called social Monadism, the desperate incorporation of complex and diffuse relations into the related terms or individuals, then it must be admitted to be true 'in a sense'. 'Algy met a bear, the bear was bulgy, the bulge was Algy'; the individual may consume what Durkheim and others have called social facts, but he will bulge most uncomfortably, and Algy will still be there.[10] I suspect that actual investigators will often, though perhaps not always, prefer to have Algy outside the bear.[11]

The uselessness of Monadism-at-all-costs can be illustrated thus: certain tribes I know have what anthropologists call a segmentary patrilineal structure, which moreover maintains itself very well over time. I could 'explain' this by saying that the tribesmen have, all or most of them, dispositions whose effect is to maintain the system. But,

[10] Social phenomena have always been most suggestive of the Principle of Internal Relations. This principle is frequently being re-discovered by social scientists.

[11] The Individualist maintains that Algy always was in the bear. Yes, if you like. But the bear isn't Algy, though the bulge is Algy.

of course, not only have they never given the matter much thought, but it also might very well be impossible to isolate anything in the characters and conduct of the individual tribesmen which *explains* how they come to maintain the system (though of course conduct *illustrating* how the system is being maintained will be found).

The recipe for reduction which we are considering does not commit the older errors of inventing dispositions *ad hoc* for each social thing to be explained, or of deriving social conduct from alleged pre-social, pure dispositions. It claims as its explanations low-level generalizations about the conduct of individuals.

But: these dispositions are not always relevant; sometimes or often they are not isolable without this affecting the possibility of explanation; they are not independent variables, but usually depend on highly generalized social factors; and they are often not statable without reference to social facts. If Individualism does not deny all this, perhaps nothing remains to disagree with it about; but if indeed it does not deny this, its programmatic implications for historians and social scientists no longer hold.

Perhaps, in the end, there is agreement to this extent: (human) history *is* about chaps—and nothing else. But perhaps this should be written: History is *about* chaps. It does not follow that its explanations are always in terms of chaps. Societies are what people do, but social scientists are not biographers *en grande série*.

L. J. GOLDSTEIN

The Inadequacy of the Principle of Methodological Individualism[1]

INTRODUCTION

Not long ago, Mr J. W. N. Watkins expressed himself in favour of 'the principle of methodological individualism', a doctrine in the philosophical foundations of social science which demands that all of the concepts used in social science theory be exhaustively analysable in terms of the interests, activities, volitions, and so forth of individual human beings.[2] It seems to me, however, that the principle is entirely too restrictive and would preclude social scientists asking what on the face of it seems like perfectly reasonable questions. And this, in turn, would radically limit the possibilities of social science theory formation. The purpose of the present paper is to make this clear.

Few would deny that Mr Watkins' papers, together with the writings on the subject by Professors K. R. Popper[3] and F. A. Hayek,[4] are the most important attempts to provide an account of the principle. But while they do describe and even illustrate it, I fear that it cannot be said that they have attempted to provide a systematic argument in defence of it. A possible exception is Professor Hayek, who may wish his emphasis upon the subjective character of the data of social science

---

[1] The present paper is based upon a discussion first presented in my dissertation, *Form, Function and Structure: a Philosophical Study Concerning the Foundations of Theory in Anthropology* (unpublished manuscript in the Sterling Memorial Library, Yale University, 1954). Without imputing to him any responsibility for its content, I would like to thank my friend, Mr Samuel E. Gluck, for his many helpful suggestions, without which this paper would be far less readable than it is.

[2] J. W. N. Watkins, 'Ideal Types and Historical Explanation', *British Journal for the Philosophy of Science*, Vol. 3 (1952), pp. 22–43 [pp. 143–165 above]; 'The Principle of Methodological Individualism', *ibid.*, pp. 186–189 [pp. 179–184 above].

[3] Karl R. Popper, *The Open Society and Its Enemies*, Princeton, 1950 (1st English ed., 2 vols., London, 1945). References will be given to the Princeton edition, with references to the first English edition following in parentheses.

[4] F. A. Hayek, *The Counter-Revolution of Science*, Glencoe, Ill., 1952. This is a volume of papers that were first published elsewhere.

to serve as such an argument.[5] But this emphasis either results from a confusion of the psychological and the phenomenological senses of 'mind', in which the objective sociocultural *content* of thought and experience is treated exclusively from the subjective standpoint of the experiencing individual[6]; or it is an attempt to insist that no social systems are possible without people, as if to suggest that methodological collectivism[7] implies the opposite. But not even the stronger doctrine of ontological collectivism (e.g. Hegel) requires so absurd a thesis, and thus it appears that Professor Hayek's point offers no systematic support to the principle.

The present paper will attempt to point out that there are problems confronting social science that require solutions not amenable to individualistic analysis and yet are not holistic or historicistic. Methodological collectivism does not deny that there is much to be usefully learned from the study of the individualistic aspects of human action, but it does insist that merely because all human cultures are first discovered through the activities of their individual members it does not follow that there are no possible problems for which the particular individuals are irrelevant. In most of their activities people behave in culturally sanctioned ways, and this way of expressing it immediately suggests the feasibility of conceptually separating the man from his culture.[8] Unless this conceptual separation is possible, I cannot see how we can ever account theoretically for any *way* of behaving; all we can discuss are individual behavers. It is not irrelevant to point out that the references and citations in the writings of the aforementioned methodological individualists clearly suggest that they are very much interested both in history, which is largely concerned with the descriptive reconstruction of action within a given situation, and theoretical economies, which provides a highly abstract account of economic behaviour within economic and social institutions the existence of which is already assumed . To the theoretical questions of institutional development and change, of major interest to sociologists and anthropologists, they seem to have paid little attention. And it is

[5] See May Brodbeck, 'On the Philosophy of the Social Sciences', *Philosophy of Science*, Vol. 21 (1954), pp. 140–156, pp. 142 ff., for other comments on this subject [see pp. 91–110, pp. 94 ff., above].

[6] See my 'Bidney's Humanistic Anthropology', *Review of Metaphysics*, Vol. 8 (1955), pp. 493–509, pp. 501 f.

[7] I have retained the term 'methodological collectivism' inasmuch as it is the term used in the literature of our subject, but I do feel it to be an awkward expression and even a misleading one. I would have preferred to use 'sociologism', which would suggest that some concepts of social science theory are entirely sociocultural and not to be treated as individualistic or psychologistic.

[8] Cf. Georg Simmel, *The Sociology of Georg Simmel*, translated and edited by Kurt H. Wolff, Glencoe, Ill., 1950, pp. 26 ff.

precisely upon the analysis of such questions that the principle of methodological individualism breaks down.

A NON-INDIVIDUALISTIC SOCIOCULTURAL THEORY

To anthropological writers, kinship and the nomenclature of kinship have long been matters of interest. Few things may seem as trivial as the terms we use to designate the people to whom we are related; we call our aunts 'aunt' and our cousins 'cousin' and there the matter ends. Consequently a brief illustration of the anthropological view may well be in order. Were we to learn of a group that used one and the same kin-term to denote both the mother and the mother's younger sister but a separate and distinct term for the mother's older sister, our reaction would probably be one of amused indifference. To anthropologists, however, such information would suggest that the preferred choice for a second wife, is the younger sister of the first wife but not her older sister. As a potential, or even actual, stepmother of the children of her sister, having to them a sociological relationship not unlike that of their own mother, she is called by the same term. Whether or not this is true for any given society would have to be determined by empirical field research. But our example does suggest that kinship nomenclature is affected by sociological factors, and further suggests the feasibility of constructing a systematic theory about the sociocultural determination of systems of such nomenclature.[9]

Although thinking along the above lines has been suggestive and useful, it must be admitted that no small amount of it has been hit-or-miss, after-the-fact speculation attempting to rationalize seemingly strange terminologies.[10] It is, therefore, to the credit of Professor George Peter Murdock that he has attempted to bring some order into these studies through the development of a theory which attempts to show that the state or form of any given system of kinship nomenclature is determined by (or is a function of) the states or forms

---

[9] Cf. A. R. Radcliff-Brown: 'There are some who would regard this kind of terminology as "contrary to common sense", but this means no more than that it is not in accordance with our modern European ideas of kinship and its terminology. . . . The Choctaw and Omaha terminologies do call for some explanation; but so does the English terminology, in which we use the word "cousin" for all children of both brothers and sisters of both mother and father—a procedure which would probably seem to some non-Europeans to be contrary not only to common sense but also to morals. What I wish to attempt, therefore, is to show you that Choctaw and Omaha terminologies are just as reasonable and fitting in the social systems in which they occur as our terminology is in our social system.' (*Structure and Function in Primitive Society*, London, 1952, pp. 55 f.)

[10] An example of this is discussed *ibid.*, pp. 56 ff.

of certain specified sociocultural variables.[11] These are four in number: the rule of marriage, the form of the family, the rule of descent, and the rule of residence. For the purpose of the present paper we will have no need to discuss these, nor need we be concerned about the empirical adequacy of the particular theory introduced as our example.[12] My concern here is only with the kind of theory it is and the tenability of formulating such theories. For each of these variables Professor Murdock has determined the possible types—there being only a very small number of ways of reckoning descent, through either parent or through both, and similarly for the other variables—and one is thus able to determine the number of possible combinations that could be had. And this would be the number of possible types of social system, if it should prove to be theoretically advantageous to define the social system in terms of these variables. But regardless of any more widespread application of such social system types, it is clearly a *methodological* assumption of the given theory that we may talk about a system that is defined in terms of five variables, the four *relatively independent* variables mentioned and the system of kinship nomenclature.[13]

For any given empirical sociocultural system it is possible to determine which of the limited number of social system types it is. But it is also possible to talk meaningfully about system types that have never been discovered. One hypothetically, but perhaps not nomologically,[14] possible rule of residence, the 'amitalocal' rule, could be characterized as a 'cultural provision that unmarried females take up their residence with a paternal aunt and bring their husbands to their aunt's home when they marry'.[15] Since no social system having this

[11] George Peter Murdock, *Social Structure* (New York, 1949), Ch. 7, 'The Determinants of Kinship Terminology'.

[12] It might be worth while if some symbolic logician would attempt to restate in formal language the theory as it is now, in order to learn both if the theorems are a self-consistent set and if it might not be possible to derive still more of them once the limitations of the English language are overcome.

[13] Of course, we may hope that similar theories may be constructed to account for change in each of the variables of the present theory. Professor Murdock seems to think that change in the rule of residence is most important for change in the kinship system, and seeks to show in Chapter 8 how the form of the rule is related to economic matters. Could we anticipate theoretically changes of a specific kind in the rule, then we would be able, further, to anticipate changes in the nomenclature of kinship. And while all such theories would define or postulate methodologically systems or types, there is no reason to think that their theoretical use implies reification, though Mr Watkins asserts that he cannot allow the use of sociologistic concepts unless it can be shown that their reification would be justified (*loc. cit.*, p. 189). Cf. Marion J. Levy, Jr., *The Structure of Society*, Princeton, 1952, pp. 30 f.

[14] Ward H. Goodenough, 'Amitalocal Residence', *American Anthropologist*, N.S., Vol. 53 (1951), pp. 427–429.

[15] Murdock, *op. cit.*, p. 71.

feature has ever been described any characterization of such a system would not be what Mr Watkins calls an 'individualistic ideal type', that is, a type constructed out of specifically observed social experience. On his view, until you have determined empirically that such a type exists—or, for the sake of those who tend to impute strange philosophical beliefs to every use of realistic language, that the type is a model for the social behaviour in some empirical sociocultural system—it has no content and is theoretically superfluous. I fear that some thinkers have determined to insist that social science must labour under restrictions it would never occur to them to impose upon physical science. Were they more consistent they would forbid our talking about ideal gases and free swinging pendulums; we can only speculate upon what they might have said to Mendeleef about the then existing gaps in his periodic table. But no physicist would recognize any obligation to accept such guidance and there is no reason for social scientists to do so either. Professor Murdock's theory makes it perfectly proper for us to talk about systems that have never been discovered. Indeed, there are some possible occasions that may require us to believe that some determinate type of system, for which we have no evidence of a factual or individualistic nature, did exist. We are informed that the evidence is overwhelming that avunculocal residence[16] 'can never develop out of neolocal, bilocal, or patrilocal residence'.[17] In consequence, a social system having an avunculocal rule of residence cannot have been preceded by any type other than one or another of those with a matrilocal rule. Also, it may be the case that the possibilities for change at any given time are restricted by the fact that not all of the forms that any given variable may have are compatible with all of the present forms of the others. If we know, on historical evidence, that a given people had at one time a social system type out of which its present type could not have developed, we would be required—assuming Murdock's theory or some modification of it—to conclude that some other social system type, for the existence of which we have no other evidence, did in fact exist. (Here too those who would feel better about it may translate my sentence into another one, replacing the idea of an existing social system with that of a model for social behaviour. My own feeling is that the form of expression is of no consequence to my argument, but that realistic language is less complicated.)

---

[16] Under an avunculocal rule of residence a young man would settle with his maternal uncle and bring his bride to live there; under a neolocal rule a married couple establishes an independent household; and under a bilocal rule such a couple has the option of settling with the family of either the husband or the wife.

[17] Murdock, *op. cit.*, p. 207.

SOME CHARACTERISTICS OF THE THEORY

Relevant to the problem of the present paper are two characteristics of the theory of kinship nomenclature: (1) it is not amenable to analysis according to the prescription of methodological individualism and yet is not holistic or historicistic; and (2) it is not psychologistic inasmuch as all its concepts are entirely upon the sociocultural level, making no appeal to the psychological dispositions of individual people.[18]

To characterize a society in terms of the variables of the theory is to say nothing about the human individuals of whom it consists. To know that in such and such a society descent is reckoned in the female line or that residence is avunculocal provides no information about the aspirations and activities of particular persons. Finally, to discover that anticipated changes in the economy of the society will make the present rule of residence inconvenient or anachronistic, and that the present forms of other variables of the social system will make some specific form of change the most reasonable to expect, requires no reference to the personalities and psychological propensities of particular persons.[19]

[18] My own view is that methodological individualism cannot be separated from psychologism, but Professor Popper advocates an individualistic sociology which is autonomous (an incongruous position which Mr Watkins, in his recognition of the psychologistic nature of his thesis, has been consistent enough to avoid [p. 149 ff. above]. Nevertheless, he is forced to admit some psychological laws but seeks to avoid the issue by calling them trivial.

[19] In a private communication, Dr J. O. Wisdom wonders whether I perhaps 'use the phrase "methodological individualism" quite differently from Popper or Watkins'. I suppose he has in mind the recent attempt by Mr Watkins, in a rejoinder to Miss Brodbeck's paper ('Methodological Individualism: A Reply', *Philosophy of Science*, Vol. 22 (1955), pp. 58–62) [pp. 179–184 above] to distinguish between a methodological individualism which allows the use of anonymous individual concepts and detailed individualistic explaining. He claims that he means to advocate the former [p. 184 above], and rereading his earlier paper I can see that there is an element of this present. But that Miss Brodbeck and I should both have misunderstood his intention suggests that there is a basis for the misunderstanding in the paper itself. And since the paper has achieved some degree of fame, as attested by its inclusion in an important anthology of *Readings in the Philosophy of Science* (edited by H. Feigl and M. Brodbeck, New York, 1953), to warn possible readers against what I deem to be a methodological inadequacy seems perfectly justified, quite apart from Mr Watkins' clarification. The clarification, it may be noted, does not result in any methodological improvement. Mr Watkins would have social science rely heavily upon (general as well as individual) psychological dispositions in constructing its explanations, but he seems entirely to ignore the recent studies by anthropologists and psychologists of the cultural conditioning of such dispositions. And well he might, for I cannot see how he could ever deal with such matters while insisting upon a theory which makes psychological dispositions methodologically primary. Moreover, even where there may be dispositions that are universal among men, these could not be used in explaining how any given social institution of a specific people (or

But while the theory we have been considering is not individualistic, it is also not holistic or historicistic. Professor Murdock has sought to specify the variables that bear upon the sociocultural phenomena he seeks to deal with. There is no appeal to the nature of the whole, no notion that what occurs in change is the actualization of inherent potentiality. Use of the term 'methodological holism' where others speak of 'methodological collectivism' indicates that Mr Watkins views all non-individualistic theories as necessarily holistic. But this results from not paying sufficient attention to the kind of theory we are presently discussing. Professor Murdock claims no inevitable necessity for the kind of change he describes. But he does insist that whenever the theoretically necessary and sufficient conditions obtain for some determinate kind of kinship system, then we may reasonably expect that kind of system to appear.[20] The individual characteristics of the members of the society need not be taken into account.

I have said that the theory of kinship nomenclature is not psychologistic, but in view of Professor Murdock's own assertion to the effect that one 'system of organized knowledge which has significantly influenced this volume is behaviouristic psychology',[21] a remark or two on this point is necessary. I believe that we have here a confusion of two points: one concerning the enculturation of the individual and the other concerning sociocultural change. The former quite clearly requires that reference be made to psychology and in particular to the theory of learning. The other has no such requirement. The behaviour of every member of the society may be treated from the vantage point of psychological theory, and if the phenomena dealt with by social theory had no effect upon the behaviour of individuals we may be sure that

---

its particular disposition set) came to be as it is. Mr Watkins' paper, then, while it does provide illustrations of what I discuss below as synchronic social studies, remains, even as clarified, methodologically inadequate, for it does not allow the possibility of formulating the kind of a diachronic sociocultural theory of which Murdock's is an example.

[20] Mr James B. Watson ('Four Approaches to Cultural Change: A Systematic Assessment', *Social Forces*, Vol. 32 (1953), pp. 137–145) has attempted to treat Murdock's theory as historicistic or, in his term, 'developmental'. A careful reading of his paper, however, makes it clear that his error results from mistaking some theorems of the theory for the theory itself. He notes that given some antecedent state of the social system, Professor Murdock allows that only a small number of possible states may succeed it. (A really developmental theory would not permit a number of alternatives.) But he has failed to note that the reason for this is that given the forms of the variables in that antecedent state, only a limited number of the changes possible in any one of them would be compatible with the existing forms of the others taken together. Thus, we have not the paradoxical eventless change of historicistic theories, but the precise specification of the reasons for change.

[21] Murdock, *op. cit.*, p. xvi; see also p. 131.

there would be no resultant social change. But it is the experience of social science that the basic bio-psychological similarity of human beings in general makes it unnecessary to take account of the psychology of individuals when explaining sociocultural change;[22] it is enough to deal with variables that are entirely on the sociocultural level. As Miss Brodbeck well remarks, 'Psychological laws may be ubiquitous, but social laws may be formulated without taking them into account'.[23] While societies consist of human beings, the psychological basis of individual learning and behaviour plays no *logical* role in the kind of explanation represented by the theory we have been considering. Stated in another way, while the comparatively stable bio-psychological nature of the human race may be a *necessary* condition for human socio-cultural systems, it is not a *sufficient* condition for the specific forms of any of them.

SYNCHRONIC AND DIACHRONIC SOCIAL STUDIES

It was remarked earlier that the methodological individualists seemed to be interested in one kind of social study to the exclusion of any other kind. In terms more common, perhaps, among social scientists—at least among anthropologists—than philosophers, it may be said that they are more concerned with the development of synchronic social research and tend to ignore the possibilities for diachronic social theory. Logically, there is no opposition between the two, and it is not uncommon to find the same scholar concerned with both. But there are differences between the two approaches, and I raise the matter here because the assertion of the principle of methodological individualism implicitly rules out the possibility of diachronic social theory. It is concerned solely with the actions of individuals within a given sociocultural context and is incapable of recognizing as a *theoretical* problem the question of how the situation came to be as it is. To be sure, methodological individualists reiterate the so-called distinction between ideographic (historical) and nomothetic disciplines, and insist that the answer to diachronic questions must be given only by historical reconstruction. But it is clear that the logic of explanation requires, at least implicitly, the use of general laws,[24] and I cannot see that

[22] See, A. L. Kroeber, *The Nature of Culture*, Chicago, 1952, Part I; and Leslie A. White, *The Science of Culture*, New York, 1949.

[23] Brodbeck [p. 107 above].

[24] Carl G. Hempel, 'The Function of General Laws in History', *Journal of Philosophy*, Vol. 39, 1942, reprinted in H. Feigl and W. Sellars, eds., *Readings in Philosophical Analysis*, New York, 1949, pp. 459–471; Hempel and Paul Oppenheim, 'Studies in the Logic of Explanation', *Philosophy of Science*, Vol. 15 (1948), pp. 135–175; Popper, *op. cit.*, pp. 445 ff. and 720 ff. (II, pp. 248 ff. and 342 ff.); and R. B. Braithwaite, *Scientific Explanation*, Cambridge, 1953, p. 2.

historical reconstruction is an exception to the rule. (Indeed, if the well-known selective character of historical research is not to give way to promiscuous subjectivity, the utilization of sociohistorical or sociocultural laws as providing criteria of relevance is certainly both required and implied.) Professor Popper tries to avoid this difficulty to his methodological individualism by insisting that the laws required for the rational justification of the results of historical inquiry are only trivial,[25] but he never troubles to specify just what are the logical properties of trivial laws that make them more acceptable than the more weighty members of the species. Nor does he show how the latter may be left out once the former have been admitted. I suspect that he may fear that there can be no serious sociohistorical law that is not at the same time historicistic. But in this he is mistaken, as the example of Murdock's theory of kinship nomenclature clearly demonstrates.

I shall use the term 'synchronic social now' to refer to that period of time within which the given sociocultural system[26] remains more or less stable. For most purposes, the persistence of the system may be assumed, and when an individual plans his day-to-day affairs he need not be concerned about social change. Governments, however, which plan for much longer periods, might well be so concerned, and it is certainly amazing how often they are unable to anticipate the results of their own plans. Which need not mean that they ought to give up necessary planning, but rather that they should recognize the value of diachronic social research. (Professor Hayek prefers that they give up planning and conveniently opts for a doctrine that makes diachronic theory impossible.) For it is obvious that social systems do change, and accounting for such change is the task of diachronic social studies. Such studies are intended to deal with how the synchronic social now develops from the previous synchronic social now[27] and the conditions for such change in general. And while the logic of explanation is the same for both, diachronic explanations do differ materially from synchronic ones.

Consider what is involved when the social behaviour of some individual person is predicted or explained. What is required is know-ledge about relevant institutions. I know that A will do such and such

---

[25] Popper, op. cit., p. 448 (II, pp. 251 f.).

[26] I do not necessarily mean by 'sociocultural system' the sum of all the institutions available to the people of any group. Indeed, inasmuch as I doubt that we shall ever have theories about such a sum, there need be no fear that my term opens the way for holism. As indicated in note 13 and the text, I am satisfied to mean by the term nothing more than what is defined by the variables of a sociocultural theory.

[27] It seems convenient to talk about past and future synchronic social nows instead of cluttering up our terminology with such phrases as 'synchronic social then' or 'synchronic historical then'.

next week because I know that he will then be in a situation that requires that sort of behaviour, even as was B some months before. In other words, I know what sort of behaviour is expected or deemed rational under specified conditions during the synchronic social now. Thus, while my prediction of A's action, or my explanation of B's, does involve future or past time, it does clearly presuppose the relative stability or persistence of certain institutions. My explanation takes the institutional framework for granted without attempting to explain it, and focuses upon the individual actor. And this is all that Professor Popper does when he talks about the logic of the situation. The 'rational man' is able to act wisely only to the extent that his familiarity with the relevant institutions of the synchronic social now is adequate to that end. If confronted with sudden basic changes in these institutions, his knowledge of former expectations and possibilities would avail him little; nor would those who based their predictions of his behaviour on that same knowledge fare any better.

Actually, on the basis of the knowledge referred to, specific explanations or predictions of individual social behaviour are not yet possible. We require, as Professor Popper has himself said, both general statements or laws and statements of specific facts. Relative to the explanation of individual behaviour, all we have so far is the latter, and even that only in part. The account of the synchronic now is only a descriptive statement. It tells how people in a given community tend to act, how they have come to behave in certain circumstances, what is deemed by them to be the best behaviour when things are such and so. And while we may state these facts in a general way, giving the appearance of a social law of restricted scope, if our interest is in the behaviour of some specific person this will not serve as a theoretical explanation. To be sure, if in society s, all men of t type in circumstance c do some specific thing, and if A is such a t in c, we may expect him to do the same thing. But it is almost never that we can say something significant about all men of any type, and what often happens is that social scientists, rather than find out what determines the exceptions, protect their generalizations with a strong *ceteris paribus*. But this seems to reduce the generalization to the trivial point that if A is the kind of person who behaves—at least in matters of the sort under discussion—in the socially accepted manner, then he will behave in the socially accepted manner.

Whether or not any individual behaves in the accepted or in the rational manner will depend upon his personal psychological make-up. To complete our explanation, then, we must add two additional factors. First we must have specific data concerning the person himself, data of the sort that psychological theory deems to be diagnostic of the kind of person he is. And, finally, we need some system of psychological theory. It then turns out that the sociocultural data only provided us with information concerning the ways in which the members of our subject's group behave, that is, they provided factual criteria of usual behaviour. But the problem to be solved, a prediction or explanation of a specific person's action, is one that is theoretically a psychological problem.[28]

While synchronic questions are concerned with behaviour within a specific sociocultural context, which may often be amenable to individualistic analysis, diachronic questions are of another sort. They do not take the situation for granted but are rather concerned with how the situation came to be as it is. This involves, for any specific situation, an historical reconstruction. But it also requires, at least in principle, a theoretical justification for the reconstruction. And this can be provided only by a system of sociocultural laws. There is nothing absurd about the possibility of discovering such laws, and the fact that the principle of methodological individualism is not compatible with the search for them is hardly ground for the rejection of a perfectly tenable programme. Such laws would be concerned with the kinds of conditions under which determinate change may be expected in sociocultural systems, and if the theoretically necessary and sufficient conditions for some determinate kind of change were to obtain, we may reasonably expect that the change would take place. Who the people are whose institutions are changing is not relevant to the problem. The view of the methodological individualist seems to be that social change results from conscious effort, though the results are often more than people bargained for. A return to our example will suffice to cast doubt upon this view. There is evidence enough that kinship systems do change, but it is absolutely untrue that every so often the people of a society get together to discuss the feasibility of bringing change about, especially inasmuch as people tend to think that their system reflects the order of things and the true morality. And in a sense, of course, this is true, for it reflects the order of things social within their own sociocultural system and defines for them the range of the application of incest prescriptions[29] as well as the limits of the moral obligations imposed by kinship.

A brief statement must be made about people. Methodological

[28] Richard Brandt, in Part VI of his *Hopi Ethics, A Theoretical Analysis* (Chicago, 1954), deals with his subject in the manner of synchronic studies. While it often seems that he wishes to provide a sociocultural account of the Hopi value system, this system is actually assumed by him, and his main effort is to show how individual Hopi develop certain attitudes. Indeed, he calls his approach a 'contemporary context theory of ethical norms', and his theoretical apparatus is quite explicitly psychological.

[29] Cf. *ibid.*, p. 207, for an example of this.

individualists like to caricature the views of their opponents by suggesting that the latter believe in peopleless systems of culture. This is not even true of ontological collectivism,[30] and is surely false when ascribed to the methodological view. What we know about social systems we have learned from observing the behaviour and probing the thoughts of particular human beings. Furthermore, the only way to test the truth or falsity for any diachronic theory of sociocultural change would be to observe individual behaviour. Noticing that certain changes were taking place, we might predict that after a while, say a generation, a certain type of kinship system will prevail in a given society. This means that under specifiable conditions of human intercourse specific behaviour may be expected; people will be related to others in determinate social ways and will act in ways compatible with those relations. It is the task of the social scientist to work out the implications of these relationships in full, taking account of the fact that the specific content of social action will differ from culture to culture, even among cultures having the same type of kinship system.[31] The social scientists of the next generation may then seek to discover how, indeed, the individual persons in the society do behave in the specified situations. And thus the prediction will be confirmed or not, depending on how individuals do act.

What methodological collectivism does not admit is that all the general concepts of social science may be exhaustively analysed in terms of actions, interests, and volitions of specific individuals. Such a view of our concepts would leave us with theories the entire contents of which were the facts that suggested them in the first place, having no further power of prediction or explanation.[32] Nor does it admit the truth of Mr Watkin's claim that only concepts or types constructed out of observed social activity are admissible. No one has discovered a society with an amitalocal rule of residence, but, in the light of Murdock's theory, it is surely not meaningless to talk about social systems having this feature. Finally, methodological collectivism insists that inasmuch as the problems of social science differ from those of psychology—the former being concerned, at least in part, with questions

[30] Hegel, for example, begins his *Philosophy of Right* with an analysis of what he calls 'abstract right', which is concerned with the individual's subjective experience of right and value.

[31] For example, the same kind of social system type, so-called Normal Eskimo, is to be found in the Andaman, Copper Eskimo, American, and Ruthenian societies, among others (Murdock, *op. cit.*, p. 228). Surely the interests, aspirations, activities, and conscious goals of people in these widely separated groups are sufficiently different to make doubtful the thesis that it is these that determine the persistence or change of social structure.

[32] Cf. Braithwaite, *op. cit.*, pp. 67 f.; and Lewis W. Beck, 'Constructions and Inferred Entities', *Philosophy of Science*, Vol. 17 (1950), pp. 74–86.

of socio-cultural development, persistence, and change, the latter with individual behaviour—the claim that all sociocultural concepts are, in the end, psychological is untenable. While the experience of each person is subjective, neither the content nor the occasion of the experience is. The individual subjectively experiences the norms of society and its accumulated knowledge and lore, but the social scientist deals with these contents in their objective or social character. I strongly suspect that no little amount of confusion on this point stems from the failure to distinguish between the psychological or subjective and the phenomenological or sociocultural[33] concepts of mind.[34]

[33] This notion is concerned with the content of experience, and is called phenomenological in epistemological discourse and sociocultural in social science discourse. I dare say that some idealistic phenomenologists would take issue with the idea that the status of such contents is sociocultural, but this cannot be discussed here.

[34] Mr Watkins seems especially given to this confusion. In any event, he seems to treat the disposition of certain individuals to weep during the death scene in *Othello* (a psychological disposition) and the disposition of police officers or Speakers of the House of Commons to act in the manner prescribed for their offices (institutional or role behaviour) as being essentially of the same sort (*loc. cit.*, pp. 163 ff. above).

L. J. GOLDSTEIN

Two Theses of Methodological Individualism

THE ONTOLOGICAL THESIS

It has become usual in the writings of methodological individualists to suggest that there is but one alternative to their methodological prescription in social science, and this they call 'holism'.[1] Maurice Mandelbaum has sought to counter this by offering a four part classification of types of sociological theories,[2] thus showing that the alternatives of the individualists is simply an instance of the fallacy of false disjunction. However, it is not at all likely that methodological individualists will find Mandelbaum's paper to the point; it does not deal with the problem that concerns them. I am not at all certain that Watkins, for example, would object to discourse about total societies—the usual meaning of 'holism' and the one with which Mandelbaum deals. He would only insist that such discourse must, at least in principle, be analysable into discourse about individuals and their dispositions, and he does refer approvingly to Ayer's statement that 'the English State . . . is a logical construction out of individual people'.[3] We need not be concerned with what Ayer here means by logical constructions, for I want only to show, since the English state is surely a social whole, that Watkins cannot be said to oppose a social whole. In this example, a holist is one who denies Ayer's assertion, not of necessity one who is interested in the English state.

According to Watkins, 'if methodological individualism means that human beings are the only moving agents in history, and if sociological

---

[1] Cf. J. W. N. Watkins, 'Historical Explanation in the Social Sciences' [pp. 166–178 above]. In view of the many connotations of 'holism', I deem it regrettable that E. A. Gellner, in his otherwise admirable paper, 'Explanation in History' [pp. 248–263 above] continues the practice of using 'holist' for everything non-individualistic. I know of no really suitable term, but I much prefer the more cumbersome 'non-individualistic social science' to 'holism'. (And we shall see that they are by no means synonymous terms.)

[2] 'Societal Laws' [pp. 235–247 above].

[3] *Language, Truth and Logic*, London, 2nd edn., 1950, p. 63; cited in Watkins, 'Ideal Types and Historical Explanation' [pp. 143–165, 150; cf. *ibid.*, n. 18 above].

holism means that some superhuman agents or factors are supposed to be at work in history, then these two alternatives are exhaustive'.[4] He further says, 'The central assumption of the individualistic position . . . is that no social tendency exists which could not be altered *if* the individuals concerned both wanted to alter it and possessed the appropriate information . . . This assumption could also be expressed by saying that no social tendency is somehow imposed on human beings "from above" (or "from below").'[5] Holists, it appears, are those who posit non-human entities which in some unexplained way are supposed to determine what happens to men. Human history, on this view, would, paradoxically, not be the history of men and their affairs, but rather of that entity or set of entities that impose themselves upon them. Holists may well be interested in entities that are total, that is, they may conceive their holistic entity to be a unitary sort of thing, and perhaps Hegel's *Weltgeist* is an instance of this. But it is not impossible that holists of more modest pretension could be concerned with entities of a less inclusive nature. Perhaps the 'basic patterns' of the anthropologist Kroeber are such lesser entities,[6] and it may be argued that their logic is rather like that of the *logospermatikoi* of Hellenistic thought.

If methodological individualism is the thesis that denies the existence of these non-human entities, it is clear that neither Mandelbaum, Gellner, in the paper cited above in a note, nor I, in my earlier paper on this subject,[7] may be said to have opposed it. Thus, one may wonder what the controversy is all about. The fact of the matter is, however, that under the rubric 'methodological individualism' Watkins has subsumed two positions. The one we have been dealing with is not a methodological position at all. This non-methodological—ontological—version of the principle of methodological individualism is that doctrine which denies the existence of certain alleged entities. The other, more truly methodological thesis is the one which claims that all explanation in social science must, in the end, be reduced to individual dispositions. I shall attempt to deal with what this means in the following section of the paper. For the present I wish to discuss further this ontological thesis. It is not enough, it seems to me, simply to separate the two individualisms

[4] 'Historical Explanation in the Social Sciences', p. 168 above.

[5] *Ibid.*, pp. 168–169; his italics. I agree with the main point of this statement and would add only that included in the 'appropriate information' may well be non-individualistic social laws. Dr Israel Scheffler, of Harvard University, observes that what Watkins says about social tendencies is equally applicable to furniture and machines, any of which could be altered if the individuals concerned both wanted to and had suitable knowledge.

[6] A. L. Kroeber, *The Nature of Culture*, Chicago, 1952; cf. chs. 5, 9 and 23.

[7] 'The Inadequacy of the Principle of Methodological Individualism' [pp. 264–276 above].

and observe that it is quite likely that in the ontological version we discover a point of agreement for most of us who have been interested in this matter. For this, I have two reasons. The first is that the bulk of the rhetorical force of the arguments that are supposed to be in defence of the more methodological of the individualist theses comes from confusing its denial with denial of the ontological thesis, and the fact that for most of us the ontological holist thesis is untenable. The suggestion that non-individualistic social science has evil consequences for freedom and morality has never been made out. Instead, we are supposed to wonder just what can possibly be intended when we talk of freedom and morality in a social world exhaustively determined by non-human entities which impose its history upon man.

My second reason for being unwilling to end discussion of the ontological version is that we are often told that holism is inextricably bound up with another methodological evil, historicism,[8] and here, too, holism and non-individualistic social science are confused. The thesis of historicism is that nothing men do makes a difference; all that will happen happens of necessity given the nature of history, or society, or the dialectic, or the *Weltgeist*. But here 'history', 'society', 'the dialectic' or 'the *Weltgeist*' serve as possible names of a holistic entity, the existence of which both Watkins and I agree in denying. Historicism is, then, an appurtenance of holism, and neither had to do with the claim of some of us that social science must be non-individualistic. Methodological individualists have never shown that to deny the assertion that all explanation in social science must be in terms of individual dispositions entails historicism, and man's consequent helplessness, and I hope to suggest that this is not the case. If they think they have it is because they have not distinguished between their methodological and their non-methodological doctrines.

Whether or not one believes that non-individualism in social science can be defended without the risk of ontological error, it is surely the case that some social scientists have been aware of the distinctions that I have been trying to make above. Thus, Simmel says,

> No matter whether we consider the group that exists irrespective of its individual members a fiction or a reality, in order to understand certain facts one must treat it as if it actually did have its own life, and laws, and other characteristics. And if one is to justify the sociological standpoint, it is precisely the difference between these characteristics and those of the individual existence that one must clarify.[9]

[8] In Popper's sense of historicism, not Mannheim's. By 'historicism' Mannheim means the socio-historical determination of thought, which need not commit him to the view that in history we have the necessary actualization of what was potential in earlier stages.

[9] *The Sociology of Georg Simmel*, translated and edited by Kurt Wolff, Glencoe, Ill., 1950, p. 26.

In the same way, Durkheim remarks,

> So there is some superficiality about attacking our conception as scholastic and reproaching it for assigning to social phenomena a foundation in some vital principle or other of a new sort. We refuse to accept that these phenomena have as a substratum the conscience of the individual, we assign them another; that formed by all the individual consciences in union and combination. . . . Nothing is more reasonable, then, than this proposition at which such offense has been taken; that a belief or social practice may exist independently of its individual expressions. We clearly did not imply by this that society can exist without individuals, an obvious absurdity we might have been spared having attributed to us . . .[10]

In sum, there are any number of people who have given thought to this matter who would say with Professor Ginsberg, 'To assign characteristics to groups is by no means the same as to consider them as entities which exist independently of the individuals which compose them'.[11]

All of these passages show that their authors feel no need of the belief in hypostatic social entities, yet they insist that explanation in social science need not, and perhaps cannot, be individualistic. If methodological individualists want to claim that this is not a consistent set of beliefs, they must show that the rejection of what I refer to as their methodological thesis entails or strongly supports the ontological position we have discovered that Watkins intends by the term 'holism'. But this has never been done, perhaps never even attempted. And I dare say it never will be so long as methodological individualists do not trouble to distinguish between the two kinds of individualism they support.

That the rejection of the methodological thesis does not entail or support holism[12] is suggested by Durkheim's referring to the community of consciousness or sentiment as a consequence of individuals living together. There are many such passages in his writings, and his failure to take pains in expressing himself on the point has led his critics to saddle him with belief in something called 'the group mind' or an actually existing collective. We have seen that he denies that this was his intention but, that apart, he is certainly not required to

---

[10] *Suicide*, translated by Spaulding and Simpson, Glencoe, Ill., 1951, pp. 319 f.

[11] *On the Diversity of Morals*, Melbourne, London, Toronto, 1956, p. 152.

[12] That is, the decision to reject the methodological thesis leaves one uncommitted so far as the ontological thesis is concerned, though it seems most reasonable that anyone who agrees with Watkins concerning the former ought to agree concerning the latter as well. Logically, this isn't necessary, for one, being so-minded, could develop a holism in which the holistic entity had about as much to do as a deistic god after the creation.

affirm it. It seems to me that a possible construction of Durkheim's words would have him advocating a point of view that may be named 'sociological emergence'. This would claim that, for whatever reasons, when human beings live together, share common experiences, and so forth, there emerge common sentiments and modes of representation[13] which would never have arisen apart from group life and which cannot be analysed into the bio-psychological characteristics of unsocialized individuals. A view such as this does not require the support of holism. Indeed, it is entirely incompatible with that doctrine as it has been characterized by Watkins. According to Durkheim, collective sentiments emerge out of the social intercourse of human beings, but the holist view is that such sentiments are imposed upon us by non-human entities, the true source of human history. Furthermore, since on the view we are considering what men do does make a difference, there being no emergent sentiments unless there are human beings sharing common experiences, historicism is equally incompatible with it. Presumably, the kinds of sentiments, values, modes of representation, and so on, that emerge depend upon the sorts of experiences that are shared, and man is not treated as if he were caught in the grip of some strange and monstrous being whose necessary development determines the course of history.

Sociological emergence is not, to be sure, a sociological theory. It does not in any way explain how it is that social institutions emerge. Nor does it have any specifically testable consequences. But in these respects it is not unlike the methodological thesis of methodological individualism. This, too, explains nothing, nor does it purport to explain anything. No sociological theory need make explicit reference to sociological emergence; its usefulness is of another sort. When methodological individualists assail this or that theory as holistic, when in fact it simply uses concepts that are not reducible to individual dispositions, its defenders have always the possibility of pointing to methodological emergence or some variation of it. That is, since the nature of the criticism levelled against the theory is ontological rather than methodological, sociological emergence offers a way of meeting it. It affirms that social scientists may develop non-individualistic theories without being holists. And it has the further advantage of forcing the methodological individualists to defend their methodological thesis on methodological grounds. If non-individualistic social science does not commit untoward ontological sins, the methodological individualists are required to find better grounds for its rejection. The doctrine that all explanation in social science is ultimately in

---

[13] Cf. his 'Individual and Collective Representations', in *Sociology and Philosophy*, London, 1953, pp. 1–34.

terms of individual dispositions is not established, indeed, in no way supported, by the untenability of holism.

INDIVIDUAL AND ANONYMOUS DISPOSITIONS

There is, as we have seen, a properly methodological thesis included under the rubric 'methodological individualism', namely, the claim that in social science all explanation is to be individualistic. This sometimes means that we are required to carry each explanation back, step by step, until we have transformed sociological explanations into psychological ones.[14] Very often in his writings Watkins talks about *individual dispositions*, and perhaps there is in this mode of speech a reference to the ontological matters discussed above. We are said to be interested in the dispositions of individual human beings and not those of societies or other holistic entities. But this apart, it will be interesting to discover what sorts of things pass muster, in his view, as individual dispositions. Fortunately, he has himself provided us with a number of examples, and the following quotations may serve as an adequate sample.

> What Smith actually showed was that individuals in competitive economic situations are led by nothing but their *personal dispositions* to promote unintentionally the public interest . . .[15]
> Suppose that it is established that Huguenot traders were relatively prosperous in seventeenth-century France and that this is explained in terms of a wide-spread disposition among them (a disposition for which there is independent evidence) to plough back into their businesses a larger proportion of their profits than was customary among their Catholic competitors. . . .[16]

Finally, in a letter to me and by way of attempted refutation of my claim[17] that the principle of methodological individualism is not adequate to deal with such social scientific work as the theory of kinship nomenclature in G. P. Murdock's *Social Structure*, Watkins writes,

> What gives a kinship system its stability and distinctive characteristics is, as you say, certain *rules* about marriage, inheritance, residence, etc., which govern the behaviour of each member to his 'relations'. But a

[14] 'From this truism I infer the methodological principle which underlies this paper, namely, that the social scientist can continue searching for explanations of a social phenomenon until he has reduced it to psychological terms' (Watkins, *British Journal for the Philosophy of Science*, 1952, **3**, pp. 28 *et seq.*) [pp. 149 ff. above].

[15] 'Ideal Types and Historical Explanation', p. 151 above.

[16] 'Historical Explanation in the Social Sciences', p. 172.

[17] Goldstein, *op. cit.*, pp. 266–271 above.

local rule of inheritance, say, is simply a disposition shared by pretty well everybody in the locality to deal with the property of dead persons in a determinate way. I conclude that there is no difficulty in the idea of an anthropological explanation of the characteristics of a kinship system in terms of disposition and beliefs.

It may be noted that Watkins's closing remarks in the material last quoted indicate that he has misconstrued the point of my paper. I did not there challenge the view that societies or parts of them could be characterized in individualistic terms, though I must confess that I have come more and more to doubt that even this is possible,[18] but rather the view that sociocultural theory must be individualistic. The problem to which Murdock addresses himself is that of accounting for how it is that systems of kinship develop and change. This is rather different from merely characterizing or describing any given such system, and even if one believes that the characterization may be done in individualistic terms, rather than in non-reducible institutional terms, the status of the sociological laws which govern the development and change of such systems may perhaps require separate determination.

But putting aside this distinction between characterizing what I have called the 'synchronic social now', that is, the institution under study during that period of time within which it remains more or less stable,[19] and characterizing the laws that govern it, we have to consider what can be meant by calling the dispositions cited in the above passages 'individual dispositions'. It has been made amply clear by Watkins that he wishes to include as individualistic not only the dispositions of specific people about whom we may have factual knowledge, but also the dispositions of anonymous people.[20] Detailed individualistic explaining may well be an ideal for which to strive, but in most instances it is not a realizable goal, and there seems to be no point in virtually ruling the social sciences out of business by insisting upon it. All of the examples quoted are instances of these so-called anonymous dispositions. They are not only the dispositions of specific individuals with whom the social scientist may be concerned, but if his explanation is adequate we should be able to discover in many other people, concerning whom factual evidence may yet become available, the same characteristics or dispositions described.

I do not doubt that it was individual Huguenots who ploughed back their profits into their respective businesses, but it is not at all obvious

---

[18] Such characterizations would tend to blur the distinction between the roles of individuals and the domains of institutions, to use the apt expression of Mr Harold Weisberg. Cf. Mandelbaum, 'Societal Facts' [pp. 221–234 above].

[19] *Op. cit.*, pp. 272 *et seq.*

[20] Watkins, 'Methodological Individualism: a Reply' [pp. 179–184 above, p. 184].

that ploughing back—or, for that matter, being a Huguenot—is anything but a social or sociocultural characteristic. Properly to understand this kind of behaviour I am required to sknow something about the economic conditions of seventeenth-century France, the kinds of business enterprises that flourished, which of them, if any, were especially noted for the concentration in them of Huguenots, and so forth. Presumably I would wish to know other things, not of an economic nature, which bear upon such matters; e.g., if the governments of European countries were wont to interfere in economic affairs, this could be an important bit of relevant information. And thus a more or less full picture of Huguenot economic activities could be developed. But in all this no mention is made of any individual; no concern is felt for the psychological characteristics of anybody. We do not, to be sure, deny, as Watkins thinks we must, that all the time individual human beings are making decisions to buy and sell, to manufacture in greater or lesser quantity, and to export or import this or that. But it is not obvious that we need be concerned with them in reconstructing the economic conditions of seventeenth-century France.

Similar observations may be made about the characterizing of the social and kinship system of a people. Specific people are related in specific ways, but the rules governing the determination of these relations are expressed—by the ethnographer even when not fully understood by the people themselves—in ways that do not make reference to individuals or to psychological characteristics. For the most part, people are born into their kinship relationships, and it seems entirely a reversal of actual fact to say that such relations 'are the product of people's *attitudes* to each other, though these are partly determined by their *beliefs* about their biological relations'.[21] It seems more reasonable to say that for the most part the proper attitudes towards one's various kin are cultivated during the enculturation process.

The point here is that the kinds of dispositions to be found in people of any given type are socially induced dispositions. It seems odd to talk about widely recurring dispositions among Huguenot entrepreneurs and not to wonder about the coincidence of the recurrence in just this group. It was, to be sure, individual Huguenots who successfully competed in the business world of the seventeenth century. But this was presumably because the Huguenot upbringing or enculturation produced people who were adept at this sort of thing. These were people who could operate effectively within the socioeconomic framework of the time.

It seems to me that methodological individualism makes sense only

[21] From a letter from Watkins to me; it immediately precedes the long sentence quoted in the text above.

if it can demonstrate the relevance of psychological characteristics in explaining and describing social institutions, and hence I am unable to agree that anonymous dispositions are individualistic. Anonymous dispositions convey no information about anyone in particular, but individuals are individuals in particular. I am not, of course, saying that no individual is disposed to behave in such-and-such way, where 'such-and-such' refers to some anonymous disposition. Bank tellers, to use Mandelbaum's example, are disposed to behave in ways suitable to their occupation, but one cannot explain banking institutions in terms of such dispositions to behave. It is the institutional framework of banking which fixes the manner deemed suitable for tellers. And when some individual bank teller finally achieves his goal and is promoted to a junior vice-presidency, his mode of behaviour changes. But it seems rather odd to say that he has now acquired a new set of personal dispositions and mean thereby that his psychological nature has undergone some change.[22] He has merely stepped into a new role and is now prepared to act in ways suitable to his new station in life.

In insisting upon the sociological character of the concepts with which we describe institutions and the social nature of so-called anonymous dispositions, it is not my intention to say that individual people make no difference. Likewise, such insistence need not lead to any undesirable ontological results. There are people and they do make a difference, and yet they are sufficiently similar—at least so we are told by many responsible students of social science[23]—that laws of social change may be formulated. Not, to be sure, historicistic laws of development, but laws in which the relevant variables are specified and the nature of the change made determinant without recourse to oracular pronouncements that obfuscate more than they clarify. I have suggested elsewhere[24] that Murdock's theory of kinship systems is an example of this sort of theorising. This theory proclaims no necessary successions; it requires—as does any theory—only that if it is accepted as true or approximately so, then given the theoretically necessary and sufficient conditions for the development of any kinship system of determinate type, we may reasonably expect an instance of that type to develop.

Murdock himself actually thinks that behavioural psychology and

---

[22] Even if it were not odd it would not support the individualistic position inasmuch as it would suggest the dependence of personal dispositions upon non-personal institutional factors.

[23] This is implicit in a good deal of work that is done in the social sciences and has been explicitly insisted upon by a good many of those who work in those fields, especially by anthropologists. The well known comparative approach of anthropology would seem to make little sense if this were not believed.

[24] *Op. cit.*, pp. 266–271 above.

psychoanalysis are relevant to his theory,[25] but in actual fact these play no logical role in the formulation of the theory or the derivation of its results.[26] I suspect that his interest in this may be part of a desire to avoid the reification of societies, holism as we now understand it. It is precisely this concern which leads us to sociological emergence, and it may well be that if one wanted to determine in specific detail the dynamics of emergence, so to speak, it would be necessary to make use of psychological theory. But I am not able to see that we are therefore required to reduce the social to the psychological any more than we do the psychological to other so-called levels of reality. Nor does it follow that because concern with the actual dynamics of emergence brings us to psychology, psychological theory has any function at all in the formulation of sociological theories.

The notion that we can talk about the dispositions of anonymous people seems to me somewhat strange. I know what it means to characterize particular people in terms of their particular dispositions. If I am told that John is lazy, I understand that he is disposed to avoid work; if told that he is thrifty, I know him to be a careful man with a dollar (or a pound, as the case may be). These are personal dispositions, though the sort of behaviour characteristic of the expression of such dispositions seems to be cultural, not psychological. But it is one thing to attribute such tendencies to John, quite another to so-called anonymous individuals. I venture to suggest that wherever Watkins talks about anonymous dispositions or the dispositions of anonymous individuals he is simply attempting to talk about non-individual characteristics of societies or parts of societies, or of socially induced ways of behaving, without being explicit about it. Anonymous individuals are referred to as a way of avoiding holism, but we have seen that this may be done in other ways. There are specific individuals and characteristics of social phenomena; each of these raises theoretical questions of its own, and it is the business of psychology and social science to deal respectively with them. But there is no science of the anonymous. What we have are not the characteristic dispositions of people we don't know, but the social behaviour of people in given situations quite apart from their personal dispositions.

[25] *Social Structure*, New York, 1949, p. xvi.
[26] Goldstein, *op. cit.*, pp. 270 *et seq.*

MAY BRODBECK

Methodological Individualisms: Definition and Reduction

The Reformation, it has been said, changed the course of history. Most people would agree. At the very least, agree or not, they would hold the proposition to be one worth considering. They would be unlikely to reject it out of hand as incapable of being either true or false because it had no meaning. For, of course, 'everybody knows' what the Reformation was and, elaborating a little, we can make clear what we meant by changing the course of history. Yet it is just statements of this sort that cause much methodological wrangling. Their controversial nature is due, in large part, to controversy over the status of such terms as 'the Reformation' and, generally, group or macroscopic concepts. Since not only history, but sociology, political science, social psychology, and economics also widely use concepts referring to groups and their properties, rather than to individuals, the controversy has wide ramifications. And because there are, as it were, so many vested interests involved, the dispute also tends to acquire an ideological tone not altogether consonant with dispassionate inquiry. Bad temper and mutual recrimination in scientific discussion are generally a sign that ideological defences are being shored up. Just possibly, a philosopher whose substantive concern in any empirical field is minimal may hope to be considered above the battle, as one who, having no private axe to grind, can be concerned only with clarifying the logical issues involved. In this hope, I wish to explore as systematically as possible the tangled web of issues woven about the status of group concepts and their relationship to those referring to individuals. Intertwined in this controversy are two different issues. One has to do with the nature of the *terms* or concepts of social science; the other with the nature of its *laws* and *theories* and their relationship in turn to those in other areas. The first issue is one of *meaning*, the second of *reduction*. Success in unsnarling the various strands of this web may alone help abate the fury of the controversy.

TWO KINDS OF GROUP PROPERTIES

John is blond and tall. Blondness and tallness are properties or characteristics exemplified by the individual man, John. John is taller than Harry. 'Taller than' is a property jointly exemplified by the two men named. Such properties, requiring more than one individual for their exemplification, are called 'relations' or, better, descriptive relations, since, like the properties of single individuals, they refer to observable characters of things. Like all characters, relations may be either undefined, such as taller than or between, or defined, such as smarter than or married. Many terms such as 'married' or 'mother', appear grammatically to be properties of single individuals, but, like 'south', are actually relational, requiring, when defined, reference to two or more individuals. A group is an aggregate of individuals standing in certain descriptive relations to each other. The kinds of relations exemplified will, of course, depend upon, or determine, the kind of group, whether it be a family, an audience, a committee, a labour union, or a crowd. Just as the individual John Smith is to be distinguished from his attributes, say, being blond or being tall, so the group must be distinguished from its attributes such as, say, being numerous or being noisy. It is simple to tell whether a characteristic is being attributed to an individual or to a group. Compare 'Indians are red-skinned' with 'Indians are disappearing'. In the former, each and every Indian is said to be red-skinned, while in the latter Indians as a group are said to be disappearing, that is, diminishing in population. When the property is attributed to a group collectively, so that the group itself is logically the subject of the proposition, rather than distributively, in which case 'each and every' member of the group could logically be the subject of the proposition, then we have a group property. Group properties, like all others, may be either logical or descriptive. In 'The Apostles are twelve', for example, 'twelve' is a logical character of the group of apostles, that is, one whose definition can be given in terms of logical words alone, such as 'all', 'either . . . or' or 'and', without recourse to terms having observable referents. The definition is cumbrous and need not concern us here. Descriptive terms, which do particularly concern us, may be either physical, in the narrow sense, like 'loud' or 'dirty', or behavioural or sociological, like 'efficient' or 'wealthy'.

Clearly there is no issue about the *occurrence* of group characteristics. There is not even any question about the occurrence of behavioural group attributes. No one will deny that it makes sense to say of some groups that they are more efficient or more powerful than others or, of some others, that they are wealthy. The controversial question, or rather one of them, is whether or not there are any such attributes which are undefined or *undefinable*; i.e., whether there are attributes of groups not definable in terms of either the behaviour of the individuals composing the group or the relations between these individuals or both. There are, of course, undefinable terms referring to properties of individual things or persons, like colour words or other words referring to directly observable qualities. Are there similarly undefinable terms referring to properties of groups, i.e., properties which can be directly observed but which cannot be defined in terms referring to either the behaviour of the individuals constituting the group or the relations obtaining among them or both? Can we speak, for example, of a 'responsive audience' without defining the adjective in terms of the behaviour of the individual people in the audience and some more or less precise statistical notion, namely, the percentage of attentive individuals in the group? Do groups or institutions have purposes not definable in terms of individual purposes; do they have purposes of their own, as it were? Similarly, can we meaningfully speak of a 'will of the people' which is something different from either the wills of all persons or of the majority of these persons? The question can also be asked about groups themselves. Is there such a thing as the State or a University over and above their constituent individuals and the relations among them? Does this entity itself have attributes? Or, to say the same thing more precisely, are there any undefined terms referring to kinds of groups?

The two questions, about group entities and about undefinable attributes of groups, are obviously not independent. If, for instance, the efficiency of a group is not some function of the behaviour of its constituent individuals, then there must be something else that exhibits this efficiency, the group 'itself'. And if there be such a superentity as, say, a 'group-mind', then it will have characteristics of its own: allegedly, it may have political opinions. So there is really only one question. And it can be most economically posed by asking whether or not there are such undefinable descriptive properties of groups. Let us consider examples. The 'cohesiveness' of a group may be defined, say, as the ratio of the number of people within the group with whom its members say they would prefer to be stranded on a desert island to the total number of votes for people within and without the group. Can 'crowd hysteria' be similarly defined in terms of individual behaviours or is it an undefinable quality of the crowd itself? The denial that there are such undefinable group properties or such superentities is the view usually known as *methodological individualism*. Its contradictory is *metaphysical holism*. It is called 'holism' because its proponents generally maintain that there are so-called wholes, group entities which have undefinable properties of their own. The property of the whole is then also said to be emergent from the properties of its parts. The thesis that there are such properties is accordingly also called 'emergentism'.[1] Philosophically, the holistic assumption that there are group properties over and above the individuals making up the group, their properties, and the relations among them is counter to empiricism. For the latter holds that all terms must ultimately refer to what is observable, directly or indirectly, and that what we observe are people and their characteristics not supra-individual groups and their characteristics. Or, to say the same thing differently, the anti-holist maintains that the behaviour *of* groups can be defined in terms of behaviour *in* groups. Culturally, holism is intimately connected with hostility towards the liberal political individualism of the Western tradition. If 'States' have wills and purposes of their own, then counting noses is unnecessary and 'serving the State' comes to sound like 'serving Mr Jones'. Jones' will we know how to ascertain, but who is to divulge the 'will of the State'? The answers are, alas, only too familiar. The will and wisdom of the State reside in a privileged class or caste. This is the conservative variant, also called 'organicism'. Or they are 'embodied' in a charismatic leader.

Since fundamental philosophical and cultural assumptions are involved in this controversy, it is important to be crystal clear about the sense or senses in which group variables, if not hypostatized, are not only practically convenient but perhaps indispensable. Once before,[2] I attempted to show the conditions under which the use of macroscopic or group variables might be both necessary and fruitful. I was promptly charged with metaphysical holism.[3] Since the charge is patently alien both to the spirit of that particular paper and my entire philosophical position, let me try once again to clarify what, given the nature of social science, must be made clear if much fruitful behavioural research is not to be *a priori* banned.

To describe a fact is to state that one or several objects exemplify certain characters, relational and non-relational or, what amounts to the same thing, that a defin*ed* or undefin*ed* concept has an instance. The occurrence of undefin*able* properties of groups would therefore be emergence at the level of description, or descriptive emergence. The operative word, of course, is 'undefinable'. For, as already mentioned, no one denies the existence of defined properties of groups, and these properties may well be different from any possessed by the individuals.

---

[1] A good discussion of holism and related issues can be found in 'Exceptionalism in Geography: A Methodological Examination' by F. K. Schaefer, *Annals of Ass'n. of Amer. Geographers*, XLIII, 1953.

[2] 'On the Philosophy of the Social Sciences' [pp. 91–110 above].

[3] 'Methodological Individualism: A Reply', J. W. N. Watkins [pp. 179–184 above].

For instance, they may be inapplicable to individuals because they are statistical aggregates, like the 'homogeneity' of a group defined in terms of a standard deviation or generally when averaging processes are used to arrive at the value of a variable. Since such statistical or aggregative concepts are always derived from information about individuals, they trivially satisfy the requirement of methodological individualism.

Sometimes the actual or possible statistical procedures entailed by the definition of a concept are only implicit or covert in ordinary usage. This appears to be the case in those statements which have been held to refer 'anonymously' rather than specifically to individuals.[4] The statement 'an increased dividend is anticipated' is interpreted, quite correctly, to be individualistic even though it does not say anything about any particular shareholder. The expectations of the so-called anonymous individuals to whom the statement refers would, in the last resort, be ascertained by polling individual shareholders. Thus the 'anticipation' is, quite trivially, a statistical concept, even though covertly so in ordinary speech. Similarly, references to, say, 'the poor', in statements such as 'The candidate received more votes from the poor than from the rich' are implicitly statistical. In neither case is any undefinable group property or group-entity meant or suggested. Neither impersonal, unattached anticipations nor a supra-individual 'poor' are implied by the use of these locutions.

Nevertheless, there remains a class of terms frequently used in social science which are not statistical in intent but have yet to be defined in terms of individual behaviour. There is a source of error associated with but not strictly in error of measurement which is perhaps peculiar to social science. This error is due to that imprecision, not in measurement proper, but in the definition of the terms whose referents are being measured. This imprecision or vagueness may itself for each observation result in different values which can have definite probabilities. Consider the assertion that a boom in trade is always followed by slump and depression. To be sure, in some respects the economists can often do better than this, still it is a fair representative of the kind of hypotheses prevalent in social science. This is imprecise not only with respect to time; its predictive value is also restricted by the nature of its concepts. What exactly are 'boom' and 'slump' conditions? 'Depression'? No doubt in these particular cases there is a large statistical component to the meanings involved. Level of employment, average wealth, and such like are doubtless entailed. But how many such things? What else? At what proportion of unemployment and 'other' things will we say depression or boom conditions prevail? Can

---

[4] Watkins, *op. cit.*, pp. 181–182.

we be certain when we have one or the other? Of course, it may be replied, we can't be certain but roughly we can tell. And that is just the point. The roughness results not from inability to determine the facts, statistically or otherwise, but from the fringe of vagueness surrounding the applicability of the terms. The definitions within physical science leave no room for this ambience. Prediction or explanation can hardly be precise when, because our terms lack sharp referents, we can be sure neither that we have the initial conditions nor the anticipated event since they are not exactly specified. The more macroscopic the concept, the wider its penumbra of vagueness is apt to be.

Consider next such concepts as 'the Reformation', 'the Church', 'capitalism', 'mercantilism', 'cold war', 'army morale' and the like. In the meaning of these there is not even an implicit statistical reference. Such non-statistical 'institutional' or 'holistic' concepts present difficulties of definition similar to those that face the clinical or, even more, the social psychologist. The precise definition of social attitudes, like pro- or anti-authoritarianism, or of clinical states, like aggression or anxiety, requires one to choose from an almost infinite variety of symptoms those which can be used reliably to define the term in question. This means, of course, not what *really* is anti-authoritarianism or aggression, but how to find a set of symptoms which, without additions or deletions, will enter into laws, that is, enable prediction of other behaviour. There is the further difficulty that, even if we could overcome the difficulty about which symptoms should be omitted and which retained in the definition, in the case of clinical concepts the fittingness of a behaviouristic definition varies from culture to culture. Just as an 'act of war' in one social setting might not be so in another, so what is aggressive behaviour for an American might not be so for a South Sea Islander. Thus a definition of, say, aggressive behaviour, not containing reference to the culture in which the behaviour to be called aggressive is displayed is, in a sense, obviously inadequate. In the case of institutional concepts like 'the Reformation' or 'capitalism', an indefinite set of behaviours are loosely encompassed by the term. It is not that certain behaviours are 'anonymously' referred to, but that the list of these behaviours cannot yet be sharply terminated. 'The Jewish race is cohesive', runs an example for a definable macroscopic term, means 'Jews usually marry Jews, live in close communities, share religious rituals, etc.'[5]. The 'etc.' makes my point for me. True, this was only meant to be illustrative. Still, the difficulty of completely spelling out that 'etc.' would also be present in actual scientific usage. Yet, despite their open-endedness, these institutional concepts are

---

[5] Watkins, *op. cit.*, p. 183.

probably just as indispensable to many areas of social science as are clinical concepts to the psychologist. *In principle*, of course, for whatever cold comfort that may be, all such concepts must be definable in terms of individual behaviour. In practice, however, we frequently cannot do this. Are we then prepared to say that in whatever context these terms occur they are wholly ambiguous as to meaning? I hardly think so. The course of science is not always as smooth as the logical analyst would like. And it seems to me that there are cases in which the best we can do is point out the distinctions and the difficulties. The most that we can ask of the social scientist whose subject matter requires him to use such 'open' concepts is that he keep the principle of methodological individualism firmly in mind as a devoutly to be wished-for consummation, an ideal to be approximated as closely as possible. This should at least help assure that nevermore will he dally with suspect group-minds and impersonal 'forces', economic or otherwise; nevermore will non-observable properties be attributed to equally non-observable group entities. At the same time, he will not by methodological fiat be struck dumb about matters on which there is, no matter how imprecisely, a great deal to be said.

DEFINITION VS. REDUCTION

The view that all group or macroscopic concepts are in principle definable in terms of individual behaviour is a fundamental or, even, metaphysical assumption, reflecting as it does basic presuppositions of the empiricist philosophical tradition. In so far as methodological individualism is a precept for proper concept formation, it is a denial of descriptive emergence, that is, it denies that supra-individual group properties can be meaningfully attributed to things or events. The banner of methodological individualism has however also been raised in the context of laws and theories. This is a matter of explanation rather than of description. The two are disparate and should not be confounded. The belief that there are no emergent *properties* rests on our criterion of the meaningful. It is thus, broadly speaking, a matter of logic. The assumption that the *laws* of group behaviour are or are not, as the case may be, emergent with respect to laws about individuals is a matter of fact, a matter for empirical determination. But for this to be clear some further distinctions and elaborations are necessary.

The possibility of 'reduction' is the issue raised by asking whether the phenomena of one field, say chemistry or psychology, can be explained in terms of the phenomena of another, say physics or physiology respectively. Reduction, as I understand it, involves deduction. Explanation, in one firm meaning of that term, is achieved by deducing what is to be explained from true premisses. Only statements, never concepts, can serve as either premises or conclusion of a deduction. Explanation, therefore, is always of statements by means of other statements. (Obvious and trivial as this point is, as long as the confused notion of 'explanatory concepts' lingers on, it is worth remaking.) The deduction by which reduction is achieved also serves to explain. Explanation is in fact a major reason for reduction. It is consequently a matter of laws and theories, not of terms or concepts. What is sometimes called 'reduction' of terms is, strictly, definition of the kind we have just discussed. Not all deduction, however, achieves reduction. We explain a law by deducing it from another law or laws. In the classical illustration, we explain Galileo's law of falling bodies by deducing it, as a special case for terrestrial objects, from the Newtonian law of gravitation. But here nothing has been reduced to anything else. Both Newton's and Galileo's laws mention the same subject matter, physical bodies and their spatial-temporal properties. Both laws are in the same area, mechanics. A 'psychological' or an 'economic' term is one that occurs in the science of either psychology or economics respectively. One area differs from another by its terms or concepts; these determine its 'subject matter'. Deduction is also reduction only when the deduced laws are in a different area from those that serve as premises. Moreover, the latter are, for reasons that will become clear, generally microscopic relative to the former, as physiology is microscopic relative to psychology which, in turn, is microscopic relative to sociology. The distinction between the microscopic (molecular) and the macroscopic (molar) refers, as the terms suggest, to some specifiable difference in the size of the respective units of description. A social group is, in an obvious sense, macroscopic relative to its individual members. But if the laws of the reducing and reduced theory are related as axioms and theorems respectively, each covering a different area, how then does the deduction take place? For, clearly, if two laws have no terms or variables in common, then one cannot possibly be a deductive consequence of the other. The fact is that the deduction, hence the reduction, takes place in different ways, depending upon the nature of the connection between the two theories involved. The logic of the reduction of macroscopic thermodynamics to mechanics differs from that of the reduction either of chemistry to physics or of psychology to physiology, and these all differ from the way in which the reduction of sociology to psychology would take place, if we could do it. We shall here be concerned only with the last of these pairs, using, with apologies, 'sociology' as an omnibus term to include all the areas using group concepts, including in it political science, economics, and social psychology, as well as sociology proper.[6]

[6] For a discussion of the relationship between psychology and physiology, see my 'On the Philosophy of Social Sciences', *op. cit.*, pp. 100 ff.

Among chemists, reductionism is hardly a controversial issue. Naturally not, since it is an accomplished fact. But even among psychologists, where it is at best a programme, though the range from optimism to pessimism is very wide with vociferous extremes at either end, ultimate physiological reduction is accepted as a frame of reference. The area concerned with group variables is rather more sensitive, however. Further removed, both historically and systematically, from the biological sciences than are psychologists, thus further removed from the classical scientific tradition, those concerned with group sciences tend to exhibit greater emotional reactions to the reductionism issue. They are darkly suspicious that the proponents of reductionism aim primarily to put them out of business by denying them any real subject matter. Nor perhaps are their suspicions wholly unfounded. However that may be, a firm grasp of the distinctions between the definitions of terms and the reduction of laws and between perfect and imperfect knowledge should considerably reduce the decibel count of this clamour either for or against autonomous group science. But, first of all, I must explain the meaning of 'perfect knowledge'.

PERFECT VS. IMPERFECT KNOWLEDGE

Suppose that we have a theory of economic behaviour, that is, a theory concerned with phenomena such as consumption, income, saving, profits, and the like. Assume that we are given the equations (laws) of this theory, the numerical values of its constant coefficients or parameters, and a set of initial conditions, that is, the observed values of its variables at any particular time or for a specified geographical area. By a leap of imagination, assume moreover that from this system we can predict the future course of all our variables or compute their entire past history; we know how changes in any one variable produce changes in any other; we know to what extent by tinkering with the system we can bring about desired changes, to what extent we are powerless. If we knew all this, either in economics or for that matter in any other social science, there is clearly nothing else we could possibly desire to know, at least as far as these variables are concerned. Such knowledge may therefore be called 'perfect'.[7]

A theory, to summarize, consists of a set of terms or concepts, undefined and defined, and a set of statements, called generalizations

---

[7] I take the terminology of perfect vs. imperfect knowledge and the accompanying criteria from Gustav Bergmann's *Philosophy of Science*, University of Wisconsin Press, 1957. I am grateful to Professor Bergmann for permitting me to use the manuscript of this work in which a more technical elaboration of the relevant distinctions will be found.

or laws, about how the referents of some of the terms affect others. In order to make a prediction about any particular system from the theory, its laws and its definitions, there must be added to it a set of statements about the state of this system at some specified time, that is, we must know which concepts are or are not exemplified by the system at that time, or, as one says in the case of quantified theories, we must be given the values of the relevant variables. Assume that prediction is made and, as it happens, is falsified by the course of events. What are the possible sources of error? All theories in all fields are subject to the inherent frailty of empirical science. Inductive generalizations may be over-generalizations; measurement, too, has its limits and its own kinds of errors. These two frailties do not by themselves distinguish the best physical theory from the most ill-confirmed social theory, even though the probability for errors of this kind to pass undetected is, of course, considerably less in the case of a well-confirmed body of laws with a highly developed theory and fine measuring instruments. In respect to induction and measurement as two sources of error, the difference between the 'hard' and the 'soft' sciences is only one of degree. The difference in degree is in turn traceable to the characteristic *closure* and *completeness* of certain physical theories, two features which are conspicuously lacking or, at least, still lacking in social science. What makes the difference is (a) whether or not the referents of the terms of the theory interact only among themselves and with nothing else at the time and within the geographical area considered and (b) whether or not any variables that in fact do make a difference have been omitted from the expressions of the theory. These criteria of closure and completeness, respectively, are touchstones to the justifiably felt superiority of physical over social science. And, as we shall see, even this is not the whole story.

(a) *Closure and Completeness*

Celestial mechanics and non-atomic thermodynamics are two theories within classical physics with non-overlapping scopes, yet each theory is nearly 'perfect' for the variables with which it deals. In the first, mass, velocity, and distance interact only with each other; in the second, volume, temperature, and pressure and a few other variables of this sort do the same. These theories consist of process laws, that is, in each case, the values of *any one* variable at any time can be computed by means of the laws from the values of *all* the others at any other time. Nothing that happens at any other time or place than those being considered affects the behaviour of the properties with which the theory is concerned, or, at worst, we know how to take account of these outside influences in our predictions or computations. The system, in other words, is *closed*. When the planet Neptune was discovered, its presence was predicted from the Newtonian law together with the known 'perturbations' of Uranus—its deviations from the predicted path—and of course the state of the sun and the other planets at the time. Logically, this means that the system which had previously been thought to be closed actually was not. The law itself omitted nothing, for Neptune was simply another instance of variables already contained in the law. The case would be different if, say, the presence or absence of life on the planets was found to affect the laws of motion. In this case, the theory would have omitted variables which in fact make a difference. It would not be *complete*. Newtonian mechanics is complete and we know, in it, the conditions of closure for any system. Because of these features the connections among the variables are reversible or symmetrical. If, in the process theories of physics, a variable x is a function of another y, we know not only that a change in x brings about a change in y, but also conversely. We know too what happens to either variable in the absence of the other. In social science, on the other hand, if we know that A causes B, rarely are we in a position to say how changes in B affect A or even what happens to B if A is not present.

(b) *Process Laws*

The mutual dependency among the variables of classical physics is even more profound than this, marking another item in its perfection. It may be suggested that changes in pressure and volume occur simultaneously, whereas changes in the price of corn come later than the rain. The temporal development presumably marks the irreversibility and consequent utility of the notion of cause. Yet perhaps the most striking feature of process laws is their reversibility with regard to time. Newton's law, for example, permits us to compute the position and velocity of, say, a planet at all times past or future, if we know its position and velocity at a single instant. Generally, by means of these characteristic laws of physics, any two states of the system can be inferred from each other, quite regardless of which comes first in time. Nor is this reversibility with respect to time all there is to it. The more exactly a prediction can be stated, the more useful it will be both practically and theoretically. There are several dimensions in which a prediction may be more or less exact. Let me revert to the assertion that a boom in trade is always followed by slump and depression. One characteristic restricting the predictive value of such statements, mentioned before, is the vagueness of its concepts. Another is indefiniteness with respect to time. The process laws of physics are extremely specific in this respect. They permit prediction not only to 'some' future time, or computation of conditions 'sometime' in the past, but for *any* given moment of time, an instant, a day, a year or a decade before or after the time from which the computation is made. This indeed is what is meant by calling them process laws, for the values of the variables mentioned in the laws are completely determinate for every moment of the temporal sequence. The contrasting imprecision with which slump and depression are said to 'follow' a boom hardly needs comment. Exactly when it will follow and how long it will last are not at present within our purview.

PERFECTION AND SOCIAL SCIENCE

How do the social sciences stand up when measured against the criteria of closure and completeness? A system consists roughly of any group of objects or patterns of behaviour remaining constant in time. The planets, identifiable by their masses, the market with its stable procedures for buying and selling, rats in a cage, people in a community identifiable, say, by occupation and income, all constitute systems. Just as velocity and position, changing in time, are the states of a mechanical system, so consumer preferences or political opinions may be the changing states of human systems. To know the conditions for closure of these systems, that is, to know either that nothing outside of the region being considered is affecting it or else to know what is entering or leaving the system, we must first know all the relevant variables, that is, the theory being applied to the system must be complete. No variables that in fact make a difference are omitted from the theory. Since the conditions for closure will in a sense settle themselves if we know all the relevant variables, we can concentrate our attention on the completeness of theories in social science.

(a) *Imperfection and Separation of Variables*
From the point of view of the physical scientist, a curious characteristic of the social sciences is the division of its terms or variables into two classes. This division is explicit in psychology and theoretical economics, implicit in the other areas. Psychologists distinguish stimulus variables from response variables; economists, the exogenous from the endogenous. Response terms name individual behaviour which the psychologist explains in terms of stimulus variables, that is, the physical and social environment, as well as certain biological states, past habits, and perhaps hereditary factors. The individual's behaviour is held to be determined by all these, but not, of course, conversely. The stimulus conditions are either given to or, at least partly, manipulated by the observer, but his theory does not purport to explain them. This is left to other areas of either social, biological, or physical science. The economist's distinction though not the same is similar. The economic

or 'endogenous' variables influence each other and are influenced by the 'exogenous', non-economic, physical, technological, institutional variables, but not conversely. The latter are 'predetermined' data or conditions in terms of which the economist explains changes in economic factors. This division among the variables is patently artificial, a convenient way of speaking only, for nothing is in itself either a stimulus or a response, endogeneous or exogenous. In neither case is the distinction a hard and fast one. The stimulus conditions may consist in part of one's own and other people's behaviour. Similarly, an exogenous factor, say, the imposition of tariffs by Congress, may be affected by economic conditions such as decreasing demand, as well as by political pressures. It is easy to see in a preliminary way why this division of the variables reflects a departure from 'perfection'. Clearly, there is no question here of symmetry between the terms in each class. Changes in the response or economic factors do not generally change the stimulus or noneconomic factors respectively. The category into which a term is placed depends in large part upon how much we know. Tax rates and exports, for example, are exogenous or institutional because determined by political decisions, but if economic causes were found for them, they would be treated as endogenous. In general, this division of the variables is a reflection of the inadequacy of a given theory, whether in psychology or economics, to fully account for changes in *all* the variables. The sociologist seeking to account for population distribution does not also attempt to explain the geographical formations which may influence where people live. The political scientist does not try to explain the economic factors which may in turn explain the voting behaviour in which he is interested. The limited scope of our theories reinforces this distinction while highlighting its artificiality. Given two different theories in an area, the same variable may be either dependent or 'predetermined'. What is considered exogenous in a business-cycle theory, for example, may not be so in a theory of demand. In psychology, a theory in social psychology may take as stimulus what is response in learning theory.

How does this affect completeness? Let us leave out of consideration the physical variables, like rainfall or body-type, in respect to which closure can hardly be expected, since presumably these are to be explained primarily in terms of other physical and physiological variables. Even so, what about the institutional and behavioural variables? It is evident, from all that we now know, that no individual social science can by itself expect to achieve completeness in its terms. Any theory of human behaviour will contain references to political, legal, psychological, economic, religious, and other institutional factors in the individual's environment. It is a commonplace by now that these factors all interact, so each social science is to some greater or lesser extent dependent upon the findings of others. In addition to the division in the variables, there are other clues to an acknowledged lack of completeness. Consider the generalization that other things remaining unchanged, a protective tariff on a commodity causes a rise in its price. Incompleteness is signalled here in two ways. First, 'protective tariff' is an exogenous variable whose imposition is not to be explained by the theory, but in terms of which change in the endogenous variable, price, is explained. Secondly, by the phrase 'other things remaining unchanged' the economist hedges his bets that the values of other variables influencing price, either mentioned or not in his theory, either exogenous, like changes in technology, or endogenous, like wage reductions, will remain as they were at the time the tariff was imposed. Some, perhaps most, of these changes in the 'other things' are not predictable from the theory, hence it is incomplete. To illustrate more obviously perhaps, other things being equal, demand is doubtless a function of price. But probably no decline in the price of the horse and buggy could have prevented its being superseded by the automobile. Changes in technology and in tastes unpredictable by the theory will have and, as the qualifying phrase indicates, are expected to have their effect. Completeness, in the strict sense of exclusive mutual dependency among the terms of the theory, could only be achieved by one vast social science encompassing the entire range of human behaviour.

The illustration about the discovery of the planet Neptune suggested that theories may be complete and prediction still fail because the system to which they are applied is not closed. A hypothetical example from social science may bring this closer home. Suppose an economist wishes to predict the relative demands for butter and white margarine in a state where coloured margarine is prohibited. Assume that among the relevant variables he includes people's preferences and in particular their relative preferences for butter over margarine as well as the prices of these products. Assume, quite unrealistically, that he omits to account for the fact that the region for which he wishes to make his prediction is surrounded on all sides by easily accessible states where coloured margarine is available at the same price as white at home. In this case, closure but not completeness is violated, since individual preference is one of his variables and that between white and yellow margarine would have been taken into account if the alternative were present in the home state. If, again quite unrealistically, individual preference were entirely omitted from the theory, when in fact they make a difference to demand, then his system is incomplete. Generally, if nothing is omitted that actually makes a difference to the behaviour of the variables with which the theory is concerned, then the theory is complete. If and only if this condition is satisfied, then all the other true laws of the area staked out by the terms of the theory follow as deductive consequences from its axioms or fundamental laws.

(b) *Statistics and Imperfect Knowledge*

Social science has developed much more specific techniques to compensate for lapses in closure and completeness. Here we have perhaps a paradox. Statistical knowledge, certainly the most extensive we have in social science, is conspicuously imperfect. Yet, statistics is perhaps the most promising method available for smoothing out the obstructive complexities in subject matter which make the road to perfection so rocky. Despite the great gap between what statistical knowledge can tell us and what we would like to know, statistical techniques do suggest, within their limitations, a method for achieving that semblance of closure and completeness which is at once the despair and, as it is for any theory, the *sine qua non* of behaviour theory. Social scientists take the use of statistical techniques so much for granted that they are not always able to articulate clearly just why these techniques are indispensable tools of the trade. The logical basis of this indispensability lies in large part, though not entirely, in the incompleteness of our explanations. The exception is the use of statistical concepts because of errors of measurement. But there is no difference in this respect between the social and physical sciences. The result of a measurement of, say, length is as much a so-called 'chance' or random variable[8] with a frequency distribution determined by the nature of the measurement as is the result of the measurement or computation of an individual's learning ability or a firm's income, though of course neither length nor for that matter Jones' 1956 income nor his learning ability are random variables. The latter, unlike 'yearly number of automobile accidents', 'income of farmers' or 'learning ability of five-year-olds', have a single value and not a frequency distribution. But errors of measurement are not unique to social science, thus not germane to our present preoccupation. The use of random variables as a consequence of incompleteness is. There are two ways in which the use of statistical concepts betrays incompleteness.

Without some abstraction or selection from all the possibilities the world presents there can be no science at all. By their very nature scientific laws describe only certain features of the kinds of things or events they hold to be connected. How much can safely be ignored

---

[8] In the jargon of the trade, statistical variables are usually called 'chance', stochastic, or random, meaning any magnitude, like 'yearly number of accidents,' which takes different values with definite probabilities. A philosopher aware of the woes associated with words like 'chance' is impelled to put the technical term in quotation marks. It means only what it is said to mean, of course, and has nothing to do with 'freedom' in the sense of uncaused.

depends upon the way things are. Even in human behaviour not everything makes a difference. An individual's taste in music may be a function of many variables, but the colour of his eyes is probably not one of them. Even so, the number of different things such as education, age, family background, heredity, special training, and so on, may be so large and so difficult to assign relative importance that we may well despair of formulating an exact functional relationship between such tastes and these other factors. To say, in consequence, that abstraction is all very well for the physical sciences but will not do for the study of man and society is the counsel of desperation, that is, no solution at all. The social scientist, striving to merit the honorific half of that title, settles for something less than perfection. Completeness being far beyond his grasp, he renounces it as a goal. The renunciation has its price and its rewards. Which face will turn up when a die is cast is determined by numerous causes, the centre of gravity of the die, the force with which it is thrown, and so on. An attempt to calculate the results of each throw by means of the laws of mechanics is practically hopeless, because of the difficulty in precisely measuring all the initial conditions. Instead, we represent, as it were, this multiplicity of causes by a probability distribution for the attribute in question. The use of the statistical concept marks our ignorance of all the influencing factors, a failure in either completeness or closure or, usually, both. Similarly, the social scientist, deliberately selecting for study fewer factors than actually influence the behaviour in which he is interested shifts his goal from predicting individual events or behaviours to predicting a random variable, that is, to predicting the frequency with which this kind of behaviour occurs in a large group of individuals possessing the circumscribed number of factors. This is the price. The reward, of course, is that instead of helplessly gazing in dumb wonder at the infinite complexity of man and society, he has knowledge, imperfect rather than perfect, to be sure, but knowledge not to be scorned none the less, of a probability distribution rather than of individual events. After all, while we might much prefer to know the exact conditions under which cancer develops in a particular person, it is far from valueless to know the factors which are statistically cor-related to the frequency of its occurrence.

The relationship between statistical prediction and incompleteness is strikingly explicit in the relatively recent use of so-called stochastic equations, where 'stochastic' means not any statistical concept but a specific form of such. The probability of success in school, let us say, is expressed as a function of I.Q. The observed values of the frequency of such success will be affected by errors of observation. If we know the probability distribution of these errors, then we can make a prediction about the probability of success in school for a given I.Q. or range of

I.Q.s. Our predicted attribute is thus a function both of I.Q. and the distribution of the error. In physics, for example, measured pressure at constant temperature will be a function of the volume plus or minus a known error component associated with the measurement of volume. And of nothing else. If there were no errors of observation, then the connection stated between pressure and volume is exact, with no statistical component. In our illustration, however, as in social science generally, even if there were no errors or if our theory of errors permitted us to separate out the error component, we would *still* be able to predict only a probability distribution and not individual values. There is, as the physicist might say, a systematic component to the error which is not associated with any particular variable but with the asserted connection, an error in the equation itself. Because of a great many other factors, not all children with the same I.Q. will be equally successful. Just as with measurement errors, all these omitted influences, each one of which may be small in itself, may be expressed as a separate variable. In this case, we may say that the connection holds with a 'disturbance'. Of course, any two things can be said to be related with a 'disturbance', so long as the latter is unspecified. To rescue these equations from vacuity, to make them empirically meaningful, the disturbance must have a known probability distribution which does not change with changes in the observed variables. Thus, success in school would be expressed as a function of I.Q. *and* a random variable. This latter probability term would express the aggregate effects of factors as yet unspecified. Thus, incompleteness is at once explicitly built into the system and, given our ignorance either of what these omitted factors are or how much weight they each carry, accounted for in the best possible way. Theoretical economics and, to a much lesser extent, experimental psychology are as yet the only social sciences adapting this technique of further dividing their variables into those which are named by the theory, called 'systematic', and those which are only latently expressed, as it were, in the 'disturbance'.

The lucidity with which stochastic equations betray the incompleteness and consequent statistical character of the theories in which they occur is, of course, not the reason why they are used. I suggested earlier that the dichotomies stimulus-response and exogenous-endogenous were at once recognition of the absence of completeness and an attempt to achieve an approximation to it for the variables of the area, psychology or economics respectively. The split by means of stochastic equations into systematic and disturbance components also serves this purpose. It does so with greater precision by assigning a definite and testable probability to the magnitude of the unknown external factors. Also, packed into the disturbance in the equation may be not only factors which the theory does not seek to explain, such as physical or institutional influences, but also as yet unnoticed variables of the area itself. With increasing knowledge of the sources of error of observation and the improvement in our measuring instruments we are able to reduce the error in the variable due to these factors. In the same way, increasing knowledge may lead to reducing the amount of error in the equation by analysing the disturbance into its components, resulting in a greater degree of completeness for the variables of the area.

To illustrate more concretely, assuming perfect observation, let us say that the amount consumed of some commodity is expressed as a function of the price of the commodity and an error factor in the connection. This error of disturbance incorporates many other causal factors, both noneconomic, like fashion, and economic, like income. Though there may always remain a residual noneconomic cause of error, with increasing knowledge and accuracy the economic factors influencing the relation may be spelled out and added to the systematic variables, leaving only noneconomic factors in the random variable. In the ideal, all economic variables would be included in the set of systematic variables. Consumption, price, and income, be it noticed, are all economic or endogenous variables. If the disturbance in their connection becomes very small, we may well say that they are relatively autonomous, that is, that they interact primarily only with each other. For complete autonomy, the disturbance would have to be zero and probably only the most extreme economic determinist envisages this as a real possibility. The more comprehensive the social science, say a science incorporating economic and sociological phenomena, the greater the degree of autonomy to be envisaged. Since physical, geographical, and physiological factors can be expected to participate in what happens, a wholly autonomous social science, closed and complete by itself, is, to put it moderately, not likely. But relative autonomy would, again to put it moderately, be no small achievement.

COMPOSITION LAWS AND GROUP BEHAVIOUR:
REDUCTION

Closure, completeness, precisely identifiable referents, temporal definiteness of prediction or computation, these then are the ingredients of knowledge at its best. The question about the possibility of an autonomous group science may thus be more precisely reworded in the light of these criteria. Is it possible to have perfect knowledge of society, that is, is it possible to have a process theory containing only group variables which will be both closed and complete?

Group concepts refer, as we saw, to complex patterns of descriptive, empirical relations among individuals. Study of the behaviour of these complexes results in the formation of laws which we may call macroscopic from the nature of their terms. Such laws will be different from laws about the behaviour of single individuals. There need not be and in general will not be any similarity between the behaviour of a complex and the behaviour of the elements of the complex. The behaviour of a substance subject to the laws of chemistry differs from the behaviour of its particles subject to the laws of mechanics. Groups may be cohesive, which individuals cannot be, and cohesiveness may affect the stability of the group, which is again something individuals, in this meaning of 'stability', cannot have. Both terms in this law, if such it be, refer to congeries of individuals exemplifying descriptive relations, such as choosing each other as friends in the first case and faithfully attending meetings with other members of the group, in the second. The law states that whenever a group has the first set of relational attributes, then it also has the other. Laws may also be found connecting individual behaviour or characteristics with that of groups. Ambitious individuals, suppose, are attracted to stratified groups offering opportunity for leadership. This would be an example of an *empirical* connection between individual and group attributes. However, since there are no undefinable group entities or properties, every group term will also be *definitionally* connected with a set of (relational individual behaviours. These latter need not necessarily be 'psychologcal' in the sense that they are technical concepts within the science of psychology. Characteristics occurring in the definitions of macroscopic concepts, such as choosing friends, communicating, buying or selling, need not be, though of course they may be accounted for by an existing psychological theory. It is therefore misleading to say that because group concepts must be defined in terms of individuals they are 'really' psychological. Only if 'psychological' is broadly defined to include all human behaviour is this the case. In this sense, 'selling short on the stock market' is psychological. But then the term is so broad as to be virtually useless. Only if this behaviour can be explained within the context of a theory in psychology is it significantly called psychological rather than, say, economic. These considerations should all help to bring into proper focus the issues connected with the possibility of reduction. What then is the logic of the connection between the group sciences and psychology? How, in principle, would the reduction of the one to the other take place?

A process theory, to repeat, is one permitting the computation of the states of a system at all times from its state at any given time. All such theories contain, in addition to laws for so-called elementary situations, another type of law which increases its scope, securing for it a range of widely different systems whose laws are deducible from the theory. The Newtonian law of attraction between *two* bodies is the elementary law of the system. One does not independently, however, have to discover the law for *three, four*, or any larger number of bodies. These are derivable from the two-body law. They are so, not by logical or arithmetical methods alone, nor from the two-body law alone, but by the addition of a special kind of empirical law, the so-called parallelogram rule. By imaginary decomposition of a system consisting of any number of bodies into pairs of two-body systems, this rule together with the elementary law permits us to compute the accelerations of each body in the complex system. Laws permitting such computation from the elementary to more complex systems may be called composition laws or, a bit misleadingly, composition rules.[9] The latter is misleading because, of course, the 'rule' by which the state of a system containing any number of bodies is computed from the law for the elementary, two-body, system is itself an empirical generalization or law. The term 'vector addition' applied to this particular rule adds to the confusion by making appear purely arithmetical what is an empirical matter, namely, that the resultant of the forces is their vector sum. Another illustration may help clarify the situation. In chemistry, we have laws for the behaviour of hydrogen and laws for the behaviour of oxygen. We also have the law of their interaction, that is, the law stating what happens when oxygen and hydrogen occur together under certain conditions. They form water, for instance. The properties of water are predictable from the laws of its elements in addition to the law of their interaction. Let us take still another example. Airplanes, despite Galileo, often stay up in the air for long periods of time. We know of course that this is not a 'violation' of the law of gravity. The fact that they stay up is explained by applying to this situation all the laws involving the variables believed to be relevant to the situation. The rules for combining these laws, which form the subject matter of aerodynamics, are themselves empirical generalizations or regularities. Such composition rules obviously give to the theories containing them tremendous power and scope. When applied to social science, they are, as I shall now show, the means by which reduction would take place.

Macroscopic laws are laws containing group variables. Assume, for instance, that sociologists find a group law to the effect that stratification causes increased efficiency. The kinds of individual behaviour, like the giving and taking of orders, who communicates with whom, etc., in terms of which the group variable, stratification, is defined, constitute the undefined terms of the sociological system. But, for two reasons,

[9] For a more detailed discussion of composition rules, see Bergmann, *op. cit.*, Ch. III.

this definition alone would not enable us to deduce the law from those of psychology. First, as mentioned before, such individual behaviours need not also be terms of an existing psychological theory. Psychologists, in other words, might not have knowledge about the causes and effects of issuing orders, direction of communication, etc. But suppose that these are terms of psychological theory. The definition, though necessary, is still not sufficient for the deduction to be made. In addition to elementary laws telling how an individual acts in the presence of one or a few others, we must also have composition laws stating what happens, under certain conditions, as the number of people he is with increases. The latter, of course, state how he behaves in a group. Assume, more particularly, that we have the elementary laws, none of which mentions stratified groups, about how Jones, that is, an individual with certain characteristics, behaves in the presence of a person like Smith and about how Jones behaves in the presence of a person like Brown. In addition, assume we have a composition law revealing how Jones behaves when he is confronted with both Smith and Brown under the conditions defined as 'stratified'. We would then know how one individual with certain characteristics behaves as a member of a certain layer of a stratified group. If in addition to these composition laws about the interactions of various kinds of people and the definitions of the group concepts, we are also given the (statistical) description of the initial composition of the group, then we can predict the behaviour of the group, that is, we may derive laws of group behaviour.

We see now why the reducing area, psychology, is said to be microscopic (molecular) relative to the reduced area. The composition laws state what happens when several elementary situations are combined in specified ways. These combined situations are the macroscopic (molar) complexes referred to by the group terms of the reduced area. The definitions of the group terms provide the common language necessary for the derivation of macroscopic statements from microscopic ones. The composition laws then supply the empirical premises from which the deduction is made. The reduction of group laws to those about individuals thus supplies an explanation of group behaviour in terms of the behaviour of individuals in groups. Given the composition laws, the reduction of sociology to psychology is a purely logical matter, following as it does from these composition laws jointly only with the definitions. Or, to say the same thing differently, just as, given the law of vector addition, we do not independently have to discover the law of a three-body system in mechanics, so, given the definitions and the composition laws, we do not independently have to investigate the behaviour of groups. And this of course is what we mean by saying that one area has been 'reduced' to another. The definitions of the group terms are all that connect the two areas.[10] Since all definitions are in principle dispensable and the composition laws contain only psychological terms, there is thus a sense in which there is 'really' only one area. It does not follow, however, that we can scrap the macroscopic social sciences. In addition to the difficulty already discussed about the vagueness or openendedness of group terms, there are even more fundamental reasons, having to do with the nature of composition laws, why the group sciences are probably here to stay.

REDUCTION: FACT VS. PRINCIPLE

Since these composition laws are empirical generalizations, they may fail at some point. Absurd as physicists might find the idea at this stage of the game, it is nevertheless logically possible that the parallelogram rule would no longer work as one went from a system containing, say, 999 bodies to one containing 1000. The prediction for the more complex system, made by means of the composition rule, might be proven false. Psychologists similarly might be able to predict the behaviour of an individual in groups of a given size, but as soon as another person was added to the group, the prediction failed. There are several reasons— apart from the theoretically uninteresting case of errors in induction and measurement—why this might happen. Possibly, but *just* possibly, there aren't any laws of human behaviour after a certain level of complexity is reached. In this case, the behaviour of groups of a certain complexity marks a level of breakdown not only of the composition law, but also of determinism. No sociologist, no matter how fervently devoted to groups he might be, would be happy about this. In fact, if there were any reason to believe it were true, his devotion to groups would wane rapidly. More realistically, perhaps we need a different composition rule. This new law might be different either because it has a different form or because it contains variables not present in the law for groups of lesser complexity. In our imaginary physical case, for instance, it might be that for systems containing 1000 or more bodies their mutual attraction turned out to be a function of the cube rather than the square of the distances between them. Or for 1000-body systems, to pile absurdity upon absurdity, the presence or absence of life might make a difference to the acceleration. Similarly,

[10] This is in contrast with the connection between psychology and physiology. In this case, the two areas are joined by cross-sectional laws, that is empirical laws connecting a physiological variable with an undefined psychological (behavioural) variable. If these laws and the appropriate physiological composition rules are known, then independent discovery of psychological laws would also be unnecessary. But psychological concepts, unlike group terms, would not be dispensable. The logical pattern of the reduction in each case is radically different.

the composition law about the behaviour of individuals in groups might either change in form or some new variable, like fear of being together with large masses of people, might begin to be operative only after the population reaches a given magnitude. The variable is 'new' not in the sense that instances of it did not exist before, but because it did not affect the behaviour we are interested in predicting, that is, it did not occur in any complete set of relevant variables of a system of lesser complexity. Finally, it might be that even though group behaviour is itself lawful there is no composition rule from which it can be predicted. I shall return to this alternative in a moment. In any case, for whatever reason, the composition rule might break down. If it should, then we have an instance of *explanatory* emergency! Emergence at the level of explanation should be carefully distinguished from what we earlier called descriptive emergence. The latter phrase refers to the occurrence of a property of groups, like the so-called group-mind, which is not definable in terms of the individuals making up the group. Explanatory emergence, however, refers to laws of group behaviour, which *even though their terms are defined as they should be*, are still not derivable from the laws, including whatever composition laws there are, about individual behaviour. This is *in fact* the case at present. The anti-emergentist, in the context of explanation, merely denies that *in principle* laws about groups are not derivable from laws about individuals. The 'emergentist' accordingly, holds that the composition rules necessary for reduction are lacking because on logical grounds there cannot be any such laws, even though group behaviour is itself lawful. This view is held, for instance, by those who maintain that society or history has laws of 'its own' for which the behaviour of individuals is not relevant. If this were the case, then it would make sense to say that there are *sui generis* laws of the social process. But this, of course, only pushes the indeterminism back from groups to individuals. It is, therefore, not a view any scientist can comfortably live with.

Two Meanings of Methodological Individualism
Sometimes the phrase 'methodological individualism' is applied both to the view that there are no undefinable group concepts and to the view that the laws of the group sciences are in principle reducible to those about individuals. The former is a denial of descriptive emergence; the latter denies that there are any logical grounds for belief in explanatory emergence.[11] Both positions are, indeed, very much a part of the general empiricist tradition. Nevertheless, they are not identical, nor are they equally fundamental. The first, as we saw, is required by the

[11] Watkins' misunderstanding (*op. cit.*) of my argument (*op. cit.*) that holism is not entailed by the possibility of an autonomous group science stems from confusing these two positions.

logic of concept formation within the individualistic, empiricist framework. But, as to the second, whether or not there are composition laws is not something that can be *a priori* decided. Descriptive emergence is compatible with and may be used as an argument for the necessity of explanatory emergence. But it is not a good argument. If the alleged emergent properties are lawfully connected with those properties of individuals from which they emerge, as, analogously, psychological properties are lawfully connected with physiological ones, then by means of such cross-sectional laws and the microscopic ones, the macroscopic laws could be derived. In any case, the denial of descriptive emergence does not entail the denial of explanatory emergence. The latter is a matter of fact. And matters of fact cannot be legislated into existence. In other words, the empiricist commitment to *definitional* methodological individualism does not logically imply a commitment to *explanatory* methodological individualism, that is, to reduction. In the context of explanation, methodological individualism is a matter of principle only in that broad sense in which determinism itself is a matter of principle. These issues are often confounded because it is not fully realized that the two alternatives, the successful working of composition rules or their breakdown at some level of complexity, are both 'individualistic', in that broad sense of the term denoting a basic metaphysical assumption. As long as it is granted that groups are composed of individuals, their characteristics, and the relations between these individuals, and of nothing else, then there is no question of violating this basic assumption. The fact is that we do not as yet, and, for all we know, may never have the psychological laws permitting reduction. This does not and cannot in any way militate against that individualism which empiricists are rightly so anxious to preserve. Happily that frame of reference does not depend, at least not logically, upon the state of our knowledge at any particular moment in history.

Whichever alternative turns out to be the case, the optimistic one that reduction of laws is achievable or its contrary pessimistic one, two possibilities still remain for social science. First, whether or not our concepts are defined or, at least, in principle definable, it is still logically possible that a class of group concepts form a complete set of relevant variables of the social process. A process theory is logically possible with any kind of variables as, for instance, non-atomic thermodynamics demonstrates. It is thus logically possible, even if most unlikely, that we could have a complete theory of psychology with only behavioural, non-physiological variables. Similarly, it is logically possible that, irrespective of definitional reduction, we may have perfect knowledge of society in the sense of having a process theory whose laws contain only macroscopic or group variables. The reduction of chemistry to physics is by now a fairly well-accomplished fact. At one time chemistry was at a stage analogous to that of the group sciences. The microscopic structure of the molecules in terms of atoms was known, just as we know the composition of our groups, but the laws of quantum physics by which atoms combine into molecules were not known. Once they were known, however, it turned out that the (chemical) laws by which molecules combine could be derived from them. Yet, organic chemistry appears to be here to stay. In principle, the interactions of the complex molecules can be derived from the laws of physics about the fundamental particles. However, the mathematics of the relevant composition laws is so involved that it is much simpler to study directly the behaviour of these organic complexes. Similarly, even if we had reduction, it might still be practically more feasible to study group behaviour. Conceivably, there might be a set of macroscopic laws permitting the prediction of the 'state' of society (i.e., the values of the group variables) at all times from its state at any given time. This possibility is to be sure most implausible. It is implausible not only because the discovery of such a complete set of relevant variables seems a formidable task, but also because it is rather more than likely that changes in the social process do not depend only upon group or macroscopic units, Marxism to the contrary notwithstanding. People are not like molecules in a gas. Some are different from others and some have more effect upon society than others. It is still a good question whether without Lenin there would have been the October Revolution. If this variance among individuals makes sufficient difference, then the laws have to take the occurrence of a particular kind of individual into account. In this case, a complete set of variables could not all be macroscopic. The unlikelihood of perfect knowledge by macroscopic laws alone is probably a source of the mistaken conviction that reduction of laws is *necessary* for empiricist individualism. But, again, it is merely a matter of fact that this possibility is most unlikely.

But if perfect knowledge with group variables alone is unlikely, there is still another possibility. It may be that approximate laws of all kinds can be stated in these variables. These laws would of course bear some or all of the marks of imperfection. They would be indefinite with respect to time, hedged in by qualification, and, above all, they would be statistical. The remarkable success of statistical knowledge is a measure of how much can be ignored, particularly of the individual variance, and prediction still be possible. If there be, as in principle there probably are, composition rules from which the behaviour of groups may be predicted, these are most likely of such complexity and difficulty that it may well be the better part of wisdom for social scientists to look for whatever imperfect connections may exist among the group variables. These, in turn, may suggest the appropriate composition rules of individual behaviour. But this is not for the philosopher to say.

M.I.C.—11

A. C. DANTO

Methodological Individualism and Methodological Socialism

I have sought to make out a case against substantive philosophy of history by emphasizing certain logical features of what one might call the language of time.* And in the course of this I have tried to explicate our concept of history, suggesting that it is the illicit extension of modes of description which are essentially historical beyond the domain in which they have application which defines the aspiration of substantive philosophy of history. I have sought, then, to draw a borderline which we are tempted to cross but cannot. The analyses of history and of substantive philosophy of history are interdependent, roughly in the manner in which the Transcendental Analytical and the Transcendental Dialectic are in Kant's *Critique of Pure Reason*: for the Dialectic exhibits the unhappy destiny which attends Reason when it seeks to extend those forms of understanding specified in the Analytic beyond the domain where they have application, the domain, namely, of experience. It is in the spirit of critical philosophy that I should wish to have my argument understood.

To this case, however inadequately it may have been stated, I have nothing further to add. But before ending I should like to dismiss another kind of charge, which is sometimes made against substantive philosophy of history, namely that it holds the view that history is not something which men make, but that the moving agents of history are certain superhuman or superorganic entities. I do not wish to say that it is innocent of this charge, but rather that it is no philosophical crime to be guilty of it; and if philosophical historians subscribe to such entities, they may or may not be wrong, but their wrongness will be factual and empirical, and not conceptual and philosophical. To show this, however, requires some detailed conceptual analysis, for the issues here are exceedingly tangled, and the discussion is composed of topics in ontology, meaning, methodology, and language which resemble one another almost too much for us to expect enthusiasts to take the time to sort them out. I shall endeavour to do this now, hoping, in transit, to contribute somewhat further to the correct analysis of historical sentences.

* Danto, A. C. *Analytical Philosophy of History*, London, Cambridge University Press (1965).

312

By *historical sentence* I shall mean: a sentence which states some fact about the past. Historical writings consist chiefly of historical sentences, and are further distinguished by the fact that a considerable number of the historical sentences which compose them employ, as grammatical subjects, proper names (e.g., 'Frederick V') or definite descriptions (e.g., 'The Elector Palatine in 1618') of individual human beings who actually existed. Neither of these linguistic features carries us very far towards an adequate characterization of historical writings. Historical sentences do not uniquely occur in historical writings, and while it is perhaps (logically) inconceivable that there should be an historical writing which contained *no* historical sentences, there is little difficulty in conceiving an historical writing in which *none* of the historical sentences which compose it employs expressions which refer directly to individual human beings who actually existed. Indeed, an historical writing *all* the sentences of which employed such expressions would be far more difficult to imagine.

Individual human beings are not the only individuals directly referred to by the subjects of historical sentences. There are, in addition, what I shall term *social individuals*, individuals which we may provisionally characterize as containing individual human beings amongst their parts. Examples of social individuals might be social classes (the German *bourgeoisie* in 1618), national groups (the Bavarians), religious organizations (the Protestant Church), large-scale events (the Thirty Years War), large-scale social movements (the Counter-Reformation), and so on. Social individuals are not the only kind of individuals, other than individual human beings, which may be referred to by the subjects of historical sentences, so these two kinds of individual-referring historical sentences do not make up the entire class of historical sentences. Nevertheless, it is with just these two kinds of sentence that I shall be concerned here.

It will, I think, be universally admitted that, from the point of view of ready communication, neither kind of sentence could easily be eliminated from the language of the historian. It is difficult to see how, for example, an historian could convey, by means only of sentences which referred directly to individual human beings, the information so neatly and intelligibly communicated by 'the Thirty Years War began in 1618'. Nevertheless, ease of communication and considerations of narrative economy notwithstanding, certain philosophers and historians have expressed a certain mistrust with regard to this latter kind of sentence—a mistrust the source of which lies in mistrust with regard to social individuals as such. These thinkers exhibit a pardonable reluctance to concede that the social world is made up of individual human beings *and* other, super-human individuals which, though they may be said to contain human beings amongst their parts, none the less are not wholly to be identified with these parts, and which enjoy, so to speak, a life of their own. In some sense or other, they appear to be saying that the social world is made up of individual human beings alone, and that there is nothing which both contains individual human beings amongst its parts and is itself an ultimate occupant of the social world. So at first glance what seems to be in issue is a question in ontology. Thus Mr J. W. N. Watkins, a philosopher, writes:

> The ultimate constituents of the social world are individual people who act more or less appropriately in the light of their dispositions and understanding of their situation. Every complex social situation, institution, or event is the result of a particular configuration of individuals, their dispositions, situations, beliefs, and physical resources and environments.[1]

And Professor H.-I. Marrou, an historian who otherwise never wearies of cautioning us that there are more things on earth and in heaven than are dreamed of in our philosophy, writes:

> Ce qui 'a réelment existé', ce n'est ni le fait de civilisation, ni le système ou le supersystème, mais l'être humain dont l'individualité est le seul véritable organisme authentiquement fourni pa l'expérience.[2]

The use of the word 'civilisation' here is almost certainly polemical, to be taken in antagonistic reference to Professor Toynbee's well-known thesis that civilizations do indeed have a life of their own, and that they, moreover, constitute the least units of historical study. But in fact he is rejecting all allegedly superhuman entities in history:

> A lire certains travaux contemporains, on a l'impression que les acteurs de l'histoire ne sont plus *des* hommes, mais des entitiés, la Cité antique, la féodalité, la bourgoisie capitaliste, le proletariat révolutionnaire. Il y a la un excès.[3]

And Watkins impugns in general the view that 'some superhuman agents or factors are supposed to be at work in history'—for example 'the alleged long-term cyclical wave in economic life which is supposed to be self-propelling, uncontrollable and inexplicable in terms of human

---

[1] J. W. N. Watkins, 'Historical Explanation in the Social Sciences', *British Journal for the Philosophy of Science* (1957). Reprinted in P. Gardiner (ed.), *Theories of History* [pp. 167–178]. The passage cited is on pp. 167–178.

[2] H.-I. Marrou, *De la Connaissance Historique* (Paris; Editions du Seuil, 1959), p. 177. Strictly speaking the cited sentence is plainly false: experience furnishes examples of masses of organisms other than human individuals. It indeed furnishes us with examples of organisms which have other organisms as parts of themselves. It is a moot point whether it furnishes examples of organisms which have human individuals as parts of themselves. But surely it is only this point that Marrou is concerned with.

[3] *Ibid.*

activity'—and insists that 'human beings are . . . the sole moving agents in history'.[4]

These writers exhibit in these passages such an essential unanimity of attitude, that it must seem sheer pedantry to distinguish between their positions. Nevertheless, it seems to me that they are in fact maintaining distinct, and possibly even independent views. Professor Marrou's views seem quite unequivocally to be a thesis in ontology. He is insisting that, in the social world, *only* human individuals are real, and superhuman, or social individuals, are not. His criterion for applying '*x* is real' is patently an epistemological one: '*x* is real' if, and only if, we experience *x*. Mr Watkins, by contrast, *may or may not* be defending an ontological thesis. He has said only that human beings are the *ultimate* constituents of the social world, and the context quite clearly implies that he means, by 'ultimate', that human beings are the only *moving agents* in the social world. It does not follow from the fact that human individuals are the sole moving agents in the social world, that they are the only members of the social world, but only that, whatever else may be a member of the social world is not a moving agent. So Watkins, whether in addition he would also subscribe to Marrou's ontological thesis, is actually concerned with a thesis about *explanation*. What he seems to be saying is this: if indeed there are such things as social individuals, their behaviour is to be explained, ultimately, with reference only to the behaviour of individual human beings, and *not* with reference to the behaviour of other social individuals. This is because (he would claim) human beings alone are *causal* agents in history.

There are, as we shall see, further differences it will be useful for us to emphasize. But, because each of their positions bears a similarity to a third possible thesis, namely, that sentences which ostensibly refer to social individuals are 'reducible' to sentences which only refer to individual human beings, it is important to recognize that neither of them is advocating this sort of reductionist programme. The strategy of such philosophical reductionism in current or recent philosophical discussion is this: if we have a set (S) of sentences which employ terms of kind T ostensibly referring to objects of kind O, and another set (s) of sentences employing terms of kind t ostensibly referring to objects of kind o, then, if we can replace every context . . . T . . . in (S) with one or more contexts . . . t . . . in (s), we will only need to admit objects of kind o in our ontology. If such a programme were in fact to succeed, of course it would not *follow* that there are no objects of kind O, but only that we do not require to *suppose* that there are such objects. Neither author is suggesting that sentences ostensibly referring to

---

[4] Watkins, *loc. cit.* p. 168.

social individuals is eliminable in this or *in any other sense* from the language of historians. Indeed, I think, even if Professor Marrou were adamant in rejecting social individuals, he might still feel that sentences of this sort have an indispensable role to play in historical writings. And for him, at least, this role does not consist in expressing some fact about social individuals but perhaps, instead, in expressing, in some fashion or other, facts about individual human beings which perhaps could not as readily be expressed by means of sentences which directly are about individual human beings, if indeed those facts can be expressed by means of those sentences at all.

At this point I deem it advisable to introduce a concrete example in which it seems to me that an historian is expressing some fact about a social individual, however we are finally to analyse the concept of a social individual. In this example, the historian is seeking to explain a change, in which, to be sure, masses of individual human beings were in one manner or other involved, but a change, nevertheless, which they were very likely not aware of. This change took place 'insensibly', and was completed after roughly seventeen years.[5] It is a change described as follows: the loss of 'whatever spiritual meaning the [Thirty Years War] had'. It will prove particularly instructive to note in what way reference to individual human beings is made. Miss Wedgewood describes the background of the change in this way:

> While increasing pre-occupation with natural science had opened up a new philosophy to the educated world, the tragic results of applied religion had discredited the Churches as the directors of the state. It was not that faith had grown less among the masses; even among the educated and the speculative, it maintained a rigid hold; but it had grown more personal, had become essentially a matter between the individual and his creator. . . .
>
> Inevitably, the spiritual force went out of public life, while religion ran to seed amid private conjecture, and priests and pastors, abandoned by the state, fought a losing battle against philosophy and science. While Germany suffered in sterility, the new dawn rose over Europe, irradiating from Italy over France, England, and the North. Descartes and Hobbes were already writing, the discoveries of Galileo, Kepler, and Harvey had taken their places as part of the accepted stock of common knowledge. Everywhere, lip-service to reason replaced the blind impulses of the spirit.
>
> Essentially, it was only lip service. The small group of educated men who appreciated the value of the new learning disseminated little save the shadow of their knowledge. A new emotional urge had to be found to fill the place of spiritual conviction; national feeling welled up to fill the gap.

[5] C. V. Wedgwood, *The Thirty Years War* (Pelican Books, 1957), p. 339.

The absolutist and representative principles were losing the support of religion; they gained that of nationalism. That is the key to the development of the war in the latter period. The terms Protestant and Catholic gradually lose their vigour, the terms German, Frenchman, and Swede assume a gathering menace. The struggle of the Hapsburg dynasty and its opponents ceased to be the conflict of two religions and became the struggle of nations for a balance of power. . . .[6]

Briefly, and with extraordinary sure touches, Miss Wedgewood is here describing and explaining the way in which the Thirty Years War changed from a religious to a political conflict, and when she makes reference to individuals, it is mainly in order to *illustrate* this change, or to provide evidence that a change has in fact taken place. It is, as it were, taking soundings in the flow of history. Here are some examples:

The aging Emperor, the Electors, of Saxony, Brandenberg, and Bavaria, the Swedish Chancellor, Richelieu . . . still held their course. But all around them had grown up a new generation of soldiers and statesmen. War-bred, they carried the mark of their training in a caution, a cynicism, and a contempt for spiritual ideals foreign to their fathers.[7]

And again:

Frederick of Bohemia had lost his crown because he had offended subjects in order to obey his Calvinist chaplain; his son, Prince Rupert, Calvinist in religion and morality, fought in England against Presbyterians and Independents, because his religion was for him, as for most of his generation, nobody's business but his own.[8]

These various individuals are selected for special mention, and certain facts about them singled out and contrasted with one another, not because of any intrinsic interest they may have—for indeed they may have no intrinsic interest—but because of their *historical* significance: they make clear to us that a great change in attitude and behaviour of individuals in roughly the same social positions has taken place. Consider one further example. The battle-cry shouted by soldiers at White Hill was 'Sancta Maria!' The battle-cry shouted, later, at Nordlingen, was 'Viva España'. Those who might have witnessed these two battles would almost certainly not have seen the significance of these shouts. For the significance lies in the contrast between them, a contrast which is significant to an historian who sees in them signs that 'insensibly and rapidly, the Cross gave way to the flag'.

I think it reasonably certain that very few of these changes were *intended* by anyone. Men followed their own purposes, acted in the light of their views of their situations, were not alive to the 'sig-

[6] *Ibid.* pp. 339–340.
[7] *Ibid.*
[8] *Ibid.*

nificance' of what they were doing. Moreover, the changes here described may not have been reproduced within the biography of any *single* individual who lived through the change: to modify slightly an example as old as Leibniz, we may change the colour of a dish of blue powder by the device of adding yellow powder, so that the content of the dish changes from blue to green without any *single* particle having to change colour. Even if certain individuals did in fact change, we still could not, from this alone, deduce the scope of the changes which incontestably took place. Even if we had complete biographies of every individual human being alive during this period, we would still have to make careful comparisons and contrasts to infer that changes of this sort had happened. To put the matter baldly, the change took place, not in individuals, but in *society*.

Now it seems to me that what took place in the period covered by this account is a fairly clear example of what Watkins terms 'organic-like social behaviour', which is to say that

> Members of some social system (that is a collection of people whose activities disturb and influence each other) mutually adjust themselves to the situations created by the others in a way which, without direction from above, conduces to the equilibrium or preservation or development of the system.[9]

Watkins further says that

> Such far-flung organic-like behaviour involving people widely separated in space and largely ignorant of one another, cannot be simply observed. It can only be theoretically reconstructed—by deducing the distant social consequences of the typical responses of a large number of people to certain repetitive situations.

Miss Wedgewood's account is an instance of this for a variety of reasons, but for the present I wish to draw attention to the fact that the social changes she has drawn our attention to are *not*, as such, observable. All that can be observed, indeed—waiving for now questions concerning problems of verifying, through observation, statements about the past—is the behaviour of individual human beings. But this behaviour is nevertheless to be appreciated and understood with reference to a social system in course of modification, and is to be taken as *evidence* for the fact that the system itself is being modified. It would only be through accepting the most thoroughgoing verificationism that we could say that her account was *about* the individuals, statements about whose behaviour provide, perhaps, the only evidence in the nature of the case available for the verification of statements about the changing social system.

[9] Watkins, *loc. cit.* p. 175.

With this in mind, we may now recognize those further differences, earlier alluded to, between the positions of Watkins and Marrou. The fact that we cannot observe social systems as such, but only the behaviour of a set of individuals, must entail, by Marrou's criterion, that social systems as such are not 'real'. Nevertheless, he is prepared to concede that the concept of a social system may have a theoretical use, in the sense that we might require such a concept in order to explain the behaviour of individual human beings. Consistent with this, I suppose, he would insist that electro-magnetic fields are not 'real' either, and that the use of field theories in no way commits us to supposing fields part of the physical world. Fields, like social systems, would be 'abstractions'. Thus:

> Même s'il apparaît a l'examen de toutes données documentaires, que te phénomène historique s'explique par l'un de ces abstraits socio-culturels, l'historien devra toujours se garder d'oublier et de laisser oublier, que ce n'est là qu'un construction de l'esprit, inévitable, sans doute (comme étant le seul moyen de saisir la complexité du réel) et, dans les limites d'emploi, légitime—mais tout de même une abstraction, un produit dérivé, et non pas le réel lui-même, ni, comme on finit toujours par le croire, du surréal![10]

Watkins, by contrast, seems quite prepared to allow that the social world contains, in addition to individual human beings (who may nevertheless be its 'ultimate components'), social systems, the behaviour of which is 'organic-like'. In fact he is concerned precisely with the explanation of just such things as these but, quite oppositely to Professor Marrou, he does not believe—and this is his main contention —that we in any ultimate way require reference to facts about such social systems in order to explain other facts about them. Theories which do make that sort of reference are what he terms 'half way theories', and these are contrasted with 'rock-bottom explanations':

> We shall not have arrived at rock-bottom explanations of such large-scale [social] phenomena until we have deduced an account of them from statements about the dispositions, beliefs, resources, and inter-relations of individuals.[11]

And the plain suggestion here is that Watkins does not believe that, in speaking of such large-scale social phenomena, we are merely speaking of individual human beings and their beliefs, dispositions, resources, and interrelations, for then the distinction between 'half-way' and 'rock-bottom' explanations collapses.

[10] H.-I. Marrou, *op. cit.* p. 177. Cf. pp. 163 ff.
[11] Watkins, *loc. cit.* p. 168.

I shall now begin to concern myself in a critical way with Watkins's position, which he has termed *Methodological Individualism*,[12] for it seems to me that Professor Marrou's views can best be appreciated and assessed in the light of such a discussion.

Let me begin by emphasizing that there are a number of closely related but nevertheless distinguishable thesis which must be carefully kept apart from Methodological Individualism. Here are some things it is *not*.

(1) It is *not* a theory of meaning. It does not hold that every statement about social phenomena is 'really' or 'ultimately' a statement about individual human beings. Nor does it propose to demonstrate that every *predicate*, nominally true of social individuals, may be explicitly defined by means of predicates which range over individual human beings. Hence it is not an *analytical* theory, in accordance with which *sentences* about social individuals are held to be, at least in principle, translatable, without loss of meaning, into sentences wholly about individual human beings. On the other hand, it *does* require that there be *some* kind of relation between these two classes of sentence. For instance, it may very well be that only through verifying, by observation, certain sentences about individuals, shall we ever be able to confirm a sentence about social systems. But this does not mean that sentences about social individuals are really to be understood as about that, the observation of which will confirm them. The Methodological Individualist is not necessarily committed to the Verifiability Criterion of meaning. Indeed, as we shall see, it is important that these two classes of sentences have, and retain, their distinctive sorts of meanings. In general then, it would be irrelevant to demonstrate that sentences about social individuals (or social phenomena however understood) are 'irreducible'.

(2) If it is not an analytical theory, neither is it a constructionist theory. It does not subscribe to Russell's celebrated dictum that inferred entities should always, in the interests of parsimony, be

---

[12] The literature on Methodological Individualism is substantial, but much of it fails to make the distinctions I feel are crucial. For background, see Watkins's earlier paper, 'Ideal Types and Historical Explanation' [pp. 143–165 above]. Criticisms may be found in M. Mandelbaum, 'Societal Facts' [pp. 221–234 above]; L. Goldstein, 'The Inadequacy of the Principle of Methodological Individualism', *Journal of Philosophy* (1956); E. Gellner, 'Holism versus Individualism in History and Sociology', *Proceedings of the Aristotelian Society* (1956) [pp. 248–263 above]. The papers of Mandelbaum (which I shall discuss on p. 325 ff.) and of Gellner are both reprinted in Gardiner, *op. cit.* which also contains a brief note—'Reply to Mr. Watkins'—by Gellner. In addition see the earlier discussions. See F. A. Hayek's two books, *Individualism and the Economic Order* and *The Counter-Revolution of Science*, as well as Karl Popper's *The Open Society and its Enemies* and *The Poverty of Historicism*.

replaced with logical constructions. It does *not* hold that societies are logical constructions out of individuals in the way in which Russell used to say that stars and tables are logical constructions out of sense-data. The Methodological Individualist is not after a *Logische Aufbau der Gemeinsschaftswelt*. Such a programme, like its analytical counterpart, might be philosophically interesting and intellectually challenging and possibly even important, but the viability of Methodological Individualism does not depend upon *its* viability, nor would the shipwreck of such a programme be of more than external interest to the Methodological Individualist. When Watkins speaks of *constructions*, he has in mind the construction of a theory of a scientific, and not a metaphysical sort, and whose purpose is not to eliminate, but to account for social systems. Such a theory indeed has sentences about individual human beings in its *base*, but we must distinguish between the base of a theory and the rest of the theory; quite clearly the concept of a *base* loses all meaning if there is not something else, distinguishable from it, for which it *is* the base: a building cannot be *all* foundation.

(3) Methodological Individualism is not an ontological theory, in accordance with which only human beings are real in the social world. Someone may wish to say that societies, or social individuals, depend for their existence upon individual human beings, and that if there were no individual human beings, there would be no social individuals either. But plainly, if something exists contingently, it still exists. The Methodological Individualist is not motivated by a metaphysical monism, and the controversy between him and his opponents is not analogous to the controversy between those who hold that images *are* simply brain-states, and those who deny they are brain-states. Indeed, he is almost militantly dualist. His position *is* analogous to the epiphenomenalist who, holding that images (and mental events generally) are distinct from brain processes (and physical events generally), still insists that the former are causally connected with the latter in a unilateral way, and can only be *explained* with reference to the latter.

(4) Accordingly, the Methodologist Individualist does not deny in advance that there are, or may be found, general law-like sentences which relate various properties of social systems. Nor does he maintain that such laws, should they be found, would really only be laws describing the behaviour of individual human beings. He might, indeed, as I have already suggested, insist that such laws can be confirmed only through the verification of sentences about human beings. But this would in no way entail that the laws in question are not really laws which describe the gross behaviour of social individuals.

So we see that Methodological Individualism has nothing whatsoever to do with a number of interesting and exciting positions it might·be thought to resemble. Very briefly, it appears to hold (a) that sentences about social individuals are logically independent of sentences about individual human beings, (b) that social individuals are ontologically distinct from individual human beings, (c) that social individuals are causally dependent upon the behaviour of individual human beings and not the other way about, (d) that explanations of the behaviour of social individuals are always to be rejected as ultimate unless these explanations are framed exclusively in terms of the behaviour of individual human beings, and (e) the explanation of the behaviour of individual human beings must never be in terms of the behaviour of social individuals; (a) is a thesis about meaning, (b) and (c) are theses about the world, and (d) and (e) are theses about the ideal form of a social science.

Now the natural methodological position which is opposed to Methodological Individualism I shall term *Methodological Socialism*. And once again, there may be positions, analogous to (1)–(4), which resemble but are nevertheless distinct from Methodological Socialism. Thus someone might hold that sentences about individual human beings can be translated into sentences about social individuals, or that social individuals are real and that human beings are not, and so on; Hegel seems to have subscribed to such views as these. But to avoid any pointless diversions from our main concern, I shall characterize Methodological Socialism as follows: simply replace every occurrence of 'individual human beings' in the theses (a) through (e) in the preceding paragraph, with the expression 'social individuals', and every occurrence of 'social individuals' with 'individual human beings'. The resulting sentences (a)–(e) will now characterize Methodological Socialism. Notice that (a) and (b) are left unaffected by the substitutions. The controversy between the two positions turns, accordingly, on (c), (d), and (e), and in whatever sense the Individualist will say that individual human beings are *ultimate* in the social world, the Socialist will say that *social individuals* are ultimate in the social world.

Not surprisingly, the most conspicuous example of a theory which satisfies this specification of Methodological Socialism is Marxism, and not surprisingly, Marxism has been one of the main targets of the Methodological Individualists, e.g. Watkins and Popper. One need but think of how subscribers to either of our methodological positions would *explain* this fact, in order to produce specific explanations which very nicely fit the characterizations I have given of these two positions. Now that in Marxism which primarily illustrates Methodological Socialism is the part of Marx's theory known as *historical materialism*. Marx believed (and believed himself to have shown) that there is a one-way interaction between social processes and at least some psychological processes, so that what we think, and how we act, are to be explained by reference to our relations *vis-à-vis* the prevailing system of production; and whatever it is that causes changes in the system of production, it is *not* something which is brought about by individual human action. Crudely put, we explain some facts about systems of production with reference to other facts about systems of production; and we explain some facts about individual human beings with reference to some facts about systems of production; but we never explain any facts about systems of production with reference to any facts about individual human behaviour; and finally, we never explain any facts about individual human behaviour with reference to other facts about individual human behaviour.

Letting S stand for some fact about a social individual, and P some fact about individual human psychology, we may represent this position schematically as follows:

$$P_1 \qquad P_2 \qquad P_3$$

(A)

$$S_1 \longrightarrow S_2 \longrightarrow S_3 \longrightarrow$$

where the arrows indicate the directions of causality, and where the *absence* of an arrow between any two points signifies the absence of a causal tie.

A theory which, on the other hand, satisfies the conditions of Methodological Individualism, would look schematically as follows (using just the same conventions as above):

$$P_1 \longrightarrow P_2 \longrightarrow P_3 \longrightarrow$$

(B)

$$S_1 \qquad S_2 \qquad S_3$$

Meanwhile, Methodological Socialism will tolerate provisional, or 'half-way' theories of this form:

$$P_1 \ldots \ldots \quad P_2 \ldots \ldots \quad P_3 \ldots \ldots$$ (C)

where the broken lines indicate only apparently causal ligatures. And *mutandis mutandum*, Methodological Individualism will allow provisional or halfway theories of this form:

$$S_1 \ldots \ldots \quad S_2 \ldots \ldots \quad S_3 \ldots \ldots$$ (D)

It is important to stress that Marxism is only an *example* of a theory which could satisfy Methodological Socialism, and that (B) is only an *example* of a theory which would satisfy Methodological Individualism. So the latter is not in fact committed in any sense whatsoever to the *independent* thesis that we can explain facts about social individuals with reference to *psychological* facts about individual human beings. That is to say, Psychologism is only a particular example of a theory which satisfies the criteria of Methodological Individualism.[13] But surely no one, not even the most militant Individualist, would say that for this reason alone it is *correct*. At best he would say that such a theory is *acceptable*.

The issue now before us is whether there is any good reason for choosing between Methodological Individualism and Methodological Socialism. I shall examine at this point an extremely interesting discussion, by Professor Maurice Mandelbaum,[14] which, if I understand it properly, is intended to furnish just such good reasons for *rejecting* Methodological Individualism, at least as a general methodological programme. Professor Mandelbaum has argued for the existence and autonomy of what he terms *societal facts* which, he maintains, are 'as ultimate as psychological facts' and 'cannot be reduced without remainder to concepts which refer to the thoughts and actions of specific individuals'.[15] Societal facts 'are facts concerning the forms of organization present in society'.[16] About the relations between psychological and societal facts, Mandelbaum says a number of things. I shall set down those that strike me as his four main theses.

(i) Sentences about societal facts cannot be translated into sentences about psychological facts without leaving a societal remainder.[17]

(ii) Sentences about societal facts must be ('it is . . . necessary to . . .') partially translated into sentences about individual facts, for 'unless we do so we have no means of verifying any statements we may make concerning societal facts'.[18]

(iii) Societal facts *may* depend for their existence 'upon the existence of human beings who possess certain capacities for thought and for action'.

---

[13] Hence Professor Popper is perfectly justified when, in ch. 14 of *The Open Society and its Enemies*, he condemns Psychologism and recommends Methodological Individualism, and Mr Gellner is in logical error when he seeks to rebut Methodological Individualism through arguing against Psychologism, feeling that the two cannot be distinguished. See 'Holism versus Individualism in History and the Social Sciences' [p. 261 above] and n. 9.

[14] Page references will be to this volume.

[15] *Ibid.* p. 223. I do not believe that the adjective 'specific' is to be taken as a rejection of reference to anonymous individuals.

[16] *Ibid.* p. 229.

[17] *Ibid.* p. 229.

[18] *Ibid.*

But this does not entail that the former set of facts is *identical* with the set of facts upon whose existence it is contingent.[19]

(iv) The existence of societal facts does not entail that there *are* no individual facts, or that individuals are not 'real'. Rather, there are these two distinct sets of facts which may be said 'to interact'. Thus: 'There are societal facts which exercise external constraints over individuals, no less than there are facts concerning individual volition which often come into conflict with these restraints.'[20]

Now it should be plain that very little of this is incompatible with Methodological Individualism as I have characterized it, but at best it is incompatible with some of the things which might be thought to *resemble* Methodological Individualism. The sole point of conflict comes in thesis (iv) where, since quite clearly *two* way interactionism is intended, there is an incompatability with (c), and with the thesis which animates Mandelbaum's argument, namely:

(v) In understanding or explaining an individual's actions, we must often refer to societal facts, i.e., facts concerning the organization of the society in which he lives.[21]

Let us now take a close look at Mandelbaum's arguments for (v). It consists of two parts, an informal (or Wittgensteinian) part, and a formal (non-Wittgensteinian) part. The informal part is this: one could not teach someone, who is strange to our culture, what a member of our culture is doing when he presents a withdrawal-slip to a bank-clerk, without, in process of doing so, teaching him something about the way in which withdrawal-slips function in that system of operations which make up our banking system. But since reference to a banking system is *ipso facto* reference to a societal fact, we cannot explain to someone, who is strange to our culture, what such a man is doing, without bringing into our explanation reference to a societal fact. Now notice how the word *explain* is being used here. It is being used in *this sense*: explaining *to* someone what that person does not understand. It is the sense in which a teacher explains a lesson, or the meaning of a word. In Mandelbaum's example, the teacher is making explicit what members of our own culture take for granted, and apply, perhaps, in a categorical kind of way when they are engaged in banking operations.

[19] *Ibid.* p. 231.
[20] *Ibid.* p. 234. A philosophical puritan would strenuously object to the notion that facts are able to interact, or that facts can possibly come into conflict. *Things* can interact, things and propositions can come into conflict. But this relaxed use of 'fact' does not intrinsically damage Mandelbaum's argument, and can readily be reconstructed.
[21] *Ibid.* p. 228.

The *formal* part of the argument is essentially the translatability thesis (i). What Mandelbaum says here is this. Suppose we have a language L_s in which only terms designating societal facts appear, e.g., 'institution', 'mores', 'ideologies', 'status', 'class'; and suppose there is another language L_i which contains terms only for describing the thoughts, actions, and capabilities of individual human beings. Now Mandelbaum insists that we cannot translate sentences from L_s to L_i 'without remainder'. In fact, Mandelbaum is not quite sure of this point. He even suggests that it may be theoretically possible to effect this translation after all, only it would be immensely difficult in practice, and of no scientific interest.[22] But the point, he admits, is not really a matter of how societal concepts are to be analysed, but how individual actions are to be *explained*, so this brings us back to the informal part of the argument.

The two-language thesis I regard as a confusion. It merits a few words on that account, despite Mandelbaum's concession that, since no matter of principle may be involved, but only a matter of practice, no philosophical importance attaches to it. The fact is, that if we could not make the translation, this would be more damaging to his position than if we could. For we use L_s to talk about societal facts, and L_i to talk about individuals, and what he wants is a way of talking about individuals which makes reference to societal facts. So what he requires, I think, is this. We have some terms which refer to individual human thought and action which presuppose something about societal facts, and some terms which refer to individual human thought and action which do *not* involve that sort of presupposition. I do not know if there is in fact the latter sort of term, but let us suppose there is. Now any term, the correct application of which to an individual human being presupposes some fact about the organization of society, I shall call an S-predicate, and any term the correct application of which to an individual does *not* involve such a presupposition, I shall call an I-predicate. A sentence which employs an S-predicate will be called an S-sentence. Any sentence which uses I-predicates *alone* (i.e. as non-logical terms) I shall call an I-sentence. Thus:

(s-1)   The bank-teller certifies the withdrawal-slip,
(s-2)   The man makes marks on the piece of paper.

are respectively instances of an S- and an I-sentence. But

(s-3)   The man certifies the withdrawal-slip

---

[22] *Ibid.* p. 228. Should the 'theoretical possibility', though 'practical impossibility', of such a translation be demonstrated this would 'be significant from the point of view of a general ontology, but would not affect my argument regarding the autonomy of the societal sciences'.

is also an *S*-sentence, since it does not use an *I*-predicate *alone*, but also uses an *S*-predicate.

We may use all three of these sentences to describe one and the same event. We may further say that (s-1) and (s-3) do, but that (s-2) does *not*, presuppose some fact about the organization of our society. A Trobriand Islander could be taught to understand (s-2) without being taught, in the process, any such facts. We may indeed say that *I*-predicates are trans-cultural. Any term, the meaning of which can be taught without bringing in some fact about the organizational peculiarity of a given society, naturally belongs to the *I*-vocabulary. We may now reconstruct Mandelbaum's thesis as follows: an *S*-sentence cannot be translated without remainder into an *I*-sentence or a set of *I*-sentences. The question now is how 'without remainder' is to be interpreted. I shall interpret it in a way which will, I hope, not merely be congenial to Mandelbaum, but which will demonstrate my revised version of his thesis.

Consider the following lists of terms, the ones in the right-hand column being *I*-terms which correspond to the *S*-terms in the left-hand column. The terms in either column refer to an individual human being, an action, and a material object respectively:

bank-teller	man
certifies	makes marks on
withdrawal-slip	piece of paper

Between the correspondent terms in either column, there are no entailment relations. We cannot deduce that someone is a man from only the information that someone is a bank-teller, nor vice versa. Not every bank-teller is a man nor every man a bank-teller; not every piece of paper is a withdrawal-slip, and even if every withdrawal-slip were *per accidens* a piece of paper, no logical difficulty would face a bank which resolved to introduce plastic withdrawal-slips; and finally, one may certify a withdrawal-slip without making marks on anything (the bank-teller could just say 'O.K.'), and it is plainly true that not every instance of making marks on something is a case of certifying something (not even when the marks are made on a withdrawal slip: the teller might write 'No good.') Hence it is quite feasible that if '. . . man . . .' is offered as a translation of '. . . bank-teller . . .', the former could be false, while the latter is true; and since the weakest condition we can place upon translations is that they be *equivalent*, the former would not be a translation of the latter.

But now there *may* be societies in which such entailments hold. Thus, it may have been the case in a certain period in English history, that only males could be bank-tellers. But this would be only in virtue of some organizational feature, hence societal fact, having to do with a temporary peculiarity of British society. So the translation could go through only through presupposing *this* sentence: 'All bank-tellers in this society are male.' And *this* would be an S-sentence.

By 'without remainder' I shall therefore mean: you cannot translate an S-sentence into an I-sentence without presupposing another S-sentence. This is generally true. Hence anyone who proposed to *eliminate*, by translation, S-predicates in favour of I-predicates, could only do so on the basis of allowing exactly the sort of sentences he proposed to eliminate. Hence any such programme is inherently self-defeating, and the programme is demonstrably impossible.

What, however, are we more precisely to understand by these societal facts, implicit reference to which is presupposed in any such translation or, for that matter, in instructing cultural outsiders? I suggest that they are rules, norms, and conventions, as, 'Only males can be bank-tellers.' Indeed, it seems to me that this is the most natural way in which we may interpret Mandelbaum's thesis (iv), for we naturally speak of people being constrained to act in accordance with this rule or that, and of people chafing under these rules and wishing to have them changed. Thus a woman whose great ambition in life is to become a bank-teller in a major bank might find herself frustrated by such a rule, and this might, with some latitude, be regarded as an instance of the interaction between an individual and a social fact.

But understood in this way, it is hard to see how either (iv) or (v) is any longer incompatible with Methodological Individualism. The Methodological Individualist is clearly not denying that there are rules, that people act in conformity with them, change them, are frustrated by them, and so on. As for (v) it has turned out to be very little more than a thesis about *meaning*, and the Individualist may very well agree with Mandelbaum that, when called upon to explain a given piece of behaviour to a stranger, in exactly the sense of 'explain' which applies in such contexts, we may have to tell him some of the rules, norms, and conventions. It may further be agreed that, in the categorial sense mentioned earlier, we understand actions, under *certain* descriptions of them, with reference to some rules, norms, and conventions. But this is *not* the sense of 'explain' which interests the Methodological Individualist. Rules, he may go on to point out, are broken all the time, and when a rule is broken, it is not by that fact alone to be considered *abrogated*. Only rules which *hold* can be broken. But he will add that his interest lies in *laws*, in the precise sense in which we speak of scientific laws. When such a law is broken, this demonstrates that the 'law' does not hold, and that is the end of the matter. The question for him is not whether there are rules in the former sense, nor whether we understand actions with reference to them. The question, rather, is whether there are *laws* covering the behaviour of societies, whether these laws are ultimate, and whether, in the social sciences, we are to be able to explain the workings of societies simply by reference to the behaviour of individual human beings. Even when tightened up, therefore, Mandelbaum's theses are not merely compatible with Methodological Individualism, but they are utterly irrelevant to questions concerning the latter's status. The fact that they could have been so much as considered to be relevant is due, in the end, to an equivocation on the word 'explain'.

The natural wish of the Methodological Individualist is to demonstrate the *logical impossibility* of Methodological Socialism—a wish, whose fulfilment would very nearly confer, upon his own position, the accolade of logical necessity. Watkins has attempted to demonstrate the logical impossibility of historical materialism, and while it is true that the refutation of historical materialism would no more demolish Methodological Socialism than a refutation of Psychologism would demolish Methodological Individualism—since these are only *instances* of the main positions—the fact is that Watkins's argument could easily bear transfer to the more general position. The demonstration presupposes four distinct theses:

(α) There are predicates which range over social individuals.
(β) There are predicates which range over individuals.
(γ) It is a necessary condition for E to be an adequate explanation of a phenomenon e, that a sentence describing e be exhibited as a deductive consequence of premises.
(δ) There can be no non-logical term in the conclusion of a deductive argument which does not appear in that argument's premises.

Now, if there is to be an explanation E of some piece of individual behaviour e, the explanandum, i.e., the sentence which is used to formulate e, must employ predicates which range over individual human beings. Let S be such a sentence. The explanation will minimally require that S be exhibited as a deductive consequence $(γ)$ of premises, and amongst these premises must appear at least one sentence which contains at least one predicate which ranges over individual human beings $(δ)$. Accordingly, from premises containing sentences which employ *only* predicates ranging over social individuals, S cannot be deduced, and hence e cannot be explained. As Watkins puts it,

> No description, however complete, of the productive apparatus of society, or of any other non-psychological factors, will enable you to deduce a single psychological conclusion from it, because psychological

statements logically cannot be deduced from wholly non-psychological statements.[23]

And he adds:

> That an explanation which begins by imputing some social phenomenon to human factors cannot go on to explain those factors in terms of some inhuman determinant of them is a necessary truth.[24]

I do not in fact think it is a necessary truth, though I do agree that it is a necessary consequence of the theses (a)–(δ), but the chief difficulty with this, for the Methodological Individualist, is that an *exactly analogous argument will show that Methodological Individualism fails.* This argument is easily constructed by substituting, in the above proof, 'predicates which range over social individuals' for 'predicates which range over individual human beings', and vice versa. Thus the argument boomerangs. If it is cogent, and entails the impossibility of Methodological Socialism, it also entails the impossibility of Methodological Individualism. The wisest course at this point appears to be logical disarmament and peaceful philosophical co-existence.

On the other hand, the conflict between our methodologies, if we are now to assume that each of them is possible, can be pitched at another point. Let us accept the general correction of the four theses (a)–(δ), but consider in more detail precisely what is required if we are both to accept them and regard each of our methodologies as possible. It seems to me that the following adjustment must be made: an explanation, acceptable to Methodological Individualism, of the behaviour of some social individual, must employ, amongst its premisses, at least *one* sentence which employs at least one predicate ranging over social individuals. Similarly for Methodological Socialism. It must allow, amongst the premisses of *its* explanations, at least *one* sentence which employs at least *one* predicate which ranges over individual human beings. Not merely can this condition be met, but in meeting it, we will have something which seems to me a far more plausible way of representing either methodology than any we have so far discussed. The condition could be met if, amongst the premisses of the explanations, we had at least one law-like sentence of the following forms:

$$(L\text{-}1) \quad (x)\,(y)\,(P_i x \supset P_s y)$$
$$(L\text{-}2) \quad (y)\,(x)\,(P_s y \supset P_i x),$$

where P_i is a predicate which ranges over individual human beings, and where P_s is a predicate which ranges over social individuals, and where

---

[23] Watkins, 'Historical Explanation in the Social Sciences', pp. 172–173.
[24] *Ibid.*

the antecedent is understood as describing a set of initial conditions for the state of affairs described by the consequent. Now any explanation, which included a law-like sentence of the form $(L$-$1)$ amongst its premises, would to that extent satisfy Methodological Individualism, for certain facts about the behaviour of individual human beings would then be initial conditions for certain facts pertaining for social individuals, and, for exactly similar considerations, an explanation containing, amongst its premises, a law-like sentence of the form $(L$-$2)$ would to that extent satisfy Methodological Socialism. Historical Materialism, incidentally, is precisely the claim that there are known laws of the form $(L$-$2)$, in which certain facts about the prevailing productive systems are initial conditions for certain psychological facts pertaining for individual human beings.

Now we can give a more general interpretation of these law-like sentences. We can simply lay down the rule that the predicates in the antecedent range over a *different kind* of phenomena than the predicates in the consequent. Such law-like sentences then would be understood to describe causal connections between phenomena of different kinds; for example, that causal connections hold between certain brain-states of an individual, and certain psychological states of that same individual—assuming that 'brain-states' and 'psychological states' are instances of different kinds of phenomena. It is through the establishment of law-like sentences of this sort that we speak of *reduction* in a scientific sense. And it is important to stress that we can *only* speak of reduction, distinct from ordinary causal explanation, when we are dealing with essentially different kinds of phenomena. *Reduction* in this sense will mean: explaining one kind of phenomena with reference to phenomena of a different kind. This is *causal* reduction, of course, and must be distinguished from philosophical reduction, i.e., where a given set of terms is held to be translatable into another, and favoured set of terms. I have stressed that Methodological Individualism is *not* a thesis about philosophical reductionism, and is not concerned to demonstrate that the *meaning* of predicates which range over social individuals is to be rendered by means of predicates which range over individual human beings. But I am now saying that it is a thesis about *scientific* reduction; indeed it could not well subscribe to both kinds of reductionist programmes, for scientific reduction clearly presupposes that we are dealing with distinct kinds of phenomena: otherwise we could effect any reduction we chose by the simple device of making definitions. I am further suggesting that Methodological Socialism is also a thesis about scientific reduction, and if this construction of the matter is correct, Methodological Individualism is the claim that explanations employing laws of the form $(L$-$1)$ are to be alone accepted as ultimate, or 'rock-bottom' explanations in the social sciences, and that laws of the form (*L*-2), and all so-called explanations which employ them, are to be rejected. Exactly the reverse of this will then be the claim of Methodological Socialism.

Having put the conflict in this form, we may once again ask whether any good reason may be found for choosing between Methodological Individualism and Methodological Socialism, and I shall say in advance that I am quite unable to find one. Nevertheless, a few words more might profitably be devoted to analysing the conflict in the form it has taken, and so to suggesting why it is hard to find good reasons for deciding it one way or another.

The concept of reduction in science has been analysed in considerable detail by Ernest Nagel, and in what follows I shall assume the essential correctness of his analysis,[25] and shall refer the reader to his work for arguments I shall not seek to summarize here. He is, of course, not responsible for the following remarks.

Suppose we were to speak of macro- and of micro-properties of societies. As a model, one might think of individual human beings as standing to societies in something like the relation in which molecules stand to gases. This might ultimately prove a misleading analogy, but for the moment it will be convenient to employ it to raise some problems. Now, in the case of gases, we speak of reduction in the following sense: some relationships and proportions between some macro-properties of gases are explained with reference to some relationships and proportions between molecules, for example variations in the temperature of a gas are explained with reference to variations in the mean kinetic energy of molecules in random motion, and hence with reference to the mechanical behaviour of aggregates of molecules. I suppose the Methodological Individualist, so far as he would accept this analogy, would speak of reduction in an exactly similar sense: relations between properties of societies, considered macroscopically, arc to be explained with reference to relations between individual human beings, i.e., to societies considered 'microscopically'.

Now before the reduction of thermodynamics to mechanics was achieved, in the nineteenth century, scientists had reasonably clear criteria for applying the terms of the former theory to gases; reasonably clear laboratory procedures for measuring variations in the properties denoted by these terms, and hence reasonably clear ways of confirming, or disconfirming, law-like sentences intended correctly to describe relationships of co-variation amongst these properties. All of this was

[25] See in particular ch. 11 of his *The Structure of Science: Problems in the Logic of Scientific Explanation* (New York, Harcourt, Brace & World, 1961).

retained after the reduction was effected. All the known laws of thermodynamics were preserved. What had been achieved (in unspeakably rough terms) was this: the behaviour of gases, as described by thermodynamics, had been explained with reference to the behaviour of molecules, as described by mechanics, and so one might, if one wished, speak of mechanics as the more 'ultimate' of the two theories, and of molecules as 'the ultimate constituents' of gases. In general, we could speak as follows: if T-1 is a theory which explains and predicts the behaviour of phenomena, P-1, and T-2 is a theory which explains and predicts the behaviour of phenomena P-2, then, if T-2 is reduced to T-1, in the sense that we can now also explain and predict the behaviour of P-2 with reference to P-1, T-1 is a more ultimate theory than T-2. Or, to revert to Watkins's language, T-2 may be considered a half-way theory for P-2, and T-1 a 'rock-bottom' theory for P-2. This does not, of course, mean that either P-2's are not 'real' or that sentences about P-2's are 'really about' P-1's.

Now let us suppose there were a theory of society comparable to thermodynamics, i.e., a theory which is concerned with societies in a macroscopic way. Imagine that such terms as 'social density' and 'cultural-economic elasticity' were among the terms of this theory, and that there were well-confirmed laws like 'Social density varies inversely as the cube of cultural economic elasticity'. *Should there be* such a theory, the Methodological Individualist would say: one can ultimately explain the variations in these properties, one can ultimately account for co-variations between them, by means of a theory concerned with the behaviour of individual human beings. To this theory we shall be able ultimately to reduce the macro-theory of society. But, of course, for us to speak of reductions in the scientific sense, it is first required that we have two theories. Of course, one *might* interpret Methodological Individualism as a negative injunction *against* seeking macro-theories of society. If so, it becomes extremely difficult to see what could now be meant by 'reduction' or by 'individuals being ultimate'. Moreover, by the Methodological Individualist's own admission, there are properties of societies which are different altogether from the properties of individuals. Are these properties to be left unaccounted for? Surely the whole point of Methodological Individualism is that all relations and proportions between such properties are to be explained, ultimately, by reference to the behaviour of individual human beings. So the Methodological Individualist would find it self-defeating to adhere to such a negative injunction. When Watkins says, of Methodological Individualism, that it is a regulative principle, part of whose purpose is to discourage research in certain directions, he places himself in the ironic position of making the viability of his methodological programme dependent upon the success of exactly the sort of research it is calculated to discourage, and we can complete this uncanny dialectic by making exactly similar points about the Methodological Socialist.

But let us suppose that the social sciences advance, and that one day a reduction is achieved which is exactly of the sort to bring joy to the Methodological Socialist's heart! The behaviour of *individual human beings* really is explained with reference to large-scale variations in the macro-properties of societies! The result would be in many ways the reverse of the example of gases. Not merely would the direction of explanation—*von oben bis unten*—be different, but the operational problems would be different as well. For while the macro-properties of gases lie within the realm of observables, the micro-properties do not. Conversely, the behaviour of human individuals lies within the realm of observables, while it has long since been agreed that we do not observe the workings of societies as such. So it is with this difference that I shall now concern myself.

It is a commonplace consideration, I should think, that when a casual theory is advanced in the sciences, asserting, say, that changes in a dependent variable v-1 are explained and predictable by reference to changes in an independent variable v-2, it is necessary that we have some independent means of measuring variations in these two variables. The Boyle-Charles law is thus confirmable by observations on pressure-gauges and thermometers. Yet suppose the *sole* way in which we could assign a value to the mean kinetic energy of unobservable molecules was by measuring the temperature of an observable body of gas. One might begin to wonder about the status of a law which held that variations in temperature were explained and predictable by reference to variation in the mean kinetic energy of gas molecules. Imagine someone were to assert that the motion of an eel through water is due to the simultaneous motion of millions of sub-microscopic limbs connected to the eel's side, like an immense galley. As the rotational frequency of the unobservable oars increases, the eel moves faster in proportion, but unhappily, the only way in which we can assign a value to the 'mean rotational frequency' of the 'ultimate constituents' of the eel would be by measuring the rate at which the eel moves through the water. Scientists might decently reject the entire account as a fairy-tale, but in fact the reduction of thermodynamics to mechanics did not consist in asserting a simple connection of co-variation between the micro- and macro-properties of gases. The relation was far more complex, and mechanics itself had a long and distinguished history before it was modified and extended to account for thermal phenomena. The fact is that there are various ways in which we can assign values to the mean kinetic energy of molecules in random motion, but, of course, never by directly applying yardsticks to molecules. These remain beyond observation, and our relations to them are indirect, and via elaborate pieces of laboratory and mathematical apparatus. Nevertheless, it remains possible to raise doubts about molecules. A radical empiricist retains the option of trying to eliminate reference to them in favour of a reconstructed theory which makes use only of observational predicates. Or one may regard them, as Professor Marrou regards those '*abstraits socio-culturels*', as concepts only, though of an unquestioned use for the organization of experience. But these options have to do with issues in ontology and in meaning, and it will be common ground that the theory, meanwhile, has an uncontested explanatory and predictive power.

Now precisely such options would remain with the sort of reductive theory I am supposing. The radical empiricist and the instrumentalist alike can specify interpretations of the laws and language of this theory of an exactly analogous sort to those which they would specify in the kinetic theory of heat. In point of unobservability, there would be little for them to choose between molecules and organic social systems. Their positions, in either case, are quite independent indeed from that of the Methodological Individualist, whose claim, only, is that such a theory is not 'ultimate', even if, *pro tempore* it might be supposed to have genuine predictive and explanatory power. His objection certainly cannot be based on ontological grounds, nor upon the sort of reservations concerning meaningfulness which animates the radical empiricist. But what is it exactly that his objections *are* based on? What exactly would be wrong with such a theory? It is this I find very hard to determine. I *think* I know what he *fears* such a theory would entail. I shall turn to this in a moment. But I should like, before doing so, to point out how very little philosophical interest remains in this controversy. The philosophical interest it might *appear* to have derives from the other, interesting, issues which resemble it. Once isolated from these, it quickly degenerates into a quite unphilosophical preoccupation with science-fiction. But it is a *dangerous* preoccupation, for it might become a self-fulfilling thesis. Social scientists, persuaded in advance that a certain sort of theory is suspect, might abandon the quest for such theories. And this might, in the end, have consequences of exactly the sort feared by the Methodological Individualist.

What the Individualist fears, I submit, is this. He feels that theories of the sort he wishes to reject would entail that we do not hold our destinies in our own hands, that we are, as it were, dragged along by the development of the social individuals we are part of, and which have a life of their own.[26] Now even if this were entailed by such theories, it would

[26] 'What I regard as the real issue is something like this: social scientists can be roughly and crudely divided into two main groups: those who regard social processes as proceeding, so to speak, under their own steam, according to their

be wholly contrary to the spirit of Philosophy to refuse to look for such theories. We may sympathize with, but scarcely approve of the attitude which, according to legend, led Pythagorians to do away with the man who discovered that there is no rational number, the square of which is equal to 2. On the other hand, it seems to me that the theories in issue entail no such thing, and an important step towards seizing our destinies in our own hands might be taken with the discovery of exactly these sorts of theories. It does not follow, from the fact that we success-fully explain the gross, thermal behaviour of gases with reference to the mechanical behaviour of molecules, that we cannot control the mech-anical behaviour of molecules. By applying gross heating and cooling apparatuses to bodies of gas, we may modify the value of the mean kinetic energy of the molecules contained in it, but, by symmetrical analogy, should we ever be able to explain the behaviour of individual human beings with reference to the behaviour of large-scale processes in *social* individuals, nothing would prevent us from similarly *controlling* those large-scale processes by operating at the 'micro-level', i.e., upon individual human beings. Science is not noted for *diminishing* our control over things.

Nevertheless, even were we to assume the correctness of method-ological individualism in assuming that social processes are but the complicated outcome of individual actions, the extent to which we do have control over our own destinies is in some measure limited. For usually, I have argued, the outcomes of our actions is seldom intended by us, and actors, unless they survive, and know restrospectively, are blind to the significance of their actions because they are blind to the future. We see this nowhere more clearly than in the sort of historical account at the beginning of this chapter. The changes Miss Wedgewood described were 'insensible' and few were aware they were taking place. This, not because a more delicate instrument could have detected them, for no such instrument could be built: the changes could not have been detected at the time, for it is only in the light of future events that they could so much as have been described. To have been able to control or modify these changes would accordingly have required that men see their own actions in a perspective unfortunately not available to them, the perspective, namely, of historians future to their actions. Not knowing how our actions will be seen from the vantage point of history, we to that degree lack control over the present. If there is such a thing as inevitability in history, it is not so much due to social processes moving forward under their own steam and in accordance with their own

own nature and laws, and dragging the people involved along with them; and those who regard social processes as the complicated outcome of the behaviour of human beings.' J. W. N. Watkins, personal letter, dated 11 January 1962.

natures, as it is to the fact that by the time it is clear what we have done, it is too late to do anything about it. 'The owl of Minerva takes flight only with the falling of the dusk.' Philosophies of history attempt to capture the future without realizing that if we knew the future, we could control the present, and so falsify statements about the future, and so such discoveries would be useless. We capture the future only when it is too late to do anything about the relevant present, for *it* is then past and beyond our control. We can but find out what its significance was, and this is the work of historians: history is made by them.

Bibliography

Abel, Theodore F., 'The Operation Called Verstehen', *American Journal of Sociology*, 54, 1948, 211–218; reprinted in Herbert Feigl and May Brodbeck, eds., *Readings in the Philosophy of Science*, New York, Appleton-Century-Crofts, 1953, 677–687.

Acton, H. B., *The Illusion of the Epoch: Marxism-Leninism as a Philosophical Creed*, London, Cohen and West, 1955.

Aron, Raymond, *German Sociology*, Translated by M. and T. Bottomore, Glencoe, Ill., Free Press, 1957.

Bash, Harry H., 'Determinism and Avoidability in Sociohistorical Analysis', *Ethics*, 74, 1964, 186–199.

Barbu, Zevedei, *Problems of Historical Psychology*, New York, Grove, 1961.

Bradley, F. H., *The Presuppositions of Critical History*, ed. with an introduction by L. Rubinoff, Toronto, J. N. Dent, 1968; Chicago, Quadrangle Books, 1968.

Beattie, J. H. M., 'Understanding and Explanation in Social Anthropology', *British Journal of Sociology*, 10, 1959, 45–60.

Beck, R. N. and Lee, D. H., 'The Meaning of "Historicism" ', *American Historical Review*, 59, 1954, 568–577.

Beck, Lewis W., 'The "Natural Science Ideal" in the Social Sciences', *Scientific Monthly*, LXVIII, 1949, pp. 386–394.

Becker, Howard, 'Constructive Typology in the Social Sciences', in H. E. Barnes *et al.*, eds., *Contemporary Social Theory*, New York, Appleton Century Crofts, 1940, 17–46.

Bendix R., 'Max Weber's Interpretation of Conduct and History', *American Journal of Sociology*, 51, 1946, 518–526.

Bendix, R., *Social Science and the Distrust of Reason*, Berkeley, University of California Press, 1951.

Bennett, Jonathan, *Rationality*, London, Routledge and Kegan Paul; New York, Humanities Press, 1964.

Bergmann, Gustav, *Philosophy of Science*, Madison, University of Wisconsin Press, 1957; Chapter 3, 'Configurations and Reduction'.

Bergmann, Gustav, 'Holism, Historicism and Emergence', *Philosophy of Science*, 11, 1944, 209–221.

Bergstrasser, Arnold, 'Wilhelm Dilthey and Max Weber: An Historical Approach to Historical Synthesis', *Ethics*, 57, 1947, 92–110.

Berlin, Isaiah, *The Hedgehog and the Fox*, New York: Simon and Schuster, 1953.

Berlin, Isaiah, *Historical Inevitability*, New York, Oxford University Press, 1954.

Berlin, Isaiah, 'History and Theory: The Concept of Scientific History', *History and Theory*, 1, 1960, 1–31.

Bisbee, Eleanor, 'Objectivity in the Social Sciences', *Philosophy of Science*, 4, 1937, 371–382.

Blake, Christopher, 'Can History Be Objective?', *Mind*, 64, 1955, 61–78.

Bock, Kenneth E., *The Acceptance of Histories: Toward a Perspective for Social Science*, Berkeley, University of California Press, 1956.

Braybrooke, David, ed., *Philosophical Problems of the Social Sciences*, New York, Macmillan, 1965.

Brown, Robert, *Explanation in Social Science*, Chicago, Aldone Publishing Co., 1963.

Brown, Robert, 'Explanations by Laws in the Social Sciences', *Philosophy of Science*, 21, 1954, 125–132.

Butterfield, Herbert, 'The Role of the Individual in History', *History*, 40, 1955, 1–17.

Carr, Edward Hallett, *What is History?*, New York, Knopf, 1962.

Cassirer, Ernst, *The Problem of Knowledge: Philosophy, Science, and History Since Hegel*, New Haven, Yale University Press, 1950.

Cassirer, Ernst, *The Logic of the Humanities*, Translated by Clarence Smith Howe, New Haven, Yale University Press, 1961.

Cohen, Carl, 'Naturalism and the Method of Verstehen', *Journal of Philosophy*, 51, 1954, 220–225.

Cohen, Percy S., 'The Aims and Interests of Sociology', *British Journal for the Philosophy of Science*, 14, 1963, 246–261. (Review discussion of *The Poverty of Historicism*, by K. R. Popper.)

Creegan, R. F., 'Radical Empiricism and Radical Historicism', *Journal of Philosophy*, 41, 1944, 126–131.

Croce, B., *History—Its Theory and Practice*, Translated by D. Ainslee, New York, Russell and Russell, 1960.

Daniels, Robert V., 'Fate and Will in Marx', *Journal of the History of Ideas*, 21, 1960, 538–552.

Danto, Arthur C., 'On Explanations in History', *Philosophy of Science*, 23, 1956, 15–30.

Davy, Georges, 'L'Explication Sociologique et Le Recours à L'Histoire, D'Aprés Comte, Mill et Durkheim', *Revue de Métaphysique et de Morale*, 54, 1949, 330–362.

Diesing, Paul, 'Objectivism vs. Subjectivism in the Social Sciences', *Philosophy of Science*, 33, 1966, 124–133.

Dobb, Maurice, 'Historical Materialism and the Role of the Economic Factor', *History*, 36, 1951, 1–11.

Donagan, Alan, 'Social Science and Historical Antinomianism', *Revue Internationale de Philosophie*, 11, 1957, 433–449.

Donagan, Alan, 'Are the Social Sciences Really Historical?', in B. Baumrin, ed., *Philosophy of Science: The Delaware Seminar*, 1, New York, John Wiley and Sons, 1963.

Donagan, Alan, 'Historical Explanation: The Popper Hempel Theory Reconsidered', in W. H. Dray, ed., *Philosophical Analysis and History*, pp. 127–159.

Dray, William H., ed., *Philosophical Analysis and History*, New York, Harper & Row, 1966.

Durkheim, Emile, *The Rules of Sociological Method*, New York, Free Press, 1950.

Easton, Lloyd, 'Alienation and History in Early Marx', *Philosophy and Phenomenological Research*, 22, 1961, 193–205.

Edel, Abraham, 'The Concept of Levels in Social Theory', in L. Gross, ed., *Symposium on Sociological Theory*, New York, Harper & Row, 1959, 167–195.

Engel-Janosi, Friedrich, *The Growth of German Historicism*, Johns Hopkins University Studies in History and Political Science, Series 62, No. 2, Baltimore, Johns Hopkins Press, 1944.

Erdmann, Karl Dietrich, 'Das Problem des Historismus in der neureren englischen Geschichtswissenschaft', *Historische Zeitschrift*, 170, 1950, 73–88.

Feigl, Herbert and May Brodbeck, eds., *Readings in the Philosophy of Science*, New York, Appleton-Century-Crofts, 1953.

Feuer, Lewis S., 'Causality in the Social Sciences', *Journal of Philosophy*, 51, 1954, 681–695.

Frankel, Charles, 'Philosophy and the Social Sciences', in C. E. Boewe and R. F. Nichols, eds., *Both Human and Humane*, University of Pennsylvania Press, 1960, 94–117.

Gardiner, P., 'Critical Study of Popper's Poverty of Historicism', *Philosophical Quarterly*, 9, 1959, 172–180.

Gibson, Quentin, *The Logic of Social Enquiry*, London, Routledge and Kegan Paul, 1960.

Ginsberg, Morris, 'Individual and Collective Representations', *Sociology and Philosophy*, London, 1953, 1–34.

Ginsberg, Morris, 'The Individual and Society', *The Diversity of Morals*, London, 1956, 149–162.

Goldstein, L., 'Mr Watkins on the Two Theses', *British Journal for the Philosophy fo Science*, 10, 1959, 240–241.

Gross, Llewellyn, ed., *Symposium on Sociological Theory*, New York, Harper & Row, 1959.

Grünbaum, Adolf, 'Comments on Professor Roger Buck's paper "Reflexive Predictions" ', *Philosophy of Science*, 30, 1963, 370–372.

Grünbaum, Adolf, 'Causality and the Science of Human Behaviour', *American Scientist*, 40, 1952, 665–676. Reprinted in *Philosophic Problems*, edited by M. Mandelbaum, F. W. Gramlich, and A. R. Anderson, New York, Macmillan, 1957, 328–338.

Grünbaum, Adolf, 'Historical Determinism, Social Activism, and Predictions in the Social Sciences', *British Journal for the Philosophy of Science*, 7, 1956.

Grünberg, E. and Modigliani, F., 'The Predictability of Social Events', *Journal of Political Economy*, 62, 1954, 465–478.

Gruner, R., 'Understanding in the Social Sciences and in History', *Inquiry*, 10, 2, Summer 1967.

Grushin, B. A., 'Karl Marx und die modernen Methoden der Geschichtsforschung', *Sowjetwissenschaft. Gesellschaftwissenschaftliche Beitrage*, No. 10, 1958, 1155–1172.

Halpern, Ben, ' "Myth" and "Ideology" in Modern Usage', *History and Theory*, 1, 1961, 129–150.

Hayek, Friedrich von, ed., *Capitalism and the Historians*, Chicago, University of Chicago Press, 1954.

Hayek, Friedrich von, *Individualism and the Economic Order*, London, Routledge and Kegan Paul, 1949.

Heilbroner, Robert L., *The Future as History:* The Historic Currents of our Time and the Direction in Which They Are Taking America, New York, Harper, 1960.

Heimann, E., *Reason and Faith in Modern Society*, Liberalism, Marxism and Democracy, Wesleyan University Press, Middletown, Connecticut, 1961.

Heinemann, F. H., 'Reply to Historicism', *Philosophy*, 21, 1946, 245–257.

Hempel, Carl G., 'Typological Procedures in the Natural and Social Sciences' in 'Symposium: Problems of Concept and Theory Formation in the Social Sciences', *Science, Language, and Human Rights*, Philadelphia, University of Pennsylvania for the American Philosophical Association, 1952.

Hempel, Carl G., *Aspects of Scientific Explanation*, New York, Free Press, 1965.

Henle, Paul, 'The Status of Emergence', *Journal of Philosophy*, 39, 1942, 486–493.

Hughes, H. S., *Consciousness and Society*, New York, Vintage Books, 1958.

Iggers, G. G., *The German Conception of History*, The National Tradition of Historical Thought from Herder to the Present, Middletown, Wesleyan University Press, 1968.

Jarvie, I. C., 'Explanation in Social Science', *British Journal for the Philosophy of Science*, 15, 1964, 62–72. (Review discussion of *Explanation in Social Science* by Robert Brown.)

Joynt, C. B. and Rescher, N., 'The Problem of Uniqueness in History', *History and Theory*, 1, 1961, 150–163.

Kaplan, Abraham, *The Conduct of Inquiry*, San Francisco, Chandler Publishing Co., 1964.

Kaufmann, Felix, *Methodology of the Social Sciences*, New York, Oxford University Press, 1944.

Kaufmann, Felix, 'The Significance of Methodology for the Social Sciences', *Social Research*, V, 1938, 442–463.

Kaufmann, Walter A., 'The Hegel Myth and Its Method', *Philosophical Review*, 60, 1951, 459–486.

Kluver, H., 'Max Weber's "Ideal Type" in Psychology', *Journal of Philosophy*, 23, 1926, 29–35.

Krieger, Leonard, 'The Uses of Marx for History', *Political Science Quarterly*, 75, 1960, 255–278.

Krieger, Leonard, 'Marx and Engels as Historians', *Journal of the History of Ideas*, 14, 1953, 381–403.

Kuhn, Helmut, 'Dialectic in History', *Journal of the History of Ideas*, 10, 1949, 14–31.

Kuznets, Simon, 'Statistical Trends and Historical Changes', *Economic History Review*, 3, 1951, 265–278.

Landheer, Bart, *Mind and Society:* Epistemological Essays on Sociology, The Hague, Martinus Nijhoff, 1952.

Lee, Dwight E. and Beck, Robert N., 'The Meaning of Historicism', *American Historical Review*, 59, 1954, 568–578.

Leibel, H., 'Philosophical Idealism in the *Historiche Zeitschrift* 1859–1914', *Theory and History*, III, 316–330.

Lerner, Daniel, ed., *Parts and Wholes*, New York, Free Press, 1963.

Lévi-Strauss, Claude, 'Histoire et Ethnologie', *Revue de Métaphysique et de Morale*, 54, 1949, 363–391.

Lévi-Strauss, Claude, 'L'Anthropologie Sociale Devant L'Histoire', *Annales*, 15, 1960, 625–637.

Levy, Marion, 'Some Basic Methodological Difficulties in the Social Sciences', *Philosophy of Science*, 17, 1950, 287–301.

Lewis, David K. and Richardson, Jane S., 'Scriven on Human Unpredictability', *Philosophical Studies*, 17, 1966, 69–74.

Lichtheim, George, 'The Concept of Ideology', *History and Theory*, 4, 1965, 164–195; reprinted in G. H. Nadel, ed., *Studies in the Philosophy of History*, New York, Harper Torchbooks, 1965, 148–179.

Lichtman, R., 'Indeterminacy in the Social Sciences', *Inquiry*, 10, 2, Summer, 1967.

Louch, A. R., 'On Misunderstanding Mr Winch', *Inquiry*, 8, 1965, 212–216.

Louch, A. R., 'The Very Idea of a Social Science', *Inquiry*, 6, 4, 1963.

Lovejoy, A. O., 'The meaning of "Emergence" and Its Modes', in P. P. Wiener, ed., *Readings in Philosophy of Science*, New York, Scribner's, 1953.

Lukes, Stephen, 'Methodological Individualism Reconsidered', *British Journal of Sociology*, Vol. 19, 1968, 119–130.

MacIntyre, A., 'A Mistake About Causality in Social Science', in P. Laslett and W. G. Runciman, eds., *Philosophy, Politics and Society* (Second Series), Oxford, B. Blackwell, 1962, 48–70.

Mannheim, Karl, *Man and Society in an Age of Reconstruction*, London, Routledge and Kegan Paul, 1940.

Marcuse, H., *Reason and Revolution*, New York, Humanities Press, 1954.

Martin, M., 'Winch on Philosophy, Social Science and Explanation', *The Philosophical Forum*, 23, 1965–66, 29–41.

Martindale, Don, 'Sociological Theory and the Ideal Type', in L. Gross, ed., *Symposium on Sociological Theory*, New York, Harper & Row, 1959, 57–91.

Martindale, Don, ed., *Functionalism in the Social Sciences*, Monograph No. 5 of the American Academy of Political and Social Science, Philadelphia, 1965.

Mayo, H. B., 'Marxism as a Philosophy of History', *Canadian Historical Review*, 34, 1953, 1–17.

McCloskey, H. J., 'The State as an Organism, as a Person, and as an End in Itself', *Philosophical Review*, 72, 1963, 306–326.

Meehl, P. E. and Sellars, W., 'The Concept of Emergence', in H. Feigl and M. Scriven, eds., *Minnesota Studies in the Philosophy of Science*, Vol. I, 1956.

Meinecke, F., *Die Enstehung des Historismus*, Munchen, 1936.

Merton, Robert K., 'The Unanticipated Consequences of Purposive Social Action', *American Sociological Review*, 1, 1936, 894–904.

Merton, Robert K., 'The Self-Fulfilling Prophecy', in *Social Theory and Social Structure*, New York, Free Press, 1957, 421–436.

Mill, John Stuart, *A System of Logic*, London and New York, Longmans, Green and Co., 1947 (originally published in 1843), Book 6, 'The Logic of the Moral Sciences'; abridged version in John Stuart Mill's *Philosophy of Scientific Method*, ed. E. Nagel, New York, Hafner, 1950.

Myrdal, Gunnar, *Value in Social Theory: A Selection of Essays on Methodology*, New York, Harper & Row, 1958.

Nadel, G. H., 'Philosophy of History Before Historicism' in *Studies in the Philosophy of History*, ed. G. H. Nadel, Harper Torchbooks, 1965, 49–73.

Nagel, Ernest, 'Wholes, Sums and Organic Unities', *Philosophical Studies*, 3, 1952, 17–32.

Nagel, Ernest, *The Structure of Science*, New York, Harcourt, Brace and World, 1961.

Nagel, Ernest and Hempel, Carl, 'Symposium; Problems of Concept and Theory Formation in the Social Sciences' in *Science, Language and Human Rights*, Philadelphia: University of Pennsylvania for the American Philosophical Association, 1952.

Natanson, Maurice, ed., *Philosophy of the Social Sciences; A Reader*, New York, Random House, 1963.

Olafson, F. A., 'Existentialism, Marxism and Historical Justification', *Ethics*, 65, 1955, 126–134.

Parsons, T., 'Evaluation and Objectivity in Social Science: An Interpretation of Max Weber's Contrition', in T. Parsons, *Sociological Theory and Modern Society*, The Free Press, New York, 1967.

Passmore, J. A., 'History, the Individual and Inevitability', *Philosophical Review*, 68, 1959, 93–102.

Plekhanov, G. V., *The Role of the Individual in History*, Moscow: Foreign Languages Publishing House, 1946.

Plekhanov, G. V., *In Defense of Materialism: The Development of the Monist View of History*, Translated by Andrew Rothstein, London, Lawrence and Wishart, 1947.

Popper, Karl R., *The Poverty of Historicism*, London, Routledge and Kegan Paul, 1961.

Radcliffe-Brown, A. R., *A Natural Science of Society*, The Free Press, New York, 1957.

Ricoeur, Paul, 'Husserl et Le Sens de L'Histoire', *Revue de Métaphysique et de Morale*, 54, 1944, 280–316.

Rieff, Philip, 'History, Psychoanalysis and the Social Sciences', *Ethics*, 63, 1953, 107–120.

Róheim, Géza, ed., *Psychoanalysis and the Social Sciences*, 3 vols., New York, International Universities Press, 1947–51.

Rothenstreich, N., 'Historicism and Philosophy, Reflections on R. G. Collingwood', *Revue Internationale de Philosophie*, 11, 1957, 401–419.

Rubinoff, L., 'Historicism and the A Priori of History', *Dialogue: The Canadian Philosophical Review*, V, 1, June 1966.

Rubinoff, L., 'Philosophy and the Logic of Social Inquiry', *Queen's Quarterly*, Winter, 1967.

Rudner, R. S., 'Value Judgment in the Acceptance of Theories', *Scientific Monthly*, 79, 1954.

Rudner, R. S., *Philosophy of Social Science*, Englewood Cliffs, New Jersey, Prentice-Hall, 1966.

Saran, A. K., 'Wittgensteinian Sociology', *Ethics*, LXXV, 3, April 1965, 195–200.

Schaaf, Julius Jakob, *Geschichte und Begriff. Eine kritische Studie zur Geschichtsmethodologie von Ernst Troeltsch und Max Weber*. Tübingen, Mohr, 1946.

Scheffler, Israel, *The Anatomy of Inquiry*; New York, Alfred A. Knopf, 1963.

Schargo, Nelly, *History in the Encyclopédie*, New York, Columbia University Press, 1947.

Shils, Edward A., 'Social Inquiry and the Autonomy of the Individual', in *The Human Meaning of the Social Sciences*, ed., Daniel Lerner, New York, Meridian Books, 1959, pp. 114–157.

Schoek, H. and Wiggins, J. W., *Scientism and Values*, New York, Van Nostrand, 1960.

Schumpeter, Joseph A., *Capitalism, Socialism and Democracy*, 3rd ed., New York, Harper, 1950.

Schutz, Alfred, 'Concept and Theory Formation in the Social Sciences', *Journal of Philosophy*, 51, 1954, 257–273.

Scriven, Michael, 'An Essential Unpredictability in Human Behaviour', in B. B. Wolman and E. Nagel, eds., *Scientific Psychology; Principles and Approaches*, New York, Basic Books, 1964, 411–425.

Scriven, Michael, 'Causes, Connections and Conditions in History', in W. H. Dray, ed., *Philosophical Analysis and History*.

Scriven, Michael, 'Explanations, Predictions, and Law', in *Minnesota Studies in the Philosophy of Science*, Vol. III, 1962, 172–230.

Scriven, Michael, 'Truisms as the Grounds for Historical Explanation', in P. Gardiner, ed., *Theories of History*.

Solo, Robert, 'Prediction, Projection, and Social Prognosis', *Journal of Philosophy*, 52, 1955, 459–464.

Steward, Julian, 'Cultural Causality and Law', *American Anthropologist*, 51, 1949, 1–27.

Strauss, L., *Natural Right and History*, Chicago, 1953.

Suppes, Patrick, 'On an Example of Unpredictability in Human Behaviour', *Philosophy of Science*, 31, 1964, 143–148.

Taylor, Charles, *The Explanation of Behaviour*, London, Routledge and Kegan Paul; New York, The Humanities Press, 1964.

Tiryakian, Edward A., *Sociologism and Existentialism:* Two Perspectives on the Individual and Society, Englewood Cliffs, N.J., Prentice-Hall, 1962.

Tran-Duc-Thao, 'Existentialisme et Matérialisme Dialectique', *Revue de Métaphysique et de Morale*, 54, 1949, 317–329.

Troeltsch, E., *Der Historismus und seine Probleme*, Tübingen, 1922.

Urbánek, E., 'Roles, Masks and Characters: A Contribution to Marx's Idea of the Social Role', *Social Research*, 34, 3, Autumn 1967, 529–562.

Voeglin, Eric, 'The Origins of Scientism', *Social Research*, 1948, 462–494.

Vyverberg, Henry, *Historical Pessimism in the French Enlightenment*, Cambridge, Mass., Harvard University Press, 1958.

Wagner, Helmut, 'Mannheim's Historicism', *Social Research*, 19, 1952, 300–321.

Watkins, J. W. N., 'The Alleged Inadequacy of Methodological Individualism', *Journal of Philosophy*, 55, 1958, 390–395.

Watkins, J. W. N., 'Third Reply to Mr Goldstein', *British Journal for the Philosophy of Science*, 10, 1959, 242–244.

Weber, Max, *From Max Weber: Essays in Sociology*, Trans. and ed. by H. Gerth, C. W. Mills, New York, Oxford University Press, 1962.

Weber, Max, *Max Weber on the Methodology of the Social Sciences*, ed. E. A. Shils and H. A. Finch, Glencoe, Free Press, Ill., 1949.

Williamson, C., 'Ideology and the Problem of Knowledge', *Inquiry*, 10, 2, Summer 1967.

Winch, Peter, *The Idea of a Social Science*, London, Routledge and Kegan Paul, 1958.

Winch, Peter, 'Mr Louch's Idea of a Social Science', *Inquiry*, 7, 1964, 202–208.

Wolff, Kurt H., 'The Sociology of Knowledge and Sociological Theory', in L. Gross, ed., *Symposium on Sociological Theory*, New York, Harper & Row, 1959, 567–602.

Wollheim, R., 'Historicism Reconsidered', *The Sociological Review*, 2, 1954, 76–97.

Zilsel, Edgar, 'Physics and the Problem of Historico-sociological Laws', *Philosophy of Science*, 8, 1941, 567–579; reprinted in H. Feigl and M. Brodbeck, ed., *Readings in the Philosophy of Science*, New York, Appleton-Century-Crofts, 1953, 714–722.

Author Index

Subject Index